S0-AWV-397

# Drugs Affecting the Respiratory System

# Drugs Affecting the Respiratory System

**Davis L. Temple, Jr.,** EDITOR
*Mead Johnson Pharmaceuticals*

Based on a symposium sponsored by the Division of Medicinal Chemistry at the 175th Meeting of the American Chemical Society, Anaheim, California, March 13–16, 1978.

ACS SYMPOSIUM SERIES **118**

AMERICAN CHEMICAL SOCIETY
WASHINGTON, D. C. 1980

Library of Congress CIP Data

Drugs affecting the respiratory system.
(ACS symposium series; 118 ISSN 0097-6156)

Includes bibliographies and index.

1. Respiratory agents—Congresses. 2. Structures—activity relationship (Pharmacology)—Congresses.
I. Temple, Davis L., 1943- . II. American Chemical Society. Division of Medicinal Chemistry. III. Series: American Chemical Society. ACS symposium series; 118.

RM388.D78 615'.72 79-24958
ISBN 0-8412-0536-1 ASCMC8 118 1–396 1980



PRINTED IN THE UNITED STATES OF AMERICA

# ACS Symposium Series

**M. Joan Comstock,** *Series Editor*

# FOREWORD

The ACS Symposium Series was founded in 1974 to provide a medium for publishing symposia quickly in book form. The format of the Series parallels that of the continuing Advances in Chemistry Series except that in order to save time the papers are not typeset but are reproduced as they are submitted by the authors in camera-ready form. Papers are reviewed under the supervision of the Editors with the assistance of the Series Advisory Board and are selected to maintain the integrity of the symposia; however, verbatim reproductions of previously published papers are not accepted. Both reviews and reports of research are acceptable since symposia may embrace both types of presentation.

# CONTENTS

BRONCHODILATORS AND OTHER PHARMACODYNAMIC AGENTS

# PREFACE

The importance of the lungs as effector organs of respiration cannot be denied. Respiration and life itself depend ultimately on absorption of oxygen from the atmosphere and excretion of carbon dioxide through pulmonary ventilation. Good health depends on the quality of this vital system. Thus impairment of the respiratory system through loss of respiratory muscle function, increased airway resistance, decreased lung compliance, alveolar destruction, or physical obstruction leads to a general loss of one's ability to function. Certain disease states such as emphysema are progressive and may ultimately prove fatal, whereas a mild case of bronchial asthma may merely limit one's capacity to exercise. However, in every untreated case of respiratory disease the quality of life invariably is lowered.

Respiratory disease may often be traced to an external source such as an inhaled allergen, pathogen, particulate matter, chemical irritant, or other, undefined material. Ideally, the resulting disease state would be abolished by removing the suspect material from the environment; however, often this is not possible. We are left then to define effective drugs for the treatment of bronchial asthma, chronic bronchitis, chronic pulmonary emphysema, and a variety of other debilitating respiratory diseases.

It is the purpose of this book to explore the contemporary development of drugs affecting the respiratory system and their application to modern medicine. The volume is divided into two parts: mediator release inhibitors, and bronchodilators and other pharmacodynamic agents. In the introduction to the first section, the historical importance of the evolution of cromolyn sodium from the naturally occurring compound khellin is discussed. These mediator release inhibitors are useful prophylactic drugs for the treatment of asthma, and their development has provided both a new avenue for therapy and a new direction for the medicinal chemist. Extensive efforts to develop an orally active, more effective cromolyn-like drug by much of the pharmaceutical industry resulted in a plethora of promising compounds; many of these were poorly effective in the clinic and subsequently abandoned. Fortunately a number of these agents did perform well in human clinical studies and are now in advanced study. Successes in this area have come as a result of a better understanding of the biologic mechanisms of action of antiallergic agents and the inherent limitations of animal screening methods used to select clinical candidates. The development of several of the more promising compounds is described also. The significant chemistry and structure–activity relationships that led to the selection of these compounds are highlighted.

The final chapter in this section deals with oxatomide, an antiallergic antihistamine. This agent may act by a different mechanism than the cromolyn-related antiallergics or the classical antihistamines. Such compounds are clinically effective and seem to offer yet a new direction for exploration.

The second part of "Drugs Affecting the Respiratory System" focuses on drugs that not only may inhibit immunologically induced release of mediators from target cells, but more importantly, that may inhibit the consequences of mediator release. Such drugs include bronchodilators and other pharmacodynamic agents. In the introduction to this second part, the multipartite nature of asthma and respiratory disease in general are discussed. This sets the stage for the following chapter in which pathophysiologic derangements in chronic obstructive pulmonary disease are discussed from a clinical point of view. The need for agents, such as bronchodilators, for chronic disease therapy and the deficiencies in existing therapy are well illustrated.

The following two chapters deal with the historical and contemporary aspects of both adrenergic and theophylline-related bronchodilator drugs. Several new structural types are considered that may indicate future trends in these areas. The problems with theophylline therapy are well documented and the need for improved agents of this class is emphasized.

The last chapter of the book explores in depth an important new area —prostanoid bronchodilator drugs. An extensive review of the chemistry and structure–activity relationships of the prostaglandin bronchodilators is presented for the first time and prospects for a useful clinical agent are discussed.

In recent years drug research in the respiratory area has been at an all-time high. Much of this work has stemmed from the discovery of cromolyn sodium as a truly new therapeutic modality as well as from a better appreciation of the pharmacodynamics of theophylline. Newer agents such as prostaglandin bronchodilators are now being studied extensively. One must feel that these extensive efforts will culminate in the development of better therapy for the patient suffering from respiratory disease.

Mead Johnson Pharmaceuticals
Evansville, Indiana 47721
August 6, 1979

DAVIS L. TEMPLE, JR.

# MEDIATOR RELEASE INHIBITORS

1

# Introduction: Perspectives on Antiallergic Agents

H. F. HODSON

The Wellcome Research Laboratories, Langley Court, Beckenham, Kent BR3 3BS, England

It is now more than ten years since Fisons, U.K. introduced the compound Intal, cromolyn sodium, or disodium cromoglycate as it will be referred to in this introduction, as an effective agent for the prophylaxis of asthma in man. This introduction caused considerable excitement and activity in the rest of the pharmaceutical industry as well as in academic medical circles. There were several reasons for this interest but one of the most important was that cromoglycate appeared to be a drug with a completely novel mode of action in asthma therapy.

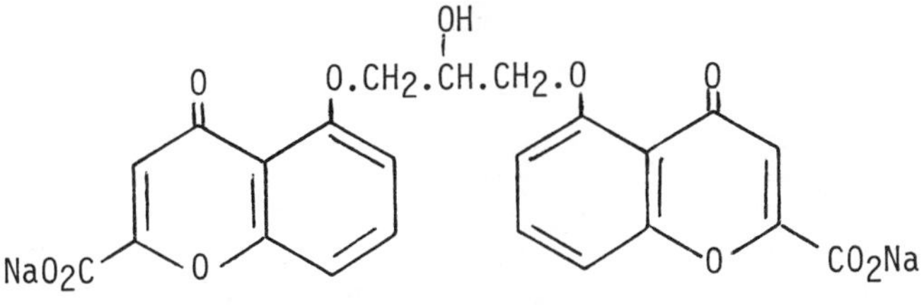

OH
O.CH$_2$.CH.CH$_2$.O
NaO$_2$C ... CO$_2$Na

Intal; disodium cromoglycate

To see how novel this mode of action was we must briefly consider the processes which are believed to be involved in allergic asthma. The basis of the disease is thought to be an immunological process. The asthmatic individual has become sensitised to an external agent, or antigen, usually protein in nature, such as house dust mite, pollen, feathers, animal scurf, *etc.* by producing antibodies towards the antigen. When the sensitised individual comes into contact with the antigen these antibodies combine with the antigen and the formation of antigen-antibody complexes is followed by the release of a number of substances, collectively called mediators, which together are responsible for the bronchospasm and other symptoms of an asthmatic attack. Among these mediators are histamine, serotonin, kinins, and the so-called SRS-A. SRS-A is an as yet chemically uncharacterised substance,* although considerable effort has been

0-8412-0536-1/80/47-118-003$05.00/0

and is currently being spent, on attempts to elucidate its structure; the initials stand for *Slow Reacting Substance of Anaphylaxis*. Anaphylaxis is a general term covering the full set of reactions which are triggered off by the mediators.

The sequence of events, then, is as follows. An individual reacts to an external agent or antigen by producing antibodies. These antibodies become attached to the membrane of specialised cells, for example mast cells, which contain the mediators in granules. Once these antibodies are formed and have become attached to the mast cell membrane the individual has become sensitised. On further contact with antigen, or challenge, the antigen combines with the cell-bound antibody, the antigen-antibody complex remaining attached to the cell. The next event is release of the mediators from the cells by a process known as degranulation. This is not a break-down of the cells but is an active secretory process; degranulated mast cells are able to regenerate themselves. The released mediators provoke an anaphylaxis or anaphylactic shock which in the case of asthma is primarily a contraction of the smooth muscle of the bronchioles which leads to bronchoconstriction. In addition the lining of the bronchioles swells and mucous is secreted. These and associated reactions combine to reduce the passage of air and lead to the typical asthmatic reaction.

If we accept this sequence of events, then, we can see that there are several points at which it is theoretically possible to interfere with the process and thereby to prevent or relieve an asthmatic attack. The first point is the end organ, the bronchioles. Before cromoglycate was introduced the most widely used therapy in asthma employed bronchodilators, in the form of β-adrenergic agents. These physiological antagonists act at the final stage of the process by relaxing the smooth muscle of bronchioles and thus counteracting the bronchoconstrictor effect of the allergic mediators. However, in general β-adrenergic stimulants have poor selectivity of action. In particular they have effects on the cardiovascular system, particularly the heart.

A second possible point of attack is not at the end organ but on the mediators themselves, by the use of competitive antagonists. In this case, of course, we would need either an agent which antagonised all the mediators or a mixture of agents, each one antagonising one or more mediators. Antihistamines have never been widely used in the clinical treatment of allergic asthma suggesting that histamine does not play a dominant role in this disease in man, although it is certainly important in anaphylactic reactions in other species. There is, though, a great deal of indirect evidence to show that SRS-A does play an important role in inducing the symptoms of human allergic asthma. A specific antagonist of SRS-A could therefore be of therapeutic value in asthma and could also help to define the role of SRS-A in asthma. The first such specific antagonist, FPL 55712, was reported by Fisons, some four years ago but there have been no reports of its clinical application.

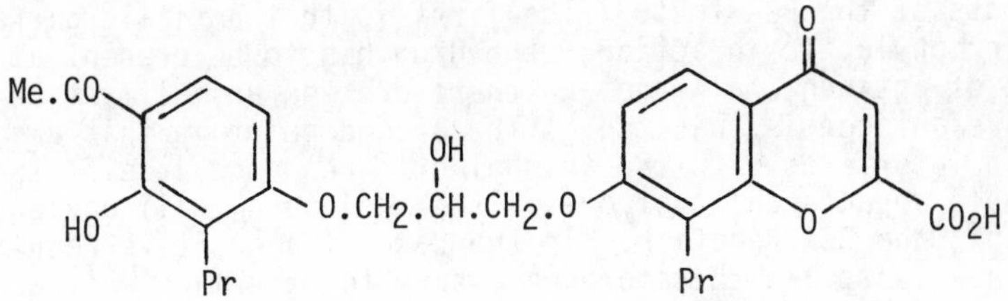

Me.CO, HO, Pr — O.$CH_2$.CH(OH).$CH_2$.O — Pr, O, O, $CO_2H$

FPL 55712

It was early demonstrated that although cromoglycate was effective as an asthma prophylactic in man it had no pharmacological action either as a bronchodilator or as a competitive antagonist to the mediators of anaphylaxis. The Fisons' workers concluded that it acted at a third point, the mediator release step; it did not prevent the combination of antigen with antibody but inhibited the release of the mediators which normally follows formation of the antigen-antibody complex.

Cromoglycate appeared to have, then, what at the time was a completely novel mode of action which has given us the title of this Symposium - Mediator Release Inhibitors. This type of action quickly became known as antiallergic activity, a term which increasingly became familiar to medicinal chemists during the 1970's.

At this point we must appreciate, however, that the effectiveness of Intal in allergic asthma was first demonstrated directly in man and that much of the work establishing its mode of action came later. Out of this work also came a number of laboratory test systems for detecting antiallergic activity of which the most widely used has been the so-called passive cutaneous anaphylaxis or PCA reaction in rats. In this test rats are sensitised towards a particular antigen; ovalbumin is usually used, together with *B. pertussis* as an adjuvant. In becoming sensitised these rats have produced antibodies of a particular type, the so-called IgE antibodies, which are believed to be of the same type as those involved in human allergic asthma. When serum from these rats is injected into other rats these latter animals now carry the antibodies, and are said to be passively sensitised. In the PCA test injection of antigen into these rats produces a characteristic skin reaction, or cutaneous anaphylaxis which can readily be measured. The PCA reaction, then, involves a skin, or cutaneous, anaphylaxis in animals which have been passively sensitised. It was assumed that the basic mechanism of mediator release which operates in the PCA reaction is the same as the mediator release step in human allergic asthma. It was shown that cromoglycate given intravenously before antigen challenge is a potent inhibitor of the rat PCA reaction and this animal model rapidly became established as a test system for the detection of antiallergic activity.

At this stage it is necessary to emphasise two important aspects of the PCA test. The first is that antiallergic agents are prophylactic in action; the drug has to be present at the time of antigen challenge and therefore the animal must be dosed before antigen is injected. The second point is that a compound which interferes with the anaphylactic response itself, for example an antagonist of one of the mediators, will obviously inhibit the PCA reaction; in the case of a positive result further tests are therefore necessary to determine whether the inhibition is caused solely by blocking mediator release.

Many other tests have been designed to detect or to confirm inhibition of mediator release. They cannot be discussed in this introduction but it is sufficient to say that all of them involve the establishing of an *in vivo* or an *in vitro* system in which an organism, a tissue, or a group of cells, is sensitised to a particular antigen. When challenged with this antigen the release of mediators can be measured either by observing a physiological response or by assaying one or more of the mediators themselves. Antiallergic activity of a compound can be assessed by its ability to supress the response or to prevent the formation of the mediator which is assayed.

Cromoglycate, then, appeared to be unique in its mode of action but at the time of its introduction it was also unique in its mode of administration - it was given by inhalation of a dry powder and had no demonstrable therapeutic effects when given by mouth. At the time this method of administration was thought not to be ideal, particularly for the therapy of a disease in which there is a reduced capability for inhalation. The appearance of cromoglycate thus not only stimulated most major pharmaceutical companies into a search for alternative antiallergic agents but provided an extra incentive in the expectation that an orally effective drug could be discovered. Just as cromoglycate is ineffective in man when given orally it shows no effect as an inhibitor of PCA reaction in rats after oral administration although when given intravenously powerful inhibition of the PCA reaction is seen. It was expected, therefore, that if a compound could be produced which was an effective inhibitor of PCA in rats after oral dosing, then this compound could be an effective oral antiasthmatic drug.

Several factors determined the way in which the search for antiallergic agents developed over the next few years. Many companies started a search for alternative antiallergic drugs, desirably orally active, but all started at about the same time and from roughly the same point. This starting point was the knowledge that cromoglycate and a few closely related compounds were effective against allergic asthma in man and were also effective at inhibiting the PCA reaction in rats. Little was known about the actual mechanism of mediator release so there was no available knowledge on which to base the rational design of drugs in this area. It is not surprising, therefore, that during the first 5 or 6 years of the search for antiallergic drugs it was evident from patent specifications and publications that most of the active compounds were similar to each other and had obviously been inspired by the chemical structure of cromoglycate itself. The direction of this work can be seen conveniently by using the development of one of our own antiallergic drugs, doxantrazole, as a framework.

Early in our work we found that xanthone-2-carboxylic acid (1) had significant activity as an inhibitor of the PCA reaction in rats - of the order of 100 mg/kg after i.v. administration. Only the 2-carboxylic acid had appreciable activity - the 1,3 and 4-carboxylic acids were inactive or only poorly active.

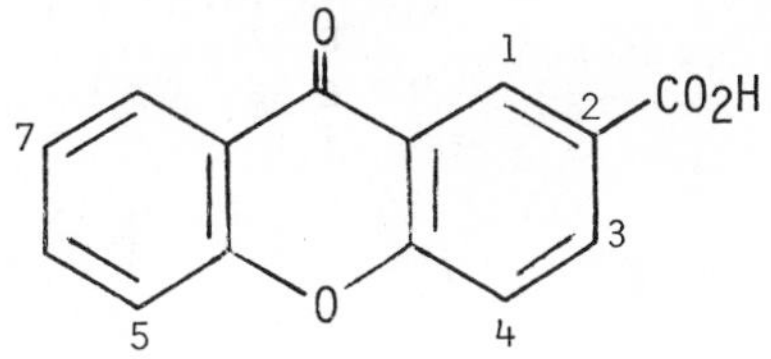

O 1 2 $CO_2H$ 7 3 O 5 4

(1)

It soon became clear that, not surprisingly, many other groups, notably Allen and Hanburys in England and Syntex in the States, had arrived at similar conclusions. Patent specifications and publications showed that a large number of substituted xanthone-2-carboxylic acids were being investigated and significantly in some cases, notably those with 7-substituents or 5,7-substituents, oraly activity was claimed. Some of these compounds were thought to be sufficiently active to be taken to trial in man and feature in comparative discussions in several contributions to this Symposium.

Further work showed that other tricyclic systems provided compounds which were equally active. Thus, we found that thioxanthone-(2, X = S) acridone-(2, X = NH) anthraquinone-(2, X = CO) and flurenone-(2, X = bond)-2-carboxylic acids all had activity comparable with that of the xanthone acid and similar findings were reported by other groups. Only those compounds with the carboxylic acid function in the 2-position were significantly active; the other isomers were weakly active or inactive.

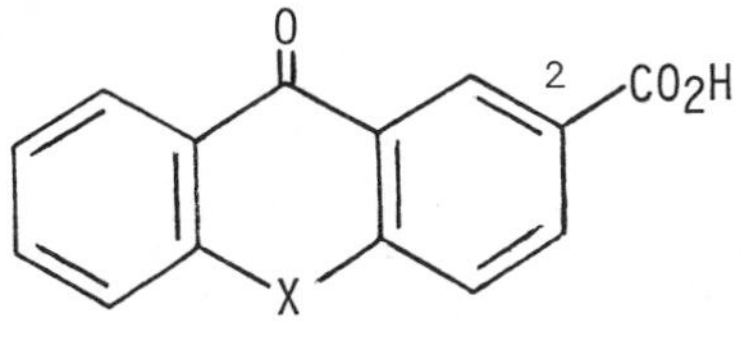

O 2 $CO_2H$ X

(2)

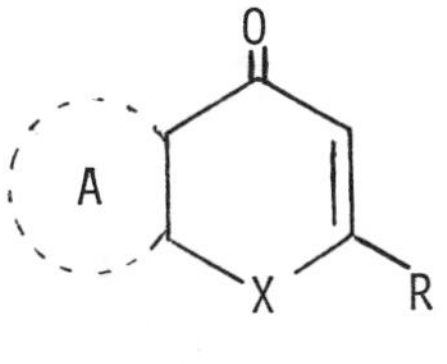

O A X R

(3)

At this stage the known antiallergic agents fell into two broad groups - the tricyclic acids just discussed and a huge range of compounds which were formally more closely related to the chromonecarboxylic acid moiety of cromoglycate itself. Most of this latter group can be accommodated in the general formula (3) in which X can be O, NH or S and A may be monocyclic, polycyclic or heterocyclic but is usually aromatic and therefore planar, and R is a carboxylic acid or other acid function. In a number of cases the acid function is adjacent to the carbonyl group.

These compounds come from the work of many groups and further examples are still appearing. It appears that if one can imagine this partial formula (3) or, in some cases two such moieties, incorporated into any kind of essentially planar di, tri or tetracyclic system then the resulting compound will have anti-allergic activity - and most of the structures which one could imagine have been prepared. In some cases individual compounds have been claimed to have appreciable oral activity - at a level which was thought high enough for trial in man. Examples of these will appear in later contributions but are not discussed here mainly because there are no readily discernible relationships between structure and oral activity.

A significant general observation on all these structural types is that i.v. activity was compatible with a wide range of substituents. In none of the early series was there an obvious relationship between activity and the physicochemical parameters of substituents; a surprisingly wide range of lipophilic - hydrophilic or electronic character was compatible with high activity. The structural factors governing oral activity were even less obvious.

Many dicarboxylic acids are particularly potent after i.v. administration; thus fluorenone 2,7-dicarboxylic acid (4) and the heterocyclic dicarboxylic acid ICI 74917, bufrolin, had activity greater than cromoglycate by factors of 4 and 300 respectively.

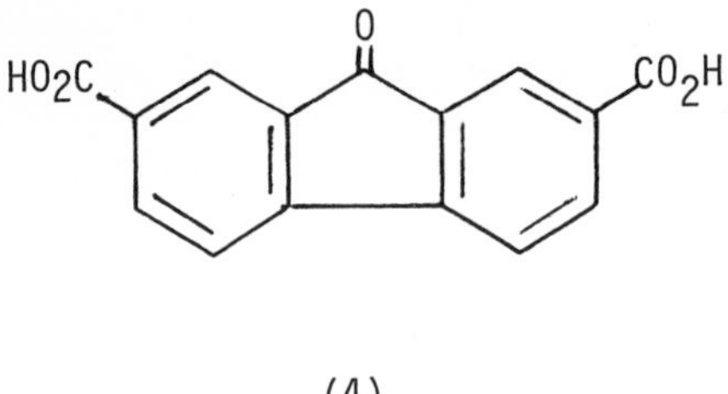

$HO_2C$ O $CO_2H$

(4)

O $CO_2H$ $HO_2C$ H N NH Bu O

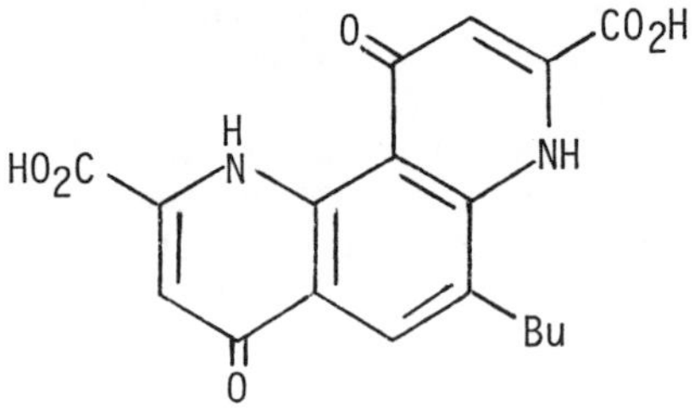

ICI 74917, bufrolin

These dicarboxylic acids and others prepared by the Upjohn and other groups, although highly active by the intravenous route, in general lacked oral activity.

Although these broad generalisations cover most of the compounds for which antiallergic activity has been described there are a number which fall outside this area. In some cases there are planar polycyclic systems incorporating an oxo-group but with a carboxyl function attached not directly to the planar system but carried on a side chain. In other cases we have structures which at first glance appear to be completely different but on closer examination can be seen to have features compatible with our broad generalisations. One of these is illustrated by the nitroindandione BRL 10833 from Beecham, which, although chemically distinct from the preceding compounds has a planar system, a carbonyl function and a strongly acidic group. Another is provided by the azapurinone series, exemplified by M & B 22948 and discussed in a later contribution; again we have a planar system, one held planar by hydrogen bonding, and an acidic function. A different example is furnished by W8011 of Warner Lambert which, although not acidic, is metabolised to the corresponding carboxylic acid which is believed to be responsible for the antiallergic activity.

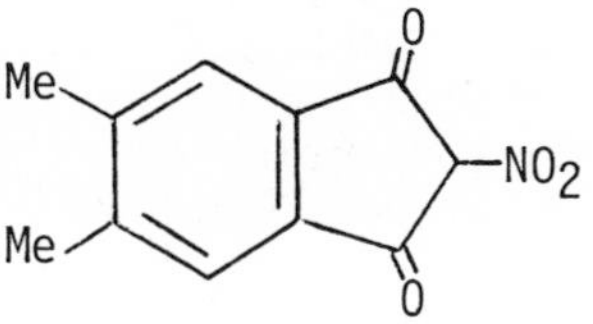

Me, Me, O, O, $NO_2$

BRL 10833

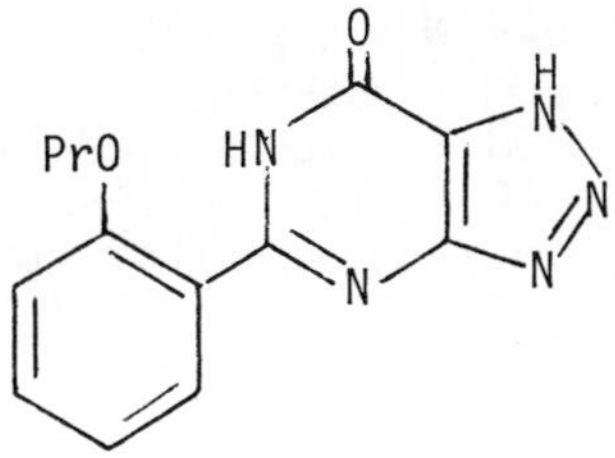

O, PrO, HN, H, N, N, N, N

M & B 22948

O, $CH_2OH$, O, OMe

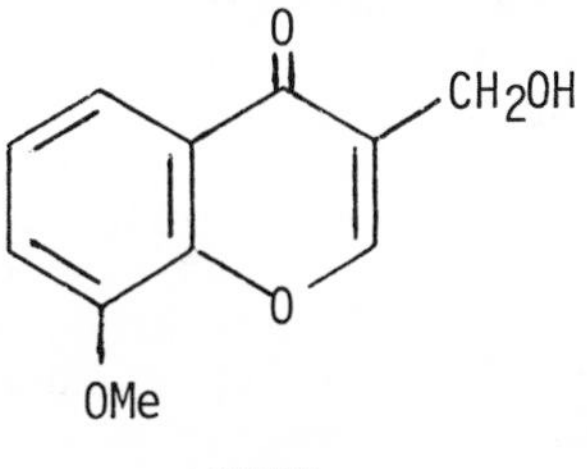

W8011

At this point I would like to return to our own work and consider how we arrived at a compound with appreciable oral activity. Two independent observations contributed to this goal.

The first came from a continuing investigation of alternative tricyclic systems as carriers of the carboxylic acid function and the finding that compounds (5) in which X or Y equals sulphone, for example, had high activity. One of these, the thioxanthone dioxide BW 437C, had a higher ratio of oral to intravenous activity than we had observed before.

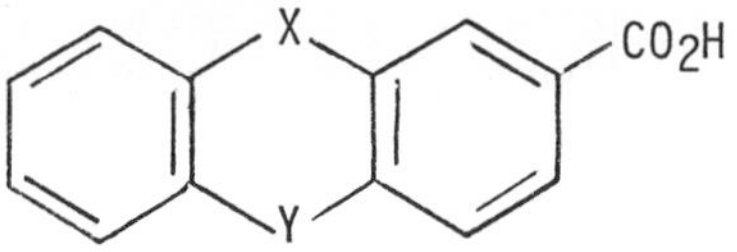

(5)

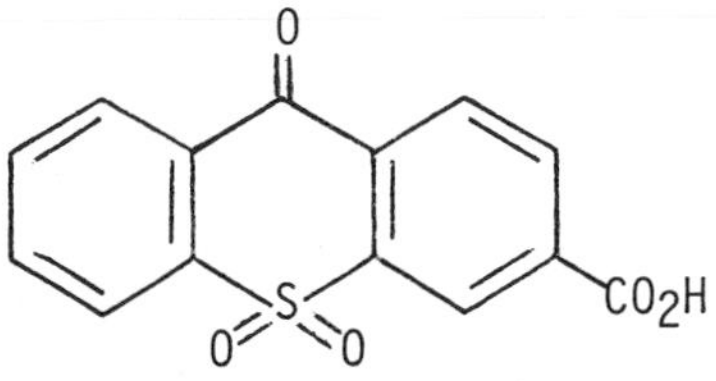

BW 437C

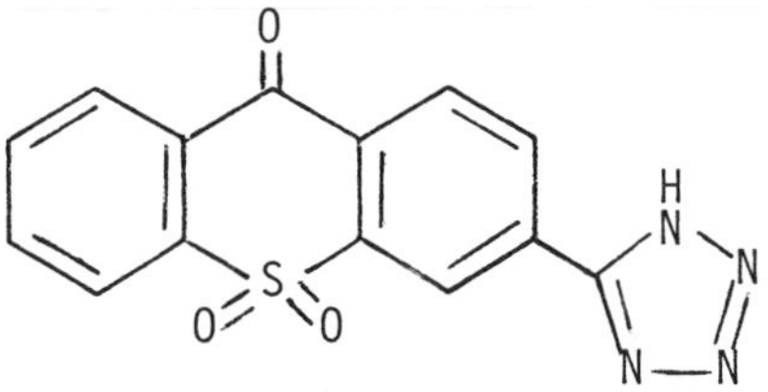

Doxantrazole

The second observation came from our attempts to see if we could find alternatives to the carboxylic acid function. Several such alternatives were investigated but only with the tetrazole function did we find compounds with activity comparable with that of the corresponding carboxylic acids. It has been known for many years that 5-substituted tetrazoles are acidic and that for any given carboxylic and tetrazole pair the difference in pKA is generally less than 0.2. Since the overall bulk of the two functions, and perhaps more importantly that of the anions derived from them is not dissimilar it was suggested that in a biologically active molecule with a carboxyl group, that group could be replaced by a 5-tetrazole moiety with retention of biological activity. This principle has been applied by many workers, particularly in the anti-inflammatory area where carboxylic acids abound, and more recently, for example, to prostaglandin analogues; not surprisingly it has also been exploited by several groups working in the antiallergic area. With our compounds not only were tetrazoles as active as carboxylic acids but in general they had greater oral potency. This observation led us to the thioxanthone dioxide tetrazole doxantrazole which had relatively high oral activity, with an $ED_{50}$ at *ca.* 10 mg/kg in the rat PCA test.

This appeared at the time to be the highest oral activity we could reach in this series. It is not perhaps startling in comparison with compounds which have subsequently been discovered by other groups - this will be quite clear from some of the contributions which follow. Despite this it appeared that with this level of activity oral doses of between 200 and 400 mg in man would be high enough to give plasma levels sufficient for a therapeutic effect.

It was mentioned earlier that many other tests had been developed to detect inhibition of mediator release and doxantrazole was effective in some of these systems. One of these, although an *in vitro* test, seemed to be of particular relevance to the problem of allergic asthma in man. Isolated, chopped, human lung can be passively sensitised by exposure to serum obtained from individuals containing antibodies to a specific antigen. On challenge with this antigen the isolated tissue releases anaphylactic mediators and a measure of the total mediator release can be obtained by assaying histamine, one of these mediators. Cromoglycate is effective in inhibiting mediator release in this system and it was found that doxantrazole was also effective, being at least 8 times as potent as cromoglycate.

Finally, doxantrazole was tested in selected human asthmatic volunteers known to be sensitive to specific antigens. Antigen challenge of such asthmatics produces an immediate bronchoconstriction which can be measured by recording the fall in $FEV_1$ and peak expiratory flow rate. In eight such volunteers, allergic to house dust mite, a single oral dose of 200 mg gave significant protection against the bronchoconstriction caused by challenge with specific antigen.

Following this demonstration of activity in a single dose challenge study doxantrazole was taken to full scale clinical trials against asthma. In several carefully controlled trials conducted throughout the world it was shown that doxantrazole was no better than placebo in protecting patients from asthmatic symptoms.

There now appear to be many examples of potent antiallergic compounds which, like doxantrazole, have shown activity in systems designed to detect inhibition of mediator release but have not yet proved themselves clinically as effective antiasthmatic drugs. Several of these agents have been shown to protect asthmatic individuals against the immediate bronchoconstrictor reaction provoked by a single antigen challenge, but have not yet succeeded in long-term asthma prophylaxis. It is interesting to compare this field with other therapeutic areas; in the ten years following the introduction of propranolol, for example, no fewer than nine other β-adrenergic antagonists reached the market in the U.K. alone.

There are many possible reasons for the non-appearance to date of successors to cromoglycate and it could be that there is a different reason or set of reasons for each individual compound. Problems of absorption, transport, distribution or metabolism may play more or less important roles in different cases. It may be that inhibition of mediator release is not the most important factor in the clinical effectiveness of cromoglycate. Most of the effort devoted to antiallergic research has assumed that inhibition of mediator release was the sole requirement of an effective prophylactic drug for allergic asthma. Only the next few years, and clinical work with highly active compounds like those described in the following contributions, will tell us whether this assumption is valid.

Finally, in this context we should watch closely the clinical development of compounds of a type not covered in this introduction. These are basic compounds, structurally more similar to histamine $H_1$-antagonists, which inhibit mediator release but which are also potent physiological or competitive antagonists; ketotifen, from Sandoz, and oxatomide from Janssen are two recent examples of this type of compound.

*Editor's note: The structure of SRS-A was disclosed subsequent to the preparation of this manuscript at the Fourth International Prostaglandin Congress in Washington, D. C. Samuelson and his colleagues of Karolinska Institutet showed SRS-A to be a product of arachidonic acid cascade which they called Leukotriene C. The material is derived by ring-opening of the epoxide bond of Leukotriene A by cysteine.

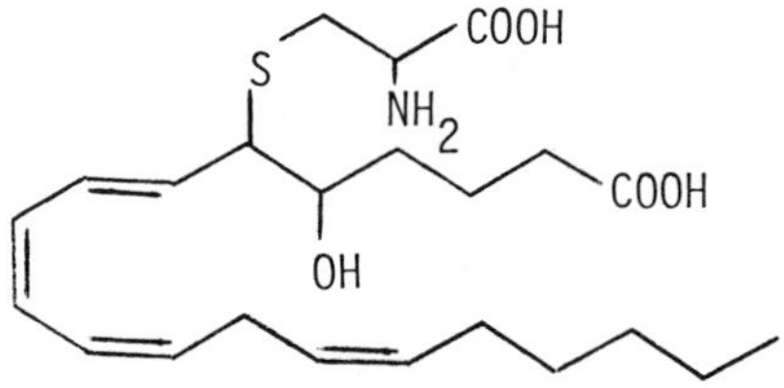

S
COOH
$NH_2$
COOH
OH

SRS-A (Leukotriene C)

RECEIVED August 6, 1979.

2

# The Mechanism of Histamine Release from Mast Cells with Reference to the Action of Antiallergic Drugs

J. C. FOREMAN

Division of Clinical Immunology, Department of Medicine, The Johns Hopkins University School of Medicine, 5601 Loch Raven Boulevard, Baltimore, MD 21239

It is now over a decade since the description of the antiallergic properties of cromoglycate (1) and it is worthy of note that, like many other drug actions, they were discovered in man and not in experimental animals. It became apparent shortly after the description of the drug that it possessed a novel mechanism of action, quite different from the classical drugs used to treat allergic disorders such as β-adrenoceptor agonists, anticholinergics, directly-acting smooth muscle relaxants and steroids (2). The novel mechanism of action of cromoglycate has become synonymous with the phrase "antiallergic activity" and a vast effort has been expended in the past ten years by drug houses worldwide to discover other antiallergic drugs, and in particular, orally active antiallergic drugs, since cromoglycate is only active when applied topically. No new antiallergic drugs have been marketed. Does this reflect our ignorance of the mechanism of action of this type of drug? Certainly, whatever the mechanism of action of antiallergic drugs is at the cellular and molecular level, it has eluded us and this has not made easier the task of developing appropriate screens for finding new compounds with antiallergic activity which are potent and orally active in man. In an attempt to promote further thought, I propose to describe some of our current knowledge of the mechanism of the allergic reaction and to relate this to some of the observations on the mode of action of antiallergic drugs.

## Mechanism of Mediator Release

Immune Stimulus. The immediate-type allergic reaction is one of the immunological responses to antigen, and is characterized by the involvement of the specific class of antibodies designated IgE (3). The initial event in the generation of an immune response is the invasion by the antigen. The host response is classically the generation of circulating IgG antibody or the production of a cellular (lymphocyte) response. In some individuals and for certain antigens, however, cytophilic IgE antibody is produced,

0-8412-0536-1/80/47-118-013$06.00/0

and while we know quite a lot about the control of IgE antibody production (4,5,6), the factors which determine why some individuals mount an IgE-response and become allergic remains unknown. Figure 1 depicts what happens to the IgE antibody produced in response to the initial antigen challenge.

Specific receptors on tissue mast cells or circulating basophil leukocytes bind the Fc portion of the IgE molecule and the antibody becomes cell-fixed. The Fc receptors for IgE have been isolated and purified from a rat basophil leukemia (7,8). There are about 2 to 8 x $10^5$ of these receptors on a mast cell (9) and it appears that the receptor protein is deeply embedded in the membrane with little exposure to the external milieu (9,10). The receptors appear to behave independently of one another and are mobile within the membrane: possibly being connected with cellular microfilaments (12). The size of the receptor is the source of some debate and it is uncertain whether it is a monomer or dimer (8,13): molecular weight estimates are in the range of 60,000 to 100,000, but it does seem fairly clear that the receptor is monovalent with respect to IgE binding (11). Thus far, the major importance of the isolated receptor has been in providing antibody against it (see below) (14,15).

Having bound IgE antibody, the sensitized cells are now primed to react when the host encounters a second challenge with antigen. Antigen binds to the Fab regions of the cell-fixed IgE antibody and it is this antigen-antibody reaction which provides the signal to the cell to release materials which mediate the effects that we recognize as an immediate-hypersensitivity reaction.

It has been shown that for the immunological signal to the mast cell or basophil to be effective in releasing mediators, at least bivalent antigen is required. It was recognized many years ago that univalent haptens could not elicit an immediate hypersensitivity reaction (16) and it has subsequently been shown that a hapten or antigen must be bivalent or polyvalent in order to stimulate mast cells and basophils to release their histamine (17). Some elegant experiments by Magro and Alexander (18) showed that IgE antibodies on rabbit leukocytes to two haptens: benzylpenicillolyl- and dinitrophenyl- were freely distributed on the cell membrane and that the cell could be triggered to secrete by joining either two BPO, two DNP or linking together BPO and DNP. Furthermore, since release by the mixed divalent hapten (DNP-BPO) could be inhibited equally well with either univalent BPO or DNP it was evident that two separate molecules of IgE were bridged rather than internal bridging between the two arms of the Y-shaped IgE molecule. Similar results have been obtained with DNP and BPO haptens in human cells (19).

Further evidence that cross linking antibody molecules is a fundamental process in triggering mast cells and basophils has come from three different approaches. Firstly, release of histamine from mast cells or basophils can be induced by anti-IgE antibody (20). Antibodies directed at IgE or Fab (IgE) were both ef-

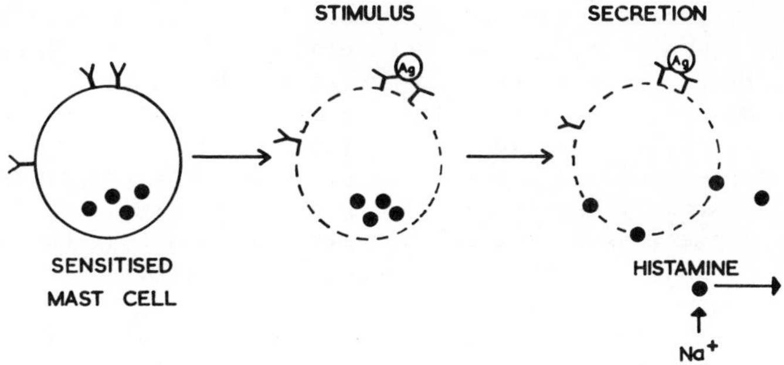


*Figure 1. Sequence of events in the secretion of mediators from mast cells or basophil leukocytes. IgE antibody (Y) binds to the cell membrane at specific receptor sites to sensitize the cell. Antigen cross-linking IgE molecules provide a membrane signal to the cell which sets in motion a chain of biochemical events. The membrane surrounding the granules (●), which contains the mediators, fuses with the cell membrane (exocytosis) to allow the mediators to escape into the surrounding medium. The granule matrix behaves as an ion-exchange resin releasing histamine and taking up Na* (75).

fective in inducing secretion. Ishizaka and Ishizaka (21) then demonstrated that only the $F(ab')_2$ portion of anti-IgE could cause cell triggering: the Fab' (monovalent) portion was not active. Thus, two antigen combining sites must be present on an anti-IgE molecule for activity and it was concluded that anti-IgE activates cells by linking together two or more IgE molecules.

The lectin, concanavalin A, binds to sugar moieties (22) and the IgE molecule has associated carbohydrate (23). Keller (24) showed that concanavalin A released histamine only from mast cells which had been sensitized by fixation of IgE to the cell membrane. The trypsinized derivative of concanavalin A which has a reduced valency relative to the untreated tetramer was not active in triggering mast cells. It was concluded, therefore, that concanavalin A probably stimulated histamine release by cross-linking IgE molecule bound to the cell membrane, by binding sugar moieties associated with the antibody carbohydrate. Siraganian and Siraganian (25) showed, using human basophils, that concanavalin A released histamine from only those cells with surface bound IgE.

The final, very interesting approach, has been to use antibody directed against IgE receptor (15). The fact that this antibody causes cell activation demonstrates that it is unnecessary for IgE to be bound to the receptor in order for triggering to occur: only the IgE receptors need be cross-linked. Again, the $F(ab')_2$ fragment of anti-receptor antibody is active but Fab' is not active: that is, a bivalent molecule is required for activation (15).

Several lines of evidence have, thus, led to the view that mast cells and basophils are triggered to secrete by a membrane signal which consists, at least in part, of a cross-linking of two or more membrane protein complexes referred to as IgE receptors. As already pointed out, it is not yet known whether these receptors are single proteins or a complex of proteins with specific functions. The coupling of this membrane signal to the event which follows is currently the problem of major interest.

Calcium and Histamine Secretion. Histamine secretion from basophil and mast cells requires the presence of calcium in the extracellular medium (26,27,39). Figure 2 shows that there is a graded increase in the range 0.1 mM to 1 mM. It was considered that one possible mechanism for the coupling of the membrane signal (cross-linking IgE receptors) to the release of secretory granules containing histamine could be the opening of membrane calcium channels which would allow the passage of calcium from outside to inside the cell where the calcium could then activate the process of exocytosis (28,45). Indirect evidence compatible with such a model was obtained using lanthanum, which is known to have a high affinity for calcium channels and to block calcium movement across membranes (29,30). Figure 3 shows that lanthanum in the concentration range 1 to 1000 nM inhibits antigen-induced histamine release, and it has been shown (31) that this action of

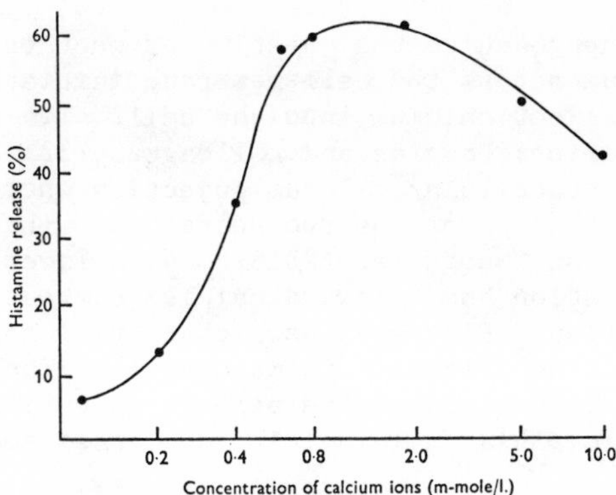


Journal of Physiology

*Figure 2. Concentration–response relationship for Ca and antigen-induced histamine release from rat mast cells* (39)

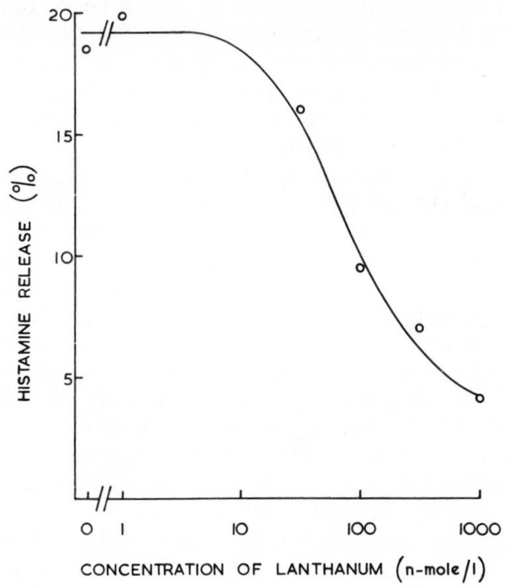


British Journal of Pharmacology

*Figure 3. Concentration–response relationship for the inhibition by lanthanum of antigen-induced histamine release* (31)

lanthanum is due to direct competition for calcium binding sites in mast cells.

One direct approach to the question of whether the inward current of calcium across the cell membrane initiates histamine secretion is to inject calcium into the cell. Two published reports are conflicting: Douglas and colleagues (32) observed secretion following intracellular calcium injection whereas Yamasaki and colleagues (33) did not observe secretion. The discovery of the specific calcium ionophore, A23187 (34) allowed a second approach to the question about inward calcium current and the initiation of secretion. Figure 4 shows that the ionophore A23187 produces an influx of calcium into mast cells. The ionophore itself does not produce histamine release (Figure 5) but in the presence of extracellular calcium, A23187 causes secretion of histamine.

It appears, therefore, that influx of calcium into the mast cell or basophil (35,36) is sufficient to initiate exocytotic secretion of histamine. What then is the evidence that the membrane signal of cross-linking IgE receptors induces opening of calcium channels to allow calcium to enter the cell from the extracellular compartment? Some pertinent information has been obtained using 45-calcium as a tracer and also using strontium as a probe for calcium. Figure 6 shows an antigen concentration-response curve for histamine secretion and for 45-calcium uptake by mast cells. There is an increase in 45-calcium associated with mast cells following the membrane signal and this increased 45-calcium uptake may be dissociated from the actual exocytosis of granules (37). In other words, when exocytosis has been inhibited by preventing intracellular ATP generation, the membrane signal still produces a change which results in 45-calcium being taken up into the cell. Using strontium in place of calcium and measuring total cell strontium by atomic absorption spectroscopy, it has been shown that there is a direct relationship between the amount of strontium entering the cell and the degree of secretion (38). Since strontium entry into cells occurs spontaneously and also following antigen stimulation, it was possible to show that the mode of entry of strontium was independent of the relationship between the amount of strontium entering the cell and the degree of histamine secreted (Figure 7). As with 45-calcium uptake, inhibition of exocytosis did not prevent the accumulation of alkaline earth ion, in this case strontium, by the cell (38). Foreman and Mongar (39) have provided evidence that calcium and strontium act at a common site in histamine secretion and so it follows that the membrane signal of cross-linking IgE receptors results in an increased permeability of mast cells to calcium, and the magnitude of this permeability change is proportional to the degree of histamine secretion. Further, the magnitude of the change of membrane permeability to calcium is proportional to the magnitude of the membrane signal (Figure 6). It is not possible to state that it is the net amount of calcium taken up by the cell

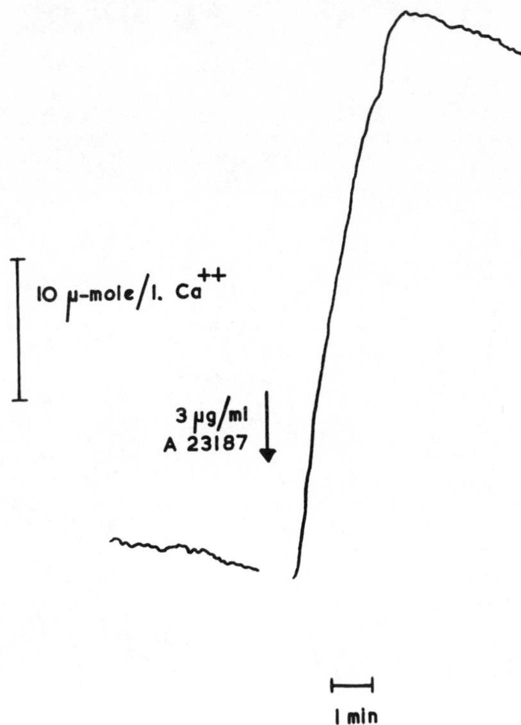


Macmillan

*Figure 4. Uptake of Ca by a mixed rat peritoneal cell suspension. The trace is of the change in absorbance of murexide, 80µM in the extracellular medium, with 1mM Ca. A23187 (6µM) was added at the point indicated with an arrow (76).*

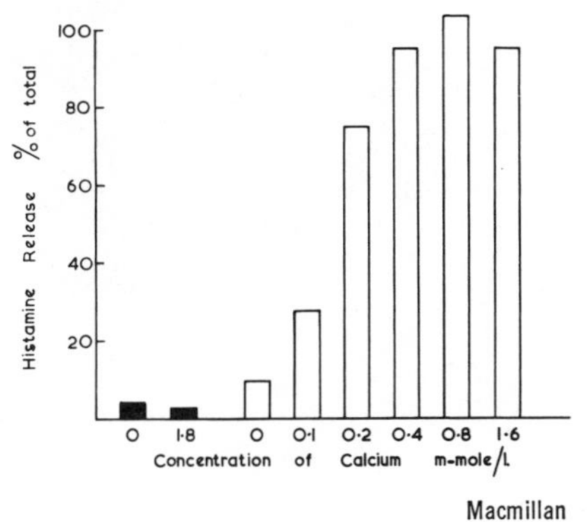


Macmillan

*Figure 5. Release of histamine from rat mast cells by Ca ions and the ionophore A23187 (0.6µM) ((■) no A23187; (□) A23187 at 0–3µg/mL) (76)*

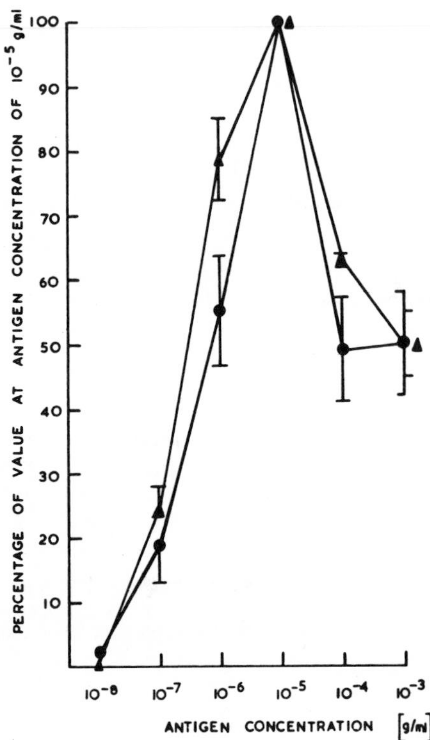


Journal of Physiology

*Figure 6. Concentration–effect curve for antigen-induced histamine release (▲—▲) and 45-Ca uptake (●—●) measured after 5-min incubation. Response is expressed as a percentage of the value obtained at an antigen concentration of 10 μg/mL, which was 43 ± 3% for histamine release and 4025 ± 820 cpm/$10^6$ cells for 45-Ca uptake. Means (± S.E.M.) from four experiments are shown (37).*

which determines histamine secretion since this has not been measured. The measurements made do not distinguish net uptake from exchange across the membrane and can thus only be interpreted in terms of change in membrane permeability to calcium brought about by the stimulus. Nevertheless, considered together, the evidence from the experiments with A23187, 45-calcium and strontium is consistent with a hypothesis in which cross-linked IgE receptors open calcium channels in the cell membrane to allow calcium to move into the cell from the extracellular medium and thereby initiate secretion.

Metabolic Energy. It has already been mentioned that exocytosis fails to occur if ATP generation within the cell is prevented. Either inhibition of glycolysis or inhibition of oxidative phosphorylation will inhibit histamine release (Figure 8) and inhibition of both processes allows virtually no histamine secretion following either antigen or ionophore stimulation (35,36,40, 41,42,43). The observation that antigen-induced and A23187-mediated secretion required ATP generation suggests that ATP is required at a point in the secretory sequence after the entry of calcium into the cell. If ATP were required for calcium entry through the channels operated by the membrane signal, then inhibitors of metabolism would be expected to block antigen-induced release but not that release caused by A23187.

Decay of Response Following Membrane Signal. If a rise in the intracellular calcium ion concentration initiates the cellular events of exocytosis, it follows that there must be a means of limiting the rise in intracellular calcium concentration and also a means of removing the calcium that is active, otherwise cellular homeostasis could not be maintained.

After the immunological membrane signal to a mast cell, there is not a continuing release of histamine until the cell content is exhausted: there is some process for limiting the degree of secretion. The experiment shown in Figure 9 demonstrates a declining sensitivity of mast cells with time after the immunological signal. Cells were stimulated in calcium-free medium by adding antigen at time t = 0 and then at the times shown on the abscissa calcium was added. The "control" degree of secretion is taken as that observed when calcium and antigen are added together. As the time between antigen addition and calcium addition is increased there is a progressive decay in the response of the cells so that at an interval of 4 min, virtually no response is seen. Decay is not due to dissociation of antigen from antibody since readding antigen after decay does not increase the response (45). A suggestion that decay might involve membrane permeability to calcium was obtained from the action of phosphatidyl serine on the decay process. Phosphatidyl serine potentiates histamine release by a mechanism which involved the response of the cells to calcium (44) and this phospholipid probably increases the membrane permeability change

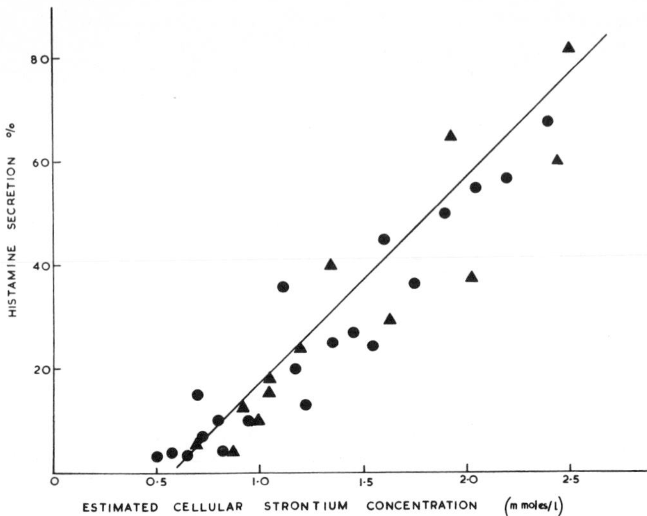


Journal of Physiology

*Figure 7. Relationship between histamine secretion and Sr accumulation determined by atomic absorption spectroscopy for antigen-stimulated cells incubated for 5 min (●) and nonstimulated cells (▲) incubated for various times. Extracellular Sr concentration was 10m*M *(38).*

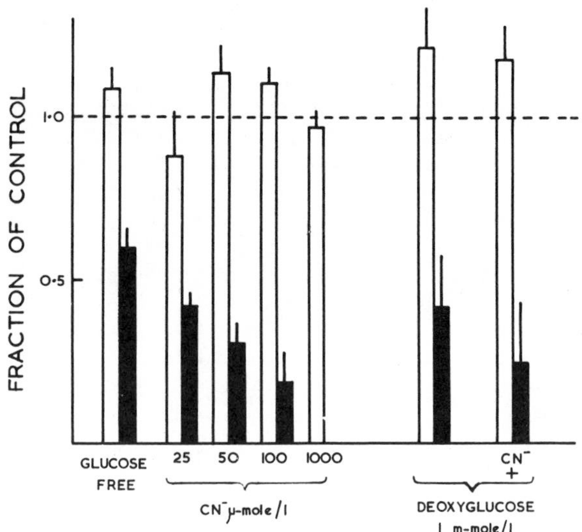


*Figure 8. Inhibition of histamine release induced by the Ca ionophore A23187 (0.6µM) (■) by removal of glucose and addition of cyanide (CN⁻) or 2-deoxy-D-glucose. Cells were preincubated with inhibitors for 30 min before addition of A23187. The action of inhibitors on release caused by a non-Ca-dependent ionophore, X537A is shown for comparison (□).*

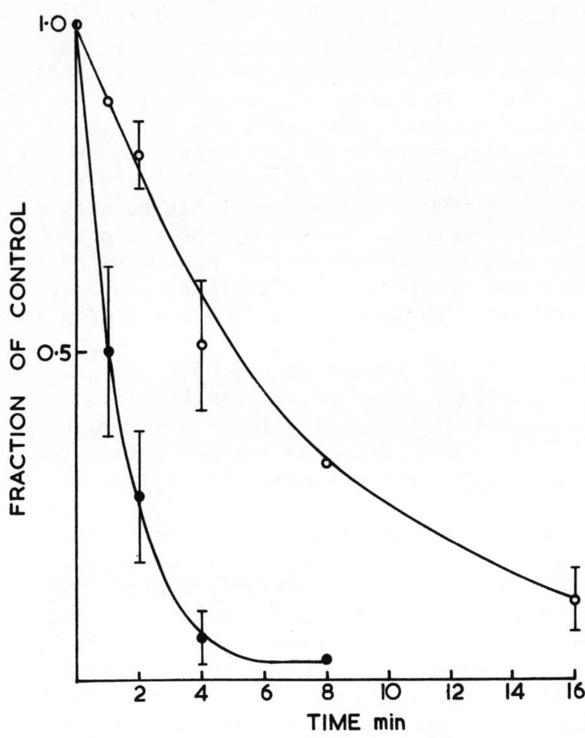


Journal of Physiology

*Figure 9. Decay of response of rat mast cells stimulated by an antigen–antibody reaction to Ca, with time: (●—●) without phosphatidyl serine; (○—○) with phosphatidyl serine, 10μg/mL. Control histamine releases were 18–54% of total without phospholipid and 37–64% in the presence of phospholipid (45).*

to calcium caused by the cross-linking membrane stimulus (37). The phospholipid caused a slowing of the decay in the response to calcium (Figure 9) which would be consistent with the view that decay represents calcium channel closure if phosphatidyl serine is able to increase calcium influx through channels which are closing.

Direct measurement of membrane permeability to 45-calcium reveals (Figure 10) that the increase in membrane permeability to 45-calcium brought about by the immunological stimulus decays with a time-course identical to the time-course of the decay of the cells' responsiveness towards calcium. Assuming that the phenomenon of decay represents closure of the calcium channels opened by a membrane signal, it follows (i) that artificial calcium channels should bypass the decay and cause the cell to respond and (ii) that release induced by artificial channels should not show decay. It has been demonstrated that cells whose response to calcium following an immunological stimulus has totally decayed are still fully responsive to the action of the ionophore A23187 (45). Figure 11 shows that histamine release induced by A23187 does not decay: calcium added up to 16 min after the ionophore was equally effective in causing secretion as calcium added with A23187 (compare Figure 9).

Thus, mast cells and basophils (26,45,46) appear to have a mechanism for limiting calcium entry into the cell which follows the cross-linking membrane signal. It is presumed that calcium already entered is removed from the intracellular site of action by mitochondria (47,48) or a plasma-membrane calcium pump (48).

Cyclic AMP. Drugs such as the β-adrenoceptor agonists, methylxanthines, prostaglandins and histamine itself cause an increase in mast cell or basophil levels of cyclic adenosine 3':5' monophosphate, and this is associated with inhibition of histamine secretion induced by an immunological stimulus (49,50,51). Whilst cyclic AMP itself does not inhibit histamine secretion induced by an immunological stimulus, the dibutyryl derivative which is able to pass through cell membranes is an inhibitor of secretion (52, 54), as is adenosine 3':5' cyclic phosphorothioate, which also passes into cells (53).

Figure 12 shows an interesting contrast in the inhibition of histamine secretion by dibutyryl cyclic AMP when two different means of releasing histamine are compared. Histamine secretion induced by the immunoligical stimulus is inhibited, whereas that induced by the ionophore A23187 is not. It follows that cyclic AMP must inhibit histamine secretion at, or before, the entry of calcium into the cell since if it acted after calcium entry, the secretion induced by both immunological stimulus and ionophore would be inhibited.

There is no evidence that cyclic AMP interferes with the antigen-antibody reaction and so it is plausible that cyclic AMP inhibits histamine secretion either by blocking directly the calcium channels or by interfering with the coupling between the

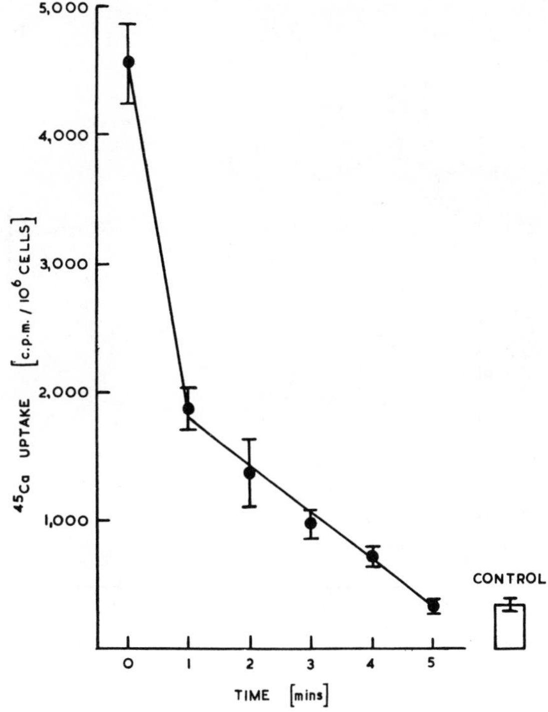


Journal of Physiology

*Figure 10. Time-course of the change in 45-Ca uptake after antigen-stimulation of rat mast cells. The 45-Ca was added at time* t *(min) to cells challenged with antigen in the presence of Ca, 1mM (non-labeled) at* t = *0. Incubation proceeded for 5 min after the addition of 45-Ca. The control bar is the uptake of 45-Ca in the absence of antigen stimulation* (37)*.*

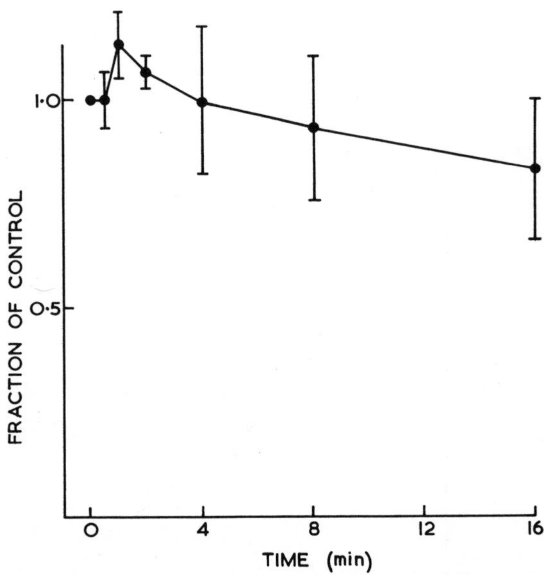


*Figure 11. Response to Ca added at various times to mast cells treated with ionophore A23187 (0.6μM at* t = *0). Histamine release obtained after adding Ca is expressed as a fraction of the release obtained by adding Ca and ionophore simultaneously to the cells (44–77% of total) (45).*

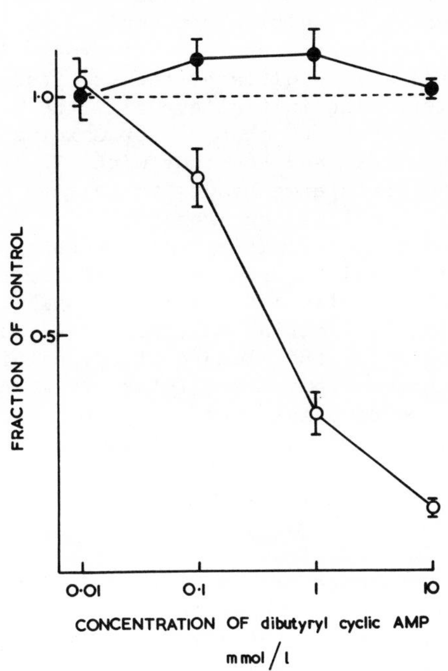


Biochemical Pharmacology

*Figure 12. Concentration–response relationship for the action of dibutyryl cyclic AMP on histamine release induced by antigen (22% of total in the absence of dibutyryl cyclic AMP) (○—○) and A23187 (77% of total in the absence of dibutyryl cyclic AMP) (●—●). Cells with or without dibutyryl cyclic AMP were incubated for 30 min before the addition of the histamine release agent (54).*

cross-linking of IgE receptors and the opening of calcium channels. Figure 13 shows that dibutyryl cyclic AMP and the phosphodiesterase inhibitor, theophylline, which cause increased intracellular levels of cyclic AMP, both inhibit the increased membrane permeability to 45-calcium caused by the immunological stimulus. No inhibition of 45-calcium transport by A23187 was observed.

To summarize what has been said about the mechanism of histamine release. Specific IgE binds to discrete receptors in the membrane of mast cells or basophils and these receptors are cross-linked by the binding of multivalent antigen to the bivalent IgE antibody attached to the receptors. The cross-linking constitutes the membrane signal which initiates the exocytosis of histamine containing granules. The initial event in the secretory process is the opening of a membrane channel for calcium through which this ion enters the cell and together with ATP brings about the fusion of cell and granule membranes to release the granule contents into the extracellular environment. The degree of secretion is controlled by (i) limiting calcium entry by closure of the calcium channels (ii) by removal of calcium from its active site. Intracellular cyclic AMP exerts an inhibitory modulating effect on secretion by limiting calcium entry and this agent is a possible messenger for the closure of the calcium channels. The kinetics of changes in intracellular cyclic AMP namely, a fall followed by a return to basal level (55) is consistent with a model in which cyclic AMP controls calcium channel opening.

## Mechanism of Action of Antiallergic Drugs

Possible Sites of Action. It will be evident from what has been said above that there are several possibilities for the use of drugs to interfere with the sequence of events leading to release of preformed mediators of allergic reactions. Possible modes of action for antiallergic drugs include: inhibition of antibody synthesis, inhibition of antibody binding to its Fc receptor, interference with the coupling between membrane signal and calcium channels, blocking calcium channels, inhibition of cellular metabolism, increase of intracellular cyclic AMP levels, and antagonism of released mediators themselves.

Cromoglycate-like drugs inhibit mediator release from tissues which have been sensitized with exogenous IgE antibody (passive sensitization) (56) so it is unlikely that these drugs exert their antiallergic activity by interfering with antibody synthesis. Furthermore, there is no evidence that antiallergic drugs are capable of inhibiting the binding of antigen to antibody, or the binding of antibody to Fc receptors (57).

Cromoglycate and many of the other antiallergic drugs have little or no antagonistic action against the mediators of allergic reactions, that is, they have no demonstrable antihistamine, anti-SRS (Slow Reacting Substance) or anti-5-hydroxy tryptamine

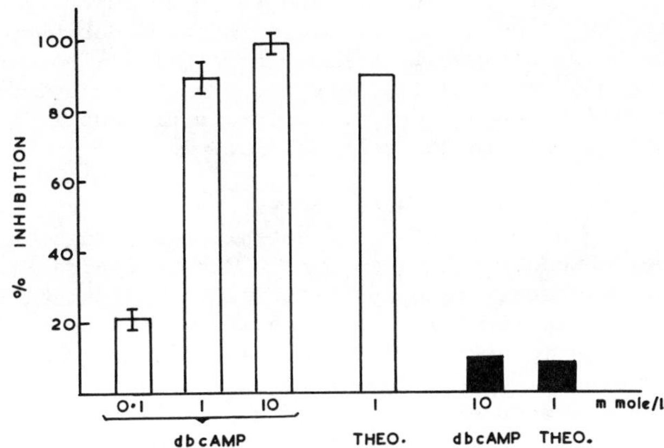


Journal of Physiology

*Figure 13. Inhibition by dibutyryl cyclic AMP and theophylline of antigen-induced 45-Ca uptake (□) and A23187-induced 45-Ca uptake (■) into rat mast cells. Uninhibited values from which percent inhibition was calculated were: 3150 ± 300 cpm/$10^6$ cells and 5550 ± 350 cpm/$10^6$ cells for 45-Ca uptake induced by antigen and A23187, respectively. Corresponding histamine releases were 43 ± 11% and 62 ± 2% (37).*

activity (58,59,60,61).

Action on Mast Cells. From these experimental observations it follows that antiallergic drugs act by preventing the mediator release from mast cells through an action at a stage between the binding of antigen to IgE and the release of the granule content from the cell.

It has been shown that cromoglycate, 1-30 μM inhibits histamine release from rat peritoneal mast cells (62,63,64) and similar concentrations inhibit release from the mast cells of human and monkey lung *in vitro* (65). The clinically active antiallergic drugs are only effective when applied directly to the lung by inhalation and so the relationship between clinically active concentrations at the mast cell surface and those concentrations effective *in vitro* is unknown. It should be pointed out that histamine release induced by antigen from human basophils is not inhibited by cromoglycate or other antiallergic drugs (65,66), indicating a rather specific receptor for cromoglycate present in human mast cells and not present in human basophils.

Inhibition of A23187-Induced Release. Some light has been shed on the mechanism of action of antiallergic drugs using histamine release induced by the ionophore A23187. Figure 14 shows that concentrations of cromoglycate which inhibit histamine release induced by an immunological-type stimulus fail to inhibit histamine release induced by A23187: these findings have been confirmed at several different ionophore and calcium concentrations (43). By the argument already used, this implies that cromoglycate acts to inhibit antigen-induced histamine release at the level of calcium entry into the mast cell through the calcium channel opened by the immunological stimulus. The same findings were obtained with the antiallergic drugs doxantrazole and bufrolin (43,67). There are, however, reports that cromoglycate will inhibit release induced by A23187 (68,69) but in those studies no direct comparison between immunologically-mediated and ionophore-induced release was made, and only a limited inhibition of A23187-induced release was achieved. It has been confirmed that doxantrazole (up to 0.3 nM) does not inhibit A23187-induced histamine release (69). It appears that cromoglycate has some inhibitory activity on A23187-induced histamine release but it should be emphasized that at concentrations which almost totally inhibit immunologically-mediated release, there is in the same experiment, no inhibition of A23187-induced release (Figure 14).

Inhibition of Calcium Movement. Figure 15 shows that cromoglycate inhibits membrane permeability to 45-calcium over the same concentration range for the inhibition of histamine release. Furthermore when cromoglycate was compared with dibutyryl cyclic AMP and doxantrazole, the relative potencies of the drugs for inhibition of histamine release (doxantrazole:cromoglycate:dibutyryl

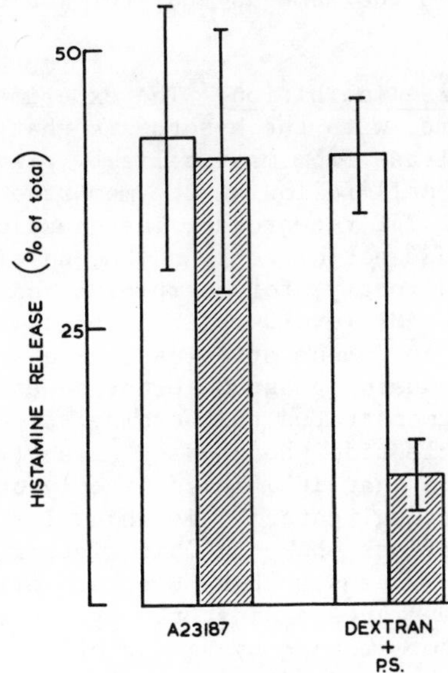


Biochemical Pharmacology

*Figure 14. Action of cromoglycate (60μM) (▨) on histamine release induced by either A23187 (2.5μM) or dextran and phosphatidyl serine. Open columns are releases in the absence of cromoglycate. Cromoglycate was added together with the releasing agent (54).*

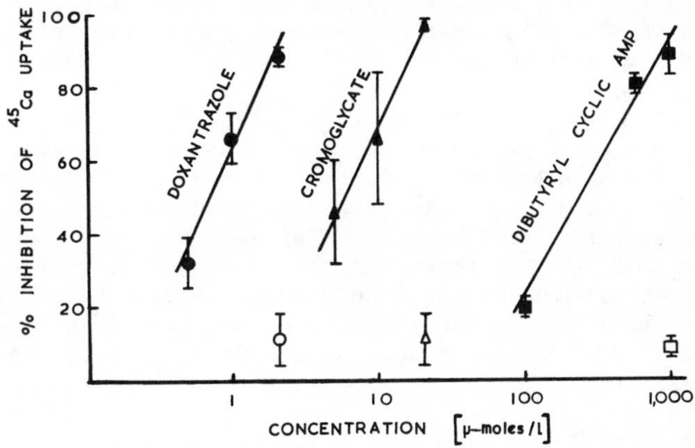


British Journal of Pharmacology

*Figure 15. Inhibition by doxantrazole, cromoglycate, and dibutyryl cyclic AMP of 45-Ca uptake induced by antigen (filled symbols) or A23187 (open symbols). The 45-Ca uptakes in the absence of inhibitor were 924 cpm/$10^6$ cells for antigen and 5274 cpm/$10^6$ cells for A23187. Corresponding histamine secretions were 26% and 55% (70).*

cAMP = 20:1:0.02) was the same as that for inhibition of calcium uptake (70).

Phosphodiesterase Inhibition. The experimental evidence is consistent, therefore, with the hypothesis that antiallergic drugs inhibit mediator release from mast cells by preventing the influx of calcium into the cell following the membrane signal provided by the cross-linking of IgE receptors. The question then arises as to whether these drugs act directly on the calcium channels or whether they act indirectly, for example, by causing a rise of intracellular cyclic AMP levels which in turn would block calcium transport following an immune stimulus (see above).

Several studies using phosphodiesterase enzymes from non-mast cell sources have demonstrated that cromoglycate inhibits the activity of cyclic nucleotide phosphodiesterase (71,72,73). However, it must be emphasized that inhibition is only obtained at high concentrations of cromoglycate ($K_i$ is about 1 mM); much higher than those concentrations which inhibit histamine and SRS-A release from *in vitro* systems such as the rat peritoneal mast cell. Whilst this evidence argues against the hypothesis that cromoglycate inhibits mediator release by virtue of its action on phosphodiesterase, it must be pointed out that the clinically active concentrations of cromoglycate in human lung are unknown. It is possible that the active concentration in man could be very high because cromoglycate is inhaled as solid particles which could give rise to high local concentrations at the human lung mast cell surface. Furthermore, the studies on phosphodiesterase have been done on broken cell preparations from tissues far removed from those where the drug is active. The only relevant model for the valid test of the hypothesis is the pure preparation of human lung mast cells and some progress towards this has been made.

Synergism with Activators of Adenylate Cyclase. Cromoglycate (30 μM) caused an elevation of cyclic AMP levels in human lymphocytes and it has also been shown that cromoglycate acts synergistically with isoprenaline (β-adrenoceptor agonist) to inhibit immunologically-mediated histamine release (63,74). Isoprenaline stimulates adenylate cyclase, and thus a phosphodiesterase inhibitor would be expected to act synergistically with such a drug in the elevation of cyclic AMP levels. However, at least one study (77) has failed to obtain synergistic effects with cromoglycate and isoprenaline.

Kinetics of Inhibitory Activity. Antiallergic drugs exibit some unique characteristics with respect to their kinetics of action. Figure 16 shows that the inhibitory activity by cromoglycate is maximal when it is added together with the immunological stimulus. Thereafter, with increasing interval between stimulation and addition of cromoglycate, the inhibitory activity declines to virtually zero before making a partial recovery. The

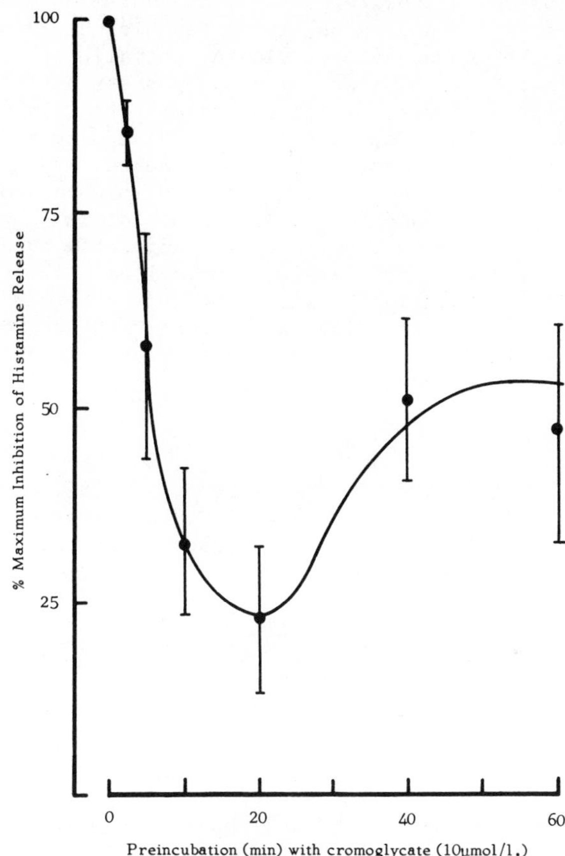


*Figure 16. Inhibition of histamine release by cromoglycate (10μM) added to cells either mixed with, or at various intervals prior to, the stimulus to release histamine. Each point is the mean and SE mean of 4 experiments and is expressed as a percentage of the maximum inhibition in each experiment. (Data supplied by Dr. L. G. Garland—unpublished).*

time course of changing inhibitory activity has been reported for several antiallergic drugs and also for the phosphodiesterase inhibitor theophylline (57).

In conclusion, a knowledge of the mechanism of mediator release from mast cells and basophils has enabled us to produce a hypothesis on the mechansim of action of antiallergic drugs. Cromoglycate and other similar compounds possess antiallergic activity by virtue of their ability to prevent the release of mediators from mast cells which have been stimulated by an antigen - IgE reaction on the membrane. The drugs prevent mediator release by blocking the calcium uptake into mast cells which follows the immunological stimulus and this blocking of calcium channels by antiallergic drugs may be brought about indirectly by an elevation of intracellular cyclic AMP levels. Cromoglycate is a phosphodiesterase inhibitor, and in the absence of any other evidence, it is suggested that this activity may represent the action of the drug at a molecular level, although this hypothesis still has to be tested in isolated human mast cells.

## Literature Cited


1. Altounyan, R.E.C. Acta Allerg. (1967). 22, 487.
2. Cox, J.S.G., Beach, J.E., Blair, A.M.J.N., Clarke, A.J., King, J., Lee, T.B., Loveday, D.E.E., Moss, G.F., Orr, T.S.C., Ritchie, J.T. & Sheard, P. Adv. Drug Res. (1970). 5, 115.
3. Ishizaka, K. & Ishizaka, T. J. Immun. (1967). 99, 1187.
4. Tada, T. Progr. Allergy (1975). 19, 122.
5. Katz, D.H. J. Allergy clin. Immun. (1978). 62, 44.
6. Ishizaka, K. Adv. Immun. (1976). 23, 1.
7. Carson, D.A., Kulczycki, A. & Metzger, H. J. Immun. (1975). 114, 158.
8. Conrad, D.H., Berczi, I. & Froese, A. Immunochemistry (1976). 13, 329.
9. Ishizaka, T., König, W., Kurata, M., Mauser, L. & Ishizaka, K. J. Immun. (1975). 115, 1078.
10. Metzger, H., Budman, D. & Lucky, P. Immunochemistry (1976). 13, 417.
11. Mendoza, G. & Metzger, H. Nature (1976). 264, 548.
12. Mendoza, G. & Metzger, H. Nature (1976). 264, 550.
13. Newman, S.A., Rossi, G. & Metzger, H. Proc. Natl. Acad. Sci. U.S.A. (1977). 74, 869.
14. Isersky, C., Mendoza, G. & Metzger, H. J. Immun. (1977). 119, 123.
15. Ishizaka, T. & Ishizaka, D. J. Immun. (1978). 120, 800.
16. Landsteiner, K. J. exp. Med. (1924). 39, 631.
17. Levine, B.B. J. Immun. (1965). 94, 111.
18. Magro, A. & Alexander, A. J. Immun. (1974). 112, 1757.
19. Siraganian, R.P., Hook, W.A. & Levine, B.B. Immunochemistry

(1975). 12, 149.
20. Ishizaka, T., Ishizaka, K., Johansson, S.G.O. & Bennich, H. J. Immun. (1969). 102, 884.
21. Ishizaka, K. & Ishizaka, T. J. Immun. (1969). 103, 588.
22. Goldstein, I.J., Hollerman, C.E. & Smith, E.E. Biochemistry (1965). 4, 876.
23. Kochwa, S., Terry, W.D., Capra, J.D. & Yang, N.L. Ann. N.Y. Acad. Sci., (1971). 190, 49.
24. Keller, R. Clin. exp. Immun. (1973). 13, 139.
25. Siraganian, R.P. & Siraganian, P.A. J. Immun. (1975). 114, 886.
26. Mongar, J.L. & Schild, H.O. J. Physiol. (1958). 140, 272.
27. Lichtenstein, L.M. & Osler, A.G. J. exp. Med. (1964). 120, 507.
28. Douglas, W.W. Br. J. Pharmac. (1968). 34, 451.
29. Weiss, G.B. Ann. Rev. Pharmac. (1974). 14, 343.
30. Van Breemen, C. Arch, int. physiol. biochem. (1969). 77, 710.
31. Foreman, J.C. & Mongar, J.L. Br. J. Pharmac. (1973). 48, 527.
32. Kanno. T., Cochrane, D.E. & Douglas, W.W. Cand. J. Physiol. Pharmac. (1973). 57, 1001.
33. Tasaka, K., Sugiyama, K., Komoto, S. & Yamasaka, H. Proc. Japan Acad. (1970). 46, 317.
34. Reed, P.W. & Lardy, H.A. J. Biol. Chem. (1972). 247, 6970.
35. Foreman, J.C., Mongar, J.L. & Gomperts, B.D. Nature (1973). 245, 249.
36. Lichtenstein L.M. J. Immun. (1975). 114, 1692.
37. Foreman, J.C., Hallett, M.B. & Mongar, J.L. J. Physiol. (1977). 271, 193.
38. Foreman, J.C., Hallett, M.B. & Mongar, J.L. J. Physiol. (1977). 271, 233.
39. Foreman, J.C. & Mongar, J.L. J. Physiol. (1972). 224, 753.
40. Diamant, B., Norn, S., Felding, P., Olsen, N., Ziebell, A. & Nissen, J. Int. Archs. Allergy appl. Immun. (1974). 47, 894.
41. Mongar, J.L. & Schild, H.O. J. Physiol. (1957). 135, 301.
42. Johansen, T. & Chakravarty, N. Naunyn Schmiedebergs Arch. exp. Path. Pharmak. (1972). 275, 457.
43. Garland, L.G. & Mongar, J.L. Int. Archs. Allergy Appl. Immun. (1976). 50, 27.
44. Mongar, J.L. & Svec, P. Br. J. Pharmac. (1972). 46, 741.
45. Foreman, J.C. & Garland, L.G. J. Physiol. (1974). 239, 381.
46. Lichtenstein, L.M. J. Immun. (1971). 107, 1122.
47. Carafoli, E. & Crompton, M. Ann. N.Y. Acad. Sci. (1978). 307, 269.
48. Baker, P.F. Ann. N.Y. Acad. Sci. (1978). 307, 250.
49. Assem, E.S.K. & Schild, H.O. Br. J. Pharmac. (1971). 42, 620.
50. Lichtenstein, L.M. & Margolis, S. Science (1968). 161, 902.
51. Bourne, H.R., Lichtenstein, L.M. & Melmon, K.L. J. Immun. (1972). 108, 695.
52. Lichtenstein, L.M. & DeBernardo, R. J. Immun. (1972). 107, 1131.
53. Eckstein, F. & Foreman, J.C. FEBS Lett. (1978). 91, 182.
54. Foreman, J.C., Mongar, J.L., Gomperts, B.D. & Garland, L.G.

Biochem. Pharmac. (1975). 24, 538.
55. Kaliner, M. & Austen, K.F. J. Immun. (1974). 112, 664.
56. Orr, T.S.C., Gwilliam, J. & Cox, J.S.G. Immunology (1970). 19, 469.
57. Garland, L.G. Ph.D. Thesis:Univ. Lond. (1975).
58. Broughton, B.A., Chaplan, P., Knowles, P., Lunt, E., Pain, D., Wooldridge, K.R., Ford, R., Marshall, S., Walker, J.L. & Maxwell, D.R. Nature (1974). 251, 650.
59. Evans, D.P., Gilman, D.J., Thomson, D.S. & Waring, W.S. Nature (1974). 250, 592.
60. Batchelor, J.F., Garland, L.G., Green, A.F., Hughes, D.T.D., Follenfant, M.J., Gorvin, J.H., Hodson, H.F. & Tateson, J.E. Lancet (1975). 1, 1169.
61. Cox, J.S.G. Nature (1967). 216, 1328.
62. Herzig, D.J. & Kusner, E.J. J. Pharmac. exp. ther. (1975). 194, 457.
63. Taylor, W.A., Francis, D.H., Sheldon, D. & Roitt, I.M. Int. Archs. Allergy appl. Immun. (1974). 46, 104.
64. Garland, L.G. Br. J. Pharmac. (1973). 49, 128.
65. Assem, E.S.K. & Mongar, J.L. Int. Archs. Allergy Appl. Immun. (1970). 38, 68.
66. Lichtenstein, L.M. & Adkinson, N.F. J. Immun. (1969). 103, 866.
67. Garland, L.G. Unpublished observations.
68. Johnson, H.G. & Bach, M.K. J. Immun. (1975). 114, 514.
69. Nagai, H., Kelly, K. & Sehon, A.H. Int. Archs. Allergy appl. Immun. (1978). 56, 307.
70. Foreman, J.C., Hallett, M.B. & Mongar, J.L. Br. J. Pharmac. (1977). 59, 473.
71. Lavin, N., Rachelefsky, G.S. & Kaplan, S.A. J. Allergy clin. Immun. (1978). 57, 80.
72. Roy, A.C. & Warren, B.T. Biochem. Pharmac. (1974). 23, 917.
73. Tateson, J.E. & Trist, D.G. Life Sciences (1976). 18, 153.
74. Assem, E.S.K. & Richter, A.W. Immunology (1971). 21, 729.
75. Thon, I-L. & Uvnäs, B. Acta Physiol. Scand. (1966). 67, 455.
76. Foreman, J.C. In Drugs and Transport Processes ed. B.A. Callingham. (1974). Macmillan: London, p. 222.
77. Koopman, W.J., Orange, R.P. & Austen, K.F. J. Immun. (1970). 105, 1096.

RECEIVED August 6, 1979.

# 3

# Structure-Activity Relationships in a New Class of Pyrimido[4,5-*b*]quinoline Antiallergy Agents

T. H. ALTHUIS, S. B. KADIN, L. J. CZUBA, P. F. MOORE, and H.-J. HESS

Central Research, Pfizer Inc., Groton, CT 06340

The discovery of Intal (I, disodium cromoglycate, DSCG) a decade ago provided a new therapeutic approach to the treatment of asthma (1,2). Pharmacologically, Intal differs from previously used drugs in that it is not a bronchodilator, antihistamine, or antiinflammatory agent. Intal acts by inhibiting the release of the mediators of anaphylaxis and thus offers an alternative to the conventional approach which seeks to alleviate the symptoms of an allergic attack with bronchodilators (3).

**INTAL**

**Structure:**

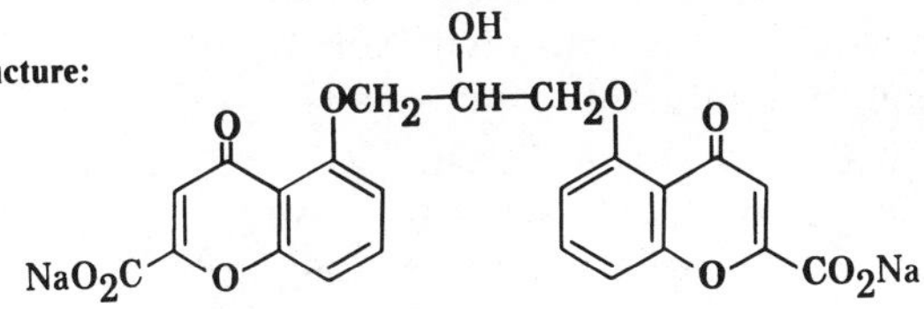

OH | $OCH_2$—CH—$CH_2O$ ... $NaO_2C$ ... $CO_2Na$

I

**Disodium Cromoglycate (DSCG)**

However, Intal does not provide relief in all asthmatic patients (4) and is not active following oral administration. It is administered by a specially developed Spinhaler which is designed to deliver the drug into the lung as a dry powder which, it has been suggested, may further irritate already hypersensitive bronchial tissue (5).

Therefore, much of the past decade's research seeking new drugs for the treatment of obstructive lung diseases has been directed toward the development of an orally active Intal-like agent. As a result, several agents with oral activity in experimental animal models or in man have now been reported. Among these are the novel pyrimido[4,5-b]quinoline-2-carboxylic acid esters described in this chapter.

0-8412-0536-1/80/47-118-037$08.00/0

The antiallergy activity of the pyrimido[4,5-b]quinolines was determined using the 48-hour IgE-mediated rat passive cutaneous anaphylaxis (PCA) procedure (6,7), which is widely used as a screen to identify agents with a pharmacological profile similar to Intal. The compounds were administered to groups of 5 to 7 rats either intravenously in saline at pH 7.2-8.0 or orally in an aqueous solution near physiological pH (8). Since these compounds did not demonstrate antagonism toward the anaphylactic mediators, histamine and serotonin, their activity is an indication of inhibition of mediator release.

Following is an account of the discovery of this series and of the structure activity relationships that have been established (9). The activity of representative members is compared with that of other orally active experimental agents reported in the literature.

## The Discovery of Ethyl 3,4-Dihydro-4-oxopyrimido[4,5-b]-quinoline-2-carboxylate

The steps leading to the discovery of the pyrimido[4,5-b]quinoline-2-carboxylic acid series are summarized in Figure 1. This series was developed by several successive structural modifications that started with 3,4-dihydro-4-oxoquinazoline-2-carboxylic acid (**II**). This acid displays an intravenous $ED_{50}$ of 10 mg/kg, thus being about one-tenth as potent as DSCG. Like DSCG it is inactive by oral administration. Other related quinazoline acids and esters with substituents in the carbocyclic ring did not exhibit significantly increased potency intravenously or have oral activity (8).

Next examined were novel acid and ester prototypes of fused pyrimidines expected to exhibit different degrees of lipophilicity from that of the quinazolines. An example is the pyrido[2,3-d]pyrimidine ester III, which exhibits 5 times greater intravenous potency than the quinazoline acid II, and, in fact, approaches the activity of DSCG, although again no oral activity was observed. A 2-3 fold increase in intravenous potency was obtained when a highly lipophilic aromatic carbocyclic ring was fused to the quinazoline, to give benzo[g]quinazoline-2-carboxylic acid IV. The ethyl ester (V) of this acid, however, was the first compound in this series which demonstrated oral activity, albeit at the relatively high dose of 100 mg/kg.

The increased potency of the pyrido[2,3-d]pyrimidine ester (III) and the achievement of oral activity with the benzo[g]quinazoline ester (V) suggested the preparation of 3,4-dihydro-4-oxopyrimido[4,5-b]quinoline-2-carboxylic acid (VI) and its corresponding ethyl ester (VII) which combine the features of III and V. This new acid and ethyl ester exhibit PCA activity 4 to 8 times that of DSCG and thus are about 50 to 100 times

| COMPOUND | STRUCTURE | R | RAT PCA, $ED_{50}$, mg/kg i.v. | RAT PCA, $ED_{50}$, mg/kg p.o. |
|---|---|---|---|---|
| I | DSCG | | 0.8 | Inactive at 300 mg/kg |
| II | 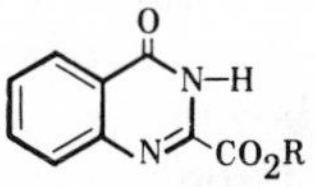 quinazolinone, N–H, $CO_2R$ | H | 10 | Inactive at 100 mg/kg |
| III | 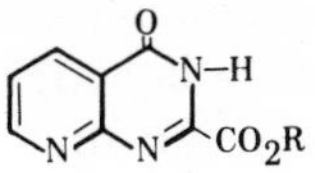 pyrido-pyrimidinone, N–H, $CO_2R$ | Et | 2 | Inactive at 100 mg/kg |
| IV | 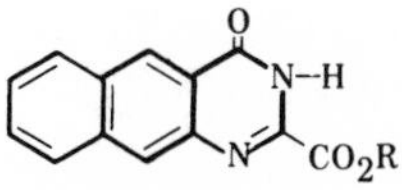 benzo[g]quinazolinone, N–H, $CO_2R$ | Na | 5 | Inactive at 100 mg/kg |
| V | | Et | — | >100 (38% at 100 mg/kg) |
| VI | 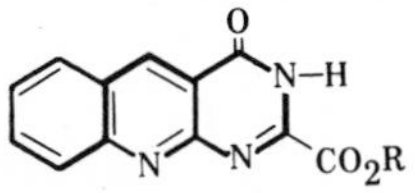 pyrimido[4,5-b]quinolinone, N–H, $CO_2R$ | Na | 0.2 | 25 |
| VII | | Et | 0.1 | 3 |

*Figure 1. Antiallergy activity of fused 4-oxopyrimidine-2-carboxylic acids and esters*

more potent than II, our original quinazoline lead. However, while the acid (VI) displayed only moderate oral activity ($ED_{50}$ = 25 mg/kg), the ethyl ester (VII) had an oral $ED_{50}$ of 3 mg/kg. Additionally, VII did not antagonize the increase in vascular permeability caused by intradermally administered histamine in the rat (10 mg/kg i.v. or 100 mg/kg p.o.), did not antagonize histamine induced bronchoconstriction in conscious guinea pigs (100 mg/kg p.o.), and had no antiinflammatory activity against carrageenin-induced rat foot edema (10 mg/kg, p.o.).

These results suggested that, like DSCG, the ethyl ester VII inhibits the release of the mediators of anaphylaxis and that an in depth pursuit of this lead was warranted.

## Chemistry of 3,4-Dihydro-4-oxopyrimido[4,5-b]quinoline-2-carboxylic Acids

Synthetic routes employed in the preparation of various substituted compounds of this new series are shown in Figures 2-4. The critical intermediates for synthesis are the appropriately substituted 2-aminoquinoline-3-carboxamides (XI, Figure 2). These intermediates were prepared from substituted 2-nitrobenzaldehydes (VIII) by two complementary routes. First, the nitrobenzaldehydes may be reduced with ferrous sulfate and ammonia to the 2-aminobenzaldehydes (IX), which are then condensed with cyanoacetamide in a Knoevenagel reaction to afford the respective 2-aminoquinoline-3-carboxamides (XI) (10). A more versatile route involves the condensation of the 2-nitrobenzaldehyde with cyanoacetamide to give the α-cyanocinnamamide, X. This method avoids the difficulties of working with aminoaldehydes and, in cases where the benzene ring has a suitable halogen substituent, permits the use of nucleophilic aromatic substitution reactions to introduce other substituents, such as sulfur. Amide X is then reduced with iron and acetic acid to give the 2-aminoquinoline-3-carboxamides, XI (11).

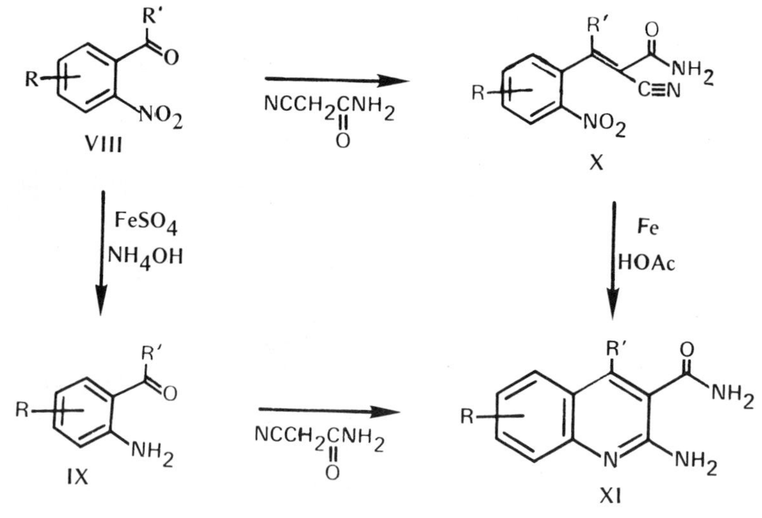

*Figure 2. Synthesis of substituted 2-aminoquinoline-3-carboxamides*

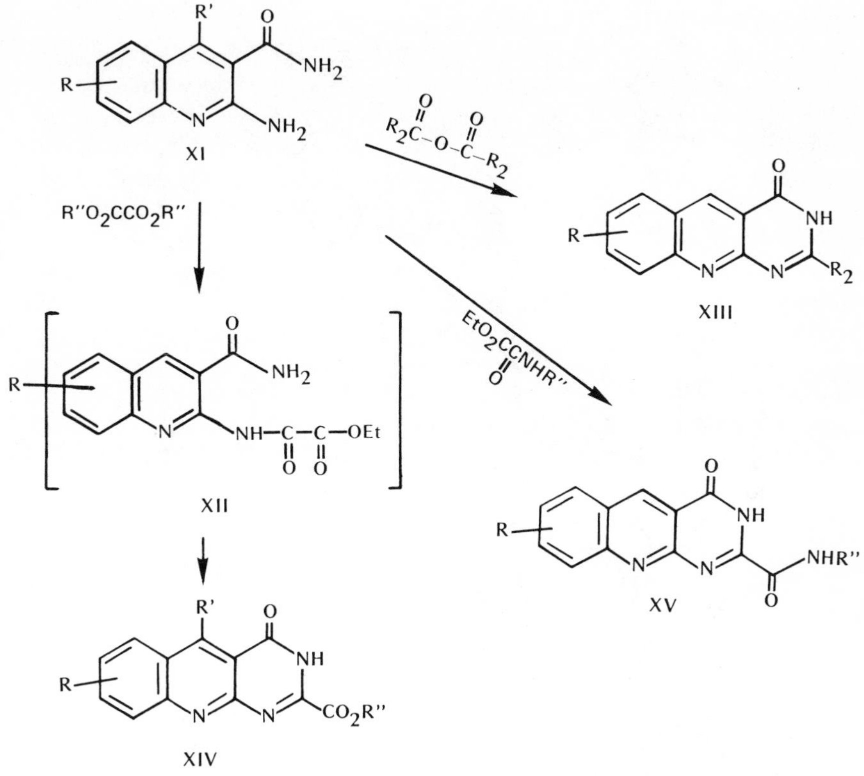

*Figure 3. Synthesis of substituted 3,4-dihydro-4-oxopyrimido[4,5-*b*]quinoline-2-carboxylic acids and related compounds*

The condensation of 2-aminoquinoline-3-carboxamides (XI) with acetic anhydride was reported to yield 2-methylpyrimido[4,5-b]quinolin-4(3H)-ones (XIII) (**12**). In an extension of this reaction (Figure 3), heating aminoamides XI with alkyl oxalates or alkyl oxamates yielded the new pyrimido[4,5-b]quinoline-2-carboxylic acid esters (XIV) and amides (XV), respectively.

Figure 4 depicts a number of standard transformations in which these pyrimido[4,5-b]quinoline-2-carboxylic acid esters (XIV) are shown to be useful synthetic intermediates. They may be transesterified to other esters in cases where dialkyl oxalates are not readily available. They also react directly with amines at room temperature or at slightly elevated temperatures to afford amides (XV), and undergo rapid hydrolysis in

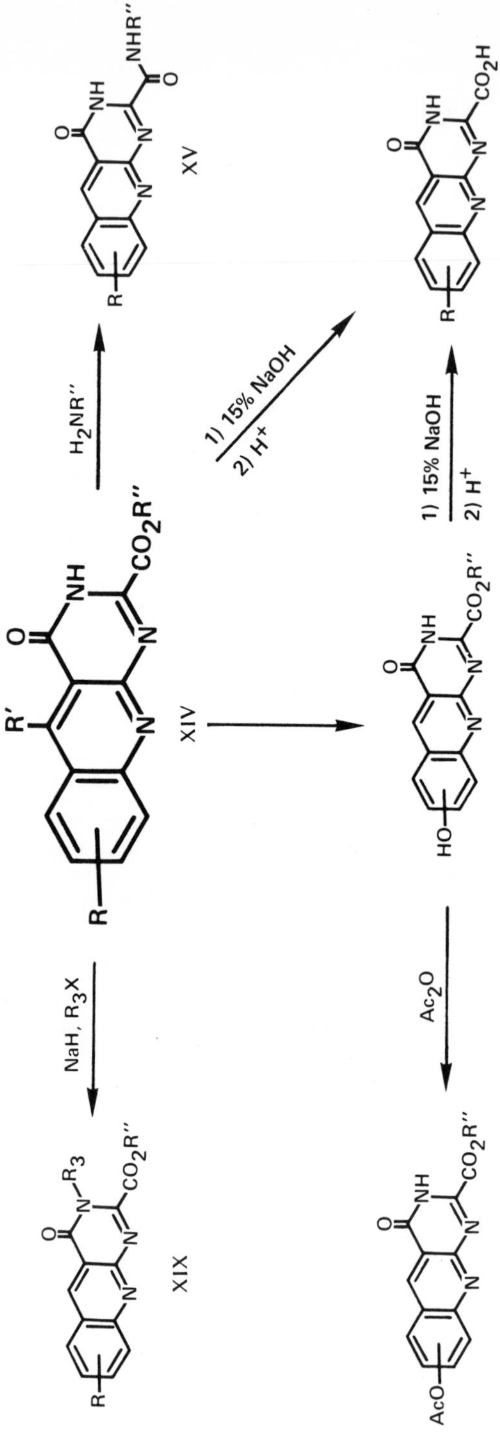

*Figure 4. Reactions of 3,4-dihydro-4-oxopyrimido[4,5-b]quinoline-2-carboxylic acid derivatives*

dilute aqueous sodium hydroxide at room temperature to give the corresponding acids (XVI). Upon heating, these acids undergo decarboxylation to give pyrimido[4,5-b]quinolin-4(3H)-ones (XIII, Figure 3, $R_2$ = H).

Hydrolysis of esters XIV to the acids XVI is considerably slower in aqueous acid than in base. As weak bases, these compounds are sparingly soluble in weak organic acids, such as acetic acid, and in aqueous mineral acids. This contrasts with their solubility in strong non-aqueous acids, such as sulfuric and trifluoroacetic acid. Esters are generally soluble in dilute sodium hydroxide because of the acidic proton at position 3 of the heterocyclic nucleus.

In cases where R is a benzyloxy substituent, the use of strong non-aqueous acids, particularly sulfuric and trifluoroacetic acids, provides a convenient means of preparing the hydroxy quinolines XVII by debenzylation (13). The hydroxy compounds may be acetylated by standard techniques to afford XVIII. Formation of the sodium salt of XIV using sodium hydride in DMF, followed by reaction with an alkyl halide, leads to the 3-substituted compounds (XIX).

## Pyrimido[4,5-b]quinoline SAR

The reaction sequence described in the foregoing section was used to synthesize compounds which are up to 400 times more potent intravenously than Intal and 10 times more potent orally than the parent pyrimido[4,5-b]quinoline ester. Figures 5-10 depict the effects of substituent variation on activity in the PCA procedure.

**Acid derivatives:** First, various pyrimido[4,5-b]quinoline-2-carboxylic acid derivatives were examined (Figure 5). The nearly equal activity of the acid VI and corresponding ethyl (VII) and butyl (XX) esters suggests that the acid is the active species. However, the ethyl ester is definitely advantageous for oral activity, being nearly 10 times more potent than the butyl ester or the carboxylic acid. This suggests that the lipophilic character of the ester is important for oral absorption. The carboxamide (XXI) which may not be readily hydrolyzed to the acid *in vivo* exhibits significantly reduced potency both intravenously and orally, and the N-ethyl carboxamide (XXII) is inactive at comparable doses.

**Quinoline ring substitution:** Using the carbethoxy group as the preferred 2-substituent, the effect of substitution at other positions of the pyrimido[4,5-b]quinoline nucleus was examined (Figure 6). Halogen (XXIII, XXIV, XXV, XXVI) or phenyl (XXVII) substitution at positions 5, 6, 7 or 8 generally retained intravenous activity, these analogs being only slightly less potent than the parent, although they were more than 10 times less potent orally.

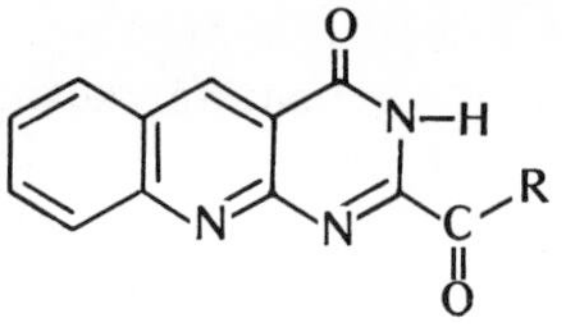

| COMPOUND | STRUCTURE | RAT PCA, $ED_{50}$, mg/kg | |
|---|---|---|---|
| | R | i.v. | p.o. |
| I | DSCG | 0.8 | (300)[a] |
| VII | OEt | 0.1 | 3 |
| VI | OH | 0.2 | 25 |
| XX | OnBu | 0.06 | 30 |
| XXI | $NH_2$ | 1.3 | 60 |
| XXII | NHEt | (3)[a] | NT[b] |

[a]Highest dose tested at which the compound was inactive.
[b]Not tested.

*Figure 5. Pyrimido[4,5-*b*]quinoline-2-carboxylic acid derivatives*

Introduction of a methoxy substituent in the 7-position (XXVIII) results in a 3-fold increase in intravenous activity while the bioisosteric 7-methylthio analog (XXIX) has potency similar to that of the parent. Both of these compounds are somewhat less potent on oral administration than the parent pyrimido[4,5-b]quinoline ester (VII). Changing the electronic and steric properties of the methylthio compound XXIX by oxidation to the sulfoxide (XXX) retains good intravenous activity, but this more polar substituent renders the compound inactive orally. The larger p-methoxyphenylthio substituent (XXXI) results in an inactive compound at comparable intravenous doses. The 7-benzyloxy (XXXII), 7-hydroxy (XXXIII) and 8-methoxy (XXXIV) compounds are equipotent with DSCG, but only the hydroxy and methoxy derivatives display significant oral activity.

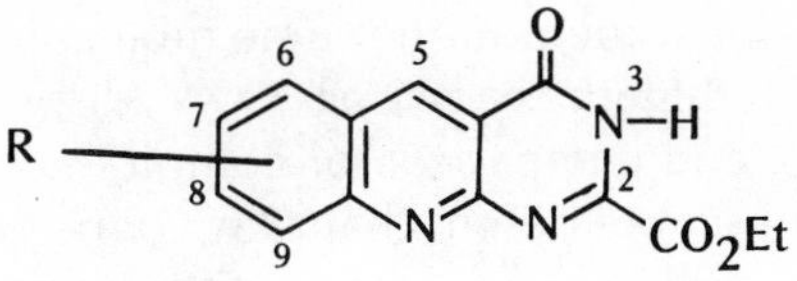

| COMPOUND | STRUCTURE | RAT PCA, $ED_{50}$, mg/kg | |
|---|---|---|---|
| | R | i.v. | p.o. |
| VII | H | 0.1 | 3 |
| XXIII | 6-Cl | 0.2 | 30 |
| XXIV | 7-Cl | 0.4 | 30 |
| XXV | 7-F | 0.3 | (30)[a] |
| XXVI | 8-F | 0.3 | 30 |
| XXVII | 5-phenyl | 0.3 | (10)[a] |
| XXVIII | 7-MeO | 0.03 | 20 |
| XXIX | 7-MeS | 0.1 | 8 |
| XXX | 7-MeS(=O)- | 0.2 | (30)[a] |
| XXXI | 7-MeO-C6H4-S- | (3)[a] | (30)[a] |
| XXXII | 7-C6H5-CH2O | 0.9 | (10)[a] |
| XXXIII | 7-OH | 0.7 | 10 |
| XXXIV | 8-MeO | 0.8 | 10 |

[a]Highest dose tested at which the compound was inactive.

*Figure 6. The 5-,6-,7-, or 8-substituted ethyl 4-oxo-3,4-dihydropyrimido[4,5-b]-quinoline-2-carboxylates*

**Alkoxy substitution:** Since methoxy substitution has a favorable influence on activity, this lead was pursued (Figure 7). Introduction of both a 7- and 8-methoxy substituent in the same molecule enhanced potency dramatically. The 7,8-dimethoxy analog (XXXV) displayed an intravenous $ED_{50}$ of 0.007 mg/kg and comparison of complete dose response curves indicates it is 84 times more potent than DSCG. In contrast to DSCG, it is orally active, having an $ED_{50}$ of 1.0 mg/kg. Other dimethoxy analogs (XXXVI, XXXVII, XXXVIII), as well as a trimethoxy compound (XXXIX), are at least 30 to 100 times less potent than XXXV, both intravenously and orally. In most cases, a 9 substituent decreased activity.

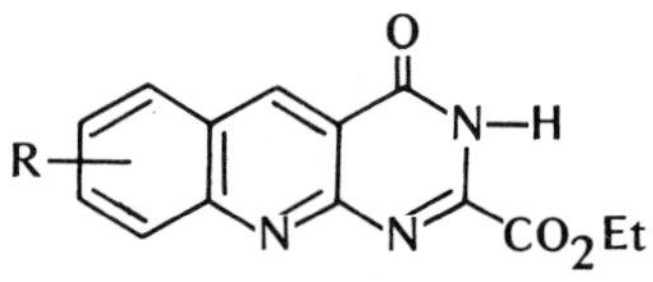

| COMPOUND | STRUCTURE | RAT PCA, $ED_{50}$, mg/kg | |
|---|---|---|---|
| | R | i.v. | p.o. |
| XXVIII | 7-MeO | 0.03 | 20 |
| XXXIV | 8-MeO | 0.8 | 10 |
| XXXV | 7,8-diMeO | 0.007 | 1.0 |
| XXXVI | 8,9-diMeO | 0.2 | (60)[a] |
| XXXVII | 7,9-diMeO | 0.5 | 30 |
| XXXVIII | 6,9-diMeO | 0.6 | (30)[a] |
| XXXIX | 7,8,9-triMeO | 0.8 | (10)[a] |
| I | DSCG | 0.8 | (300)[a] |

[a]Highest dose tested at which the compound was inactive.

*Figure 7. Methoxy-substituted ethyl pyrimido[4,5-*b*]quinoline-2-carboxylates*

Small changes in the size of the 7,8-dialkoxy substituents produced marked alterations in activity (Figure 8). The cyclic 7,8-methylenedioxy (XL) and 7,8-ethylenedioxy (XLI) compounds are 70-140 times less potent intravenously than the 7,8-dimethoxy analog (XXXV) and the methylenedioxy derivative is inactive orally. Optimal potency was observed with compounds possessing 7- and 8-substituents one

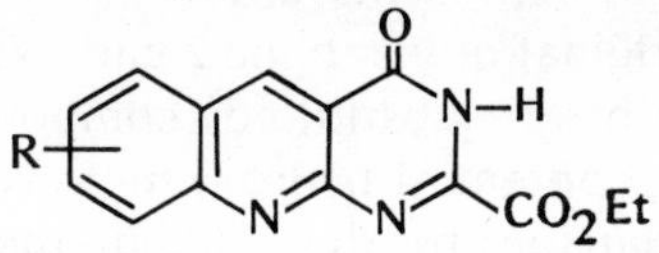

| COMPOUND | STRUCTURE | RAT PCA, $ED_{50}$, mg/kg | |
|---|---|---|---|
| | R | i.v. | p.o. |
| XXXV | 7,8-diMeO | 0.007 | 1.0 |
| XL | 7,8-$OCH_2O$ | 0.5 | (30)[a] |
| XLI | 7,8-$OCH_2CH_2O$ | 1.0 | NT[b] |
| XLII | 7-MeO, 8-EtO | 0.007 | 2.0 |
| XLIII | 7-EtO, 8-MeO | 0.002 | 0.3 |
| XLIV | 7-HO, 8-MeO | 0.002 | (10)[a] |
| XLV | 7-MeO, 8-HO | 0.1-1.0 | 10 |
| XLVI | 7,8-diEtO | 0.01 | 1.0 |
| XLVII | 7-EtO, 8-n-BuO | 0.3 | 5.0 |
| XLVIII | 7-$\phi CH_2O$, 8-Meo | (3)[a] | (10)[a] |
| XLIX | 7-MeO, 8-$\phi CH_2O$ | 0.8 | (30)[a] |
| I | DSCG | 0.8 | (300)[a] |

[a]Highest dose tested at which compound was inactive.
[b]Not tested.

*Figure 8. Ethyl 7,8-dialkoxypyrimido[4,5-*b*]quinoline-2-carboxylates*

methylene unit larger than the 7,8-dimethoxy analog. Whereas the 7-methoxy-8-ethoxy analog (XLII) is equipotent with the 7,8-dimethoxy compound, transposition of the two substituents, resulting in XLIII, increased both intravenous and oral activity by a factor of three. Thus, ethyl 7-ethoxy-8-methoxy-3,4-dihydro-4-oxopyrimido[4,5-b]quinoline-2-carboxylate (XLIII) is 400 times more potent than Intal and has an oral $ED_{50}$ of 0.3 mg/kg. It represents a 5000 fold increase in intravenous potency over the original quinazoline-2-carboxylic acid ester (II) lead.

Since many methoxy substituted compounds are metabolically dealkylated, the two potential hydroxy-methoxy metabolites were also prepared. In comparison to the 7,8-dimethoxy analog (XXXV), the 7-hydroxy-8-methoxy derivative (XLIV) is 3 times more potent intravenously, but it and its reverse isomer (XLV) are less potent on oral administration. Similar to the sulfoxide (XXX), this is another example of a highly polar substituent in this portion of the molecule causing a decrease in oral versus intravenous potency.

Large substituents decreased intravenous activity. Although the 7,8-diethoxy compound XLVI is about as potent as its dimethoxy analog, combinations of butoxy and benzyloxy with methoxy and ethoxy substituents (XLVII, XLVIII, and XLIX) resulted in decreases in intravenous activity and a loss of oral activity.

**Pyrimidine ring substitution:** Substituent effects on the pyrimidine ring were examined while retaining the 7,8-dimethoxy substitution pattern in the carbocyclic ring (Figure 9). A methyl group in the 3-position (L) decreased intravenous activity by more than 100-fold. Similarly, introduction of carbethoxyalkyl substituents in position 3 (LI and LII) resulted in compounds which are inactive or considerably less active than the N-unsubstituted analog (XXXV).

The importance of the carboxylic acid moiety for activity is clearly illustrated by the next group of compounds. Removal of the carbethoxy substituent provided 7,8-dimethoxypyrimido[4,5-b]quinolin-4(3H)-one (LIII) which is inactive at 3 mg/kg i.v. in the PCA procedure. Interestingly, the 2-methyl analog (LIV) exhibits excellent oral activity while displaying only weak intravenous activity. This may be rationalized on the basis of metabolic oxidation of this compound to the carboxylic acid (LX, Figure 10). The fact that the 2-ethyl (LV), 2-trifluoromethyl (LVI), and 2-acetyl (LVII) analogs are considerably less active, and the 2-phenyl (LVIII) and 2-hydroxy (LIX) analogs are inactive, supports this explanation.

**Esters and amides as potential prodrugs:** The ethyl ester (XXXV) (Figure 10) is at least ten times more potent orally than the carboxylic acid (LX), butyl ester (LXI), or $\beta$-hydroxy ethyl ester (LXII). However, the equipotent

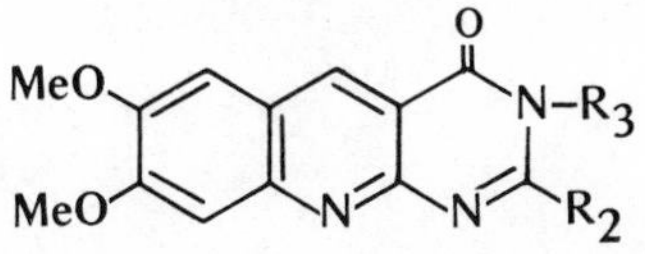

| COMPOUND | STRUCTURE | | RAT PCA, $ED_{50}$, mg/kg | |
|---|---|---|---|---|
| | $R_3$ | $R_2$ | i.v. | p.o. |
| XXXV | H | $CO_2Et$ | 0.007 | 1.0 |
| L | $CH_3$ | $CO_2Et$ | 0.8 | (30)[a] |
| LI | $CH_2CO_2Et$ | $CO_2Et$ | (3) | NT[b] |
| LII | $(CH_2)_3CO_2Et$ | $CO_2Et$ | 0.1 | (10)[a] |
| LIII | H | H | (3)[a] | NT[b] |
| LIV | H | $CH_3$ | 0.4 | 1.0 |
| LV | H | Et | 3 | (60)[a] |
| LVI | H | $CF_3$ | >10 i.p. | NT[b] |
| LVII | H | $C(=O)CH_3$ | 2 | (10)[a] |
| LVIII | H | $C_6H_5$ | (3)[a] | NT[b] |
| LIX | H | OH | (3)[a] | NT[b] |

[a]Highest dose tested at which the compound was inactive.
[b]Not tested.

*Figure 9. The 2- or 3-substituted 7,8-dimethoxypyrimido[4,5-b]quinolin-4-ones*

intravenous activity of these esters suggests that they are prodrugs and that the acid is the active species. Supporting this conclusion is the finding that a variety of amides (LXIII, LXIV, LXV, LXVI, and LXVII), which may not be readily metabolized to the acid, are considerably less active or inactive following either oral or intravenous administration.

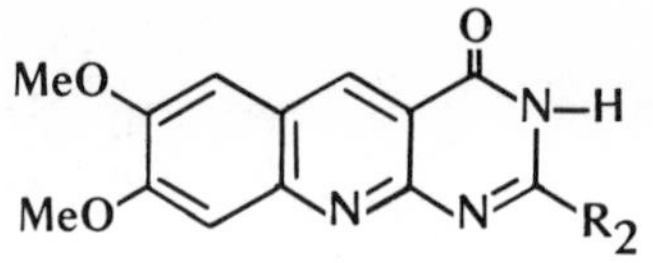

| COMPOUND | STRUCTURE | RAT PCA, $ED_{50}$, mg/kg | |
|---|---|---|---|
| | $R_2$ | i.v. | p.o. |
| LX | $-CO_2Na$ | 0.005 | (10)[a] |
| XXXV | $-CO_2Et$ | 0.007 | 1.0 |
| LXI | $-\overset{O}{\overset{\|\|}{C}}O(CH_2)_3CH_3$ | 0.003 | 10 |
| LXII | $-CO_2CH_2CH_2OH$ | <0.03 | 10 |
| LXIII | $\overset{O}{\overset{\|\|}{C}}NH_2$ | 3 | (30)[a] |
| LXIV | $\overset{O}{\overset{\|\|}{C}}NHCH_3$ | (3)[a] | NT[b] |
| LXV | $\overset{O}{\overset{\|\|}{C}}NHEt$ | (3)[a] | NT[b] |
| LXVI | $\overset{O}{\overset{\|\|}{C}}NHOH$ | <3 | (60)[a] |
| LXVII | $\overset{O}{\overset{\|\|}{C}}NHCH_2CO_2Et$ | 6 | NT |

[a]Highest dose tested at which the compound was inactive.
[b]Not tested.

*Figure 10. The 7,8-dimethoxy-4-oxo-3,4-dihydropyrimido[4,5-*b*]quinoline-2-carboxylic acid esters and amides*

**SAR summary:** Ethyl esters of 7,8-dialkoxy substituted pyrimido[4,5-b]-quinoline-2-carboxylic acids display optimal potency. The dimethoxy (XXXV), diethoxy (XLVI) and the methoxy-ethoxy isomers (XLII and XLIII) are 80-400 times more potent than DSCG intravenously. Morever, in contrast to DSCG, these compounds are active orally, having $ED_{50}$'s of 1 mg/kg or less in the PCA procedure.

The next section compares the PCA activity of these compounds with that reported for a variety of other experimental antiallergy agents which inhibit mediator release.

## Classes of Experimental Agents Orally Effective in the Rat PCA Procedure

Research sparked by the discovery of DSCG, which lacks oral activity, has indeed borne fruit over the last 6 to 7 years. Reports on orally active antiallergy agents include those on the xanthone-2-carboxylic acids (14-24), thioxanthone-10,10-dioxides (25-30), indane-1,3-diones (31-35), 3- and 4-substituted coumarins (36), naphthoquinones (37), chromone-2-carboxylic acids (38,39), other substituted chromones (40-52), 8-azapurinones (53,54), benzopyranobenzopyrane carboxylic acids (55-58), dioxopyridoquinoline-2,8-dicarboxylic acids (59-61), cinnoline-3-propionic acids (62), 4-oxoquinoline tetrazoles (63), pyranenamines (64), aryloxamates (66-69), and aroylanthranilic acids (70-72). The fused 4-oxopyrimidine-2-carboxylic acids described here (73-75) may now be added to this list. Several of these agents, together with some possessing antihistamine activity (76-81), are discussed in detail in subsequent chapters.

The following sections illustrate the compounds for which oral anti-allergy activity has been reported. Rough cross comparisons of published data can be made since most workers report an $ED_{50}$ of about 1.0 mg/kg i.v. for DSCG in the PCA test, and this seldom falls outside the range of 0.5 to 2.5 mg/kg. A number of these compounds have been reported to be in clinical trial.

**Xanthone-2-carboxylic acids:** One of the first series of orally active agents reported in the early 1970's is the xanthone-2-carboxylic acids (14-24) (Figure 11). This series has been explored primarily by workers at Allen & Hanburys (17) and Syntex (16,18). Several compounds have been studied clinically as aerosol formulations (21). AH 7725, at 500 mg, was the first agent reported to have oral activity in man (14). Oral activity in the rat PCA procedure has been reported for xanoxic acid (LXX) (19) and tixanox (LXXI) (20); these compounds also antagonize exercise-induced asthma in man (15,18). The intravenous potency of these compounds in the PCA assay is 10-30x DSCG, but oral activity appears to be relatively weak, for example, the dicarboxamide LXXII (23). An exception is the recently reported Ru 31156 (LXXIII), which has an oral $ED_{50}$ of 0.2 mg/kg and is 263x more potent than DSCG in the rat PCA test (24).

**Thioxanthones:** Another early series, the thioxanthones, is represented by Wellcome's doxantrazole (25-29). Doxantrazole has a reported oral $ED_{50}$ of $\leq 30$ mg/kg in the PCA test (26) and was initially reported to be orally active in antigen challenge studies in man at a dose of 200 mg (26), but later clinical studies have given equivocal results (27-29).

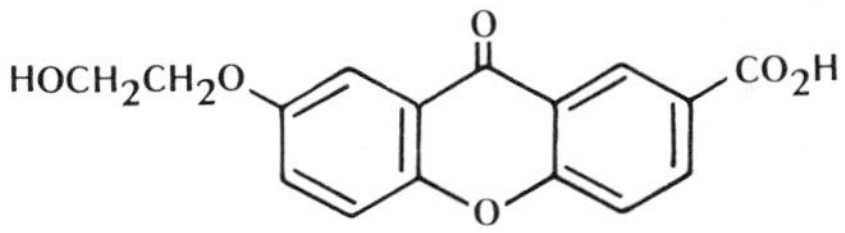

$HOCH_2CH_2O$ — $CO_2H$

LXIX

*ALLEN AND HANBURYS*

AH 7725

**RAT PCA: 13-20 x Intal**

**HUMAN: 500 mg p.o. active**

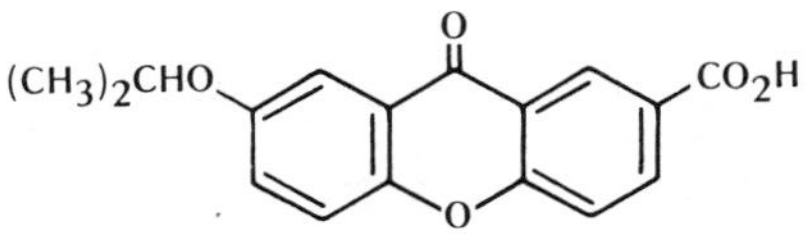

$(CH_3)_2CHO$ — $CO_2H$

LXX

*SYNTEX*

Xanoxic Acid , RS 7540

**RAT PCA: 8 x Intal**

**HUMAN: p.o. active**

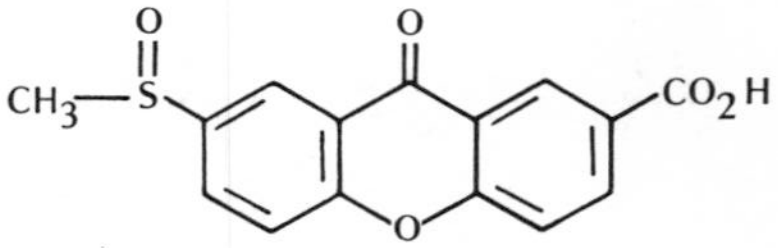

$CH_3—S(=O)$ — $CO_2H$

LXXI

*SYNTEX*

Tixanox, OTMX

**RAT PCA: 25 x Intal**
**p.o. - active**

**HUMAN: Aerosol-active**

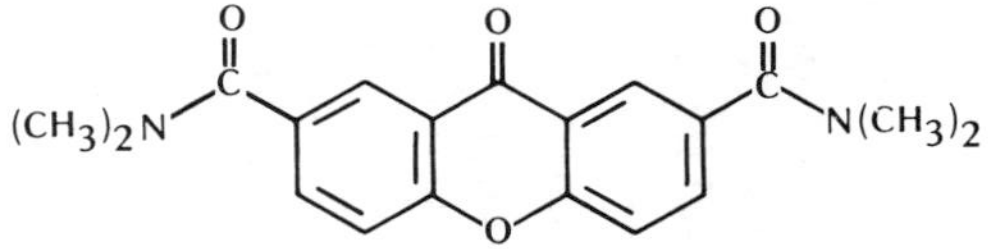

$(CH_3)_2N—C(=O)$ — $C(=O)—N(CH_3)_2$

LXXII

*MERRELL-NATIONAL*

**RAT PCA: p.o. - 69% at 100 mg/kg**

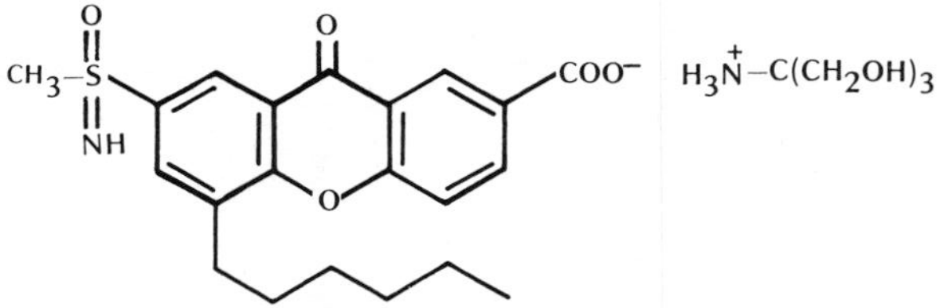

$CH_3—S(=O)(=NH)$ — $COO^-$ $H_3\overset{+}{N}—C(CH_2OH)_3$

LXXIII

Ru-31156

**RAT PCA: 203 x Intal**
**p.o. $ED_{50}$ = 0.19 mg/kg**

*Figure 11. Xanthone-2-carboxylic acids*

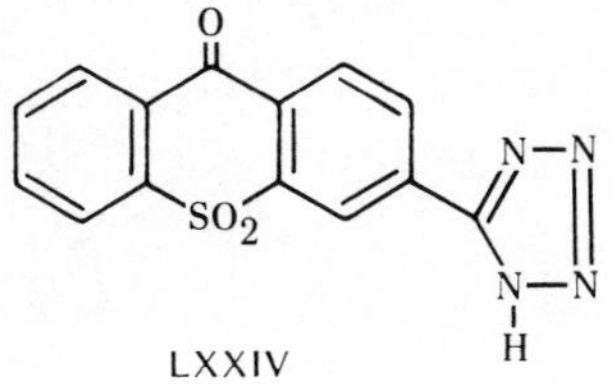

LXXIV

*WELLCOME*

Doxantrazole

**RAT PCA: 10 x Intal**
**p.o. $ED_{50} \leq$ 30 mg/kg**

**HUMAN: 200 mg p.o. active**

BW 437C, a new oral carboxythioxanthone-10,10-dioxide, is reported to be a more effective inhibitor of human leukocyte histamine release than DSCG or doxantrazole (**30**).

**Nitroindanediones and related compounds:** Beecham's nivimedone (BRL 10,833) is a nitroindanedione (**31**-**35**) that has potent oral activity in the PCA procedure. It has demonstrated activity in antigen challenge studies in man at oral doses of 2 mg/kg (**34**) and is also active by aerosol administration (**35**).

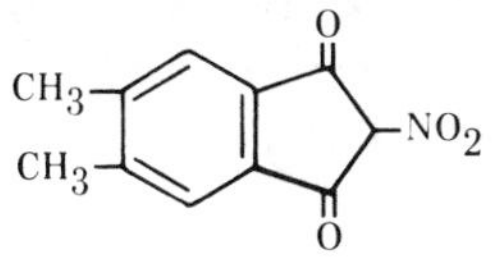

LXXV

*BEECHAM*

Nivimedone, BRL-10,833

**RAT PCA: 25-50 x Intal**
**p.o. $ED_{50}$ = 1.0 mg/kg**

**HUMAN: active at 2 mg/kg p.o.**

Several series related to the nitroindanediones, including cyanoindanediones (LXXVI) (**36**), cyanocoumarins (LXXVII) (**36**), and nitronaphthoquinones (LXXVIII) (**37**), have been reported. These compounds display moderate oral activity in the PCA procedure ($ED_{50}$ 15-25 mg/kg).

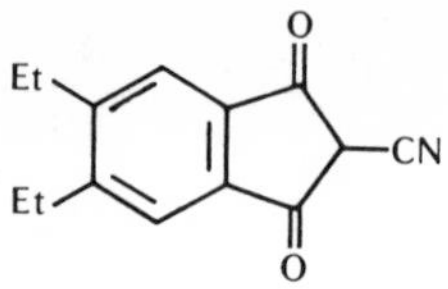

LXXVI

*BEECHAM*

RAT PCA:~Intal
p.o. $ED_{50}$≈14 mg/kg

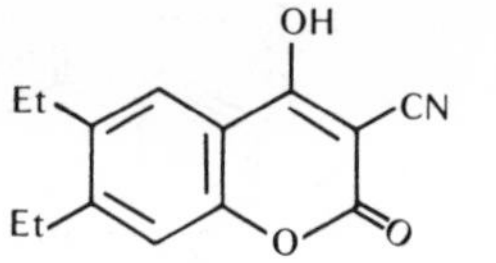

LXXVII

*BEECHAM*

RAT PCA:~Intal
p.o. $ED_{50}$≈15 mg/kg

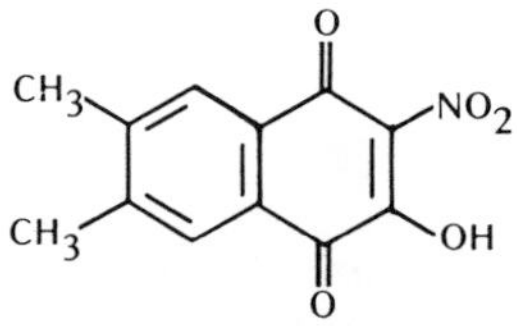

LXXVIII

*BEECHAM*

RAT PCA:~Intal
p.o. $ED_{50}$ = 25 mg/kg

**Chromone-2-carboxylic acids:** Several chromone-2-carboxylic acids (LXXIX, LXXX and LXXXI) have been reported by Fisons (38,39). These compounds have oral $ED_{50}$ values of 4-16 mg/kg in the PCA procedure and oral activity in man has been reported for two of these acids. Particularly potent is proxicromil (LXXXI) which is reported to be active in man at doses of 4-10 mg (39).

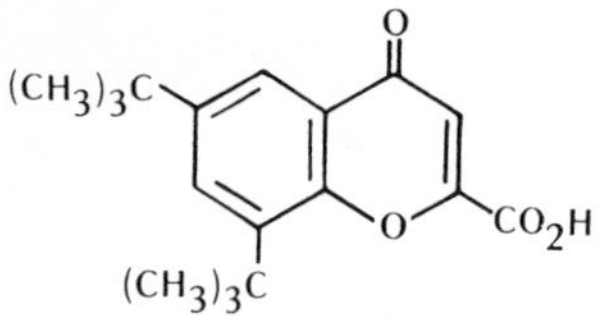

LXXIX

*FISONS*

Terbucromil, FPL 52791

RAT PCA: 6 x Intal
p.o. $ED_{50}$ = 4.2 mg/kg

HUMAN: in the clinic

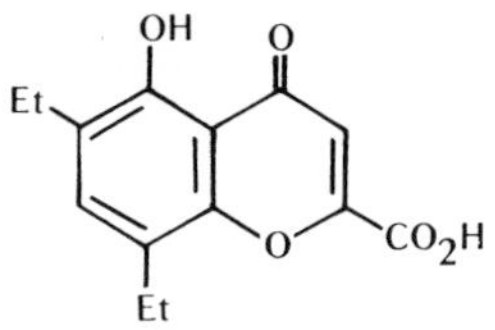

LXXX

*FISONS*

FPL 52757

RAT PCA: 1/4 x Intal
p.o. $ED_{50}$ = 5.0 mg/kg

HUMAN: 50-100 mg p.o. active in challenge studies

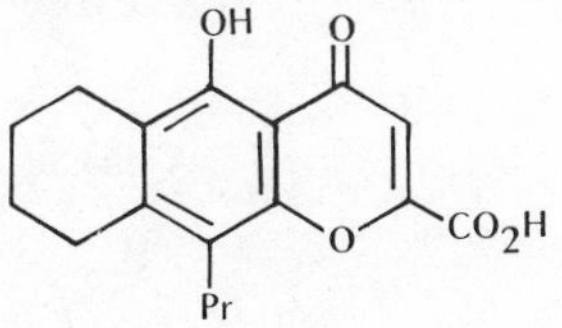

OH O

$CO_2H$

Pr

LXXXI

*FISONS*

Proxicromil, FPL 57787

RAT PCA: 1/5 x Intal
p.o. $ED_{50}$ = 15.5

HUMAN: 4-10 mg p.o. active in experimental asthma

**Other substituted chromones:** Warner-Lambert and Takeda have reported oral activity for 3-substituted chromones (**40**-**48**). Compounds with the 3-carbinol (W8011) and 3-tetrazole (AA-344) substituents are about as potent in the PCA procedure as DSCG and have oral $ED_{50}$ values in the 2-7 mg/kg range (**43**,**44**,**46**,**49**). The active form of W8011 appears to be the carboxylic acid (**49**). Tetrazole AA-344 is reported to be active after 2 or more days of oral administration of 30-60 mg/day in patients with atopic asthma (**48**).

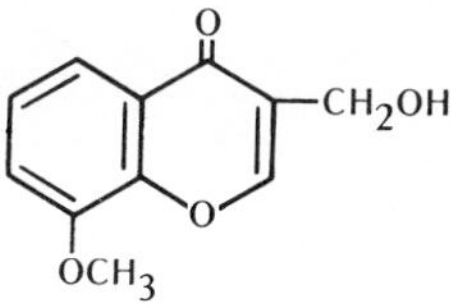

O $CH_2OH$ O $OCH_3$

LXXXII

*WARNER-LAMBERT*

W8011

RAT PCA: ≃Intal
p.o. $ED_{50}$ = 2.0 mg/kg

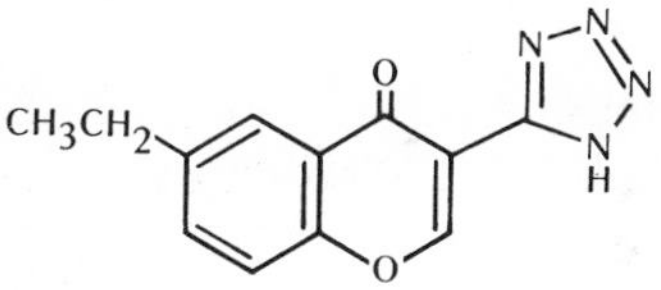

$CH_3CH_2$ O N N N N H O

LXXXIII

*TAKEDA*

AA-344

RAT PCA: 4 x Intal
p.o. $ED_{50}$ = 7 mg/kg
HUMAN: 30-60 mg/day - active

Takeda's acrylic acid (LXXXIV) (**50**), Carlo Erba's 2-phenylchromone-6-carboxylic acid (LXXXV) (**57**), and Miles' CPTC chromone tetrazole (LXXXVI) (**52**) appear to be orally active in the PCA procedure. However, precise $ED_{50}$ values have not been reported and clinical reports have not yet appeared.

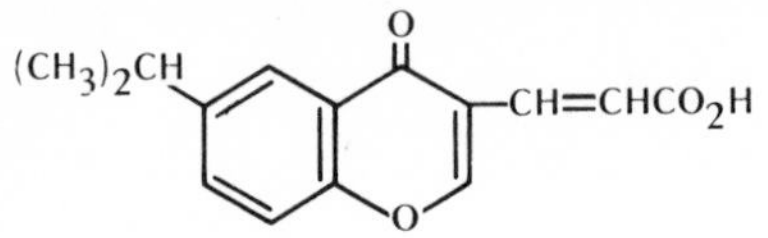

$(CH_3)_2CH$ — CH=$CHCO_2H$

LXXXIV

*TAKEDA*

RAT PCA: > Intal
p.o. - active

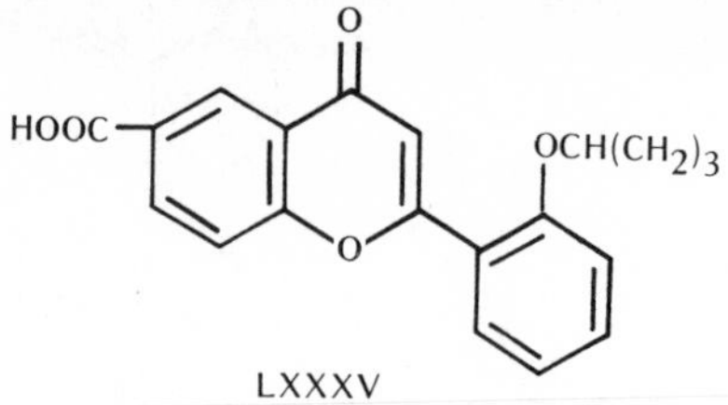

HOOC — $OCH(CH_2)_3$

LXXXV

*CARLO ERBA*

RAT PCA: ≃ Intal
p.o. $ED_{50}$ = 10 mg/kg

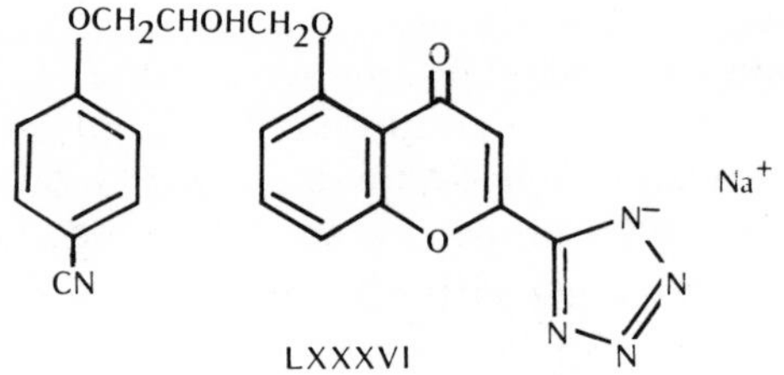

$OCH_2CHOHCH_2O$ — CN — $Na^+$

LXXXVI

*MILES*

Na CPTC

**Azapurinones:** With an oral $ED_{50}$ of 0.2 mg/kg, the May & Baker azapurinone, M&B 22,948, is one of the more potent compounds reported (53,54).

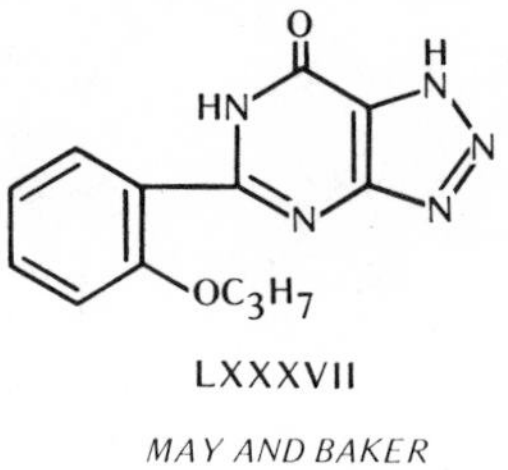

$OC_3H_7$

LXXXVII

*MAY AND BAKER*

M&B 22,948

RAT PCA: 35-50 x Intal
p.o. $ED_{50}$ = 0.2 mg/kg

**Benzopyranobenzopyrane dicarboxylic acids:** Pharma Research's benzopyranobenzopyrane, PRD-92-EA, (55-58) is about 6 times more potent than DSCG (56) and has an oral $ED_{50}$ of 22 mg/kg (58). It is active orally in the monkey, inhibiting the increase in airway resistance following antigen challenge.

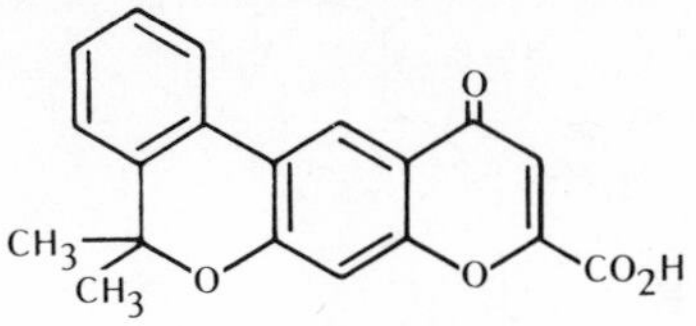

LXXXVIII

*PHARMA-RESEARCH*

PRD-92-EA

RAT PCA: 6 x Intal

MONKEY: p.o. — active — inhibits the increase in airway resistance in challenge studies

**Dioxopyridoquinoline-2,8-dicarboxylic acids, cinnoline-3-propionic acids and 4-oxoquinoline-3-tetrazoles:** The pyridoquinoline dicarboxylic acid series has been explored by Upjohn and ICI (59-61). An angular pyridoquinoline, ICI 74,917 (bufrolin), is active in man by the aerosol route (60). The linear compound A (LXXXIX) is reported by Upjohn workers to be orally active in the PCA procedure (59).

ICI workers have also reported activity for a series of cinnoline-3-propionic acid derivatives (XC), with oral $ED_{50}$ values as low as 4 mg/kg for the 6-ethyl compound (62).

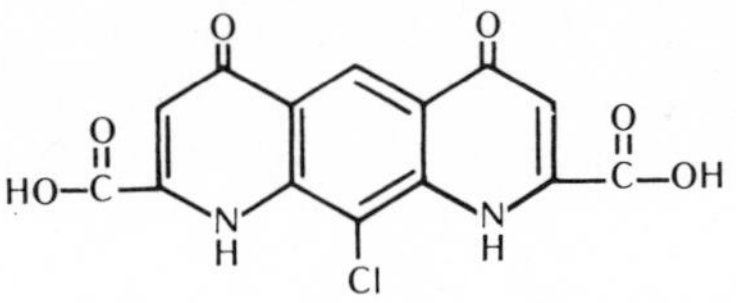

LXXXIX

*UPJOHN*

Compound A

RAT PCA: 50 x Intal

p.o. $ED_{50}$ $\leq$ 25-50 mg/kg

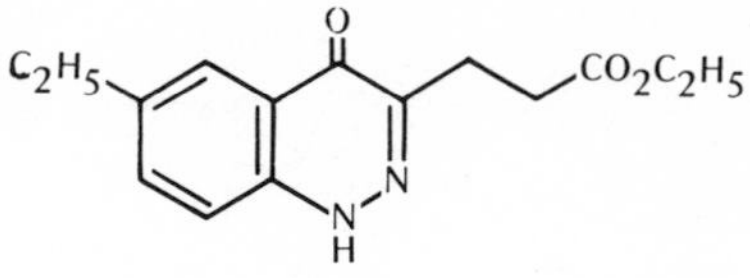

XC

*IMPERIAL CHEMICAL INDUSTRIES*

RAT PCA: $\leq$Intal

p.o. $ED_{50}$ $\simeq$ 4 mg/kg

In another related series, Riker reported that 8-chloro-4-oxo-3-(5-tetrazolyl)quinoline (XCI) was the most potent member (63). With an $ED_{50}$ of 0.078 mg/kg intraperitoneally, this compound is 32 times more potent than DSCG and has an oral $ED_{50}$ of 0.12 mg/kg. However, this compound exhibited crystalluria in toxicology studies (63).

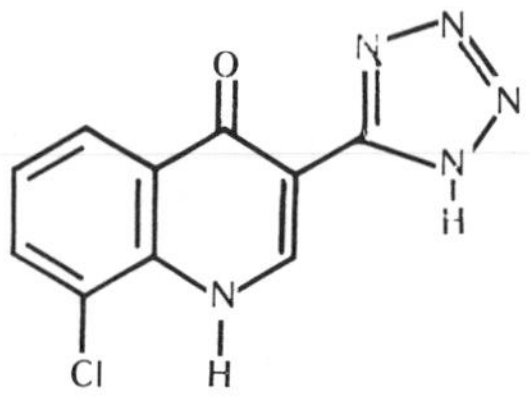

XCI

*RIKER*

**RAT PCA: 32 x Intal**
**p.o. $ED_{50}$ = 0.12**

**Pyranenamines:** SKF 78,729-A, (XCII), a potent member of a novel series of pyranenamines, has intravenous and oral $ED_{50}$ values of 0.7 mg/kg in the PCA procedure (64). This series is further discussed in a subsequent chapter.

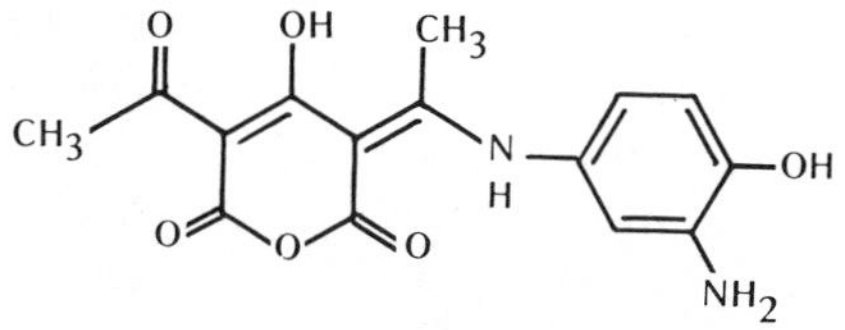

XCII

*SMITH KLINE & FRENCH*

SK&F 78,729-A

**RAT PCA: $ED_{50}$ = 0.7 mg/kg p.o. & i.v.**

**Tetrahydrocarbazole-3-carboxylic acids:** Oxarbazole (XCIII), a tetrahydrocarbazole-3-carboxylic acid, is under investigation by Winthrop and has shown activity in human challenge studies when administered at doses of 100-300 mg orally, b.i.d. for 3.5 days (65).

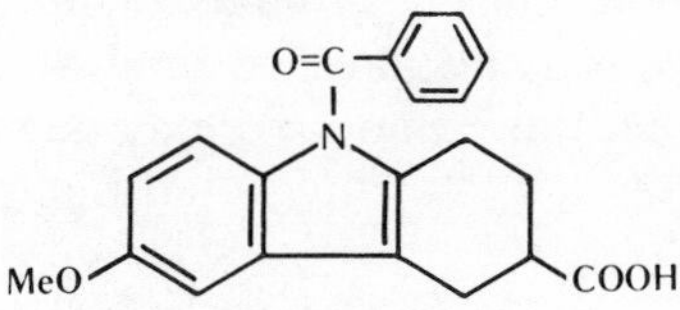

XCIII

*WINTHROP LABS*

Oxarbazole, Win 34,284

HUMAN: 100-300 mg p.o.
(bid for 3.5 days)
Active in challenge studies

**Aryloxamic acids, and aroylaminobenzoic acids:** Upjohn's aryloxamic acid, lodoxamide (U 42,585 E), (XCIV), is 2500 times more potent intravenously than DSCG (66), being the most potent agent thus far reported. However, this compound is 100-1000 fold less potent orally than intravenously, with inhibition in the PCA procedure obtained with oral doses between 0.1 and 10 mg/kg (66). Activity has been reported in man following aerosol administration (67). Further details on this series are discussed in the next chapter.

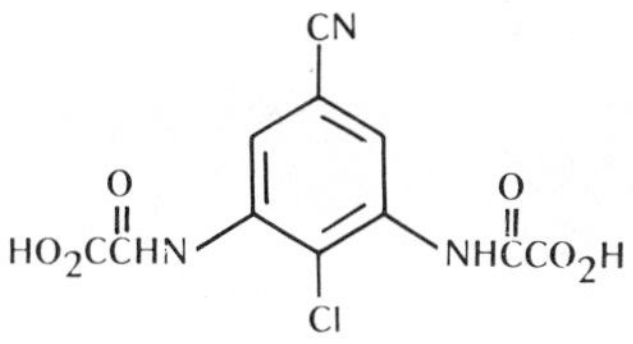

XCIV

*UPJOHN*

Lodoxamide, U-42,585 E

RAT PCA: 2500 x Intal
p.o. $ED_{50}$ = 0.1-10 mg/kg

HUMAN: 0.01, 0.10 and 1.0 mg
active by inhalation

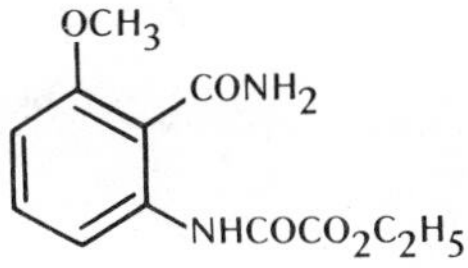

XCV

*WYETH*

WY 16,922

RAT PCA: 8 x Intal
p.o. $ED_{50} \geq 25$ mg/kg

Wy-16,922 (XCV) is a representative of an aryloxamate series which was less potent orally in the PCA procedure (68,69) than lodoxamide.

Japanese workers have explored a series of aroylaminobenzoic acids of which N-5′ (XCVI), is about equal to DSCG intravenously and has an oral $ED_{50}$ of 100-150 mg/kg (70). It should be noted, however, that this is after a 2 hour pretreatment interval, a much longer period than used by most other investigators. N-5′ displays optimal activity 30-60 minutes post-dosing (71). Therefore, this compound may be more potent relative to other compounds discussed than suggested by its reported $ED_{50}$.

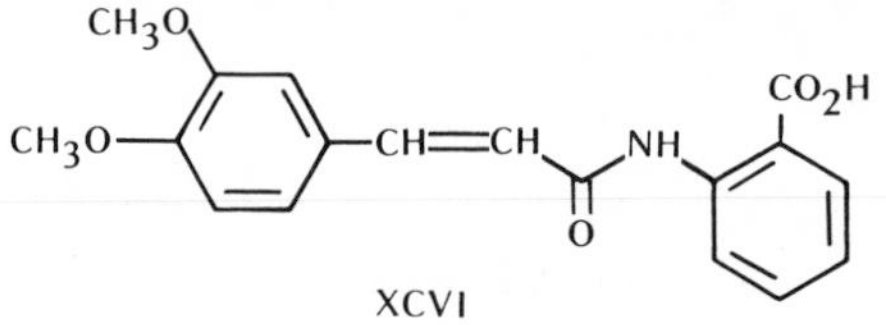

$CH_3O$ / $CH_3O$–C₆H₃–CH=CH–C(=O)–NH–C₆H₄–$CO_2H$

XCVI

*KISSEI*

N-5'

RAT PCA: ~ Intal
p.o. $ED_{50}$ = 100-150 mg/kg
(2 hr pretreatment)
HUMAN: in the clinic

AB-50 (XCVII), the active species of which is the deacetylated compound known as AB-23, is reported to be orally active although it has only weak activity intravenously, requiring a dose of 20 mg/kg to achieve nearly complete inhibition in the PCA test (72).

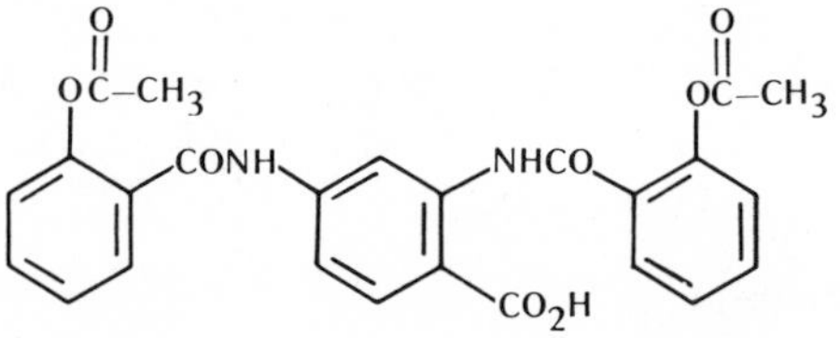

$OC(=O)CH_3$ ... CONH ... NHCO ... $OC(=O)CH_3$ ... $CO_2H$

XCVII

*CHUGAI*

AB-50

RAT PCA: 20 mg/kg i.v. - nearly complete inhibition
p.o. - active

**Fused pyrimidine-2-carboxylic acids:** Thienopyrimidines (73,74) and pyrimidoquinoxalines (75), both of which are related to our pyrimido-[4,5-b]quinoline-2-carboxylic acid esters (XXXV and XLIII), were recently reported in the patent literature by Mead Johnson and Mitsubishi, respectively. The most potent compound in the thienopyrimidine series is XCVIII which has an oral $ED_{50}$ of 3.1 mg/kg (73), while ethyl 7,8-dimethoxy-3,4-dihydro-4-oxopyrimido[5,6-b]quinoxaline-2-carboxylate (XCIX) appears to be about equipotent (75) with our compound XXXV.

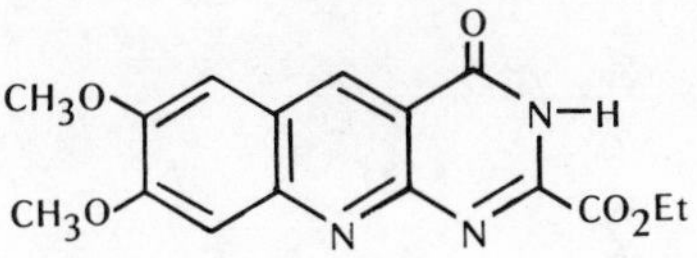

XXXV

*PFIZER*

Pirolate

**RAT PCA: 80-100 x Intal**
**p.o. $ED_{50}$ = 1.0 mg/kg**

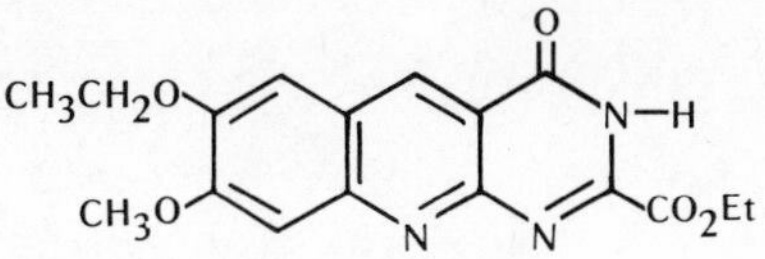

XLIII

*PFIZER*

**RAT PCA: 400 x Intal**
**p.o. $ED_{50}$ = 0.3 mg/kg**

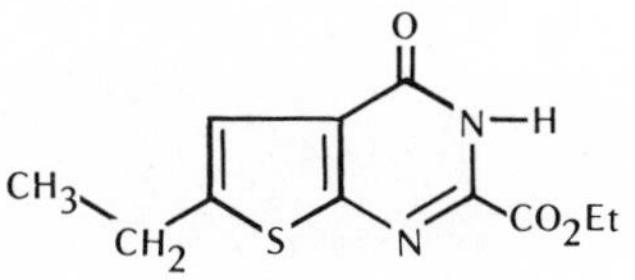

XCVIII

*MEAD JOHNSON*

**RAT PCA: p.o. $ED_{50}$ = 3.1 mg/kg**

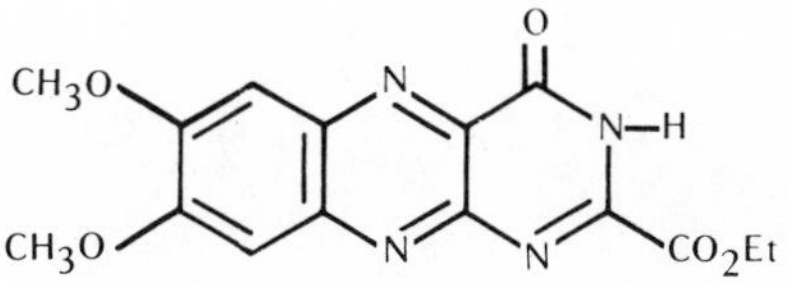

XCIX

*MITSUBISHI YUKA*

**RAT PCA: p.o. $ED_{50}$ = 1 mg/kg**

**Mediator release inhibitors with antihistamine activity:** Several agents which are both antihistamines and inhibitors of mediator release have also been reported (Figure 12). An early compound of this type was Schering 15,280 (C, azanator) (76). Three other compounds (CI, CII and CIII) have subsequently been reported (77-81). The most advanced of these is ketotifen (CI) which is structurally related to azanator. It is orally active in man at 1 mg (b.i.d.) (77) and has been marketed by Sandoz in Switzerland. Two other potent, orally active compounds in the rat PCA procedure are Janssen's oxatomide (78,79) and Boehringer Mannheim's BM 15,100 (80,81). These compounds combine the properties of mediator release inhibition with antihistamine activity.

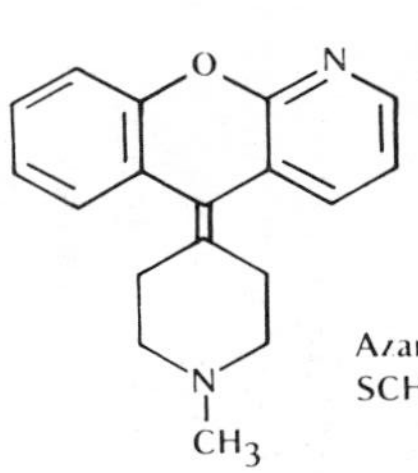

Azanator
SCH-15,280

C

*SCHERING*

**RAT PCA: p.o. $ED_{50}$ = 0.3 mg/kg**

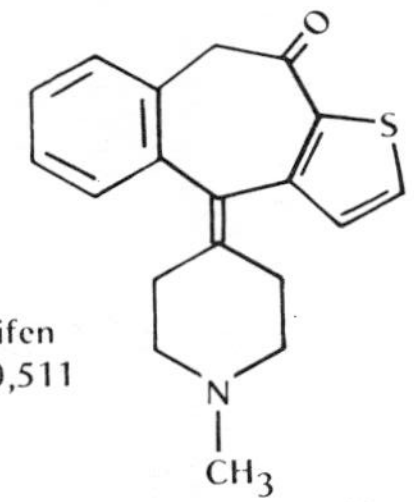

Ketotifen
HC 20,511

CI

*SANDOZ*

**HUMAN: orally active marketed in Switzerland**

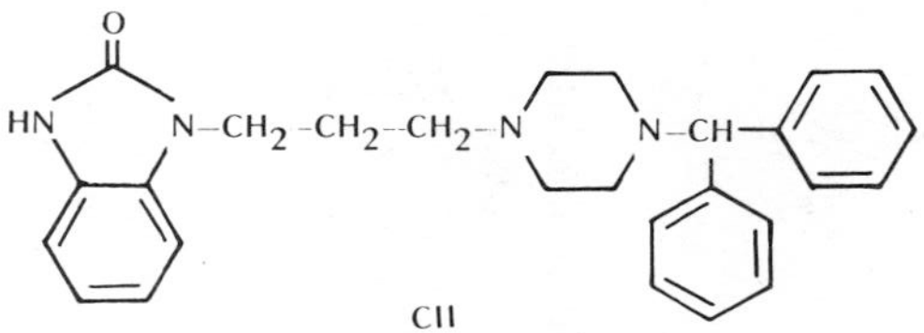

CII

*JANSSEN*

Oxatomide
R-35,443

**RAT PCA: $ED_{50}$ = 1.25-40 mg/kg**

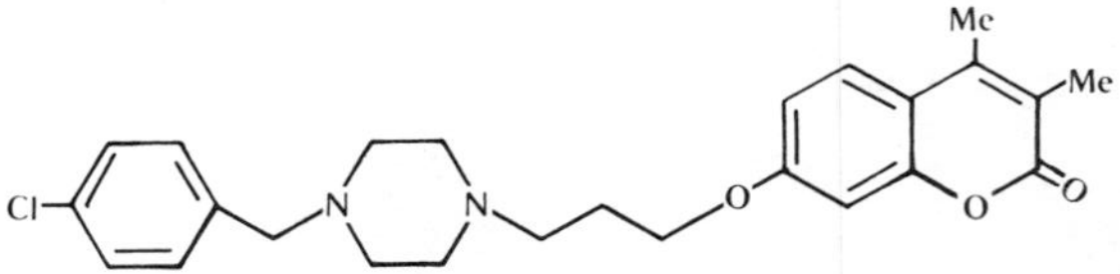

CIII

*BOEHRINGER MANNHEIM*

BM 15,100

**RAT PCA: equipotent i.v. and p.o., $ED_{50}$ = 0.75 mg/kg**

*Figure 12. Some agents with combined inhibition of mediator release and antihistaminic activity*

## Pharmacology of Ethyl 3,4-Dihydro-7,8-dimethoxy-4-oxopyrimido[4,5-b]-quinoline-2-carboxylate (XXXV)

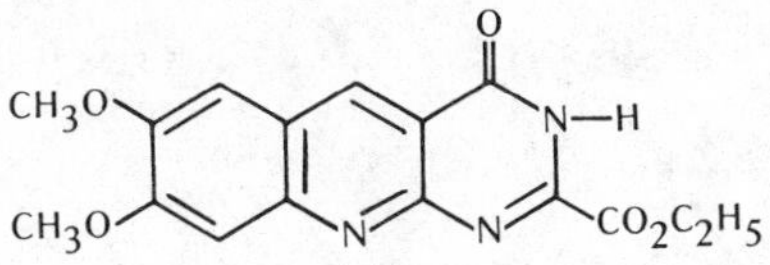

XXXV

As discussed earlier, pirolate (XXXV) has an intravenous $ED_{50}$ of 0.007 mg/kg (84 times more potent than DSCG) and an oral $ED_{50}$ of 1.0 mg/kg in the PCA assay. Pirolate doses as high as 1.0 mg/kg i.v. or 60 mg/kg p.o. do not antagonize the changes in vascular permeability induced by intradermal injections of histamine or serotonin. Pirolate inhibits the plasma histamine increases induced by antigen challenge in rats passively sensitized with homologous antisera. At 0.1 mg/kg i.v. pirolate produces 92% inhibition of histamine release while DSCG displays a similar degree of inhibition at a dose of 3 mg/kg. The bronchoconstrictive effect of a histamine aerosol in conscious guinea pigs is unaltered by pirolate at a dose of 30 mg/kg, i.v.

This profile of pharmacological activity confirms that the pyrimido-[4,5-b]quinoline ester XXXV inhibits the release of the mediators of anaphylaxis, and is neither a bronchodilator nor an antihistamine.

### Summary

Successive molecular modification of our original quinazoline-2-carboxylic acid led to compounds displaying 5000-fold increases in potency. Several 7,8-dialkoxy substituted pyrimido[4,5-b]quinoline esters are 80 to 400 times as potent as DSCG intravenously, and, more importantly, have potent oral activity in the rat PCA test with $ED_{50}$'s of 1 mg/kg or less. Comparison with other agents that display oral activity in this test shows that the pyrimido[4,5-b]quinoline series ranks among the most potent orally active inhibitors of mediator release reported to date.

## Literature Cited


1. Howell, J.B.L., and Altounyan, R.E.C., *Lancet,* **2,** 539 (1967).
2. Cox, J.S.G., *Nature* (London) **216** 1328 (1967).
3. Cox, J.S.G., Beach, J.E., Blair, A.M.J.N., Clark, A.J., King, J., Lee, T.B., Loveday, D.E.E., Moss, G.F., Orr, T.S.C., Ritchie, T. and Sheard, P., in "Advances in Drug Research," Harper, N.J., (Ed), Academic Press, 1970 p 115.
4. Brogden, R.N., Speight, T.M. and Avery, G.S., *Drugs,* **7,** 164 (1974).
5. Bergner, R.K. and Bergner, A., *J. Am. Med. Assoc.,* **235,** 288 (1976).
6. Mota, I., *Immunology,* **7,** 681 (1964).
7. Petillo, J. and Smith, S., *Int. Arch. Allergy Appl. Immunol.,* **44,** 309 (1973).
8. Althuis, T.H., Moore, P.F. and Hess, H.-J., *J. Med. Chem.,* **22,** 44 (1979).
9. Presented in part at the "Symposium on Drugs Affecting the Respiratory System" at the 175th National Meeting of the American Cancer Society, Anaheim, Calif., Mar. 13-17, 1978, see Abstract MEDI-2.
10. Taylor, E.C. and Kalenda, N.W., *J. Org. Chem.,* **18,** 1755 (1953).
11. Campaigne, E. and Randau, G., *J. Heterocyclic Chem.,* **8,** 111 (1971).
12. Taylor, E.C. and Kalenda, N.W., *J. Am. Chem. Soc.,* **78,** 5108 (1956).
13. Althuis, T.H. and Hess, H.-J., *J. Med. Chem.,* **20,** 146 (1977).
14. Assem, E.S.K., Evans, J.A. and McAllen, M., *Brit. Med. J.,* **2,** 93 (1974).
15. Sprenkle, A.C., Van Arsdel, P.P., Jr. and Bierman, C.W., *J. Allergy Clin. Immunol.,* (abstract) **55,** 118 (1975).
16. Pfister, J.R., Feraresi, R.W., Harrison, I.T., Rooks, W.H., Roszkowski, A.P., Van Horn, A. and Fried, J.H., *J. Med. Chem.,* **15,** 1032 (1972).
17. Fullarton, J., Martin, L.E. and Vardey, C., *Int. Arch. Allergy, Appl. Immunol.,* **45,** 84 (1973).
18. Pfister, J.R., Ferraresi, R.W., Harrison, I.T., Rooks, W.H. and Fried, J.H., *J. Med. Chem.,* **21,** 669 (1968).
19. Roszkowski, A.P., Ferraresi, R.W., Schuler, M.E. and Sullivan, B.J., *Fed. Proc.,* **33,** 569, (1974).
20. Ferraresi, R.W., Roszkowski, A.P. and Kepel, E., *Fed. Proc.,* **33,** 762 (1974).

21. Assem, E.S.K. and McAllen, M.K., *Int. Arch. Allergy Appl. Immunol.,* **45,** 697 (1973).

22. Assem, E.S.K., *Int. Arch Allergy Appl. Immunol.,* **45,** 708 (1973).

23. Jones, W.D., Albrecht, W.L., Munro, N.L. and Stewart, K.T., *J. Med. Chem.,* **20,** 594 (1977).

24. Miller, P. and James, G.W.L., *Arch. Intern. Pharmacodyn.,* **231,** 328 (1978).

25. Haydu, S.P., Bradley, J.L. and Hughes, D.T.D., *Brit. Med. J.,* **3,** 283 (1978).

26. Batchelor, J.F., Follenfant, M.J., Garland, L.G., Gorvin, J.H., Green, A.F., Hodson, H.F., Hughes, D.T.D. and Tateson, J.E., *Lancet,* 1169 (1975).

27. Poppins, H. and Stenius, B., *Europ. J. Clin. Pharmacol.,* **11,** 107 (1977).

28. Pauwels, R., Lamont, H. and Van Der Straeten, M., *Acta Allergologica,* **31,** 239 (1976).

29. Pauwels, R., Lamont, H. and Van Der Straeten, M., *Acta Allergologica,* **31,** 471 (1976).

30. Pinnas, J.L., Chen, T.M. and Perkins, J.G., *Clinical Research,* **26,** 293A (1978).

31. *Drugs of the Future,* **2,** 538 (1977).

32. Pauwels, R., Lamont, H. and Van Der Straeten, M., *Clin. Allergy,* **6,** 471 (1976).

33. Buckle, D.R., Morgan, N.J., Ross, J.W., Smith, H. and Spicer, B.A., *J. Med. Chem.,* **16,** 1334 (1973).

34. Spicer, B.A., Ross, J.W. and Smith, H., *Clin. Exp. Immunol.,* **21,** 419 (1975).

35. Pauwels, R., Lamont, H. and Van Der Straeten, M., *Clin. Allergy,* **6,** 463 (1976).

36. Buckle, D.R., Cantello, B.C.C., Smith, H. and Spicer, B.A., *J. Med. Chem.,* **20,** 265 (1977).

37. Buckle, D.R., Cantello, B.C.C., Smith, H., Smith, R.J. and Spicer, B.A., *J. Med. Chem.,* **20,** 1059 (1977).

38. Augstein, J., Cairns, H., Chambers, A., Burns, J.W. and Radziwonik, H., *J. Pharm. Pharmacol.,* **28,** 919 (1976).

39. Augstein, J., Cairns, H., Hunter, D., Lee, T.B., Suschitzky, J., Altounyan, R.E.C., Jackson, D.M, Mann, J., Orr, T.S.C. and Sheard, P., *Agents and Actions,* **7,** 443 (1977).

40. *Drugs of the Future,* **3,** 235 (1978).

41. von Strandtmann, M., Klutchko, S., Cohen, M.P., and Shavel, J. Jr., *J. Heterocycl. Chem.,* **9,** 171 (1972).

42. Klutchko, S., Cohen, M.P., Shavel, J. Jr. and von Strandtmann, M., *J. Heterocycl. Chem.,* **11,** 183 (1974).

43. Giles, R.E. and Herzig, D.J., in *Ann. Repts. Med. Chem.,* **10,** Heinzelman, R.V., (Ed), Academic Press, New York, N.Y. (1975) pp. 80-89.

44. Herzig, D.J., Giles, R.E., Schumann, P.R., Kusner, E.J. and Dubnick, B., *Fed. Proc.* **34,** 760 (1975).

45. *Drugs of the Future,* **3,** 7 (1978).

46. Honara, A., Kuriki, H., Saijo, T., Sugihara, H., Kanno, M. and Sanno, Y., *J. Med. Chem.,* **20,** 141 (1977).

47. Kuriki, H., Saijo, T. and Sugano, M., *Jap. J. Allergol.,* **25,** 350 (1976).

48. Kurokawa, D., Katsushiro, E., Okuda, N. and Ocubo, Y., *Jap. J. Allergol.,* **25,** 350 (1976).

49. Di Carlo, F.J., Herzig, D.J., Kusner, J., Schumann, P.R., Melgar, M.D., George, S. and Crew, M.C., *Drug Metab. Disp.,* **4,** 368 (1976).

50. Nohara, A., Kuriki, H., Saijo, T., Ukawa, K., Murato, T., Kauno, M. and Sanno, Y., *J. Med. Chem.,* **18,** 34 (1975).

51. Doria, G., Romeo, C., Giraldi, P., Lauria, F., Sberze, P., Tibolla, M., Corno, M.L., Cadelli, G. and Montoro, C., *Eur. J. Med. Chem.,* **13,** 33 (1978).

52. Muni, I.A., Leeling, J.L., Helms, R.J. and Johnson N. Jr., *Toxicol. Appl. Pharmacol.,* **43,** 527 (1978).

53. Broughton, B.J., Chaplen, P., Knowles, P., Lunt, E., Pain, D.L., Woodridge, K.R.H., Ford, R., Marshall, S., Walker, J.L. and Maxwell, D.R., *Nature,* (London), **251,** 650 (1974).

54. Broughton, B.J., Chaplen, P., Knowles, P., Lunt, E., Marshall, S.M., Pain, D.L. and Wooldridge, K.R.H., *J. Med. Chem.,* **18,** 1117 (1975).

55. Stewart, P.B., Devlin, J.P. and Freter, K.R., *Fed. Proc.,* **33,** 762, Abstr. 3129 (1974).

56. Devlin, J.P., Freter, K. and Stewart, P.B., *J. Med. Chem.,* **20,** 205 (1977).

57. Burka, J.F. and Eyre, P., *Int. Arch. Allergy Appl. Immunol.,* **49,** 774 (1975).

58. El-Azab, J. and Stewart, P.B., *Int. Arch. Allergy Appl. Immunol.,* **55,** 350 (1977).

59. Johnson, H.G. and VanHout, C.A., *Int. Arch. Allergy Appl. Immunol.,* **50,** 446 (1976).

60. Mygend, N. and Thomsen, J., *Acta Allergologica,* **30,** 298 (1975).

61. Evans, D.P., Gilman, D.J., Thomson, D.S. and Waring, W.S., *Nature,* (London) **250,** 592 (1974).

62. Holland, D., Jones, G., Marshall, P.W. and Tringham, G.D., *J. Med. Chem.,* **18,** 1225 (1976).

63. Erickson, E.H., Hainline, C.F., Matson, D.J., and Rice, T.K., 16th National Medicinal Chemistry Symposium, Kalamazoo, Michigan, June 18-22, 1978.

64. Snader, M., Chakrin, L.W., Cramer, R.D., III, Gelernt, Y.M., Miao, C.K., Shah, D.H., Sutton, B.M., Venslavsky, J.W. and Willis, C.R., Presented in the "Symposium on Drugs Affecting the Respiratory System" at the 175th National Meeting of the American Chemical Society, Anaheim, Calif., Mar. 13-17, 1978, see abstract MEDI-3.

65. Falliers, C.J. and Mingo, T.S., *J. Allergy Clin. Immunol.,* **61,** 188 (1978).

66. Johnson, H.G., VanHout, C.A. and Wright, J.B., *Intern. Arch. Allergy Appl. Immunol.,* **56,** 416 (1978).

67. Moreno, J.N., LeZotte, J.R., Johnson, H.G. and Brooks, C.D., *Allergologica et Immunopathologica,* (abstract), **5,** 441 (1977).

68. Sellstedt, J.H., Guinosso, C.J., Begany, A.J., Bell, S.C. and Rosenthale, M., *J. Med. Chem.,* **18,** 926 (1975).

69. Rosenthale, M.E., Begany, A.J., Dervinis, A., Sellstedt, J., Guinosso, C. and Gluckman, M.I., *J. Pharmacol. Exp. Ther.,* **197,** 153, (1976).

70. Koda, A., Nagai, H., Watanabe, S., Yanagihara, Y. and Sakamoto, K., *J. Allergy and Clin. Immunol.,* **57,** 396 (1976).

71. Azuma, H., Banno, K. and Yoskimura, T., *Brit. J. Pharmacol.,* **58,** 483 (1976).

72. Ohsugi, Y., Matsumo, T. and Takagaki, Y., *Chem. Pharm. Bull.,* **25,** 2437 (1977).

73. Temple, D.L., Jr., U.S. 4,054,656.

74. Yevich, J.P., Covington, R.R., Hanning, C.A., Seidehamel, R.J. and Temple, D.L., Abstr. of the 176th National Meeting of the American Chemical Society, Miami Beach, Florida Sept. 10-15, 1978, MEDI-29.

75. Belg. 862,384.

76. Smith, S.R., Tozzi, S. and Petillo, J., *J. Allergy Clin. Immunol.,* **53,** 84 (1974).

77. Gobel, P., *J. Int. Med. Res.,* **6,** 79 (1978).

78. Awouters, F., Niemegeers, C.J.E., Van den Berk, J., Van Nueten, J.M., Lenaerts, F.M., Borgers, M., Schellekens, K.H.L., Broeckaert, A., De Cree, J. and Janssen, P.A.J., *Experientia,* **33,** 1657, (1977).

79. De Beule, R., Vannieuwenhuyse, E., Callier, J., Verstraete, W., Degreef, F., Gregoire, M., Robience, Y., Stevens, W. and Libert, P., *Acta Allergologica,* **32,** 278 (1977).

80. *Drugs of the Future,* **2,** 438 (1977).

81. Roesh, A. and Roesh, E., *Brit. J. Pharmacol.,* **57,** 438P (1976).

RECEIVED January 22, 1979.

# 4

# The Development of Phenylenedioxamic Acids As Potential Antiallergy Agents

CHARLES M. HALL and H. G. JOHNSON

Hypersensitivity Diseases Research, The Upjohn Company, Kalamazoo, MI 49001

Traditional chemotherapy of the asthmatic patient has generally utilized "end organ" antagonists, that is, agents (antihistamines, bronchodilators, and steroids) which appear to block the receptors for a variety of mediators (histamine, SRS-A, ECF-A, etc), but may have little to do with the basic allergic disease. In principle, the clinical manifestations of an allergic attack may be ameliorated by prevention of mediator release. The introduction of cromolyn sodium in 1967 confirmed that inhibition of mediator release is one viable means of prophylactically treating the allergic patient. Subsequently a number of other research groups have reported (1) that other classes of compounds also prevent mediator release in standard animal models both *in vivo* and *in vitro* assays.

In the course of investigating a variety of different classes of compounds for their ability to inhibit mediator release, we found that certain aryl (2) and heteraryl(3) oxamic acids and esters were active in the rat passive cutaneous anaphylaxis (PCA) assay. It is noteworthy that other workers (4) independently, also have found similar activity in a variety of aryl and heteraryl oxanilic acid derivatives. In related work with a series of quinaldic acid derivatives (5,6), we found that activity was generally greater in compounds with "bis-functionality" incorporated into the molecular structure as compared to the "mono-functional" analog. Accordingly, we investigated a series of aryl dioxamic acid derivatives in the rat PCA assay to see if they possessed enhanced activity when compared to the monooxamic acid with a similar substitution pattern.

At first glance, the oxamic acid derivatives may appear to be unrelated structurally to other reported series of inhibitors of mediator release. However in the extended planar conformation the oxamic acids possess several structural features in common with both chromone-2-carboxylic acids and quinaldic acids.

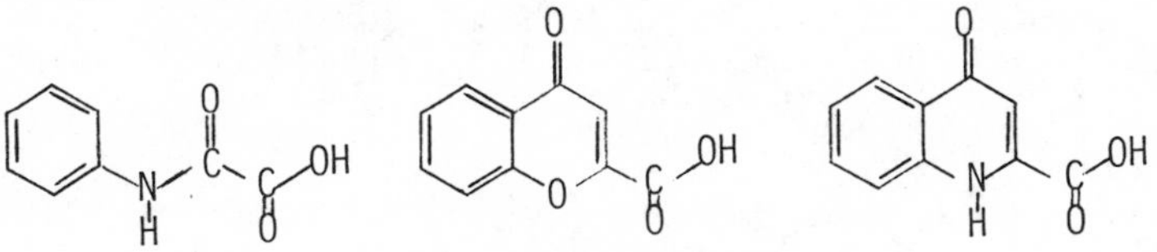

0-8412-0536-1/80/47-118-069$07.25/0

Moreover, Cheney (7) and collaborators have shown that these three structural classes possess similarity in their electronic structure as well, and that a statistically significant correlation exists between the energy of a low-lying unoccupied molecular orbital of members of all three series and the PCA activity. Structural similarity also exists between the phenylenedioxamic acids and the previously reported pyridoquinolinedicarboxylic acids (5). It should be noted that the carboxyl-carboxyl distances are approximately 10 A in both examples:

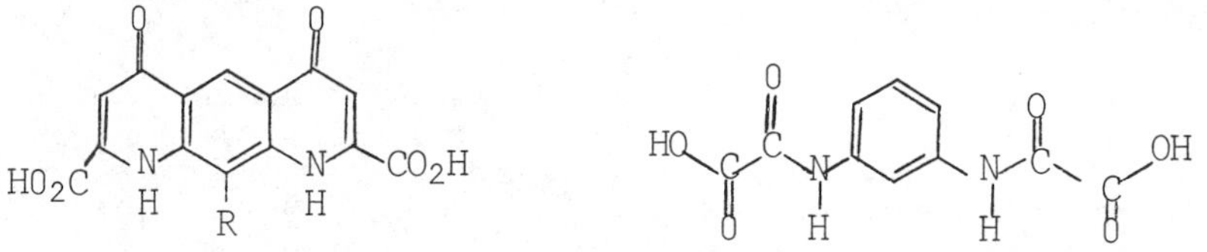

Phenylenedioxamates can be synthesized readily by either of two routes. Reaction of appropriate phenylenediamine with 2 eq. of an alkyl oxalyl chloride in the presence of 2 eq. of triethyl amine in anhydrous DMF gave the desired dialkyl diester in generally good yield. Alternatively the phenylenediamine can be heated at reflux in the dialkyl oxalate. The latter approach has the disadvantage of requiring higher temperatures and producing some oxamides and insoluble polymeric material. The isolated dioxamate can be readily hydrolyzed with dilute NaOH. Acidification to pH=2 gives the dioxamic acid in good yield. The dioxamic acids were relatively insoluble in water but dissolved readily in the presence of 2 eq. of THAM (trishydroxymethylaminomethane). The acids were administered i.v. as aqueous solutions of the THAM salts. The diesters were administered orally as suspensions.

Scheme I

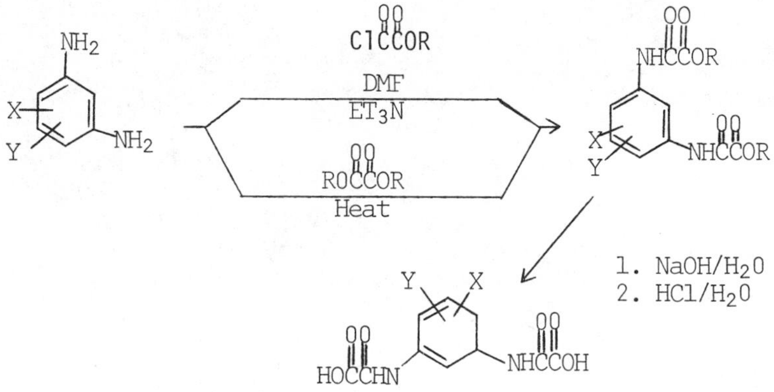

The results (8) of the rat PCA assay are given in Tables 1 and 2. Although a complete structure-activity picture does not emerge from these data, in general it appears that upon i.v. administration (Table 2) an "electron withdrawing" group at the 5 position enhances activity, (compare 37 with 43 and 38 with 48 and 49). Furthermore, a chlorine substituent at the 2 position improves activity (compare 43 with 49 and 49 with 52).

Although absorption, deposition, metabolism and excretion considerations must play a role for orally administered drugs, the oral activity of the diesters (Table 1) roughly parallels the i.v. activity of the diacids. It is interesting to note that many of these diesters exhibit their maximum activity when administered only 5 min. prior to antigen challenge and that they show little or no activity when administered one hour before challenge. The potency of compound 49 (lodoxamide tromethamine U-42,585E) led us to study its biological properties further. These studies are summarized in the next section along with a comparison of lodoxamide tromethamine and cromolyn sodium.

## Biological Evaluation of Lodoxamide Tromethamine. (49, U-42,585E)

### A. Rat Studies.

When DSCG or U-42,585E (lodoxamide tromethamine) were injected intravenously along with antigen in previously sensitized animals, the amount of compound needed to inhibit the PCA reaction was determined. Table 3 shows that under identical conditions, U-42,585E was some 2,500 times more active than DSCG. The optimal time for giving these drugs for best inhibition was either immediately before or along with antigen. Table 4 shows that U-42,585E administered orally to sensitized rats 3-10 minutes before antigen challenge also inhibited the reaction. Inhibition was obtained with oral doses of between 0.1 and 10.0 mg/kg. DSCG showed poor to negligible activity at up to 200 mg/kg orally. The onset and duration of biological activity when U-42,585E was given orally are remarkably similar to the onset seen by the intravenous route. The reason it requires 100 to 1,000 times more drug to show comparable activity by the oral route as compared to the intravenous route is thought to be due to poorer absorption by the former route. However, it is clear that the amount of drug that is required for efficacy is adsorbed by the oral route in under 5 min. Table 5 shows one possible additional explanation for the disparity between oral and intravenous doses. When animals were predosed orally with U42,585E, they developed tachyphylaxis to a secondary dose of the drug. Tachyphylaxis seemed to be time and dose dependent, but generally occurred after the biological effect of the drug had subsided (2.0 h). In Table 5, one would have expected excellent inhibition

Table 1

Diethyl N,N'-(m-Phenylene)dioxamates

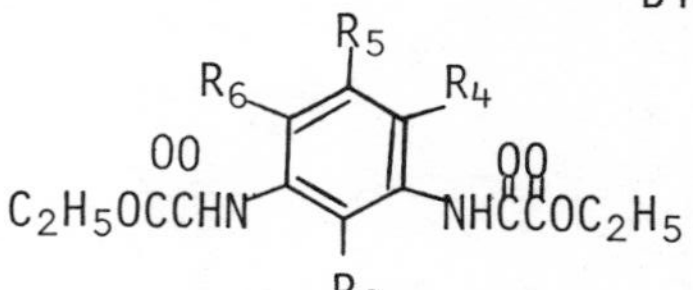

| Compd. | $R_2$ | $R_4$ | $R_5$ | $R_6$ | dose, mg/kg (P.O.) | % inhib of rat PCA, time (min) before challenge: 5 | 20 | 60 | 120 |
|---|---|---|---|---|---|---|---|---|---|
| 1 | H | H | H | H | 50 | 3 | 94 | 14 | 29 |
| 2 | F | H | H | H | 50 | | | 0 | |
| 3 | Cl | H | H | H | 50 | 53 | 17 | 1.8 | |
| 4 | $COOCH_3$ | H | H | H | 50 | | 27 | 15 | 0 |
| 5 | $CH_3$ | H | H | H | 50 | 28 | 53 | | |
| 6 | CN | H | H | H | | | | | |
| 7 | $OCH_3$ | H | H | H | 50 | 72 | 11 | 22 | |
| 8 | H | $CH_3$ | H | H | 50 | 17 | 38 | 12 | |
| 9 | H | $n-C_4H_9$ | H | H | 50 | 0 | 0 | 5 | 0 |
| 10 | H | $OCH_3$ | H | H | 50 | 50 | 70 | 11 | 45 |
| 11 | H | CN | H | H | 10 | 7 | 19 | 19 | |
| 12 | H | F | H | H | 50 | 74 | 64 | 18 | |
| 13 | H | H | $OCH_3$ | H | 50 | | 4 | 0 | 29 |
| 14 | H | H | COOH | H | 50 | 14 | 0 | 0 | 20 |
| 15 | H | H | $CONH_2$ | H | | | | | |
| 16 | H | H | CN | H | 10 | 95 | 25 | 0 | |
| 17 | H | H | $NO_2$ | H | 50 | 0 | 0 | 6 | |

Table 1 Cont'd.)

| Compd. | $R_2$ | $R_4$ | $R_5$ | $R_6$ | dose, mg/kg (P.O.) | % inhib of rat PCA time (min) before challenge | | | |
|---|---|---|---|---|---|---|---|---|---|
| | | | | | | 5 | 20 | 60 | 120 |
| 18 | H | H | NHCOCO-$OC_2H_5$ | H | 50 | | 0 | 5 | 0 |
| 19 | H | H | $NHCOCH_3$ | H | 50 | 6 | 1 | 0 | 24 |
| 20 | Cl | H | $CH_3$ | H | 50 | | 26 | 0 | 3 |
| 21 | Cl | H | COOH | H | 50 | 15 | 41 | 15 | 9 |
| 22 | Cl | H | $COOCH_3$ | H | 50 | | 7 | 0 | 0 |
| 23 | Cl | H | $CONH_2$ | H | 50 | 85 | 49 | | |
| 24 | Cl | H | $COCH_3$ | H | 50 | | 14 | 37 | 31 |
| 25 | Cl | H | $CF_3$ | H | 50 | 10 | 10 | 4 | |
| 26 | Cl | H | CN | H | 50 | 100 | 31 | 0 | |
| 27 | Cl | H | $CH_3SO_2$ | H | 50 | 0 | 0 | 0 | |
| 28 | Cl | H | $C_6H_5$ | H | 50 | 25 | 25 | | |
| 29 | Cl | $NO_2$ | H | $NO_2$ | 50 | | 25 | 0 | |
| 30 | $CH_3$ | H | COOH | H | 50 | 0 | 0 | 0 | 0 |
| 31 | CN | H | CF | H | 50 | 50 | 25 | 0 | |
| 32 | Cl | Cl | $COOCH_3$ | H | 50 | | 0 | 0 | 0 |
| 33 | H | Cl | H | Cl | 50 | | 50 | 25 | |
| 34 | H | $NO_2$ | H | $NO_2$ | 50 | | 17 | 9 | |
| 35 | H | Cl | CN | H | 50 | 100 | 20 | 0 | |
| 36 | H | Cl | $C_6H_5$ | H | 50 | 72 | 10 | 51 | |

Table 2

N,N'-(m-Phenylene)dioxamic Acids

| Compd | $R_2$ | $R_4$ | $R_5$ | $R_6$ | % inhibition of rat PCA, mg/kg iv 1.0 | 0.1 | 0.01 | 0.001 |
|---|---|---|---|---|---|---|---|---|
| 37 | H | H | H | H | 82 | 73 | 0 | |
| 38 | Cl | H | H | H | 75 | 32 | | |
| 39 | H | $OCH_3$ | H | H | 100 | 0 | | |
| 40 | H | CN | H | H | 87 | 8 | | |
| 41 | H | F | H | H | 100 | 41 | | |
| 42 | H | H | $CONH_2$ | H | 91 | 17 | | |
| 43 | H | H | CN | H | | 90 | 57 | |
| 44 | H | H | $NHCOCH_3$ | H | 47 | 11 | 0 | |
| 45 | Cl | H | $CH_3$ | H | 100 | 91 | 20 | 2 |
| 46 | Cl | H | $CONH_2$ | H | 90 | 28 | 0 | |
| 47 | Cl | H | $COCH_3$ | H | 88 | 22 | 0 | |
| 48 | Cl | H | $CF_3$ | H | | 100 | 90 | 0 |
| 49 | Cl | H | CN | H | | | 94 | 50 |
| 50 | Cl | H | $C_6H_5$ | H | 94 | 87 | 44 | |
| 51 | H | Cl | H | Cl | 81 | 25 | 0 | |
| 52 | H | Cl | CN | H | 100 | 100 | 20 | 0 |
| 53 | Cl | H | $CH_2SO_2$ | H | 85 | 10 | | |

Table 3

Comparison of activity of U-42,585E to cromolyn Na in the rat PCA assay

| Compound | Number of animals | 50% inhibition mg/kg ± SD |
|---|---|---|
| 1. Cromolyn Na | 35 | 2.5 ± 0.18 |
| 2. U-42,585E | 49 | 0.001 ± 0.00088 |

Both compounds were given intravenously along with 2 mg ovalbumin and 5 mg Evans blue to antiovalbumin-lgE-sensitized animals 72 h after sensitization. Each point is the mean ± SD 50% inhibitory concentration of the number of animals indicated.

Table 4

Inhibition of rat PCA reactions by orally administered U-42,585E

| Duration of activity oral dose 50 mg/kg | | Dose Response 5 min before challenge | |
|---|---|---|---|
| minutes before challenge | inhibition, % | U-42,585E mg/kg | inhibition, % |
| 1 | 95 | 50 | 100 |
| 3 | 100 | 25 | 92 |
| 5 | 100 | 10 | 95 |
| 10 | 69 | 5 | 59 |
| 20 | 31 | 1.0 | 25 |
| 30 | 0 | 0.1 | 12 |
| 60 | 0 | | |

Oral doses were administered in 1.0 ml of vehicle 122 by gavage to 18-hour fasted rats. Each time or dose point above represents the results from 16 amimals.

Table 5

Dose relationship of orally administered U-42,585E to development of tachyphylaxis in the rat PCA

| | Secondary oral Dose U-42,585E p.o. 3 min before challenge with antigen and dye | | |
|---|---|---|---|
| | 25 mg/kg | 0.01 mg/kg | none |
| Primary oral dose, U-42,585E (mg/kg) | | | |
| 25 (high dose) | 12 | 56 | - |
| 0.01 (low dose) | 87 | 25 | - |
| Non-predosed controls, U-42,585E orally 3 min before challenge, mg/kg | | | |
| 25 (high dose) | - | - | 96 |
| 0.01 (low dose) | - | - | 0 |

Animals were predosed as described above. These results are the mean percent inhibition calculated with 14 animals in each control group and 8 at each test variable. Drug was given orally in 1 ml vehicle 122. The oral doses were chosen to illustrate both tachyphylactic concentration (25 mg/kg) and nontachyphylactic dose (0.01 mg/kg). A 2 hr time interval was used between prinary and secondary dose.

at 25 mg/kg oral dose, however only 12% was seen. Similar results have been described for DSCG and U38,650 (23).

U-42,585E was tested for its antagonism of the effects of the mediators of anaphylaxis at the end organ and showed the following: a bath concentration of up to 50 μg/ml did not antagonize the guinea pig ileum contractions induced by either histamine or rat SRS-A. Further pharmacological profiles on U-42,585E indicated that this compound was capable of inhibiting the antigen-induced release of SRS-A in the peritoneal cavity of rats at 0.1 to 3 mg/kg. Dose responses were difficult to obtain with this drug, and there was a poor relationship between inhibition of histamine and SRS-A release.

Extensive studies were undertaken to show the effects of U-42,585E on the *in vitro* rat mast cell system using either antigen- or 48/80-induced histamine release as a model of allergic reactions. DSCG shows a bell-shaped, biphasic dose-response curve when tested against 48/80 release in mast cells (12,13,14), thus making definition of the mode of action of these drugs difficult. Table 6 shows dose responses for both DSCG and U-42,585E in the inhibition of 48/80-induced histamine release. In this comparison, U-42,585E showed approximately 100 times more activity than DSCG. However, dose comparisons are difficult when biphasic responses are seen. The apparent enhancement (52 versus 27%) of histamine release at very low concentration of DSCG (0.001 and 0.0001 μg/ml) is repeatedly seen in this assay and with these drugs the meaning is not clear at this time. Similar results have been reported in other studies (15).

A recent finding (14) that DSCG inhibited the ionophore induced movement of $^{45}$Ca into rat mast cells and additionally inhibited histamine release was extended to U-42,585E as well. Table 7 shows that U-42,585E inhibited $^{45}$Ca flux into rat mast cells maximally at 0.1 μg/ml whereas in other experiments (14), DSCG inhibited $^{45}$Ca flux in a bell-shaped dose response curve at 10 to 100 μg/ml. The stimulation by U-42,585E rather than inhibition of Ca flux into the cell seen at 1.0 and 5.0 μg/ml may explain in part the nonlinear dose-response curves seen for DSCG and U-42,585E.

### B. Mechanism of Cholinergic Stimulation at High Concentrations of U-42,585E (lodoxamide tromethamine).

The anti-allergy drugs, cromolyn sodium and lodoxamide tromethamine show *in vitro* dose responses which are bell-shaped or biphasic in mast cells. The nature of the biphasic dose response is poorly understood; however, through the use of specific antagonists it has been possible to show that at the high concentrations of these drugs leading to enhanced histamine release or

Table 6

Dose responses for U-42,585E and cromolyn Na on the inhibition of 48/80-induced histamine release from rat mast cells

| DSCG | | | U-42,585E | | |
|---|---|---|---|---|---|
| Concentration of compound µg/ml | Net histamine release % | Inhibition % | Concentration of compound µg/ml | Net histamine release % | Inhibition % |
| 100 | 27.8 ± 2.3 | 38 | 100 | 12.0 ± 1.95 | 71 |
| 50 | 13.5 ± 9.8 | 70 | 50 | 30.0 ± 3.14 | 46 |
| 25 | 15.0 ± 2.8 | 66 | 25 | 31.0 ± 1.4 | 43 |
| 5 | 17.8 ± 1.4 | 62 | 1 | 47.0 ± 2.12 | 14 |
| 1 | 25.1 ± 3.5 | 44 | 0.10 | 42.0 ± 4.97 | 23 |
| 0.01 | 27.0 ± 2.8 | 38 | 0.01 | 31.0 ± 1.4 | 44 |
| 0.001 | 48.0 ± 9.8 | 0 | 0.001 | 49.0 ± 2.19 | 11 |
| 0.0001 | 52.0 ± 3.5 | 0 | | | |

48/80 concentration 0.25 µg/ml added to the cells at the time of compound. Each point is the mean ± SD of 3 replicates. In the DSCG experiment, 0.25 µg 48/80 released 47.3 µg histamine out of a total of 106 µg. In the U-42,585E experiment, 0.25 µg 48/80 released 86.6 µg histamine out of a total of 157 µg.

Table 7

The dose-response effect of U-42,585E on $^{45}Ca$ movement into rat mast cells

| | Net $^{45}Ca$ uptake, mean ± SD, counts/min | | |
|---|---|---|---|
| | I<br>control cells | II<br>A23,187<br>1.0 μg/ml | III<br>A23,187<br>1.0 μg/ml<br>5.0 μg/ml 42,585E |
| 2 min | 5,839 ± 1,586<br>0.198[1] | 6,997 ± 999 | 6,870 ± 1,404<br>0.153 |
| 7 min | 8,299 ± 2,802<br>0.012 | 12,778 ± 933 | 10,031 ± 976<br>0.003 |
| 20 min | 7,229 ± 1,562<br>0.001 | 19,992 ± 3,935 | 23,354 ± 2,451<br>0.130 |
| Enhancement over A23,187 alone at 20 min | | | 126% over control |
| Inhibition at 20 min, % | | | 0 |

[1] The significance of each column is compared to column II (ionophore only) by Student's t test. p values of 0.05 or less are considered significant. The net (cycles/min) uptake is the mean ± SD of 5 replicate assays for radioactivity and this experiment is representative of 3 experiments.

Table 7 (Cont'd.)

| | Net $^{45}Ca$ uptake, mean ± SD, counts/min | | |
|---|---|---|---|
| | IV<br>A23,187<br>+ 42,585E<br>1.0 μg/ml | V<br>A23,187<br>+ 42,585<br>0.1 μg/ml | VI<br>A23,187<br>+ 42,585<br>0.01 μg/ml |
| 2 min | 7,068 ± 1,399<br>0.929 | 5,750 ± 477<br>0.036 | 5,780 ± 2,109<br>0.277 |
| 7 min | 14,164 ± 1,455<br>0.211 | 7,257 ± 1,164<br>0.000 | 5,841 ± 1,492<br>0.000 |
| 20 min | 28,139 ± 12,214<br>0.018 | 12,002 ± 1,111<br>0.002 | 15,907 ± 1,887<br>0.041 |
| Enhancement over A23,187 alone at 20 min | 163% | 0 | 0 |
| inhibition at 20 min, % | 0 | 63 | 37[3] |

[2] Lonophore is required for this enhancement, as 42,585 by itself caused no significant $^{45}Ca$ movement over control levels.

[3] Inhibition (%) = $\frac{\text{counts/min drug (x) + A23,187 - control counts/min}}{\text{counts/min A23,187 alone - control counts/min}}$ x 100.

multiple high dose tachyphylaxis, a cholinergic receptor is stimulated in the cell. This receptor is muscarinic in nature and can be blocked by atropine or quinuclidinyl benzilate (QNB). Prevention of multiple dose tachyphylaxis to either drug can be modulated by pretreatment with atropine or QNB. High concentrations of both drugs cause cell accumulation of cyclic-guanosine monophosphate through stimulation of guanyl cyclase and prevention of cGMP breakdown by inhibition of the phosphodiesterase (PDE) for cGMP (27).

### The Effect of Muscarinic Blockers on the DSCG and Lodoxamide Tromethamine Dose Response in Rat Mast Cell

When Ficoll-purified rat mast cells (16) are challenged with 48/80 immediately after the addition of increasing concentrations of DSCG (Fig. 1A) or lodoxamide tromethamine (Fig. 1B), the release of histamine is blocked maximally for DSCG at 50 μg/ml and for lodoxamide tromethamine at 1.0 μg/ml. Increasing the concentration of either drug then leads to a loss of efficacy and actual enhanced release if the concentration is high enough. Prior treatment with $10^{-6}$ to $10^{-7}$M atropine (5 min at 25°C) altered the dose-response curve. For DSCG the loss of efficacy (right hand) portion of the curve was totally blocked, and the curve for lodoxamide tromethamine was altered in a manner which suggested partial but not complete reversal of the loss of efficacy at high doses of drug (27), (Fig. 1A,1B).

The cholinergic stimulation by lodoxamide tromethamine was time and dose-related. Both inhibition of mediator release (5 μg/ml) and high-dose enhancement of release (500 μg/ml) were near maximal at 4 to 10 min (Fig. 2). The high dose also caused the accumulation of cGMP in P815 mastocytoma cells and the time of maximal stimulation was 6 to 12 min after drug was added (27).

### The Effect of Pretreatment of Rats with the Muscarinic Blockers Atropine and Quinuclidinyl Benzilate (QNB) on Multiple Dose DSCG and Lodoxamide Tromethamine Tachyphylaxis

Rats dosed twice with inhibiting doses of either DSCG or lodoxamide tromethamine show tachyphylaxis to an inhibition of the subsequent passive cutaneous anaphylaxis assay (10,11,13,16,17). Atropine (25 mg/kg) or QNB (0.01 mg/kg) given ip 20 min prior to the first iv dose of DSCG or lodoxamide, partially blocked this multiple dose tachyphylaxis (13,16,17,27). Atropine or QNB by themselves at these concentrations had no inhibitory effect on the PCA reaction, but markedly reduced (or almost totally eliminated) the tachyphylaxis (Fig. 3,4) to DSCG and to a lesser

*A*

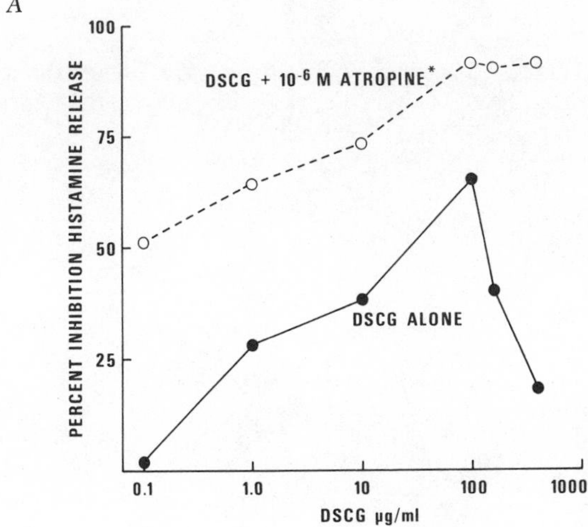


*B*

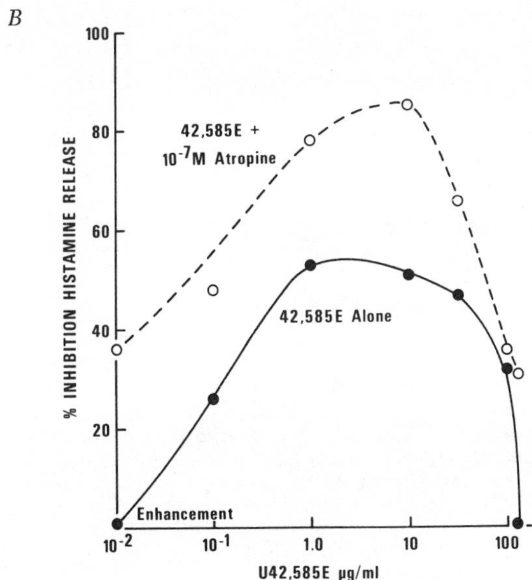


*Figure 1. Dose response for DSCG (A) or lodoxamide (B) in Ficoll-purified rat mast cells vs. 48/80-induced histamine release. Atropine was added to incubations (25°C) 5 min before DSCG or lodoxamide. DSCG or lodoxamide was prepared in distilled water and added immediately before 48/80. Histamine was determined in supernatants by an automated Technicon histamine assay and was compared to histamine content of boiled cells (boiled in 0.1N HCl for complete release). The results are expressed as net histamine release. ((A) Atrophine $10^{-6}$M alone inhibited 48/80 release; 2.8%; 0.5 µg/mL; 48/80 = 26.8% histamine release)*

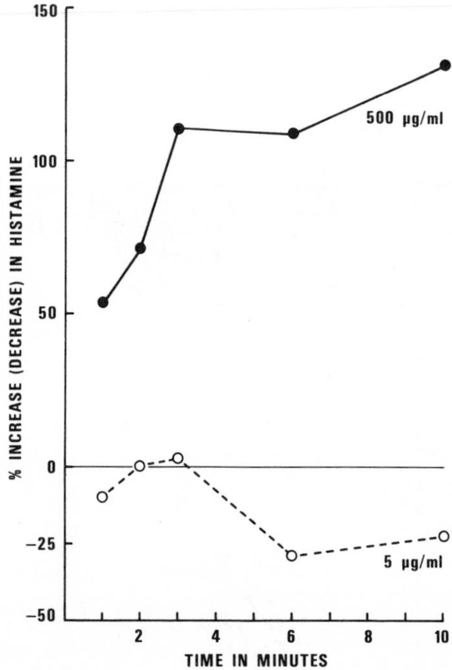


*Figure 2. Kinetics of cholinergic stimulation (enhanced histamine release) at high lodoxamide concentrations (500µg/mL) and inhibition of histamine release at low concentrations (5µg/mL). Ficoll-purified mast cells were incubated for various time periods with lodoxamide followed by 48/80. The mixture was filtered over Millipore 8-µm filters to stop the reaction. The filter was washed with 15 mL of phosphate-buffered saline, pH 7.2. The wash and filtrate were collected and analyzed for released histamine, and the release assay was compared to total levels in acid-boiled cell mixtures.*

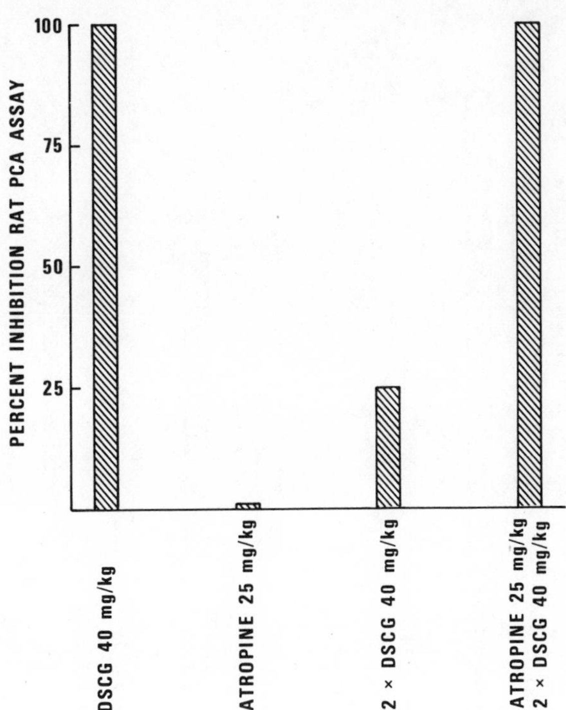


*Figure 3. Effect of atropine in blocking multiple-dose, DSCG-induced tachyphylaxis in rats. Sensitized animals were given atropine 25 mg/kg ip 20 min before iv (DSCG). After 1.0 hr the animals were given another iv dose of DSCG containing 2 mg egg albumin and 5 mg Evans blue. Eight controls of nondrug-predosed animals were also used to calculate inhibition of the PCA assay after 30-min development of the skin sites. Six animals were used for each variable. The variability of repeated assays of DSCG in these animals is approximately ± 8%.*

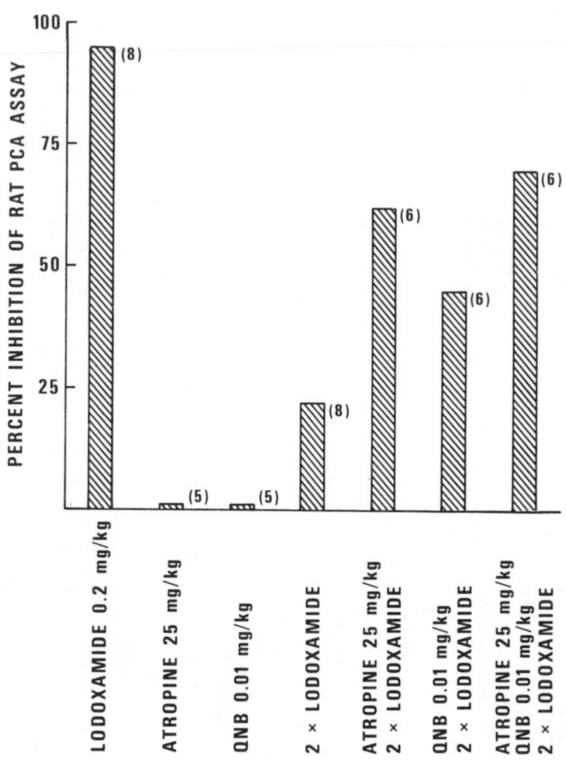


*Figure 4. Effect of muscarinic blockers atropine and QNB on multiple-dose lodoxamide tachyphylaxis. Sensitized rats were given atropine 25 mg/kg ip or QNB 0.01 mg/kg ip 20 min before the first iv dose of lodoxamide. One hr later the animals were given another iv dose of lodoxamide (0.2 mg/kg containing 2 mg egg albumin and 5 mg Evans blue), and 30 min later the skin sites of sensitization were scored and compared to nonpredosed rats as well as control rats. Numbers in parenthesis refer to number of animals per variable.*

extent to lodoxamide.

Effect of Lodoxamide Tromethamine on the Intracellular Nucleotide Levels and PDE Inhibition in Various Tissues

Since the high dose inhibition as well as the multiple dose tachyphylaxis appeared to be cholinergic in nature we looked for the corollary of raised cyclic-GMP in tissue which had been exposed to lodoxamide tromethamine. In studies on high and low affinity cAMP PDE's (phosphodiesterases) and cGMP PDE's from crude preparations of rat lung, lodoxamide tromethamine showed a low potency inhibition which was slightly selective for cGMP PDE over cAMP PDE (Table 8). Lodoxamide tromethamine was next studied for its ability to stimulate rat lung adenylate and guanylate cyclase. Table 9 shows that in both soluble and particle preparations high concentrations of the drug stimulated guanylate cyclase more than adenylate cyclase. Atropine partially blocked the stimulation of rat lung guanylate cyclase when it was added at an equivalent concentration to lodoxamide tromethamine in the low speed pellet only but not the high speed supernatant (Table 10). The kinetics of cholinergic stimulation by lodoxamide were measured in mouse P815 mastocytoma cells. The drug produced a rapid depletion of both cAMP and cGMP that was dose-related and lasted between 0-6 min.

These data indicate that DSCG and lodoxamide tromethamine exhibit biphasic dose responses for inhibition of mediator release and that both a portion of the bell-shaped curve and a part of the multiple dose tachyphylaxis can be blocked by prior treatment with atropine.

These results are consistent with the hypothesis, that this unwanted effect of the anti-allergy drug occurs through a cholinergic receptor leading to the accumulation of cGMP in the cells.

C. Comparison Between Cromolyn Sodium and Lodoxamide Tromethamine in Primates Against Aerosolized *Ascaris suum* Antigen.

Since models of reaginic hypersensitivity in rodents, although predictive for humans, have their limitations, lodoxamide tromethamine was studied in a model of active reaginic allergy in primates, and which have skin sensitivity to *Ascaris* antigen in certain Rhesus monkeys (18,19). This sensitivity was present naturally and was not induced by immunization. Comparative evaluation of the immunology of the reaginic antibody resides in the IgE type immunoglobulin, (19).

Table 8

$I_{50}$ Values of Lodoxamide ($X10^{-3}M$) versus Crude Rat Lung cAMP and cGMP Phosphodiesterases

| cAMP PDE | | cGMP PDE | |
|---|---|---|---|
| Enzyme Substrate | | Enzyme Substrate | |
| $10^{-4}M$ | $10^{-6}M$ | $10^{-4}M$ | $10^{-6}M$ |
| 7.6 | 4.7 | >10 | 1.3 |

Table 9

Effect of Lodoxamide on Rat Lung Adenylate and Guanylate Cyclases (Basal Activity = 100%)

| | Lodoxamide Concentration | |
|---|---|---|
| Enzyme Source | $8X10^{-4}M$ | $8X10^{-5}M$ |
| Adenylate Cyclase(1) | 129 | ND |
| Guanylate Cyclase | | |
| LPS(2) | 152 | 96 |
| HSS(3) | 141 | 98 |

1 = Hypotonic particle preparation

2 = Low speed pellet (10,000XG)

3 = High speed supernatant (100,000XG for 60 min)

Table 10

Effect of Atropine* on Lodoxamide Stimulation (Percent) of Rat Lung Guanylate Cyclase (Basal Activity = 100%)

| | Lodoxamide | | Atropine | | | Lodoxamide $8X10^{-4}M$ + Atropine | | |
|---|---|---|---|---|---|---|---|---|
| Enzyme Source | $8X10^{-4}M$ | $8X10^{-5}M$ | $8X10^{-4}M$ | $8X10^{-5}M$ | $8X10^{-6}M$ | $8X10^{-4}M$ | $8X10^{-5}M$ | $8X10^{-6}M$ |
| LSP(1) | 148 | 100 | 91 | 103 | 115 | 123 | 139 | 151 |
| HSS(2) | 136 | 100 | 95 | 100 | 104 | 135 | 137 | 140 |

1 = Low speed pellet (10,000XG)

2 = High speed supernatant (100,000XG for 60 min)

*Atropine alone had no effect on guanylate cyclase activity

A system for study of respiratory reactions was developed in the previously described primate with Ascaris by aerosol challenge that was reproducible (Fig. 5) simple to do, and easy to adapt to studying the effects of pharmacologic agents on the respiratory parameters involved in the Ascaris reaction (20).

Initial studies showed that the IgE-mediator primate respiratory response was partially inhibited by antihistamines, partially reversed by beta adrenergic blocking agents (20) and partially inhibited by cromolyn sodium when it was given either intravenously or by aerosol prior to antigen challenge (21).

We have reported studies on the effect of drugs on various lung parameters induced by Ascaris sensitivity (17,22). We quantitated these parameters and adapted the system to test cromolyn Na by aerosol and intravenous administration as well as lodoxamide tromethamine. Lodoxamide tromethamine in this assay showed quantitative advantages to cromolyn Na (DSCG) because it was significantly more active and was orally adsorbed.

When lodoxamide tromethamine was administered orally to reactor Ascaris monkeys, excellent inhibition of both lung function parameters was seen indicating a reversal of antigen challenge induced changes. Table 11 summarizes the activity of lodoxamide tromethamine and its duration of effect when dosed orally. This table also shows that when the optimal time (30 min.) is used to assay a dose response, inhibition can be seen as low as 5.0 mg/kg. Table 12 shows that when lodoxamide tromethamine was administered i.v. 5 min. before ascaris aerosolization (0.16 ml aerosolized in 50 respirations), protection was seen even at 0.001 mg total dose per animal (Table 13).

Multiple doses of DSCG and other similar compounds have been shown to develop a time and dose related period of tachyphylaxis in rats and primates, (12, 17, 23). Lodoxamide tromethamine also showed a similar phenomenon when multiple oral doses of 50 mg/kg were given (Table 14). Tachyphylaxis was evident if a high dose (50 mg/kg) preceded a similar high dose. Several low doses (0.1 mg/kg) appeared to give good inhibition in this assay.

## D. Human Clinical Studies With Lodoxamide Tromethamine.

The promising animal studies with lodoxamide tromethamine led to its investigation in human subjects. Two independent bronchoprovocation studies in patients with extrinsic bronchial asthma have been reported. Moreno and LeZotte (24) studied 12 patients, who had been pretreated randomly with inhaled lodoxamide tromethamine (1.0 mg, 0.1 mg, 0.01 mg) or placebo in a double blind manner, in a standard bronchial challenge. Each of the patients was treated with each drug dose and placebo in separate settings

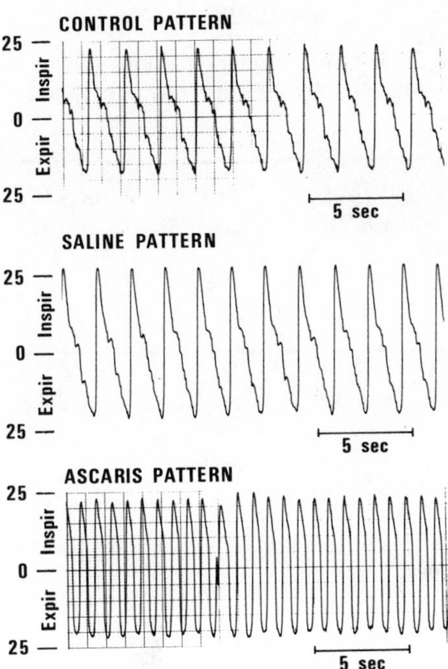


*Figure 5. Recordings of respiratory airflow rates (mL/sec) before and after aerosol challenge of an* Ascaris*-sensitive Rhesus monkey. Animals were aerosolized for 50 respirations and received 0.16 mL water containing 0.20 mg nitrogen/mL* Ascaris *antigen or saline. Average peak expiratory flow rate was 4 mL/sec/division. Tidal volume was determined by measuring the area under the inspiratory and expiratory airflow volume traces.*

Table 11

Inhibition of *Ascaris* induced lung function changes in reactor primates by orally administered U-42,585E.

| Duration of Activity P.O. dose 50 mg/kg | | Dose Response 30 min before challenge | |
|---|---|---|---|
| Time before challenge | % Inhibition | P.O. Drug mg/kg | % Inhibition |
| (min) | | | |
| 5 | 51 | 25 | 100 |
| 20 | 89 | 10 | 60 |
| 30 | 95 | 5 | 19 |
| 60 | 16 | 1.0 | 3 |
| | | 0.1 | 0 |

P.O. doses were administered in 1.0 ml vehicle 122 by gavage to 18 hr. fasted animals. Inhibition is expressed as the average inhibition of both (f) and (TV) lung function changes.

Table 12

Dose response for i.v. administered U-42,585E in the prevention of *Ascaris* induced lung function changes in primates.

| Drug mg/kg[a] | Lung Function | % Inhibition |
|---|---|---|
| 0.1 | (f) | 84 |
| | TV | 77 |
| 0.01 | (f) | 27 |
| | TV | 31 |
| 0.001 | (f) | 47 |
| | TV | 39 |
| 0.0001 | (f) | 0 |
| | TV | 10 |

(f) = respiratory rate/min increase

TV = tidal volume (ml) decrease

[a] U-42,585E was given in 1 ml water by the femoral artery 5 minutes before aerosal *Ascaris* challenge.

Table 13

The prevention of *Ascaris* induced lung function changes in primates by intrabronchial (ib) administration of U-42,585E and DSCG.

Percent Inhibition of Lung Reactivity

| Mg compound ib per 50 inspiratory cycles* | | Lung Function | % Inhibition |
|---|---|---|---|
| 1. U-42,585E | 25 | f (respiratory rate increase) | 100 |
| | | TV (tidal volume decrease) | 93 |
| | 12.5 | f | 80 |
| | | TV | 68 |
| | 5.0 | f | 78 |
| | | TV | 83 |
| | 1.0 | f | 80 |
| | | TV | 75 |
| | 0.1 | f | 71 |
| | | TV | 71 |
| | 0.01 | f | 93 |
| | | TV | 81 |
| | 0.001 | f | 100 |
| | | TV | 90 |
| 2. DSCG | 10** | f | 0 |
| | | TV | 9 |
| | 5 | f | 5 |
| | | TV | 36 |

*See text-methods for drug administration.

**When this concentration of DSCG is made up in 0.1 ml the resulting solution is very viscous and cannot be nebulized, therefore, this dosage is questionable.

Table 14

The inhibitory effect of multiple oral doses of U-42,585E given to *Ascaris* reactor monkeys 2.0 hours before challenge

| P.O. Dose U-42,585E mg/kg | Lung Function | % Inhibition |
|---|---|---|
| 1. 50 mg/kg Primary | f<br>TV | 83<br>77 |
| 2. 0.1 mg/kg Primary | f<br>TV | 7.0<br>21 |
| 3. 50 mg/kg Primary, 50 mg/kg Secondary* | f<br>TV | 0<br>21 |
| 4. 50 mg/kg Primary, 0.1 mg/kg Secondary | f<br>TV | 32<br>29 |
| 5. 0.1 mg/kg Primary, 0.1 mg/kg Secondary | f<br>TV | 51<br>59 |

f = Respiratory rate
TV = Tidal volume

* U-42,585E in vehicle 122 was given at the indicated dose by nasal stomach tube. Two hours later the secondary dose was given, followed 30 minutes later by antigen challenge. Vehicle 122 by itself had no effect on the respiratory responses.

at least 72 hrs. apart. When compared to placebo all three drug groups provided statistically significant protection against $FEV_1$ falls greater than 20% of baseline.

In a similar study, Townley and co-workers (25,26) challenged 10 extrinsic asthmatics with increasing amounts of allergen after pretreatment with inhaled placebo or lodoxamide tromethamine (1.0 mg, 0.1 mg, and 0.01 mg) in a randomized double blind fashion. Statistical analysis of the results demonstrated that the cumulative log dose of allergen which produced a 15% drop in $FEV_1$ ($PD_{15}$) was 2-65 greater for all three drug doses than for placebo.

Studies are being undertaken to determine the efficacy of lodoxamide tromethamine in exercise induced bronchospasm, allergic rhinitis and various skin allergies.

Literature Cited:

1. (a) J. J. Pfister, R. W. Ferraresi, I. T. Harrison, W. H. Rooks, A. P. Roszkowski, A. VanHorn, and J. H. Fried, J. Med. Chem. 15, 1032 (1972).
(b) C. M. Hall, H. G. Johnson, and J. B. Wright, J. Med. Chem., 17, 685 (1974). (c) D. R. Buckle, N. J. Morgan, J. W. Ross, H. Smith, and B. A. Spicer, J. Med. Chem., 16, 1334 (1973).

2. J. B. Wright, U.S. 3,987,192.

3. C. D. Blanton and H. G. Johnson, U.S. 3,838,166

4. J. H. Seldstedt, C. J. Guinosso, A. J. Begany, S. C. Bell and M. Rosenthale, J. Med. Chem., 18, 926 (1975).

5. C. M. Hall, J. B. Wright, H. G.Johnson and A. J. Taylor, J. Med. Chem., 20, 1337 (1977).

6. C. M. Hall, J. B. Wright and H. G. Johnson, J. Med. Chem., 17 685 (1974).

7. B. V. Cheney, J. B. Wright, C. M. Hall, H. G. Johnson, and R. E. Christofferson, J. Med. Chem., 21, 936 (1978).

8. J. B. Wright, C. M. Hall and H. G. Johnson, J. Med. Chem., 21, 930 (1978).

9. D. S. Thomson and D. P. Evans, Clin. exp. Immunol. 13: 537 (1973).

10. H. G. Johnson and C. A. VanHout, Proc. Soc. exp. Biol. Med. 143: 427 (1973).

11. H. G. Johnson and C. A. VanHout, Int. Archs Allergy appl. Immunol. 50: 446 (1976).

12. E. J. Kusner, B. Dubnick and D. J. Herzig, J. Pharmac. exp. Ther. 184:41 (1973).

13. H. G. Johnson and C. A. VanHout, Allergol. Et. Immunopathol. 2:33 (1973).

14. H. G. Johnson and M. K. Bach, J. Immunol. 114:514 (1975).

15. L. G. Garland, Br. J. Pharmacol. 49: 128 (1973).

16. H. G. Johnson, C. A. VanHout and J. B. Wright. Int. Arch. Allergy Appl. Immunol. 56:416 (1978).

17. H. G. Johnson and C. A. VanHout, Int. Arch. Allergy and Appl. Immunol. 50:454, (1976).

18. I. Weiszer, R. Patterson and J. D. Pruzansky, J. Allergy, 91:14 (1968).

19. R. Patterson and C. H. Talbot, J. Lab. and Clin. Med. 73: 924 (1969).

20. R. Patterson, C. H. Talbot and B. Booth, Amer. Rev. Resp. Dis. 102: 412 (1970).

21. R. Patterson, C. H. Talbot and M. Brandfonbrener, Int. Arch. Allergy Appl. Immunol. 41: 592 (1971).

22. H. G. Johnson, J. Am. Chem. Soc. (Med) 167: 24 (1974).

23. H. G. Johnson, C. A. VanHout and J. B. Wright, Int. Arch. Allergy Appl. Immunol 56: 481 (1978).

24. J. N. Moreno, L. A. Lezotte, H. G. Johnson and C. D. Brooks, Proc. International Congress of Immunology, Prague 1977.

25. N. Nair, K. Burke, G. Watt, A. Bewtra, and R. Townley, J. Allergy Clinical Immunology, 61: 189 (1978).

26. T. Bui, K. Burke, G. Watt, A. Bewtra and R. Townley J. Allergy Clinical Immunol. 61: 189 (1978).

27. H. G. Johnson, G. J. White, Monograph in Allergy 12th CIA Symposium, S. Kayer, N.Y. 1979.

RECEIVED August 16, 1979.

# 5

# New, Orally Effective Chromone Derivatives for the Treatment of Asthma

H. CAIRNS

Fisons Ltd., Pharmaceutical Division, R. & D. Laboratories, Bakewell Road, Loughborough, Leicestershire, England

It is of interest to note that, since the introduction of disodium cromoglycate (Intal, cromolyn) (I) in 1967 as the first prophylactic agent for the treatment of bronchial asthma, no successor products of this type are yet clinically available. This observation is of extreme importance from the medicinal chemist's view point, as in our interpretation it high-lights the lack of clinically predictive screening models which can be used, reliably, in structure-activity studies. Perhaps this is best exemplified by considering the following facts; (i) that in the past 10 years, at least 65 pharmaceutical companies have filed patent applications describing compounds with cromolyn-like activity, (ii) that at least 25 of these companies have published papers describing some aspect of their scientific studies on compounds of this type, and (iii) that at least 9 of these latter companies have taken selected compounds to some stage of clinical evaluation as evidenced by appropriate publications (1 - 9). Yet despite this mammoth effort, my initial comments stand.

We ourselves rank alongside the companies listed above, as for the past 10 years we have striven to identify a follow-up product to cromolyn. This paper presents a summary of our work during this period, highlighting the significant theoretical and practical achievements and failures which have marked our progress. Always our objective was to identify a new "cromolyn like" drug, i.e. a compound whose biological mode of action was similar to that of the parent drug. Early in our programme we decided to concentrate on the search for an orally effective agent as an attractive alternative to cromolyn which has to be administered by inhalation.

Despite extensive investigation, the precise mechanism of action of cromolyn in man is still unknown, but it is generally accepted that this agent exerts much of its anti-asthmatic activity by inhibiting the release of mediators from sensitised mast cells (10). It is perhaps pertinent to reflect on how this aspect of the drug's mode of action was first discovered. Cromolyn

0-8412-0536-1/80/47-118-099$05.00/0

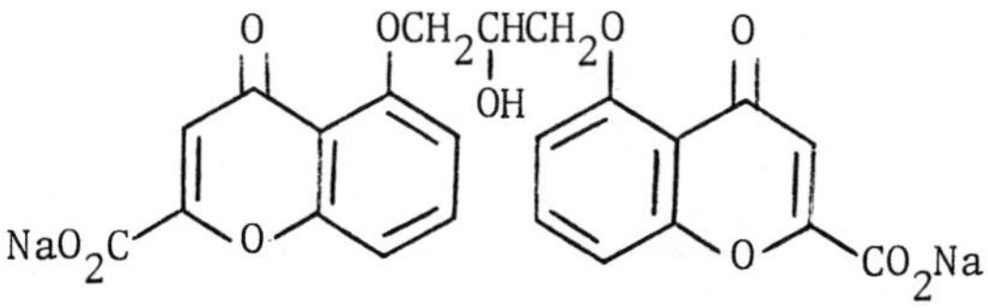

O OCH$_2$CHCH$_2$O O
OH
NaO$_2$C O O CO$_2$Na

I

MeO O
O O Me
MeO

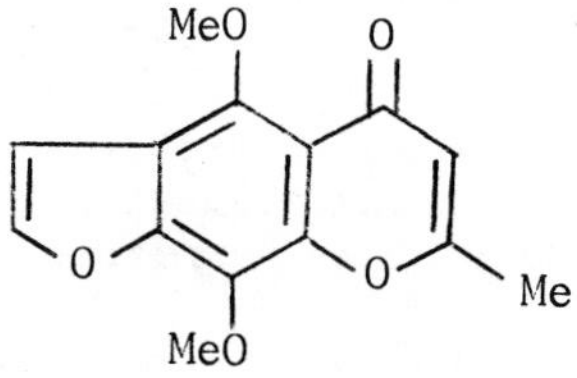

II

was synthesised during a programme of work originally designed to exploit the bronchodilating properties of a naturally occurring 2-methylchromone known as khellin (II). Part of the structural variation applied to the khellin molecule was to replace the 2-methyl substituent by a carboxy group. By so doing, it was soon apparent from our screening programme that we had lost all of khellin's bronchodilating activity, but continued investigation of the biological properties of the 2-carboxy series revealed that they possessed a novel prophylactic anti-asthmatic activity. Thus when given before antigen challenge to an asthmatic subject, these compounds inhibited the expected onset of bronchospasm. I would stress that this activity was first identified in a human asthmatic volunteer. It was only subsequent to this demonstration of the new prophylactic activity of the chromone-2-carboxylic acids in man, that we began to revise our biological testing programme — indeed cromolyn had been synthesised and identified as highly active in man before an animal model, which we could use to study the structure-activity relationships of these compounds, was identified. The animal model which Goose and Blair (11) of our laboratories used to demonstrate a possible explanation of the mode of action of cromolyn was the rat passive cutaneous anaphylaxis test (PCA test). At first sight, this PCA test seemed to be a potentially useful model of allergic asthma as it seemed to have several fundamental correlations with the human disease. Thus both systems involved mast cells; in both systems these cells were sensitised with antibodies of the IgE class; challenge of such sensitised cells with antigen resulted in the controlled release of the pharmacological mediators of anaphylaxis from these cells.

This then was the background to the beginning of our medicinal chemistry approach to the identification of an orally effective anti-asthmatic agent, which began around 1969-1970. At that time we considered our stock data on anti-asthmatic compounds from experimental asthma studies in humans. Thus, we knew that mono- and bischromones were highly active by inhalation, but that none of the compounds which we had prepared up to that time were orally effective. This lack of oral activity was, we decided, due to the high polarity and low lipophilic character of the chromone derivatives that we had prepared up to that time. For example, cromolyn had a pKa of about 1.5 and an octanol/water (pH 7.4 aqueous buffer) log D value of about -3.5. Such a compound would be expected to have a very poor absorption profile. This was reflected in its short plasma half-life following intravenous administration and the fact that its plasma levels following oral administration in a number of species were extremely low (12).

Consequently when we decided to look for orally effective analogues of cromolyn, we chose eventually to concentrate on molecular modification of the monochromones as they were rather more lipophilic than their bischromone counterparts. At the outset we decided to accept the inherent problem of the high acidity of the chromone-2-carboxylic acids and to attempt to overcome this by the introduction of lipophilic substituents into the chromone nucleus, in the hope that the net result would be the production of an active compound with an acceptable absorption profile.

As our primary test model we initially decided that we had to stay with the rat PCA screen. However, since we were now interested in orally effective compounds we studied the activity of the chromones following their administration either directly into the stomach or into the intestine of the animals, the latter following anaesthetisation and laparotomy. Experience showed that the results obtained on intra-duodenal dosing were much more reproducible than those obtained by straight oral dosing and so for a number of years we have used this route of drug administration to determine the likely oral activity of our compounds.

Our early clinical studies in the monochromone area had shown that, of the alkoxy substituted series, those derivatives which had the alkoxy group in the 5- position were the most active. An investigation of the biological activity of a large variety of 5-alkoxy substituted chromones in the rat PCA test, by the intra-duodenal route, revealed that the most active were those which carried an unsubstituted straight or branched alkyl chain, containing four carbon atoms or more, on the oxygen atom (see Table I). Our next step was to attempt to overcome the weak lipophilic character of the most active compound from this series, FPL 50419, by the introduction of alkyl and alkenyl substituents around the benzene ring of the chromone nucleus. These new compounds, like those contained in Table I, were prepared by the route shown in Scheme I. An examination of the data presented in Table II shows the success of this approach. Each of the compounds described was more active than FPL 50419 by the intra-duodenal route, with optimal activity being found in the 8-allyl derivative FPL 55618 which was 30 times more potent. Indeed FPL 55618 was 100 times more potent by the intravenous route, than cromolyn itself.

Not wishing to rely on activity data generated in only one biological screen, we tested FPL 55618 in a range of *in vitro* and *in vivo* models of immediate hypersensitivity which had been developed by our biologists. These models involved allergic reactions in the skin and in the lungs of rats, dogs, monkeys and guinea-pigs, as well as in a number of *in vitro* systems and FPL 55618 was active in several of these models of allergic disease (13). Our only worry at the time was that cromolyn did not have particularly outstanding activity in many of these new screens, so their true value as models of allergic asthma were untried. However, we decided to take FPL 55618, forward to clinical evaluation. In the event, the compound had

TABLE I

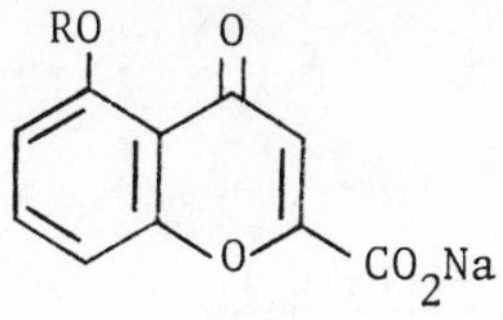

(Structure: 5-RO-chromone-2-$CO_2Na$)

| Compound No. | R | PCA $ED_{50}$* in mg/kg intraduodenal (i.d.) |
|---|---|---|
| 50268 | $CH_3CH_2CH_2$- | >10 |
| 50271 | $CH_3CHOHCH_2$- | 50 |
| 50291 | $PhOCH_2CH_2$- | 105 |
| 50419 | $Me_2CHCH_2CH_2$- | 6 |
| 50482 | $Et_2NCOCH_2$- | >>10 |
| 50485 | $CH_2$=$CHCH_2CH_2$- | 10 |
| 50489 | $PhCH_2$- | >10 |
| 50490 | $ClCH_2CH_2$- | >10 |
| 55671 | $CH_3(CH_2)_4$- | 10 |

*Compounds were given intraduodenally 7-10 min prior to antigen challenge. This was shown to be the optimal dosing schedule.

SCHEME I

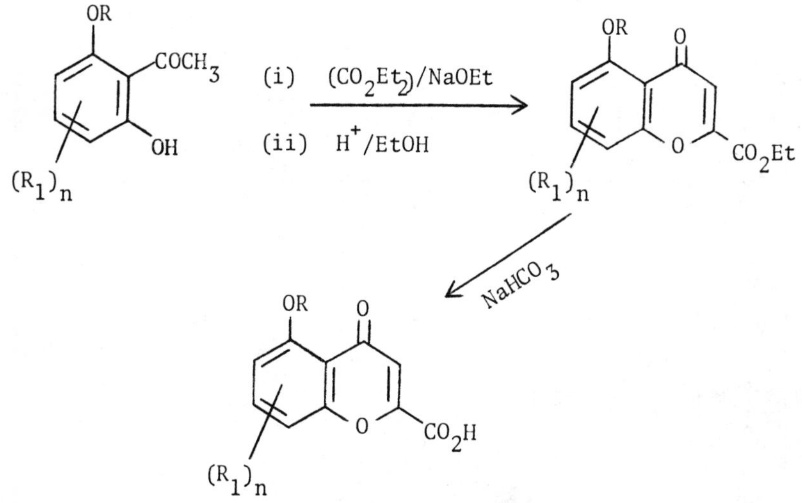

OR
$COCH_3$
OH
$(R_1)_n$

(i) $(CO_2Et)_2$/NaOEt

(ii) $H^+$/EtOH

OR O
$CO_2Et$
$(R_1)_n$

$NaHCO_3$

OR O
$CO_2H$
$(R_1)_n$

R, $R_1$, n - see Tables I and II

TABLE II



| Compound No. | $R_1$ | $R_2$ | PCA $ED_{50}$ in mg/kg (a) | |
|---|---|---|---|---|
| | | | i.v. | i.d. |
| 55618 | H | $CH_2$=$CHCH_2$- | 0.008 (0.005 - 0.01) | 0.2 (0.2 - 0.25) |
| 55636 | H | $CH_3CH_2$- | 0.07 (0.05 - 0.1) | 1.65 (1 - 3) |
| 55662 | H | $CH_3CH_2CH_2$- | 0.02 (0.01 - 0.025) | 0.86 (0.8 - 1.2) |
| 55679 | $CH_2$=$CHCH_2$- | $CH_2$=$CHCH_2$- | 0.03 (0.02 - 0.04) | 0.8 (0.5 - 1) |
| 55727 | $CH_3CH_2$- | $CH_3CH_2$- | 0.02 (0.02 - 0.03) | 0.8 (0.5 - 1) |

(a) The figures in brackets are the dose range within which the estimated $ED_{50}$ was found to lie.

only weak activity against antigen challenge in asthmatic patients (13). However, one very important point which arose from these clinical studies was the observation that, when given orally to man, FPL 55618 blocked the protective action of inhaled cromolyn. In our interpretation, we had evidence which suggested to us that these specifically designed oral chromones were being absorbed and, via systemic circulation, reaching the receptors in the human lung responsible for the protective action of their inhaled clinically effective analogues. For some reason, these newly designed compounds did not possess the ability to modify the receptor in man, in a way which would translate to inhibition of asthma. In addition, these oral derivatives appeared to have a stronger binding affinity for the receptor than did cromolyn.

It was time for our first major re-think. Basically we had shown that our general medicinal chemistry approach to oral activity had been successful. These more lipophilic chromones were indeed being absorbed from the gastro-intestinal tract and reaching their required site of action, but we concluded that one could not use the rat PCA test, or indeed any of our newly developed tests, in a quantitatively predictive sense, for the identification of compounds which would be active anti-asthmatic agents, of the cromolyn type, in humans. I suspect that others have more recently come to the same conclusion about the PCA test, following the clinical evaluation of their own selected compounds.

The above conclusions were reinforced by our next sortie in the area of the 5-alkoxy chromone-2-carboxylic acids. We decided to ignore the rat PCA data which identified the 5-isoamyloxy derivative, FPL 50419, as a lead compound. We reverted instead to our early clinical studies which had shown that though inactive orally, the 5-(2-hydroxypropoxy) derivative, FPL 50271 (III), was highly active, when given by inhalation, in bronchial antigen challenge experiments in asthmatic patients. The 8-propyl substituted analogue, FPL 52694 (IV), was prepared for clinical evaluation. By this time we recognised that FPL 52694 was not an ideal oral product as it was still a highly acidic compound and its log D value was still less than zero (-0.65), but it was significantly more fat soluble than its predecessor FPL 50271 (log D = -1.8). FPL 52694 was eventually shown to be extremely effective against antigen challenge in asthmatic patients by the oral route, but had to be given at very high doses in the order of 1 - 2 gm per dose (13). We did not consider that such a compound could be a useful therapeutic product, but from the medicinal chemist's viewpoint, we had established beyond doubt that chemical modification of the highly acidic, highly polar chromone-2-carboxylic acids could lead to orally effective agents of this series which could be useful therapeutically in the prophylactic control of bronchial asthma.

Chemically, we were moving in the right direction by attempting to increase the lipophilicity of our compounds. We knew that the compounds we were seeking would have to have relatively high log D values, probably in excess of +1.0. In terms of the PCA tests, we had by now established that well absorbed oral products would have a ratio of intra-duodenal to intravenous PCA $ED_{50}$ values of less than 10 - preferably the ratio would approach unity for very well absorbed compounds. Our experience had shown that compounds with a ratio of >10 were in general very poorly absorbed in the rat and the dog following oral administration and, as a rule, were fairly rapidly excreted following intravenous dosing in both species. But how could we select suitable compounds for further development from an activity viewpoint? None of our existing animal screens was capable of predicting activity in man!

At about this time, which was in mid-1974, we decided that the screening approach we would follow, would be one which involved the profiling of our compounds for cromolyn-like activity, whilst checking fully their oral absorption profiles. The type of screen which would best identify this activity, would be, we decided, one in which we could demonstrate that our compounds could occupy the same receptors as cromolyn. It was of little consequence, we argued, what particular action of the drug we tried to mimic in these screens, as we felt that none of them would be completely clinically predictive. The best we could hope to achieve was to identify compounds which, in some animal models, could be shown to interact with and occupy the receptors cromolyn was known to activate. Such molecules could perhaps occupy and activate the cromolyn receptors in human lung. If these compounds also possessed physico-chemical characteristics, e.g. suitable partition coefficients, which imparted acceptable absorption profiles to the entities, then we would select one or more for progression to a clinical evaluation.

The facet of cromolyn's activity profile on which we concentrated was the compound's reported tachyphylactic action in both the rat PCA screen and in producing a Bezold-Jarisch reflex induced fall in blood pressure in the anaesthetised dog (10, 14). In essence, a high dose of the compound administered to a rat 30 - 60 minutes before a second dose, given in the normal manner at the time of antigen challenge, inhibits or abolishes the protective effect of the latter dose on the rat PCA reaction. In the anaesthetised dog, we have found that a fifteen minute infusion of a low dose of cromolyn blocks the normal depressor activity of a subsequent bolus injection of the compound. The blocking action of the infused dose diminishes with time as shown in Figure 1. The loss of activity with time in these experiments probably reflects the rate of elimination of the cromolyn from the sensory receptors in the left ventricle of the heart which have been shown to be involved in the

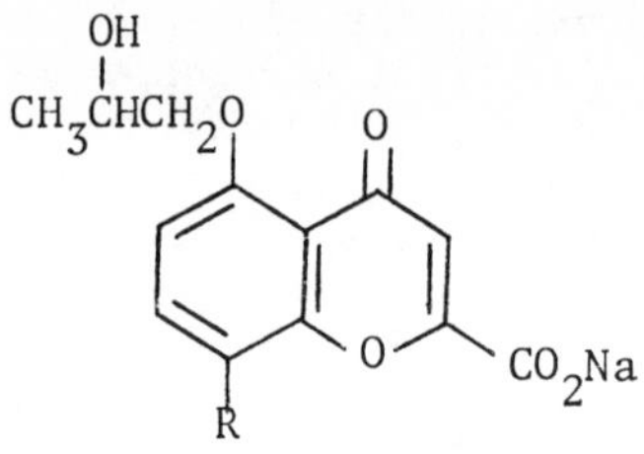

III : FPL 50271 : R = H

IV : FPL 52694 : R = $-CH_2CH_2CH_3$

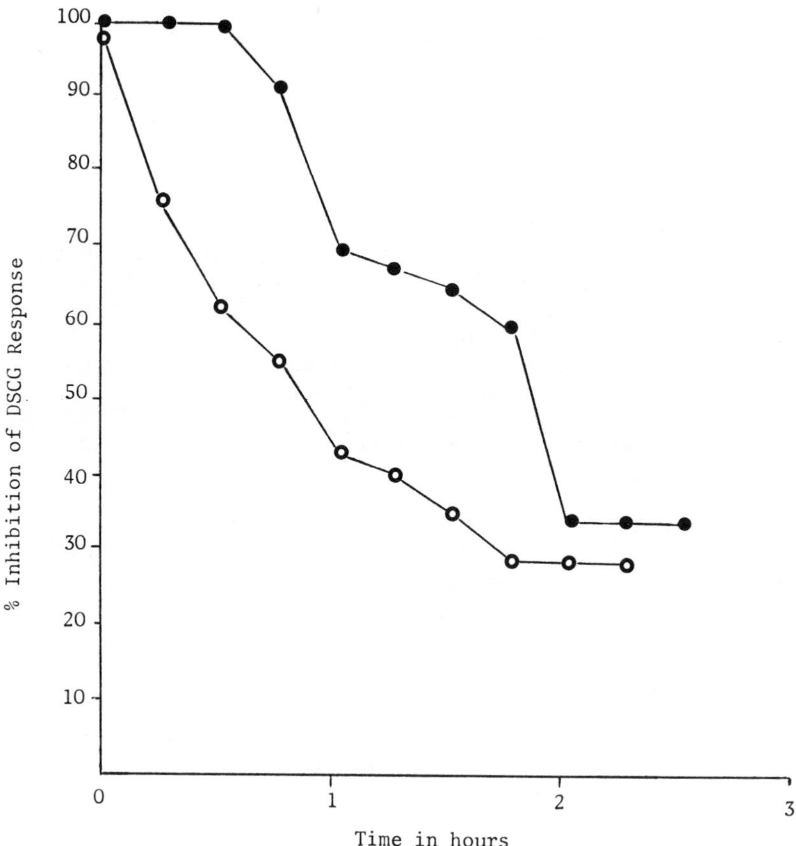


*Figure 1. Effect of infused doses of disodium cromoglycate on the depressor action of a bolus injection of disodium cromoglycate: (○—○) 20 μg/kg/min; (●—●) 100 μg/kg/min*

depressor response to bolus injections of cromolyn (15).

Rescreening of a number of our more lipophilic chromone-2-carboxylic acids along this new approach identified an already existing series of compounds which possessed an overall profile close to that which we were seeking. These compounds were principally 5-hydroxy-6,8-dialkyl chromone-2-carboxylic acids and the activity profile of one of these, FPL 52757, is shown in Table III. One can contrast this data with that for FPL 52694, which had the following profile: (i) log D = -0.65, (ii) PCA $ED_{50}$ ratio = 10, (iii) plasma levels in the dog, from an oral dose of 20 mg/kg, never exceeded 2.5 μg/ml over the 5 hour sampling period, (iv) plasma $t_{\frac{1}{2}}$ in dogs = 0.3 h. FPL 52757 was clearly a much more lipophilic compound and encouragingly had a much superior overall oral profile in the rat and the dog. In addition it was clearly capable of occupying the cromolyn receptors in these two species. Consequently, FPL 52757 was submitted for clinical evaluation and in several studies involving antigen provocation the compound was shown to be orally effective, at a dose of 50 to 100 mg t.i.d., as an anti-asthmatic agent. Unfortunately, longer term studies in dogs revealed that continued oral dosing with the compound produced an incidence of liver toxicity which was related to the metabolism of the drug and the compound was withdrawn from further clinical study (13).

Fortunately, we had not settled solely for the chance of FPL 52757 making the grade as an orally effective agent. Whilst this compound was under detailed investigation, we had begun another programme of work on the chemical modification of a further monochromone which had been identified as clinically active by inhalation back in the early 1960's. This derivative was the tricyclic compound FPL 52845; it was chosen for the present study as an alternative to the 5-alkoxy series because of its intrinsically higher fat solubility (log D of FPL 52845 being -0.2 compared to -1.8 for the 5-alkoxychromone FPL 50271).

This particular study proved extremely fruitful and many of the compounds produced were active in our screens. As can be seen in Table IV, the introduction of a propyl substituent into the 10 position of FPL 52845, to give FPL 57579, produced a noticeable improvement in the oral properties of this tricyclic compound. Thus the lipophilicity of the compound was increased over 10 fold and this was reflected in an improved PCA ratio, higher plasma levels after oral dosing in the dog and a longer plasma half-life following intravenous administration in the dog. However, the plasma $t_{\frac{1}{2}}$ of FPL 57579 was considered to be rather short for a potential oral product. A further consideration of our previous studies indicated that the introduction of a hydroxyl substituent into the 5-position of the chromones would lead to an increase in lipophilicity and this proved to be the case also in this

TABLE III

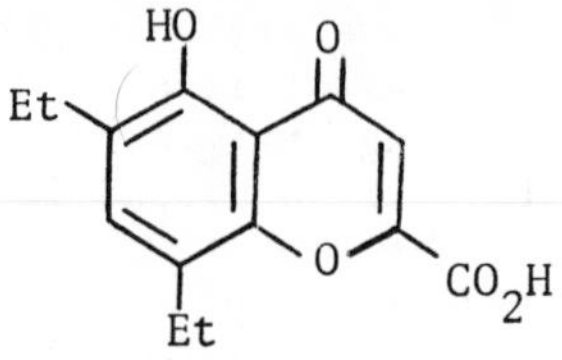

| FPL 52757 | | |
|---|---|---|
| Log D<br>Octanol/water | | + 0.65 |
| PCA $ED_{50}$ : i.v.<br>i.d.<br>ratio i.d./i.v. | | 5.0 mg/kg<br>5.0 mg/kg<br>1.0 |
| Plasma levels in dogs - dose (20 mg/kg p.o.) | Time post dosing<br>1 h<br>3 h<br>5 h | <br>3 μg/ml<br>13 μg/ml<br>13.5 μg/ml |
| Plasma $t_{\frac{1}{2}}$ in dogs | | 2.4 h |
| Cross tachyphylaxis : rat | | 70 mg/kg i.v. at 45 min blocked the effect of disodium cromoglycate 2 mg/kg |
| dog | | Infusion of 200 μg/kg/min blocked the depressor action of disodium cromoglycate for up to 3 hours |

Chemical and biological data available on FPL 52757

TABLE IV

| Compound No. | R | $R_1$ | log $D_{oct}$ | PCA $ED_{50}$ mg/kg [a] | | | Plasma levels μg/ml (dog) [b] | | | Plasma $t_{\frac{1}{2}}$ in hrs (dog) [c] |
|---|---|---|---|---|---|---|---|---|---|---|
| | | | | i.v. | i.d. | $ED_{50}$ ratio i.d./i.v. | 1 hr | 3 hr | 5 hr | |
| 52845 | H | H | -0.2 | 0.4 (<0.5) | 10.7 (10-15) | 27 | 0.2 | 0.5 | 1.5 | 0.3 |
| 57579 | H | $CH_3CH_2CH_2$- | +1.0 | 1.6 (1 - 4) | 5.5 (3 - 6) | 3.4 | 3.5 | 4.1 | 5.3 | 0.9 |
| 57787 | HO- | $CH_3CH_2CH_2$- | +1.8 | 6.4 (5 - 10) | 15.5 (15 - 20) | 2.4 | 2 | 11 | 17 | 1.9 |

(a) The figures in brackets are the dose range within which the estimated $ED_{50}$ was found to lie

(b) Plasma levels determined by sampling of peripheral blood at the times stated after an oral dose of 10 mg/kg of each compound.

(c) Plasma $t_{\frac{1}{2}}$ determined following an intravenous dose of 5 mg/kg of each compound

tricyclic series. Thus, with the synthesis of FPL 57787 (see Table IV), we obtained a compound which measured up fairly well to our pre-determined standards. It was highly lipophilic and its good absorption profile in the rat (see PCA ratio) was paralleled in the dog where plasma levels were readily maintained for up to 5 hours and its intravenous half-life was about 2 hours. It was cross tachyphylactic with cromolyn in the PCA screen (an intravenous dose of 36 mg/kg of FPL 57787 given 40 min before challenge, inhibited the protective effect of cromolyn 1 - 8 mg/kg given with challenge) and, when given by intravenous infusion in the dog, it effectively inhibited the reflex induced lowering of blood pressure produced by injection of cromolyn (Figure 2). The long duration of action of FPL 57787 in this test is, we believe, due to a combination of the much longer biological half-life (see Table IV) of this lipophilic chromone, compared to say cromolyn sodium, and to its stronger binding affinity for the cromolyn receptors (e.g. in *in vitro* studies FPL 57787 is much more highly and strongly protein bound than cromolyn, a factor which may support the above interpretation of receptor affinity).

The synthetic routes used to prepare FPL 52845, 57579 and 57787 are outlined in Scheme II.

FPL 57787 was therefore submitted for a fuller investigation, involving a study of its activity in man as an orally effective anti-asthmatic agent. These investigations are not yet complete, but we already have data from clinical studies which show that, when given in doses of 6 to 24 mg for up to 12 hours before challenge, FPL 57787 effectively inhibits antigen induced bronchoconstriction in a number of asthmatic patients (13). These investigations in experimentally induced asthma have been extended into the study of the activity of the compound in double blind therapeutic trials. Again, in these studies the protective action of the compound has been demonstrated (16) and longer term studies in humans, hopefully leading to the clinical launch of FPL 57787, are currently underway.

The work described in this presentation is only part of a programme which has taken us some 10 years to carry out and I'm sure that you will appreciate that, over this time, it has involved the combined efforts of a substantial number of scientists in our laboratories. It is only through their combined efforts and with the important background support of our research and development management that it has been possible to carry out the work described in this paper.

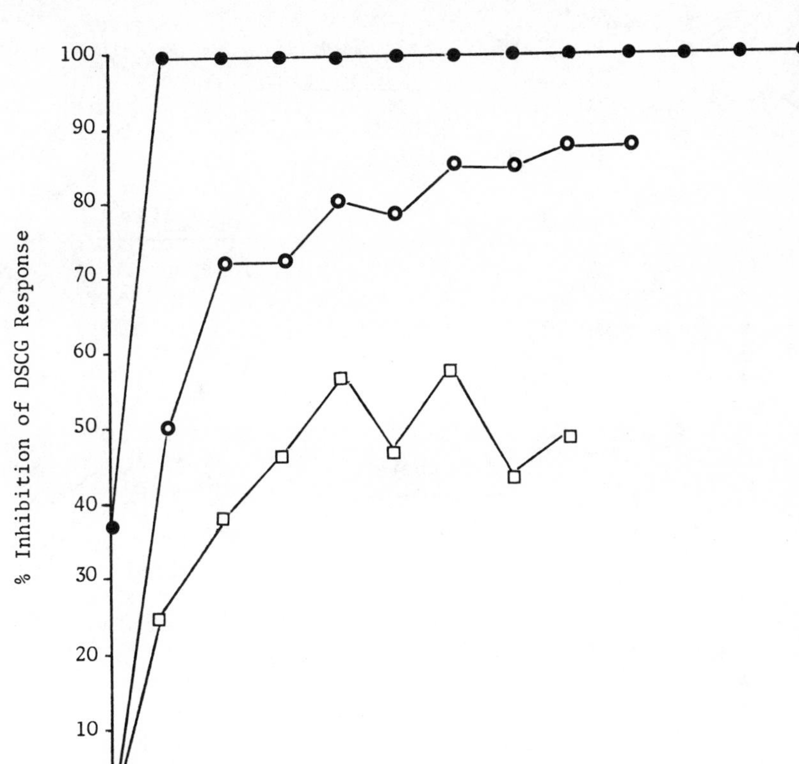


*Figure 2. Effect of infused doses of FPL 57787 on the depressor action of a bolus injection of disodium cromoglycate:(□—□) 10 μg/kg/min; (◉—◉) 20 μg/kg/min; (●—●) 50 μg/kg/min*

SCHEME II

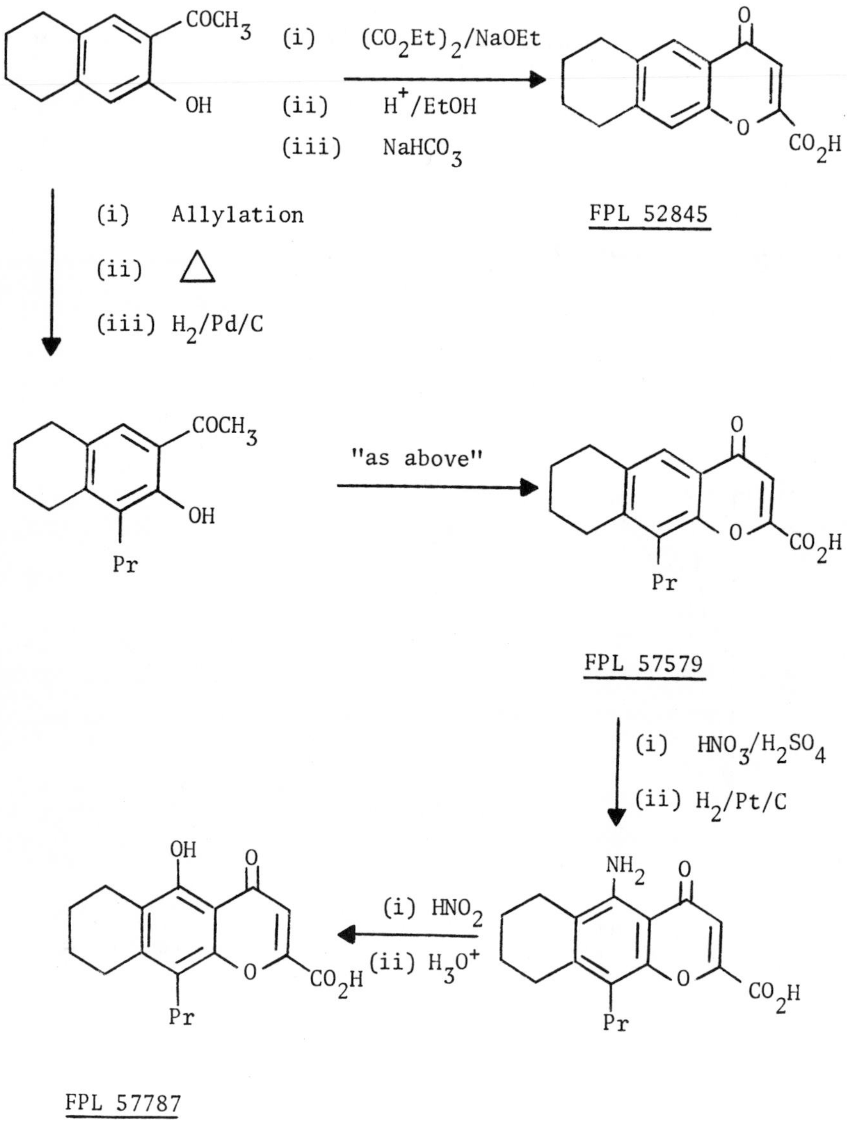

COCH$_3$ OH

(i) $(CO_2Et)_2$/NaOEt
(ii) $H^+$/EtOH
(iii) $NaHCO_3$

O O $CO_2H$

FPL 52845

(i) Allylation
(ii) $\Delta$
(iii) $H_2$/Pd/C

COCH$_3$ OH Pr

"as above"

O O $CO_2H$ Pr

FPL 57579

(i) $HNO_3/H_2SO_4$
(ii) $H_2$/Pt/C

$NH_2$ O O $CO_2H$ Pr

(i) $HNO_2$
(ii) $H_3O^+$

OH O O $CO_2H$ Pr

FPL 57787

## LITERATURE CITED

1. Assem, E.S.K., Evans, J.A. and McAllen, M., Brit. Med. J. (1974), 2, 93-95.
2. Pauwels, R., Lamont, H. and Van Der Straeten, M., Clinical Allergy, (1976), 6, 471-478.
3. Muittari, A., Ahonen, A., Kellomäki, L., Kuusisto, P., Lehtinen, J. and Veneskoski, T., Clinical Allergy, (1978), 8, 281-288.
4. Koda, A., Nagai, H., Watanabe, S., Yanagihara, Y. and Sakamoto, K., J. Allergy Clin. Immunol., (1976), 57, 396-407.
5. Wüthrich, B. and Parrott, D., Respiration, (1976), 33, 231-235.
6. Kurogawa, D. *et al*, Allergy (Japan), (1976), 25, 350-351.
7. Moreno, J.N., Le Zotte, L.A., Johnson, H.G. and Brooks, C.D., Allergologia et Immunopathologica, (1977), 5, 441.
8. Haydn, S.P., Bradley, J.L. and Hughes, D.T.D., Brit. Med. J., (1975), 3, 283-284.
9. Falliers, C.J. and Mingo, B.A., J. Allergy Clin. Immunol., (1978), 61, 188.
10. Cox, J.S.G., Beach, J.E., Blair, A.M.J.N., Clarke, A.J., King, J., Lee, T.B., Loveday, D.E.E., Moss, G.F., Orr, T.S.C., Ritchie, J.T. and Sheard, P. in "Advances in Drug Research", Vol. 5, 115-196, Academic Press, 1970.
11. Goose, J. and Blair, A.M.J.N., Immunology, (1969), 16, 749-760.
12. Ashton, M.J., Clark, B., Jones, K.M., Moss, G.F., Neale, M.G. and Ritchie, J.T., Toxicol. Appl. Pharmacol., (1973), 26, 319-328.
13. Unpublished results.
14. Thomson, D.S. and Evans, D.P., Clin. Exp. Immunol. (1973), 13, 537-544.
15. Jackson, D.M., Proceedings of an International Symposium on Cardiac receptors. University of Leeds, (U.K.). Leeds, 1976.
16. Ellul Micallef, R. and Fenech, F.F., Allergologia et Immunopathologica, (1977), 5, 519.

RECEIVED August 6, 1979.

# Antiallergic Purinones: A Successful Application of QSAR

K. R. H. WOOLDRIDGE

Pharmaceutical Division, May & Baker Ltd., Dagenham, Essex, RM10 7XS, England

When we became interested in the antiallergic field in 1971 at May & Baker, we knew from the studies of Austen et.al. (1) that the inhibition of the anaphylactic release of histamine from human lung could be related to raised tissue levels of cyclic AMP. Furthermore, Lichtenstein and Margolis (2) observed that methylxanthines such as caffeine or theophylline (I) inhibit the antigen-induced release of histamine from human basophilic leukocytes probably by their well-known ability to inhibit phosphodiesterases. We therefore examined the methylxanthines in the passive cutaneous anaphylactic (PCA) reaction mediated by reaginic antibodies in the rat, and found them to be weak inhibitors. They did not inhibit the PCA reaction reactions mediated by non-reaginic antibodies and therefore in this respect the methylxanthines resembled disodium cromoglycate (DSG). Accordingly the xanthines were regarded as a lead to compounds of potential interest for antiallergic therapy, and totally unrelated chemically to DSG.

In addition to being weak inhibitors of the rat PCA reaction, the xanthines possess a wide variety of pharmacological properties. Accordingly, available structural variants were examined in order to improve selectivity with respect to the PCA inhibition, and to increase potency. Some members of a series of 6-thioxanthines (II) previously studied as bronchodilators (3) proved to have improved potency (one hundredth of DSG) but this series still possessed a wide spectrum of pharmacological activity.

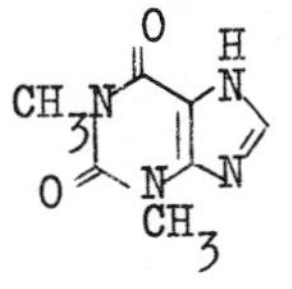

(I) 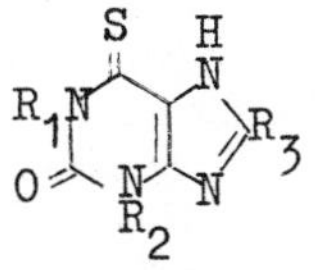 (II) 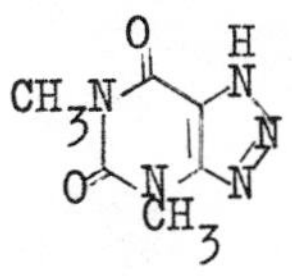 (III)

0-8412-0536-1/80/47-118-117$05.00/0

The introduction of an extra nitrogen into the xanthine system to give 8-azaxanthines had been reported to reduce cardiovascular effects (4) and we found that 8-azatheophylline (III) was 10 times more active than the corresponding theophylline or 6-thiotheophylline in inhibiting the rat PCA reaction whereas the other pharmacological properties were reduced in magnitude. A series of 8-azaxanthines (IV) were prepared and the best of these compounds was found to be the p-nitrobenzyl derivative (V) which was equiactive with DSG in the rat PCA test (5).

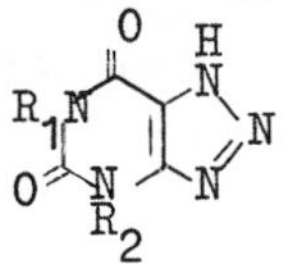

(IV)

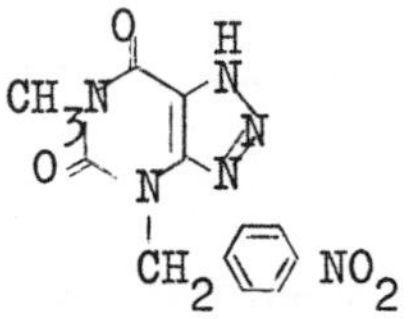

(V)

Application of the multiparameter extrathermodynamic technique to this series, where $R_1$ and $R_2$ were alkyl groups, revealed a good relationship between the PCA inhibitory potency (I=relative activity to DSG) and the substituent partition constant ($\pi$) and Taft steric factor (Es) in the $R_2$ position (equation 1, where the figures in parentheses are the Student t values for the coefficients of the equation and n, r, s, F and p have their usual statistical meaning).

Eqn. 1 $$\text{Log}\,[\text{MW} \times \text{I}] = 1.365 - \underset{(7.00)}{0.073}\,\pi^2 - \underset{(4.658)}{0.789}\,\text{Es}$$

$n=11,\ r=0.942,\ s=0.153,\ F=31.4\ (p < 0.001)$

This relationship was of interest for several reasons. Firstly it indicated that the biological assay was sufficiently precise to enable the QSAR approach to be used. Secondly the observation that only alkyl substituents $R_2$ affected the activity whereas alkyl substituents in the $R_1$ position apparently had little influence. This parallels the observations in the 6-thioxanthine series where a similar relationship was derived for the bronchodilating activity (6). Thirdly, bulky substituents in the $R_2$ position had a beneficial effect. Benzyl-substituted compounds e.g. (V) were more active than equation 1 indicated, possibly because the usual value of Es for benzyl did not reflect the buttressing effect of the adjacent triazole ring as revealed by a study of space-filling models (5).

Other 8-azapurines were tested and an isothiazolyl-8-azapurin-6-one (VI) exhibited twice the inhibitory potency of DSG. Other heterocyclic-substituted derivatives were no better (7) but the 2-phenyl-substituted congener was 4 times as potent as DSG in inhibiting the rat PCA reaction.

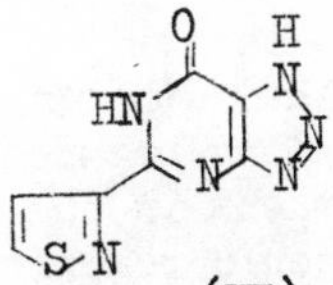

(VI) 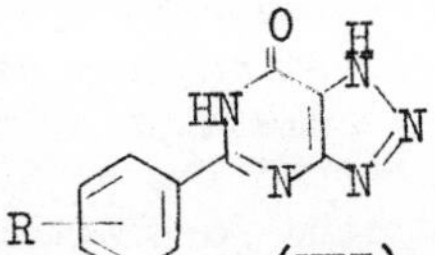 (VII)

A series of substituted 2-phenyl-8-azapurin-6-ones (VII) was prepared (Table 1) and when the results on the first 10 compounds was available, correlations were sought between the inhibitory activity and electronic, steric, and partition parameters, but without success. However the results on the azaxanthines (equation 1) suggested that bulky substituents might lead to increased activity and this was supported in the phenylazapurinone series by the higher activity of the <u>ortho</u>-methoxy compound (Table 1, No. 4) as compared with the <u>meta</u> (No. 8) and <u>para</u> (No. 10) isomers. However the <u>ortho</u>-methyl

Table 1

The inhibitory activity in the rat PCA reaction of substituted 2-phenyl-8-azapurin-6-ones relative to DSG following i.v. administration

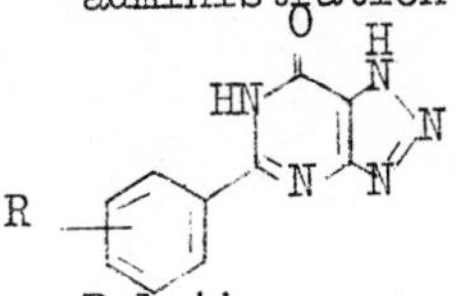

| Compound No. | Subst. | Relative Activity (DSG=1) | Es[a] | v[b] | Obs Log [MW x I] | Calc Log[c] [MW x I] |
|---|---|---|---|---|---|---|
| 1 | H | 4.0 | 1.24 | 0 | 2.932 | 2.743 |
| 2 | 2-$CH_3$ | 0.04 | 0 | 16 | 0.959 | 1.111 |
| 33 | 2-Cl | 0.2 | 0.27 | 17 | 1.695 | 1.519 |
| 4 | 2-$CH_3O$ | 10.0 | 0.69 | 108 | 3.386 | 3.201 |
| 5 | 2-i-$C_3H_2O$ | 5.0 | 0.69 | 128 | 3.132 | 3.435 |
| 6 | 2-$C_6H_5CH_2O$ | 10.0 | 0.69 | 121 | 3.504 | 3.353 |
| 7 | 3-$CH_3$ | 4.0 | 1.24 | 0 | 2.959 | 2.743 |
| 8 | 3 3-$CH_3O$ | 2.0 | 1.24 | 0 | 2.687 | 2.743 |
| 9 | 4-Cl | 2.0 | 1.24 | 0 | 2.695 | 2.743 |
| 10 | 4-$CH_3O$ | 1.0 | 1.24 | 0 | 2.386 | 2.743 |

[a]Es=Taft's steric factor of the 2-substituent

[b]Difference ($cm^{-1}$) between the 1-NH stretching frequency in the substituted compound compared with compound 1.

[c]Equation 2

compound (No. 2) showed only 1/100 of the activity of the <u>meta</u> isomer (No. 7) suggesting very strongly that other factors must be involved. Intramolecular hydrogen bonding between the proton in the 1-N position and the <u>ortho</u> substituent in the phenyl ring could be involved; and fortunately this could readily be quantified by comparison of the NH-stretching frequency in the substituted compound compared with the parent compound (No. 1). This ir shift, $\Delta\bar{\nu}$, may be regarded as an energy term and when it was used as a parameter in regression analysis, a highly significant relationship, equation 2 was obtained (8).

Eqn. 2 $$\text{Log}\,[MW \times I] = 0.924 + \underset{(7.50)}{0.012\,\Delta\bar{\nu}} + \underset{(7.72)}{1.467\,Es}$$

$n=10$, $r=0.961$, $s=0.244$, $F=42.7$, $p < 0.001$.

As the Es term decreases in numerical value with increasing size of the substituent, equation 2 indicated that antiallergic activity is increased by high hydrogen bonding and decreased by increasing size of the <u>ortho</u> substituent in the phenyl ring. The knowledge of the relevant factors rapidly led us to synthesise the most active member of the series, the <u>ortho</u>-propoxy compound, M&B 22,948 (VIII), about 40 times as potent as DSG (9).

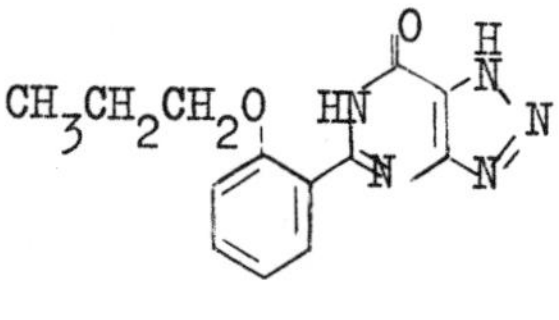

(VIII) 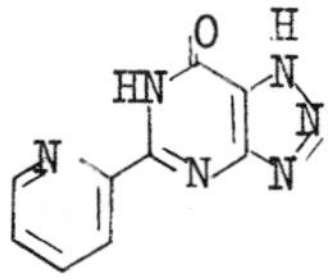 (IX) 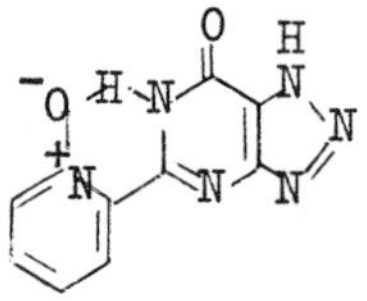 (X)

We interpreted the relationship in equation 2 to mean that coplanarity of the phenyl ring with the azapurinone system is a requirement for high antiallergic activity in the test system employed. Hydrogen bonding with a suitable <u>ortho</u> substituent in the phenyl ring would favour planarity while a bulky substituent would reduce planarity. Activity would be maximised by a high degree of hydrogen bonding coupled with small size. Simple ether substituents as in M&B 22,948 appear to be optimal in this respect. Additional evidence is provided by the fact that the activity of the 2-pyridyl analogue (IX) which does not show intramolecular hydrogen bonding is increased over 100-fold by formation of the N-oxide (X) which forms exceptionally strong intramolecular hydrogen bonds. This coplanarity hypothesis originally deduced from the QSAR equation has been substantiated by some recent work in which M&B 22,948 has been shown to be planar in the solid state by X-ray crystallography (10).

In addition to causing 100% inhibition of the rat PCA reaction following intravenous administration at 0.1 mg/kg, M&B 22,948 was also active orally. When administered to rats

15 minutes before allergen challenge, it was effective in inhibiting the PCA reaction at doses of 0.5-2 mg/kg with a bell-shaped dose response curve. This compound also inhibited the allergen-induced release of histamine and SRS-A from passively sensitised human lung tissue in vitro, and inhibited reagin-meditated anaphylactic bronchospasm in the guinea pig (9).

Toxicological studies in several species have been satisfactory and the compound is effective in man following administration in doses of 5-15 mg by aerosol administration.

Further substitution in the alkoxyphenyl-8-azapurinones gave a series of compounds in which the hydrogen bonding did not vary appreciably but in which the antiallergic potency spanned a wide range (Table 2). The activity correlated with the substituent partition value $\pi$ for the 5-position as the dominant parameter, with a smaller contribution from the resonance factor R defined by Swain and Lupton (11), equation 3.

Eqn. 3 $$\text{Log}\,[MW \times I] = 3.57 - \underset{(6.40)}{0.74} \quad + \underset{(2.79)}{0.87}\,R$$

$n=9,\ r=0.940,\ s=0.205,\ F=22.9,\ p < 0.01$

Table 2

The inhibitory activity in the rat PCA reaction of 5-substituted 2-methoxyphenyl8-azapurin-6-ones

| Compound No. | Subst. | Relative Activity (DSG=1) | $\pi$ | R[11] | Obs Log [MW x I] | Calc Log [MW x I] |
|---|---|---|---|---|---|---|
| 4 | H | 10 | 0 | 0 | 3.384 | 3.569 |
| 11 | $NO_2$ | 10 | -0.28 | 0.155 | 3.459 | 3.909 |
| 12 | $NH_2$ | 40 | -1.23 | -0.681 | 4.029 | 3.885 |
| 13 | HO | 10 | -0.67 | -0.643 | 3.413 | 3.506 |
| 14 | $CH_3O$ | 4 | -0.02 | -0.500 | 3.038 | 3.151 |
| 15 | $CH_3$ | 10 | 0.56 | -0.141 | 3.410 | 3.064 |
| 16 | $CF_3$ | 4 | 0.88 | 0.186 | 3.095 | 2.942 |
| 17 | Cl | 2 | 0.71 | -0.161 | 2.745 | 2.907 |
| 18 | t-Bu | 0.5 | 1.83 | -0.138 | 2.176 | 2.213 |

This equation suggested that electron-withdrawing hydrophilic substituents should be highly active in this test system, and as a result a number of such compounds were prepared.

Many of these compounds in fact proved to be highly potent (Table 3) and provide an example of the predictive use of multiparameter regression analysis, (12) although the analysis of the full series, which is still in progress, suggests that equation 3 is an over-simplification (13).

Table 3
5-Substituted 2-alkoxyphenyl-8-azapurines with predicted high activity

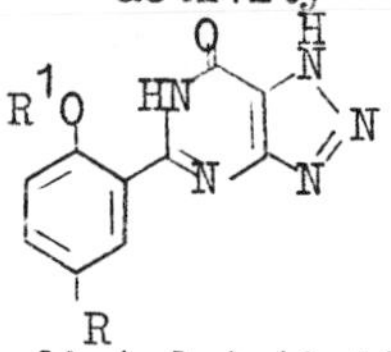

| Substituent | Predicted Activity* (DSG=1) | Observed Activity (DSG=1) |
|---|---|---|
| $SO_2NH_2$ | 336 | 150 |
| $SO_2Me$ | 138 | 200 |
| $CONH_2$ | 63 | 200 |
| $CO_2Me$ | 18 | 40 |

*Equation 3

Work on this series was initiated on the supposition that inhibition of phosphodiesterase would increase the level of cyclic AMP thereby leading to antiallergic effects. Subsequent work in our laboratories has suggested that this was a gross oversimplification. Using 25 known antiallergic agents of widely varied chemical structural features, we have shown that the more potent inhibitors of anaphylactic reactions inhibit the hydrolysis of cyclic GMP more effectively than that of cyclic AMP. The implication is that histamine release is reduced more effectively when cyclic GMP levels are increased with respect to cyclic AMP levels. The fact that highly significant correlations were obtained between selective inhibition of phosphodiesterase activity and pharmacological potency in *in vitro* and *in vivo* tests involving different species and different tissues may well reflect a basic common mechanism of fundamental importance in allergic reactions (14). However, the azapurines *in vivo* show the bell-shaped dose-response curves in antiallergic tests, typical of DSG-like compounds but unlike phosphodiesterase inhibitors. It is possible, therefore, that the antiallergic activity of the azapurines is due to a combination of mast cell stabilisation and phosphodiesterase inhibition.

## LITERATURE CITED


1. Orange, R.P., Kaliner, M.A., Laraia, P.J. and Austen, K.F. Fed.Proc., (1971), 30, 1725.

2. Lichtenstein, L.M. and Margolis, S. Science, (1968), 161, 902.

3. Wooldridge, K.R.H. and Slack, R. J.Chem.Soc., (1962), 1863.

4. Bariana, D.S. J.Med.Chem., (1971), 14, 543.

5. Coulson, C.J., Ford, R.E., Lunt, E., Marshall, S., Pain, D.L., Rogers, I.H. and Wooldridge, K.R.H. Eur.J.Med.Chem., (1974), 9, 313.

6. Bowden, K. and Wooldridge, K.R.H. Biochem.Pharmacol., (1973), 22, 1015.

7. Holland, A., Jackson, D., Chaplen, P., Lunt, E., Marshall, S., Pain, D.L. and Wooldridge, K.R.H. Eur.J.Med.Chem., (1975), 10, 447.

8. Broughton, B.J., Chaplen, P., Knowles, P., Lunt, E., Marshall, S., Pain, D.L. and Wooldridge, K.R.H. J.Med.Chem., (1975), 18, 1117.

9. Broughton, B.J., Chaplen, P., Knowles, P. Lunt, E., Pain, D.L., Wooldridge, K.R.H., Ford, R., Marshall, S., Walker, J.L. and Maxwell, D.R. Nature (London), (1974), 251, 650.

10. Hodgson, D. (University of North Carolina) unpublished work.

11. Swain, C.G. and Lupton, E.C. J.Amer.Chem.Soc., (1968), 90, 4328.

12. Ford, R.E., Knowles, P., Lunt, E., Marshall, S., Walker, J.L. and Wooldridge, K.R.H. Unpublished.

13. Coombs, T.J. and Wooldridge, K.R.H. Unpublished.

14. Bowden, K., Coombs, T.J., Coulson, C.J., Ford, R.E., Marshall, S., Walker, J.L. and Wooldridge, K.R.H. Nature (London), (1977), 265, 545.


RECEIVED August 6, 1979.

# Clinically Effective 6-Ethyl-3-(1*H*-tetrazol-5-yl)chromone (AA-344)

AKIRA NOHARA

Medicinal Research Laboratories, Central Research Division, Takeda Chemical Industries, Ltd., Yodogawa-ku, Osaka 532, Japan

It is well known that disodium cromoglycate (DSCG), a prophylactic drug for asthma, is a splendid fruit of Fisons' group effort in the structural modification of a naturally occurring oxygen heterocycle, khellin, which possesses vasodilatory and smooth muscle relaxant properties (1, 2). On the other hand, the dried radix of Scutellaria baicalensis Georg has been used since ancient times in Chinese medicine as a diuretic or an antiallergic drug. Based on this information, Koda *et al*. studied baicalein (1), a major flavonoid present in the radixes and demonstrated that the flavonoid markedly inhibited the release of the mediators (histamine, SRS-A etc.) induced by the antigen challenge of chopped guinea pig lung which had been sensitized with egg albumin (3, 4). We were interested in these reports, and started our research to improve the antiallergic potency of baicalein. Preliminary structure-activity studies on baicalein and related synthetic compounds revealed that introduction of a carbonyl group at the 3-position of the chromone ring enhanced the antiallergic activity (5). This finding along with the paucity of reports concerning chromone derivatives containing substituents at the 3-position prompted us to initiate a program of chemical investigation on 3-substituted chromones.

At that time, several preliminary screening methods for antiallergic activities had been reported. At the beginning of the following studies, we selected two assay methods, A and B: A, as mentioned above, the mediator release from chopped guinea pig lung (3, 4), and B, homologous passive cutaneous anaphylaxis (PCA) in the rat (6).

As an initial step to the introduction of a carbonyl group at the 3-position of the chromone ring, we started with the synthesis of 3-formyl derivatives on which only a few reports (7, 8, 9) had been published. The 4-oxo-4H-1-benzopyran-3-carboxaldehydes 2 synthesized by our own method (10, 11, 12) which is described later, showed an inhibitory

0-8412-0536-1/80/47-118-125$05.00/0

activity in the assay (A), but they were inactive in the PCA assay (13). Compounds of type 2 possessed desirable anti-allergic properties, but were found to be highly toxic. Therefore, 4-oxo-4H-1-benzopyran-3-carboxylic acids (3) were set as the second target in our attempt to solve the problems of the toxicity and poor solubility of 2. However, the desired products 3 (14) obtained by Jones oxidation of 2 were found to be inactive in PCA in rats and also in the assay (A). On the other hand, the isomeric 4-oxo-4H-1-benzopyran-2-carboxylic acid which is the parent compound of DSCG was inactive in the assay (A), but active in PCA in rats. We, therefore, speculated that the difference in the biological activity between the two isomers might be based on the difference in acidity. While 4-oxo-4H-1-benzopyran-2-carboxylic acid exhibited a high acidity (pKa' 4.15 in dimethyl sulfoxide-$H_2O$ or pKa 2.96 (15)), the corresponding 3-isomer showed a low acidity (pKa' 8.85 in dimethyl sulfoxide-$H_2O$ (14)) due to intramolecular hydrogen bonding.

In order to enhance the acidity, a vinylogue (4a) of 3, 3-(4-oxo-4H-1-benzopyran-3)acrylic acid, in which the formation of the hydrogen bonding between the carboxyl and the carbonyl groups is sterically hindered, was synthesized as the third target. As expected, the acrylic acid (4a) was a slightly stronger acid than 3a (pKa' 7.25 in dimethyl sulfoxide-$H_2O$) and proved to be 0.36 times as active as DSCG in the rat PCA test by intravenous administration (16). In the next step, some biological activities were investigated to characterize the profile of 4a. The compound 4a was not antagonistic to histamine, serotonin or bradykinin, and also showed no inhibitory activity in the assay (A). Thus, 4a was found to be active specifically in the rat PCA test. In addition, the fact that 4a is active not only by an intravenous administration route but also by an oral route was of particular significance because DSCG is inactive when orally administered and usually has to be administered by an inhalation route. Thus, a number of the derivatives of 4a were synthesized and the potencies studied (16).

Recently, attempts have been made to replace the carboxylic acid group by a tetrazole group in chromones (17, 18), xanthones (19), and a thioxanthone derivative (20), because 1H-tetrazoles generally show acidity comparable with the corresponding carboxylic acids (21). Since these examples indicate that biologically active tetrazoles can be obtained from the corresponding biologically active carboxylic acids, but not from the inactive acids, there was a good chance that the substitution of the tetrazole group for the carboxylic acid group in biologically inactive 4-oxo-4H-1-benzopyran-3-carboxylic acids (3) might give inactive compounds. Contrary to this assumption, however, 3-(1H-tetrazol-5-yl)chromone (5a) was found to be active in the rat

PCA test and more potent than the acrylic acid (4a). The physico-chemical properties of 5a differed from those of the acid (3a). The intramolecular hydrogen bonding between the carbonyl and tetrazole groups was not observed in 5a which showed a stronger acidity (pKa' 5.85 in dimethyl sulfoxide-$H_2O$ or pKa 4.3) than the corresponding 3a and also the acrylic acid (4a). Hence, an extensive study on the synthesis and the structure-activity relationships of this orally effective series of tetrazolylchromones 5 was conducted (22).

## Synthesis of 3-Substituted Chromones

An earlier investigation (23) demonstrated that the Vilsmeier-Haack reaction of the $ArCOCH_3$ type compounds gives the monoformylated compounds or the corresponding β-chlorovinyl aldehydes. It was found, however, that in the case of o-hydroxyacetophenones, the methyl group was doubly formylated by a Vilsmeier reagent to give our first target compounds, 4-oxo-4*H*-1-benzopyran-3-carboxaldehydes (2) in one step (10, 11, 12). The reason why double formylation took place in the case of o-hydroxyacetophenone can be interpreted as follows; while an enolated acetophenone reacts with the reagent to give the intermediate which cannot be further formylated, an o-hydroxyacetophenone in which the enolization is prohibited by the intramolecular hydrogen bonding can be doubly formylated (Figure 1).

The second target, 4-oxo-4*H*-1-benzopyran-3-carboxylic acids (3) were obtained by Jones oxidation of 2 or hydrolysis of the 3-carbonitrile derivatives (6) described below (14). The third target, 3-(4-oxo-4*H*-1-benzopyran-3)acrylic acids (4) were synthesized generally by the Knoevenagel reaction of 3-carboxaldehydes (2) with malonic acid (16). In the meantime, it was found that the 3-carboxaldehydes (2), which were able to function as β-dialdehyde compounds, were attacked by amide groups in some cases, to give 2(1*H*)-pyridone derivatives after condensation with malonic acid derivatives. Thus, condensation of 2 with malonodiamide in pyridine gave initially acrylamide derivatives which were converted into 3-carbamoyl-5-(2-hydroxybenzoyl)-2(1*H*)-pyridones (7) (24).

The final target, 3-(1*H*-tetrazol-5-yl)chromones (5), were synthesized by the reaction of sodium azide in the presence of anhydrous aluminum chloride and 4-oxo-4*H*-1-benzopyran-3-carbonitriles (6) which were obtained in one step from 2 with hydroxylamine (22, 25) (Figure 2).

## Structure-Activity Relationships in the Tetrazole (5) and Acrylic Acid (4) Series (22, 16)

While the parent acrylic acid (4a) was, as stated

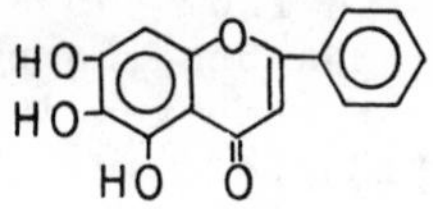

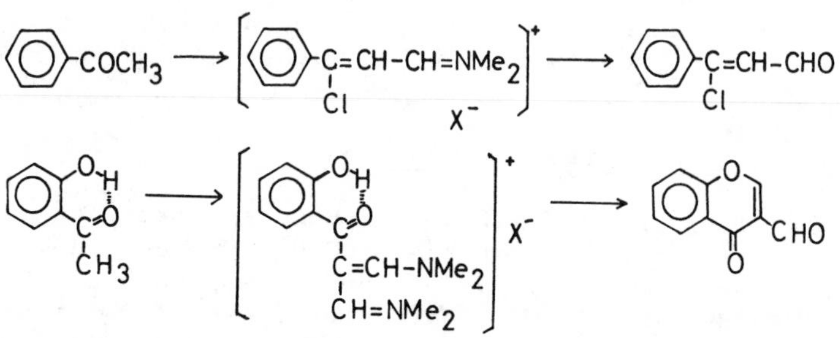

*Figure 1. Reaction of acetophenones with a Vilsmeier reagent*

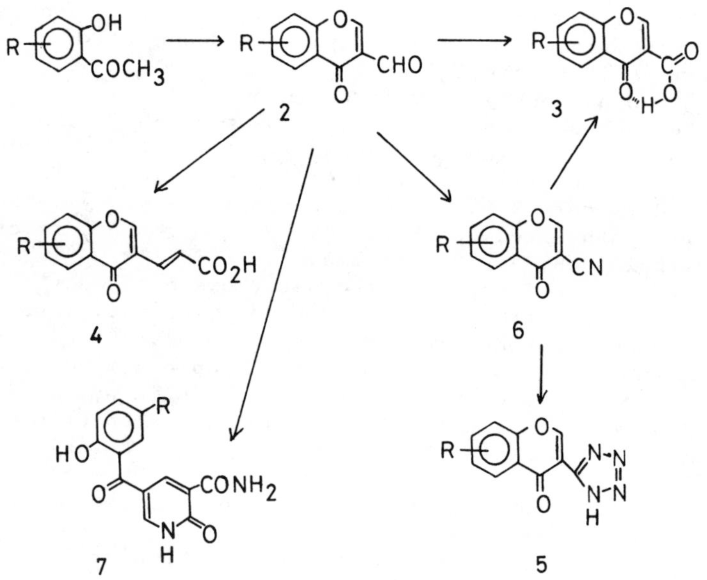

*Figure 2. Synthesis of 3-substituted chromone derivatives*

Table I. Relative Potencies against Rat Passive Cutaneous Anaphylaxis (PCA) of 3-(1H-Tetrazol-5-yl)-chromones (5), 3-(4-Oxo-4H-1-benzopyran-3)-acrylic Acids (4), and DSCG

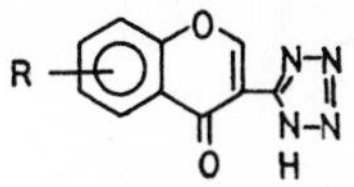

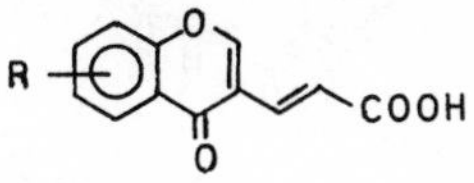

| Compd. | R and Position | PCA assay[a] (iv) | Compd. | PCA assay[a] (iv) |
|---|---|---|---|---|
| DSCG | | 1 (standard) | | |
| 5a | H | 3.5 | 4a | 0.36 |
| 5b | 8-OMe | 30 | | |
| 5c | 6,8-$Me_2$ | 11.6 | 4c | 1.4 |
| 5d | 7,8-Benzo | 8.3 | | |
| 5e | 5,6-Benzo | 5.0 | 4e | 0.4 |
| 5f | 6-Et | 4.0 | 4f | 1.1 |
| 5g | 6-Cl | 4.0 | 4g | 0.5 |
| 5h | 6-$NO_2$ | 4.0 | 4h | 0.3 |
| 5i | 6-n-Pr | 3.4 | 4i | 1.4 |
| 5j | 6-i-Pr | 3.4 | 4j | 2.4 |
| 5k | 6-COOEt | 2.9 | | |
| 5l | 7-OMe | 2.5 | 4l | 0.3 |
| 5m | 6-Me | 2.4 | 4m | 0.8 |
| 5n | 6-$NMe_2$ | 2.3 | 4n | 1.1 |
| 5o | 6-OMe | 2.2 | 4o | 1.3 |
| 5p | 6-n-Bu | 1.8 | 4p | 1.1 |
| 5q | 6-n-Hex | 0.6 | | |
| 5r | 6-cyclo-Hex | 0.5 | | |

[a] The dose giving 50% inhibition ($ID_{50}$) for each drug was calculated graphically from the dose-inhibition relationship expressed in inhibition percent of the bluing areas against doses on a logarithmic scale. At least three doses and three animals for each dose (i.e., 12 spots) were used for obtaining the dose-inhibition relationship.

Table II. Relative Potencies (DSCG=1) in Rat PCA Assay (iv route)

| Compd. | Structure | PCA assay[a] | Structure | PCA assay[a] |
|---|---|---|---|---|
| 8 | 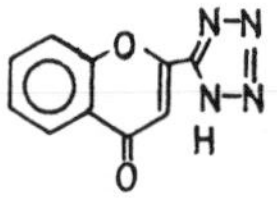 | 1.4 | 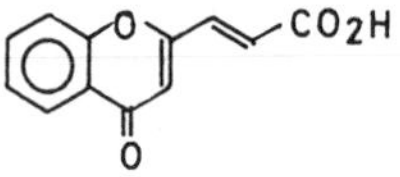 | < 0.1 |
| 9 | 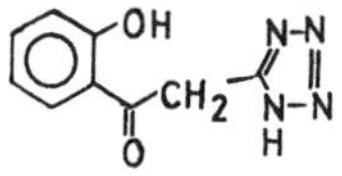 | 0.35 | | |
| 10 | 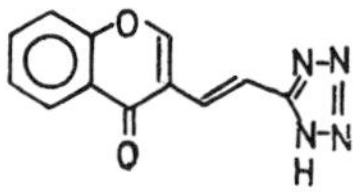 | 0.3 | | |
| 11 | 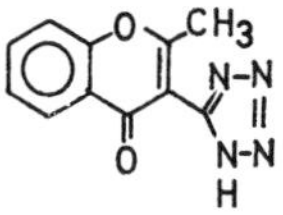 | 0.1 | 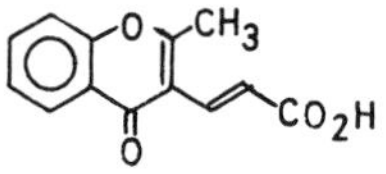 | inactive |
| 12 | 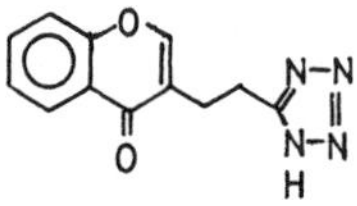 | 0.07 | 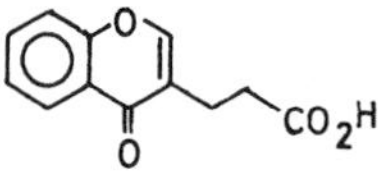 | < 0.1 |
| 13 | 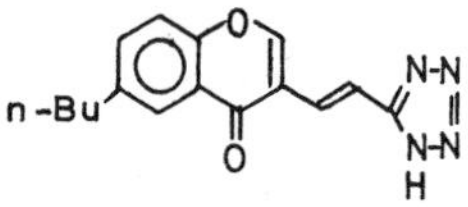 | 0.07 | | |
| 14 | 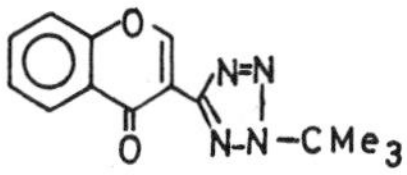 | inactive | | |
| 15 | 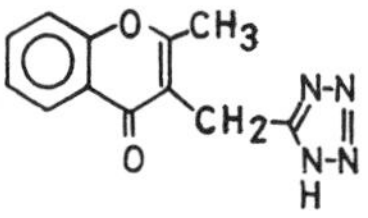 | inactive | 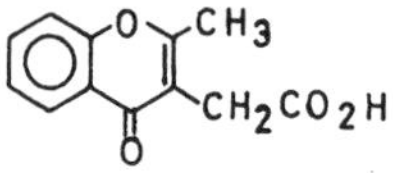 | inactive |

[a] See Table I footnote a.

before, 0.36 times as active as DSCG when administered intravenously in the rat PCA test, the corresponding tetrazole derivative (5a) was 3.5 times as active as DSCG. Thus, in a study on the relationship between the biological activity and acidity of 3a (pKa' 8.85), 4a (pKa' 7.25) and 5a (pKa' 5.85), it appeared to us that the activity would increase with the increase of the acidity. In Table I, the activities in the rat PCA assay (iv) of the tetrazole derivatives (5) along with the corresponding acrylic acid derivatives (4) are listed. Almost all the compounds in the 5 and 4 series carrying a substituent group(s) on the 6-, 7-, or 8-position of the chromone ring were highly potent inhibitors of the PCA reaction. Among them the most noteworthy compounds were 4j and 5b-5o which were 2 to 30 times as active as DSCG. When comparison was made of the biological activity among the analogues bearing a tetrazole group on the 2- or 3-positions of the chromone ring, 5a proved to be 2.5 times as active as the isomer 8. This superior activity of the 3-position for the activity was in agreement with the result observed in the 4 series. It is interesting to note that the acetophenone derivative (9) which is not as rigid in structure as 5 also shows some activity. Introduction of a long side chain like hexyl at the 6-position or of a methyl group at the 2-position of the chromone nucleus (i.e., 5q, 5r or 11) reduces the biological activity. Similar results have also been obtained with the acrylic acid derivatives (4). On the other hand, 10, 12 and 13 show the same extent of activities as the corresponding carboxylic acid derivatives. The presence of the acidic tetrazole ring is essential for the activity as is shown by the inactivity of 14 which lacks an acidic proton (Table II). All the derivatives of 5a are orally active, and typical examples are shown in Table III.

Table III. 50% Inhibition Dose ($ID_{50}$) of Orally Administered 3-(1*H*-Tetrazol-5-yl)chromones in PCA in Rats[a]

| Compd. | $ID_{50}$ (mg/kg) |
|---|---|
| DSCG | > 100 |
| 5a | 5.3 (5.5, 5.0) |
| 5b | 1.7 |
| 5c | 1.25 |
| 5d | 7.4 |
| 5e | 8.5 |
| 5f | 6.9 ± 1.7[b] |
| 5j | 17.0 |
| 5m | 10.0 |
| 5o | 7.0 |

[a] See Table I footnote a.
[b] The value is mean ± standard error of four experiments.

## Pharmacology of 6-Ethyl-3-(1H-tetrazol-5-yl)chromone (5f) (AA-344) (26)

After examination of the pharmacological and toxicological properties of 5, the 6-ethyl derivative (5f) (AA-344) was selected as one of the most promising drugs for further studies. As stated previously, AA-344 is effective orally in inhibiting the IgE-mediated PCA reaction in rats (Figure 3) (27). Also, AA-344 had an inhibitory effect on the IgGa mediated PCA reaction in rats (27) and the passive systemic anaphylaxis in guinea pigs (Table IV), but slight or little effect on the Forssman shock in guinea pigs, the complement-dependent cytolysis of mast cell in rats, the Arthus reaction in guinea pigs, and the tuberculin reaction and contact sensitivity to dinitrofluorobenzene in mice. These results indicated that AA-344 depressed selectively the anaphylactic (type I allergic) reaction, mainly IgE-mediated one. The antiallergic effect of AA-344 was not due to antihistamine or antiserotonin action (27). AA-344 markedly inhibited the antigen-induced histamine release from the sensitized rat peritoneal mast cell (28). Neither binding of IgE to mast cell receptor nor binding of antigen to membrane-bound IgE was affected by AA-344, suggesting that it acted on a step involving the process of histamine release in the mast cell after the antigen-antibody interaction (27, 28). An inhibitory effect of AA-344 on the cyclic AMP phosphodiesterase activity of the purified rat peritoneal mast cell was observed. AA-344 may prevent the histamine release by changing the intracellular cyclic AMP level.

No significant side effects were observed on one-, three- and six-month toxicity test in rats. In the general pharmacological study, AA-344 and DSCG administered intravenously induced a transient hypotensive and bradycardiac effect in the anesthetized dogs, in contrast to a transient hypertensive and tachycardiac effect in the anesthetized monkeys. In the dogs, DSCG showed an activity about 100 times as potent as AA-344 in both effects. However, in the conscious dogs no hypertensive or bradycardiac effect was observed even at a dose as high as 100 mg/kg po of AA-344.

## Metabolic Fate of AA-344 (29)

In the study on the metabolic fate of AA-344, 6-ethyl-3-(1H-tetrazol-5-yl) [4-$^{14}$C]chromone ($^{14}$C-AA-344) was used. The maximum plasma levels and half-lives ($t_{1/2}$) of the drug after oral administration (10 mg/kg) were highest and longest in dogs (45.6 μg/ml, 13.3 h), followed by monkeys (28.7 μg/ml, 2.39 h), guinea pigs (14.6 μg/ml, 1.31 h), rats (5.5 μg/ml), and rabbits (0.9 μg/ml, 1.31 h). The drug was highly bound to plasma protein. In dogs and rats, the plasma $^{14}$C was

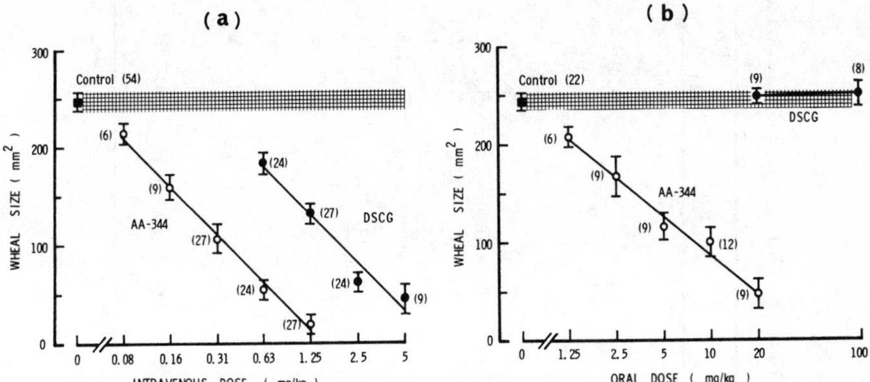


*Figure 3. Effects of AA-344 and DSCG administered intravenously (a) and orally (b) on the IgE-mediated 72-h PCA in rats AA-344 or DSCG was administered intravenously immediately before antigen challenge (a) and orally 5 min before antigen (b). The control wheal sizes (mm², mean ± SE) were 248 ± 6 for (a) and 243 ± 9 for (b). Each numeral in parenthesis represents number of animals.*

Table IV. Effect of AA-344 on the Type I Allergic Reaction

| Type I Allergic Reaction | Antiserum | Animal | Dose (mg/kg iv) | AA-344 | DSCG |
|---|---|---|---|---|---|
| In vivo | | | | | |
| Homologous 72-h PCA | Rat IgE | Rat | 0.28 (iv $ED_{50}$) | ++ | 1.30 (mg/kg) (iv $ED_{50}$) |
| | | | 5.4 (po $ED_{50}$) | ++ | - |
| Homologous 3-h PCA | Rat IgGa | Rat | 5, 20 | + | + |
| Homologous 8-d PCA | Guinea pig IgE-like | Guinea pig | 5, 20 | + | - |
| Homologous 3-h PCA | Guinea pig IgG | Guinea pig | 5, 20 | + | - |
| Heterologous 3-h PCA | Rabbit IgG | Guinea pig | 5, 20 | - | - |
| Passive systemic anaphylaxis | Rabbit IgG | Guinea pig | 5, 20 | + | - |
| Active systemic anaphylaxis | -- | Mouse | 5, 20 | - | - |
| In vitro | | | | | |
| Anaphylactic histamine release from isolated rat peritoneal mast cell | IgE | | $10^{-7}$M ($IC_{50}$) | ++ | $5x10^{-7}$M ($IC_{50}$) |
| | IgGa | | $10^{-5}$M ($IC_{50}$) | + | $10^{-3}$M ($IC_{50}$) |
| Schultz-Dale reaction | Rabbit IgG | Guinea pig ileum | $10^{-3}$M | - | - |

++ : marked inhibition + : inhibition - : no inhibition

predominantly the unchanged drug, but in guinea pigs, rabbits and monkeys, metabolites whose structures are stated later were found (Table V).

There was already a wide distribution of $^{14}C$ in tissues 10 min after oral administration of the drug to rats. At this time, the $^{14}C$ concn. was highest in the stomach, followed by kidney, liver, plasma, heart and lung, and lowest in the brain.

Almost all of the administered $^{14}C$ was eliminated from the body in 72 h. The major route of excretion was urine in the various species except guinea pigs, in which the dosed $^{14}C$ was almost equally divided between urine and faeces. Only trace amounts of the unchanged drug was found in urine and bile. The major urinary metabolites are as follows: α-hydroxy (16), α-keto (17), β-hydroxy (18), and α,β-dihydroxy (19) derivatives of AA-344 in rats; 16 and salicylic acid derivative (22) in guinea pigs; 16, 18 and a glucuronide (20) in rabbits; 16 and 20 in dogs; and 16 and 19 in monkeys (Table VI).

## Synthesis and Biological Activities of the Metabolites (32)

In the metabolism study (29, 30, 31), the following seven metabolites, 6-(1-hydroxyethyl)-3-(1*H*-tetrazol-5-yl)-chromone (16), 6-acetyl-3-(1*H*-tetrazol-5-yl)chromone (17), 6-(2-hydroxyethyl)-3-(1*H*-tetrazol-5-yl)chromone (18), 6-(1,2-dihydroxyethyl)-3-(1*H*-tetrazol-5-yl)chromone (19), glucuronide (20) (the structural elucidation is described below), 5-ethylsalicylic acid (21) and 3-carboxy-4-hydroxy-phenylacetic acid (22), were identified in the urine of rats, guinea pigs, rabbits, dogs and monkeys. These seven compounds were synthesized and used as reference compounds to unequivocally establish the structures of the urinary metabolites, and to allow evaluation of their antiallergic activity (32). The synthetic routes are shown below (Figure 4).

Bromination of AA-344 with N-bromosuccinimide (NBS) followed by alkaline hydrolysis gave the α-hydroxy metabolite (16), which was converted to 17 by Jones oxidation. While the epoxide derivative (23) (refer to reference 32) gave the β-hydroxy metabolite (18) on catalytic hydrogenation, the treatment of 23 with formic acid followed by hydrolysis with aqueous alkali yielded the α,β-dihydroxy metabolite (19). Condensation of AA-344 with methyl 1-bromo-1-deoxy-tri-O-acetyl-α-D-glucopyranuronate (24) in the presence of silver carbonate gave a mixture of 25a and 26a which were separated by fractional recrystallization. The protecting groups of 25a and 26a were removed with sodium hydroxide to give 25b and 26b, respectively. The structures of the glucuronides were confirmed to be the N-1 isomers, 25a and 25b, by the chemical shifts of the glycosydic carbons and the tetrazole

Table V. Composition of Radioactivity in Plasma after Oral Administration of $^{14}C$-AA-344 in Various Species

| Species | Time after dosage (h) | Total radioactivity (μg eq. of $^{14}C$-AA-344/ml) | Percentage of the radioactivity | | | |
|---|---|---|---|---|---|---|
| | | | Parent drug | Metabolites | | |
| | | | | 16 | 17 | 18, 19, 25b and unidentified |
| Rat | 2.0 | 5.0 | 86.7 (4.3) | 7.9 (0.4) | 1.8 (0.1) | 3.6 (0.2) |
| Guinea pig | 1.5 | 22.4 | 65.5 (14.6) | 1.8 (0.4) | 0.3 (0.1) | 32.4 (7.2) |
| Rabbit | 0.5 | 3.4 | 26.0 (0.9) | 55.0 (1.9) | 4.0 (0.1) | 15.0 (0.5) |
| Dog | 3.0 | 50.6 | 90.0 (45.6) | 4.9 (2.5) | 1.3 (0.6) | 3.8 (1.8) |
| Monkey | 1.0 | 44.4 | 64.6 (28.7) | 9.6 (4.3) | 0.5 (0.2) | 25.3 (11.2) |

Dose of the labelled drug was 10 mg (18.4 to 90.2 μCi)/kg. Percentage of the total $^{14}C$ was for pooled samples from 3 animals in each experiment. Figures in parentheses denote the plasma concn. of the drug (μg/ml) and metabolites (μg eq. of $^{14}C$-AA-344/ml).

Table VI. Composition of Radioactivity in the 48 h-urine and Bile Samples from Animals Orally given $^{14}C$-AA-344

| Species | Sample | Excretion of radio-activity (% of dose/48 h) | Parent drug | Percentage of total radioactivity as: Metabolites | | | | | | | |
|---|---|---|---|---|---|---|---|---|---|---|---|
| | | | | 16 | 17 | 18 | 19 | 21 | 22 | 25b | Others* |
| Rat | Urine | 83.1 | n.d. | 65.6 | 5.6 | 15.5 | 8.4 | n.d. | n.d. | n.d. | 4.9 |
| | Bile | 16.0 | n.d. | 52.3 | 6.1 | 5.5 | 6.1 | 0.7 | n.d. | n.d. | 29.3 |
| Guinea pig | Urine | 44.3 | 0.5 | 19.3 | n.d. | n.d. | n.d. | 1.7 | 8.0 | n.d. | 70.5 |
| Rabbit | Urine | 85.4 | n.d. | 33.1 | n.d. | 47.5 | n.d. | 2.7 | 2.3 | 5.8 | 8.6 |
| Dog | Urine | 71.3 | 1.1 | 75.0 | 1.5 | n.d. | n.d. | 1.7 | n.d. | 12.9 | 7.8 |
| | Bile | 19.8 | 1.3 | 40.7 | 1.3 | n.d. | n.d. | 4.7 | n.d. | 33.4 | 18.6 |
| Monkey | Urine | 77.6 | 0.7 | 59.6 | n.d. | n.d. | 8.1 | 0.7 | 0.9 | 2.0 | 28.0 |

Dose of the labelled drug was 10 mg/kg. The composition was determined by two-dimentional t.l.c.-autoradiography following extraction with ethyl acetate at pH 1. Percentage of $^{14}C$ was for pooled samples of 3 animals, except dog bile (n=2). n.d., Not detected.

* : Unidentified metabolites.

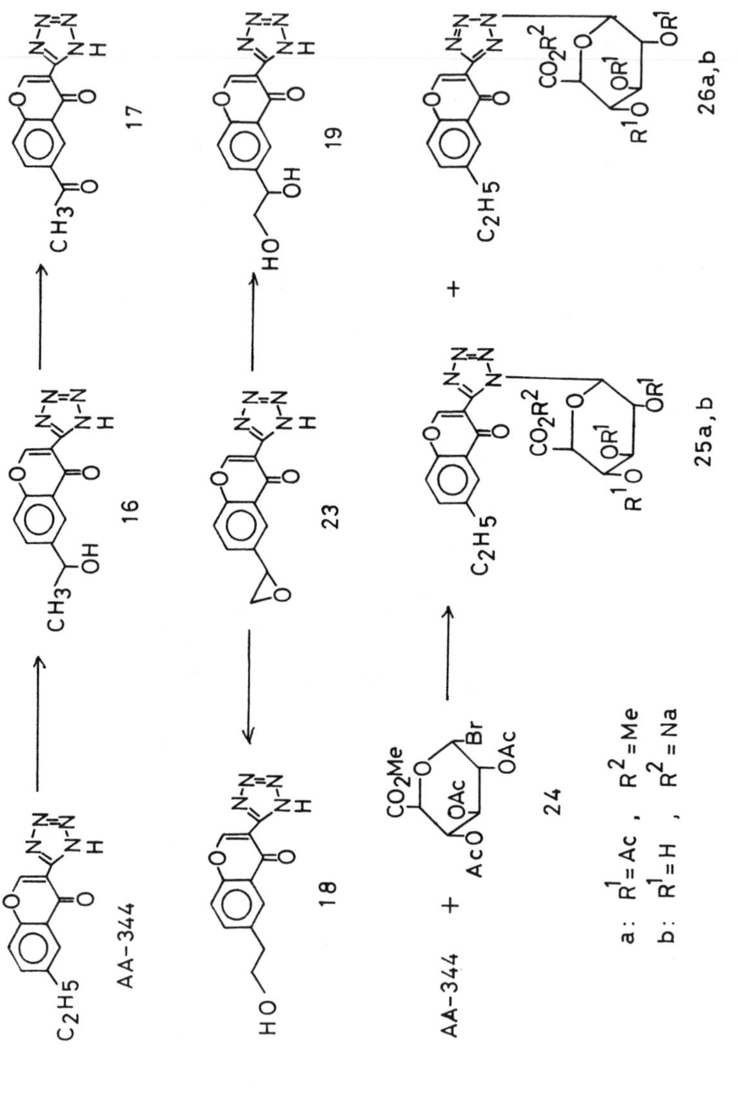

*Figure 4. Synthesis of the metabolites of AA-344*

ring carbons in $^{13}C$-nmr. When the natural glucuronide (20) treated with diazomethane and acetic anhydride was compared with authentic glucuronides, it was found to be identical with 25a and different from 26a using mass spectra and TLC (31). Therefore, the full structure of 20 was confirmed to be 1-deoxy-1-[5-(6-ethylchromon-3-yl)tetrazol-1-yl]-β-D-glucopyranuronate (25b).

The biological activities of the metabolites are shown in Table VII. Among the metabolites, activities similar to that of AA-344 were observed with the ketone (17) and the β-hydroxy derivative (18), and *ca.* half the activity with the α-hydroxy derivatives (16, 19) when administered intravenously. These results show that oxidation of the alkyl group of AA-344 gives little influence on the activity when administered intravenously. The glucuronide (25b) showed no inhibitory activity. This fact agrees with the previous finding that the acidity of the tetrazole ring is essential for the biological activity (16). The salicylic acid derivatives (21, 22) also showed no activity. In contrast to the effects on intravenous activity, modification of the alkyl side chain had a marked influence on oral activity, probably due to reduced absorption from the gastrointestinal tract. Thus, when administered orally, only the metabolites (16) and (17) showed activity.

Table VII. Activities in the Rat PCA Assay of the Metabolites of AA-344[a]

| Compd. | iv | po $ID_{50}$ (mg/kg) |
|---|---|---|
| DSCG | 1 (standard) | > 100 |
| AA-344 | 5.3 | 5.9 |
| 16 | 2.3 | 13.4 |
| 17 | 5.5 | 6.6 |
| 18 | 6.3 | > 20 |
| 19 | 2.3 | > 20 |
| 21 | inactive | -- |
| 22 | inactive | -- |
| 25b | inactive | -- |

[a] The $ID_{50}$ value was calculated from relationship between logarithmic dose and area of dye leakage by the method of least squares.

## Clinical Trials

Effect of AA-344 on Asthma. In an earlier report (33), a single blind trial in 14 subjects with atopic bronchial asthma (paroxysmal or chronic type) was carried out and the efficacy was assessed subjectively from the alleviation of the symptoms. Continuing oral administration of AA-344 at 30-60 mg/day, was markedly effective in 4 cases, effective in 3, slightly effective in 3, ineffective in 3 and assessment was impossible in 1 case. Of the 7 subjects in which AA-344 was effective, 6 were RAST positive and had high serum IgE level (RIST). The result in 10 subjects in which the cross-over test with DSCG was carried out, indicated the effect of these two drugs to be approximately equal. A 30% or more improvement in $FEV_1$ or FVC was noted in 8 cases.

In a second report (34), the clinical courses in 12 subjects with atopic asthma (paroxysmal or chronic type), extending from 7 to 22 weeks, were described. Oral administration of AA-344 at 60 mg/day was somewhat effective in 11 cases. AA-344 was effective not only in all cases of high RIST and RAST value, but also in 3 out of 4 cases in which RIST and RAST were normal. In the cross-over test with DSCG, AA-344 seemed to be superior in 5, while DSCG was better in 3 cases, and in 1 case both drugs appeared to be equipotent. During the course of administration with AA-344, alleviation of allergic rhinitis and chronic urticaria was noted.

In a clinical trial in 33 subjects with bronchial asthma (35), oral administration of AA-344 at 40 mg t.i.d. was effective in 14 (the rate of efficacy: 42.4%), and slightly effective in 5 cases (the overall rate of efficacy: 57.6%). Efficacy was assessed after 4 or more weeks administration of AA-344. The efficacy appeared to be proportional to the serum IgE level, namely, the efficacies were 83, 80, and 44% when the IgE values were >701, 301-700, and 101-300 unit/ml, respectively. The drug was ineffective when the IgE value was less than 100 unit/ml.

Effect of AA-344 on Hoya (Sea-Squirt) Asthma (36). Hoya (sea-squirt) asthma is an occupational asthma. Sea-squirt (Hoya) is a lower animal that belongs to the *phylum chordate* division. Allergic symptoms often developed in the oyster culture workers which are ascribed to Hoya. The body fluid of the sea-squirt, having been discharged upon the oyster shell, splashes during the shucking operation. Some of the workers who inhale the substance become sensitized and manifest symptoms of asthma (37).

The clinical effects of AA-344 at 60-120 mg/day oral administration (2 to 19 weeks) were studied in 22 cases of the sea-squirt asthma, a typical type I allergy. Of the 22 subjects studied, 17 received AA-344 alone, and 5 were treated with AA-344 in combination with a hyposensitization therapy with sea-squirt antigen. A total of 11 showed a marked improvement and a moderate effect was seen in 8 cases. Two cases did not show any change, and 1 case was termed as aggravated (Table VIII).

Table VIII. Clinical Study of AA-344 on a Typical Atopic Disease, Hoya Asthma

Hoya: Sea-squirt (Styela plicata, Styela clava, Ciona intestinalis, Botrylloides violaceum)

22 asthma patients: 3 men and 19 women (20-70 years old)

| Treatment | Patients | Therapeutic effect | | | |
|---|---|---|---|---|---|
| | | ++ | + | 0 | - |
| AA-344 | 17 | 9 | 7 | 0 | 1 |
| AA-344 + Hyposensitization | 5 | 2 | 1 | 2 | 0 |

++ : markedly effective + : effective
0 : no effect - : aggravated

Table IX. The Relation between Severity of Symptom of Hoya Asthma and Therapeutic Effect of AA-344

| Symptom | Therapeutic effect | | | |
|---|---|---|---|---|
| | ++ | + | 0 | - |
| Mild | 3 | 3 | | |
| Moderate | 7 | 3 | 1 | 1 |
| Severe | 1 | 2 | 1 | |

++ : markedly effective + : effective
0 : no effect - : aggravated

The effect of AA-344, irrespective of whether 60, 80 or 120 mg was used in the initial daily dose, was manifested within one week in almost all cases. The treatment proved to be effective not only in patients with mild and moderate sea-squirt asthma but also in 3 out of 4 patients with a severe condition (Table IX). Hyposensitization therapy with sea-squirt antigen solution has proved to be highly effective in treating sea-squirt asthma (37). The subjects in this trial included 15 patients on whom hyposensitization therapy had been performed in the previous seasons and the effect assessed; and the effect of AA-344 treatment was compared with that of the hyposensitization therapy. These two therapies proved to be effective, however, AA-344 treatment was superior to the hyposensitization therapy by bringing about a marked relief to a larger number of the patients.

In a clinical phase II study (271 patients), no significant adverse effect has been observed including cardiovascular effect.

## Abstract

Starting with the structure-activity study of the naturally occurring flavone, baicalein, we have synthesized a number of 3-substituted chromones. In the course of the investigation, 3-(4-oxo-4*H*-1-benzopyran-3)acrylic acids and 3-(1*H*-tetrazol-5-yl)chromones were found to be orally active antiallergic agents, and their structure-activity relationships were studied. After examination of pharmacological and toxicological properties of these compounds, AA-344 was selected as one of the most promising drugs and its metabolic fate was studied. Also, the metabolites found in the urine were synthesized and the biological activities were tested. In the clinic, AA-344 at an oral dose of 60-120 mg/day showed an efficacy in a typical type I allergy including sea-squirt asthma, a common occupational asthma among oyster culture workers.

## Literature Cited

1. Cox, J.S.G., Beach, J.E., Blair, S.M.J.N., Clarke, A.J., King, J., Lee, T.B., Loveday, D.E.E., Moss, G.F., Orr, T.S.C., and Ritchie, J.T., *Advances in Drug Research*, (1970), *5*, 115.
2. Cairns, H., Fitzmaurice, C., Hunter, D., Johnson, P.B., King, J., Lee, T.B., Lord, G.H., Minshull, R., and Cox, J.S.G., *J. Med. Chem.*, (1972), *15*, 583.
3. Koda, A., Nagai, H., and Wada, H., *Nippon Yakurigaku Zasshi*, (1970), *66*, 194, 273.
4. Koda, A., Nagai, H., Yoshida, Y., and Kiat, L.H., *ibid.*, (1970), *66*, 471.

5. Sanno, Y., Nohara, A., Kuriki, H., and Koda, A., J. Takeda Res. Lab., (1974), 33, 225.
6. Mota, I., Life Sci., (1963), 2, 917.
7. Eiden, F. and Harverland, H., Arch. Pharm. (Weinheim), (1967), 300, 806.
8. Reynolds, G.A., and Van Allan, J.A., J. Heterocycl. Chem., (1969), 6, 375.
9. Vlasov, V.M., and Jakobson, G.G., Izv. Nauk. SSSR., Ser. Khim., (1969), 893, Chem. Abstr., (1969), 71, 30322g.
10. Nohara, A., Umetani, T., and Sanno, Y., Tetrahedron Lett., (1973), 1995.
11. Idem, Tetrahedron, (1974), 30, 3563.
12. Harnisch, H., Ann. Chem., (1972), 768, 8.
13. Koda, A. et al., unpublished work.
14. Nohara, A., Umetani, T., Ukawa, K., and Sanno, Y., Chem. Pharm. Bull., (1974), 22, 2959.
15. Dauphin, J., Chatonier, D., Couquelet, J., Payard, M., and Picard, M., Lab-Pharma-Probl. Tech., (1970), 18, 58.
16. Nohara, A., Kuriki, K., Saijo, T., Ukawa, K., Murata, T., Kanno, M., and Sanno, Y., J. Med. Chem., (1975), 18, 34.
17. Ellis, G.P., and Shaw, D., ibid., (1972), 15, 865.
18. Idem, J. Chem. Soc., Perkin Trans., (1972), 1, 779.
19. Assem, E.S.K., and Mc Allen, M.K., Int. Arch. Allergy Appl. Immunol., (1973), 45, 697.
20. Batchelor, J.F., Follenfant, M.J., Garland, L.G., Govin, J.H., Green, A.F., Hodson, H.F., Hughes, D.T.D., and Tateson, J.E., Lancet, (1975), 1169.
21. Benson, F.R., Heterocyclic Compounds, (1967), 8, 8.
22. Nohara, A., Kuriki, H., Saijo, T., Sugihara, H., Kanno, M., and Sanno, Y., J. Med. Chem., (1977), 20, 141.
23. Arnold, Z., and Zemlicka, J., Coll. Czechoslov. Chem. Commun., (1959), 24, 2385.
24. Nohara, A., Ishiguro, T., and Sanno, Y., Tetrahedron Lett., (1974), 1183.
25. Nohara, A., ibid., (1974), 1187.
26. Maki, Y., Kuriki, H., Saijo, T., Ashida, Y., and Kanno, M., Seventh International Congress of Pharmacology (Paris), Abstract, (1978), 910.
27. Kuriki, H., Saijo, T., Maki, Y., and Kanno, M., Japan. J. Pharmacol., in press.
28. Saijo, T., Ashida, Y., Kuriki, H., Kanno, M., and Maki, Y., ibid., in press.
29. Kanai, Y., Nakai, Y., Nakajima, N., and Tanayama, S., Xenobiotica, in press.
30. Kuwayama, M., Itakura, K., Ito, H., Takeda, K., Nohara, A., and Kuriki, H., unpublished work.
31. Kanai, Y., Nakai, Y., Shirakawa, Y., Kobayashi, T., Nakajima, N., and Tanayama, S., unpublished work.

32. Nohara, A., Kuriki, H., Ishiguro, T., Saijo, T., Ukawa, K., Maki, Y., and Sanno, Y., J. Med. Chem., in press.
33. Kurokawa, D., Katsuki, E., Okuda, N., and Ohkubo, A., Allergy (Japan), (1976), 25, 350.
34. Kurokawa, D., Katsuki, E., Ohkubo, A., ibid., (1977), 26, 173.
35. Sasaki, Y., et al., ibid., (1978), 27, 343.
36. Katsutani, K., Jyo, T., Komoto, K., and Tsuboi, S., ibid., (1977), 26, 172.
37. Jyo, T., Komoto, K., Tsuboi, S., Katsutani, T., Otsuka, T., and Oka, S., Allergie und Immunologie, (1974/1975), 20/21, 435.

Received August 6, 1979.

# 8

# Pyranenamines: A New Series of Potent Antiallergic Compounds

K. M. SNADER, L. W. CHAKRIN, R. D. CRAMER III, Y. M. GELERNT, C. K. MIAO, D. H. SHAH, B. M. SUTTON, J. W. VENSLAVSKY, and C. R. WILLIS[1]

Research and Development Division, Smith Kline & French Laboratories, Philadelphia, PA 19101

The discovery of disodium chromoglycate (DSCG) in 1969 and its unique antiallergic activity (1) has prompted many laboratories, including our own, to search for more potent, orally active compounds with this activity (2). We reported in 1976 on a mildly active new series, the pyrantriones (I) (3).

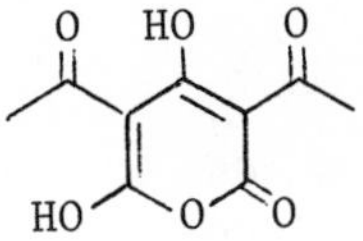

I

We now report an extension of this series, the amine adducts or pyranenamines (II) which have potent, oral, DSCG-like activity

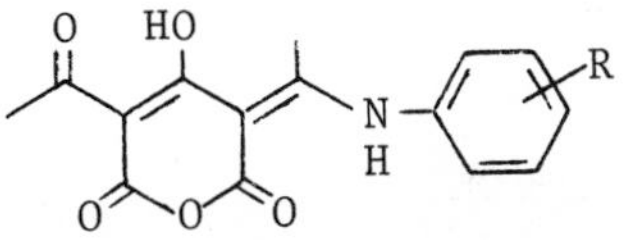

II

as demonstrated both in the rat PCA test system and in rat and primate *in vitro* systems which measure the antigen-IgE induced release of allergic mediators.

## Introductory Chemistry

Condensation of the pyrantrione I with various aromatic and aliphatic amines gives the monopyranenamine II, whose skeletal

[1] Current address: Hercules, Inc., Central Research Department, Wilmington, DE

0-8412-0536-1/80/47-118-145$05.00/0

structure and tautomeric state can be clearly demonstrated by carbon and proton nmr spectroscopy. The bisenamine can also be

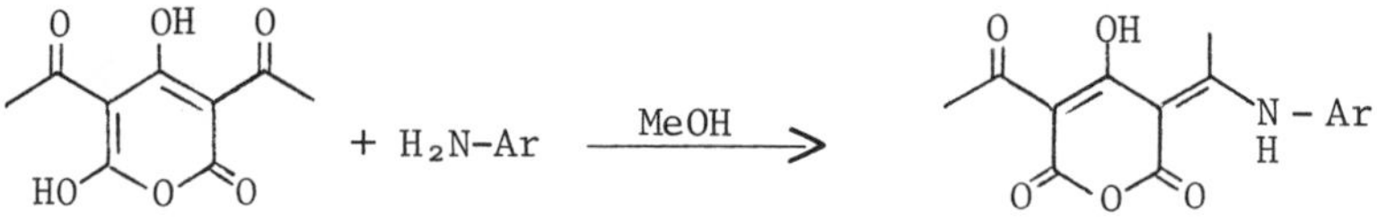

I + $H_2N$-Ar —MeOH→ II

prepared under forcing conditions such as elevated temperature and azeotropic removal of water, but in general the monoenamine is readily obtained in high (50-85%) yield by precipitation from the reaction media. The structure of II was originally suggested by Kiang and his colleagues (4) but was not rigorously proven. Examination of the proton and carbon-13 nmr spectra substantiate the tautomeric form shown here as II. Furthermore an x-ray crystallographic examination was performed on the p-hydroxy analog, 15, and agreed with our assignment.

## Test System

We use the conventional (Goose and Blair) inhibition of antigen-IgE induced passive cutaneous anaphylaxis (PCA) reaction in rats as a preliminary test system (5). Test compounds are administered at the optimum pretreatment time of 0.5 minutes prior to antigen challenge in the i.v. tests and 15 minutes prior to antigen challenge in oral tests. Generally, six animals are used in each test group. In addition, the ability of any test compound to inhibit a direct, exogenous challenge of histamine or serotonin is measured when there is significant activity in the PCA system.

## Monosubstituted Pyranenamines

In the search for improved potency, a group of simple substituents was first examined as shown in Table I. In this table the results of the PCA test are shown as a percent inhibition at the intravenous dose tested. For those compounds which were sufficiently active to test several doses, an $ID_{50}$, or a dose which gives a 50% inhibition of the PCA reaction, was calculated. The mean percent inhibition was evaluated using a one-sided Student "t" test and p is 0.01 unless otherwise noted. The column labeled $pI_{50}$ is a calculated value used for QSAR work and is defined as log $(1/ID_{50})$. The obvious difficulties in estimating the $ID_{50}$ from a single dose experiment are discussed in the following paper. The $ID_{50}$ of DSCG as determined in our system is included as compound 13 for reference purposes.

TABLE 1

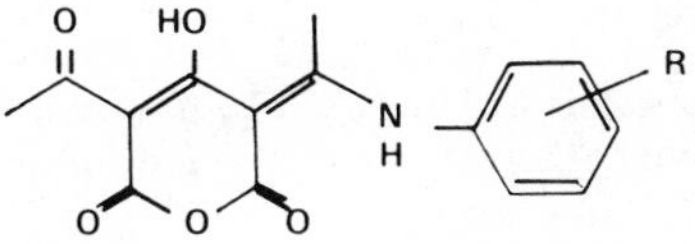

| CMPD. NO. | R | IV PCA DOSE[a] | IV PCA % INHIB.[b] | $p_{I50}$ |
|---|---|---|---|---|
| 1 | H | 10 | 76 | –0.70 |
| 2 | 2–Cl | 10 | 36 | –1.20 |
| 3 | 3–Cl | 10 | 74 | –0.70 |
| 4 | 4–Cl | 10 | 84 | –0.60 |
| 5 | 4–F | 10 | 54 | –1.00 |
| 6 | 4–Br | 0.5 | 0(NS)[c] | –1.50 |
| 7 | 4–$NO_2$ | 10 | 17(NS) | –1.34 |
| 8 | 2–$COOC_2H_5$ | 5 | 18(NS) | –0.50 |
| 9 | 4–$COOC_2H_5$ | 5 | 6(NS) | –1.50 |
| 10 | 3–$SO_2NH_2$ | 0.5 | 45 | 0.31 |
| 11 | 4–$SO_2NH_2$ | 0.5 | 12(NS) | 0.00 |
| 12 | 4–$CH_3$ | 10 | 33 | –1.15 |
| 13 | DSCG | 0.9† | 50 | |

a. dose in mg./kg.; b. p=0.01 except where noted; c. NS=Not significant; †=calculated $ID_{50}$

The analogs were prepared from readily available anilines. Halogen substitution as well as substitution with other electron withdrawing groups did not substantially improve potency in the PCA assay. Simple alkyls also had only minor impact on potency. More significant improvements were made with hydroxyl functions and their derivatives, as shown in Table II. The phenol esters were prepared by conventional methods from the phenoxide and a suitable acid halide or anhydride. The PCA activity of the various esters reached a maximum with the valerate (19) but even this was not significantly more potent than the parent 4-hydroxy derivative, 15, which was our early lead candidate.

Another significant improvement was obtained with amine substituents and their derivatives as shown in Table III. The amines were prepared by reduction of the corresponding nitro pyranenamine. Amide derivatives, III, were prepared from the corresponding nitro-aniline IV and then condensed following reduction as shown in Scheme I.

Two interesting compounds were the sulfamides 56 & 57 which were prepared from sulfamyl chloride and the corresponding nitro-aniline. The para substituted compound was straightforward but the meta isomer produced equal amounts of the sulfamide and the disulfamide intermediate. One of the driving forces in our selection of derivatives was the QSAR studies being performed and two choices made early in the series were the guanidine 36 and the glyceramide 60 both of which were quite active in the PCA assay. The most active derivatives in this series were the oxamic acid 59 and the glyceramide 60.

The 3-amido analogs were examined in more detail and other isomers were prepared as shown in Table IV. The benzylamido analog 61 was prepared from the benzylamino compound V which in turn was easily made from m-nitrobenzaldehyde as shown. The various amides, including the barbituramide 66, were prepared from m-nitrobenzoyl chloride. PCA testing of these various analogs clearly showed a decrease in activity when the amine function is displaced from the aromatic ring (see Scheme II.)

The importance of N-alkylation was determined by a short series of derivatives as shown in Table V. Preparation of the N-alkyl derivatives is accomplished in the usual manner by condensation of the pyrantrione with an N-alkylaniline but forcing conditions are necessary. Comparison of 67 & 68 with their corresponding unalkylated parents show no significant improvement. In addition, the corresponding morpholino analog and the unsubstituted amide show no significant activity.

## Multiply Substituted Pyranenamines

Based on the observed activity, the assembly of multiple groupings was a clear pathway to improved potency. Once again the QSAR study helped our decision-making process by reducing the large number of possible permutations to some workable

TABLE II

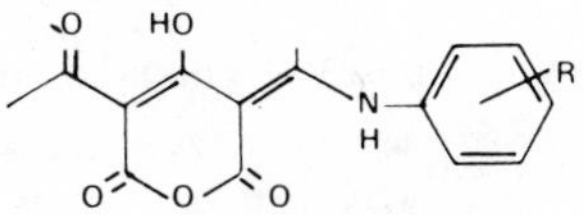

| CMPD. NO. | R | IV PCA DOSE[a] | IV PCA % INHIB.[b] | $pI_{50}$ | PO PCA DOSE[a] | PO PCA % INHIB.[b] |
|---|---|---|---|---|---|---|
| 1 | H | 10 | 76 | –0.70 | | |
| 13 | 2–OH | 2.8† | 50 | –0.45 | 25 | –12(NS)[c] |
| 14 | 3–OH | 1.6† | 50 | –0.20 | 25 | 0(NS) |
| 15 | 4–OH | 1.3† | 50 | –0.11 | 29† | 50 |
| 16 | 4–$OCOCH_3$ | 0.5 | 41 | 0.22 | | |
| 17 | 4–$OCOCH_2CH_3$ | 0.5 | 16 | –0.06 | | |
| 18 | 4–$OCO(CH_2)_2CH_3$ | 1.5† | 50 | –0.19 | | |
| 19 | 4–$OCO(CH_2)_3CH_3$ | 0.5 | 34 | 0.16 | 25 | 36 |
| 20 | 4–$OCO(CH_2)_4CH_3$ | 12.1† | 50 | –0.83 | | |
| 21 | 4–$OCO(CH_2)_5CH_3$ | 0.5 | 21 | 0.01 | | |
| 22 | 4–$OCOC(CH_3)_3$ | 0.5 | 3(NS) | –0.45 | | |
| 23 | 4–$OCOC_6H_5$ | 0.5 | 10(NS) | –0.18 | | |
| 24 | 4–$OCONH_2$ | 0.5 | 19 | –0.01 | | |
| 25 | 4–$OCONH–C_7H_7$ | 0.5 | 22 | 0.03 | | |
| 26 | 4–$OCH_3$ | 5 | 27 | –0.92 | | |
| 27 | 3–$OCH_2COOH$ | 0.5 | 6(NS) | 0.10 | | |
| 28 | 4–$OCH_2COOH$ | 0.5† | 50 | 0.30 | 25 | 2(NS) |
| 29 | 4–SH | 1.9† | 50 | | | |

a. dose in mg./kg.; b. p=0.01 except where noted; c. NS=not significant; †=calculated $ID_{50}$

TABLE III

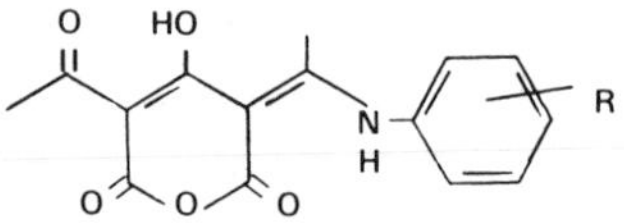

| CMPD. NO. | R | IV PCA DOSE[a] | IV PCA % INHIB.[b] | $pI_{50}$ | PO PCA DOSE[a] | PO PCA % INHIB.[b] |
|---|---|---|---|---|---|---|
| 1 | H | 10 | 76 | −0.70 | | |
| 30 | 2–$NH_2$ | 27.5† | 50 | −1.00 | | |
| 31 | 3–$NH_2$ | 0.3† | 50 | 0.68 | | |
| 32 | 3–$NHCH_3$ | 0.5 | − 8(NS)[c] | −0.30 | | |
| 33 | 4–$NH_2$ | 0.5 | 58 | 0.40 | 25 | 23 |
| 34 | 4–$N(CH_3)_2$ | 100[d] | 11(NS) | | | |
| 35 | 3–NHC(NH)–NH–TOS | 0.5 | 2(NS) | | | |
| 36 | 3–$NHC(NH)NH_2$ | 0.9† | 50 | 0.30 | 25 | − 7(NS) |
| 37 | 2–NHCHO | 0.5 | 52 | 0.32 | 25 | 31 |
| 38 | 3–NHCHO | 0.5 | 22(NS)[c] | 0.03 | | |
| 39 | 4–NHCHO | 0.5 | 49 | 0.29 | 25 | − 6(NS) |
| 40 | 2–$NHCOCH_3$ | 0.5 | −12(NS) | −0.50 | | |
| 41 | 3–$NHCOCH_3$ | 0.25 | 65 | 0.73 | 25 | 53 |
| 42 | 4–$NHCOCH_3$ | 5 | 19(NS) | −0.18 | | |
| 43 | 3–$NHCONH_2$ | 0.5 | 45 | 0.25 | 25 | 6(NS) |
| 44 | 4–$NHCONH_2$ | 0.5 | 38 | 0.19 | 25 | −17(NS) |
| 45 | 3–$NHCOCH_2CH_3$ | 0.2† | 50 | 0.79 | 25 | 70 |
| 46 | 4–$NHCOCH_2CH_3$ | 1.6† | 50 | 0.04 | | |
| 47 | 3–$NHCOCH(CH_3)_2$ | 0.5 | 72 | 0.51 | 25 | 46 |
| 48 | 4–$NHCOCH(CH_3)_2$ | 0.5 | 64 | 0.42 | 25 | 4(NS) |
| 49 | 3–$NHCO(CH_2)_2CH_3$ | 0.5 | 58 | 0.44 | | |
| 50 | 3–$NHCO(CH_2)_2COOCH_3$ | 0.4† | 50 | | | |
| 51 | 3–N–succ.[d] | 0.5 | 22 | | | |
| 52 | 3–$NHSO_2CH_3$ | 0.5 | 28 | 0.10 | | |
| 53 | 4–$NHSO_2CH_3$ | 0.5 | 20(NS) | 0.00 | | |
| 54 | 3–$NHSO_2C_6H_5$ | 1.3† | 50 | 0.00 | 25 | 7(NS) |
| 55 | 4–$NHSO_2C_6H_5$ | 0.5 | 4(NS) | −0.39 | | |
| 56 | 3–$NHSO_2NH_2$ | 0.5 | 45 | 0.50 | 25 | 13(NS) |
| 57 | 4–$NHSO_2NH_2$ | 0.3† | 50 | 0.52 | 25 | 10(NS) |
| 58 | 3–$NHCOOC_2H_5$ | 0.4† | 50 | 0.40 | | |
| 59 | 3–NHCOCOOH | 0.03† | 50 | 1.52 | 25 | 21(NS) |
| 60 | 3–NHCOOCH(OH)–$CH_2$(OH) | 0.05† | 50 | 1.30 | 25 | 55 |

a. dose in mg./kg.; b. p=0.01 except where noted; c. NS=not significant; d. N-succinimido; † calculated $ID_{50}$

*Scheme I*

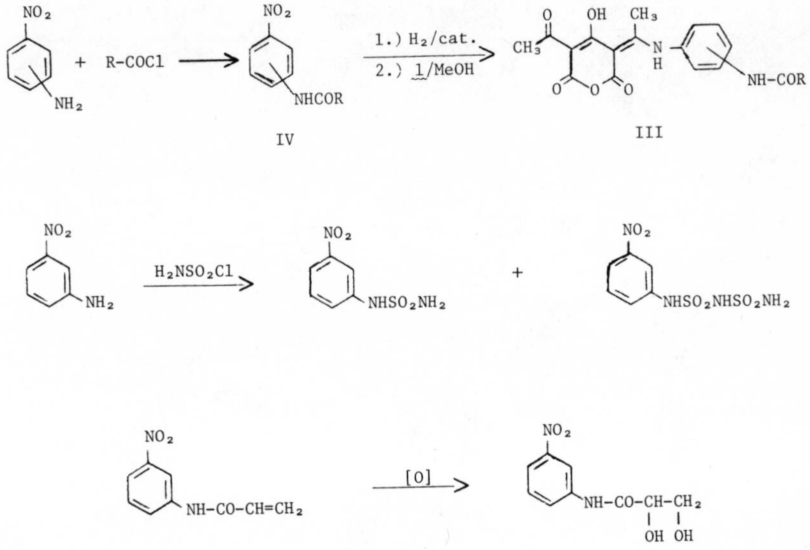

$NO_2$-aminobenzene + R-COCl → $NO_2$-C$_6$H$_4$-NHCOR (IV) → 1.) $H_2$/cat. 2.) 1/MeOH → III (NH-COR)

$NO_2$-C$_6$H$_4$-$NH_2$ → $H_2NSO_2Cl$ → $NO_2$-C$_6$H$_4$-$NHSO_2NH_2$ + $NO_2$-C$_6$H$_4$-$NHSO_2NHSO_2NH_2$

$NO_2$-C$_6$H$_4$-NH-CO-CH=$CH_2$ → [O] → $NO_2$-C$_6$H$_4$-NH-CO-CH(OH)-$CH_2$(OH)

TABLE IV

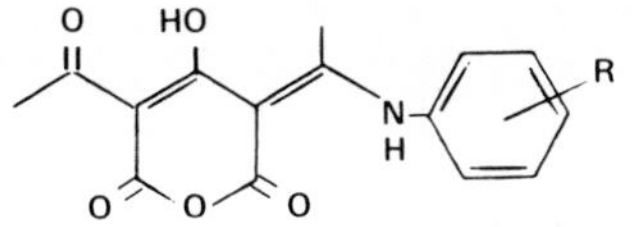

| CMPD. NO. | R | IV PCA DOSE[a] | IV PCA % INHIB.[b] | $pI_{50}$ | PO PCA DOSE[a] | PO PCA % INHIB.[b] |
|---|---|---|---|---|---|---|
| 41 | 3–$NHCOCH_3$ | 0.25 | 65 | 0.73 | 25 | 53 |
| 61 | 3–$CH_2NHCOCH_3$ | 0.5 | 4(NS)[c] | –0.39 | | |
| 62 | 3–$CONH_2$ | 0.5 | –16(NS) | –0.30 | | |
| 63 | 3–$CONHCH_3$ | 0.5 | 24 | 0.15 | 25 | 33 |
| 64 | 3–$CONHC_2H_5$ | 0.5 | – 4(NS) | –0.20 | | |
| 65 | 3–$CON(CH_3)_2$ | 0.5 | 10(NS) | 0.10 | | |
| 66 | 3–CONH–barb.[d] | 0.5 | 39 | 0.22 | 25 | 14(NS) |

a. dose in mg./kg.; b. p=0.01 except where noted; c. NS=not significant;

d. barb. = (barbituric acid-5-yl)

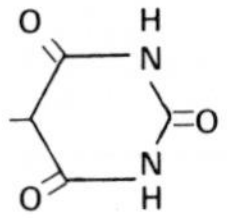

*Scheme II*

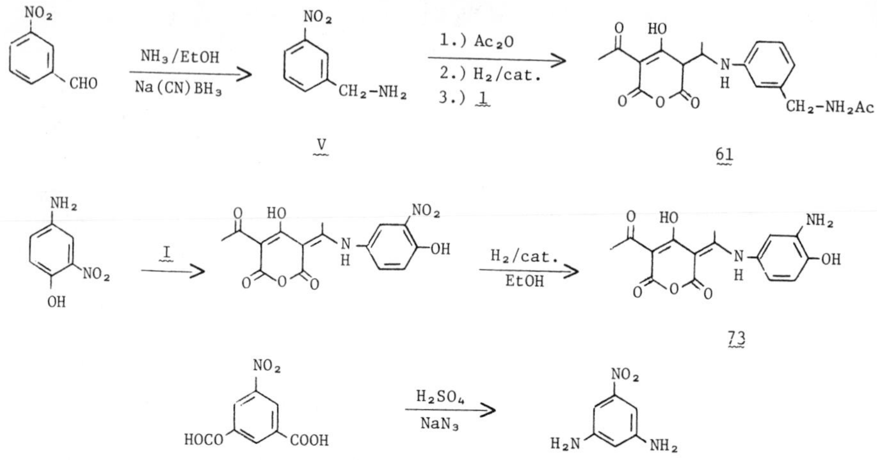

$NO_2$, CHO $\xrightarrow[Na(CN)BH_3]{NH_3/EtOH}$ $NO_2$, $CH_2$-$NH_2$ (V) $\xrightarrow{1.)\ Ac_2O;\ 2.)\ H_2/cat.;\ 3.)\ 1}$ O, HO, N-H, $CH_2$-$NH_2$Ac (61)

$NH_2$, $NO_2$, OH $\xrightarrow{I}$ O, HO, $NO_2$, N-H, OH $\xrightarrow[EtOH]{H_2/cat.}$ O, HO, $NH_2$, N-H, OH (73)

$NO_2$, HOCO, COOH $\xrightarrow[NaN_3]{H_2SO_4}$ $NO_2$, $H_2N$, $NH_2$

TABLE V

(O, HO, R; O, O, O)

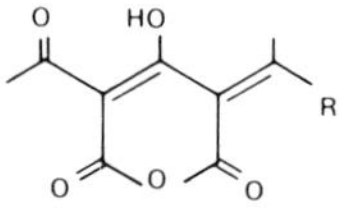

| CMPD. NO. | R | IV PCA DOSE[a] | IV PCA % INHIB.[b] |
|---|---|---|---|
| 67 | 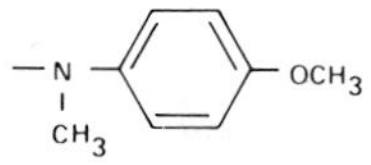 —N($CH_3$)—C₆H₄—$OCH_3$ | 5. | 37 |
| 24 |  —NH—C₆H₄—$OCH_3$ | 5 | 27 |
| 68 | 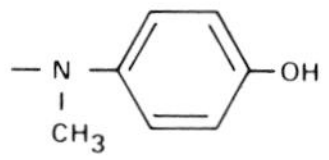 —N($CH_3$)—C₆H₄—OH | 5 | 42 |
| 13 | 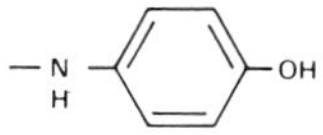 —NH—C₆H₄—OH | 1.3† | 50 |
| 69 | 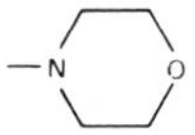 —N(morpholino)O | 0.5 | 2(NS) |
| 70 | —$NH_2$ | 5 | 17(NS) |
| 71 | 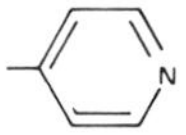 4-pyridyl (N) | 10 | 60 |

a. dose in mg./kg.; b. p=0.01 except where noted; † = calculated $ID_{50}$.

sampling. The two most promising substitution patterns were predicted to be 3,4 and 3,5-bis substitutions.

The 3,4-bis substituted derivatives are shown in Table VI. They were prepared from suitable 3,4-disubstituted nitrobenzenes as shown or in the case of 73 (SK&F 78729-A), the corresponding phenolic enamine could be nitrated in nearly quantitative yield to give the intermediate VI.

$\xrightarrow[\text{HONO, HOAc}]{HNO_3}$ VI

Once again the most active derivatives were the hydroxy and amino derivatives, and the two compounds of most significant interest were the 3-amino-4-hydroxy 73 and the 3-propionamido-4-hydroxy 81 which have very low oral to intravenous activity ratios.

The 3,5-disubstituted derivatives are shown in Table VII. Chemistry for these compounds depends upon symmetrical 1,3,5-trisubstitution and the most convenient approach to a starting material was the double Schmidt reaction which could be performed (with some precautions) on the readily available 5-nitroisophthalic acid. Either derivatization or condensation with the pyrantrione can then be performed to lead to the various symmetrical or unsymmetrical derivatives. Antiallergic activity in this series reached its maximum with the dipropionamide 90 and the diglyceramide 95 which were 300X and 1000X more potent than DSCG in the PCA test.

Additional multiply substituted analogs were made and are shown in Table VIII. As can be seen, there was no substantial improvements with these modifications.

## *In Vitro* Evaluation of Candidates

In order to select the best candidates, we used our published *in vitro* assay system (6) which employs passively sensitized lung tissue from rats or primates. In either experiment lung tissue is removed, cut into small pieces and incubated with the species-suitable immunoglobulin E. After 90 minutes the tissue is challenged (either in the presence or absence of drug) with a suitable antigen. Ovalbumin is used for the rat tissue anti-IgE for primates. The amount of histamine released is measured and in the case of primate tissue the amount of SRS-A is also measured by bioassay on guinea pig ileum. A compound's activity then is expressed as its ability to inhibit the secretion of these mediators. One distinct disadvantage to

TABLE VI

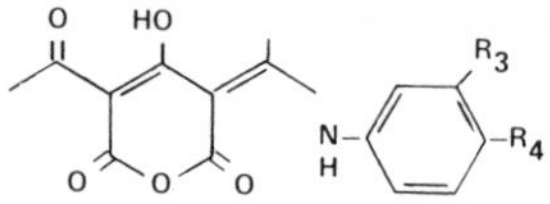

| CMPD. NO. | $R_3$ | $R_4$ | IV PCA DOSE[a] | IV PCA % INHIB.[b] | $pI_{50}$ | PO PCA DOSE[a] | PO PCA % INHIB.[b] |
|---|---|---|---|---|---|---|---|
| 72 | Cl | Cl | 10 | 10(NS)[c] | −1.50 | | |
| 73 | $NH_2$ | OH | 0.7† | 50 | −0.5 | 0.8† | 50 |
| 74 | OH | $NH_2$ | 3.4† | 50 | −0.5 | 25 | 40 |
| 75 | $NHCH_3$ | OH | 0.5 | − 6(NS) | −0.30 | | |
| 76 | $CH_2NHCH_3$ | OH | 0.5 | 1(NS) | −0.10 | | |
| 77 | $NHCOCH_3$ | OH | 0.2† | 50 | 0.82 | 25† | 50 |
| 78 | `N = C(CH_3) − O´ | | 0.5 | 13 | −0.11 | | |
| 79 | $NHCOCH_3$ | $OCH_3$ | 0.5 | 27 | 0.09 | | |
| 80 | $CONHCH_3$ | OH | 0.5 | 38 | 0.10 | | |
| 81 | $NHCOCH_2CH_3$ | OH | 0.4† | 50 | 0.43 | 0.6† | 50 |
| 82 | $NHCOCH(CH_3)_2$ | OH | 0.2† | 50 | 0.68 | 3.3† | 50 |
| 83 | $NHSO_2CH_3$ | OH | 5.0 | 38 | −0.80 | | |

a. dose in mg./kg.; b. p=0.01; c. NS=not significant; † = calculated $ID_{50}$

TABLE VII

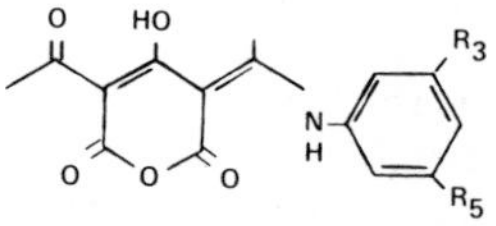

| CMPD. NO. | $R_3$ | $R_5$ | IV PCA DOSE[a] | IV PCA % INHIB.[b] | $pI_{50}$ | PO PCA DOSE[a] | PO PCA % INHIB.[b] |
|---|---|---|---|---|---|---|---|
| 84 | $CF_3$ | $CF_3$ | 5.0 | 14 | −1.09 | | |
| 85 | OH | $NH_2$ | 0.5† | 50 | 0.20 | 8.0† | 50 |
| 86 | OH | $NHCOCH_3$ | 0.02† | 50 | 1.70 | 25 | 2(NS)[d] |
| 87 | $NH_2$ | $NHCOCH_3$ | 0.1† | 50 | 0.89 | 25 | 11(NS) |
| 88 | $NH_2$ | $NH_2$ | 0.5† | 50 | 0.30 | 0.9† | 50 |
| 89 | $NHCOCH_3$ | $NHCOCH_3$ | 0.01† | 50 | 1.92 | 50 | − 1(NS) |
| 90 | $NHCOCH_2CH_3$ | $NHCOCH_2CH_3$ | 0.003† | 50 | 2.5 | 50 | 14(NS) |
| 91 | $NHCO(CH_2)_2CH_3$ | $NHCO(CH_2)_2CH_3$ | 0.05† | 50 | 1.30 | 25 | 7(NS) |
| 92 | $NHCOOC_2H_5$ | $NHCOOC_2H_5$ | 0.25† | 50 | 0.60 | 25 | −18(NS) |
| 93 | $NHCOCO_2C_2H_5$ | $NHCOCO_2C_2H_5$ | 0.03† | 50 | 1.70 | 6.5† | 50 |
| 94 | $NHCOCO_2H$ | $NHCOCO_2H$ | 0.05† | 50 | 1.20 | 19† | 50 |
| 95 | NHCOCH(OH)−$CH_2$(OH) | NHCOCH(OH)−$CH_2$(OH) | 0.0009† | 50 | 3.00 | 2.9† | 50 |
| 96 | $NHSO_2CH_3$ | $NHSO_2CH_3$ | 0.3† | 50 | 0.52 | 50 | 9(NS) |
| 97 | $NHSO_2C_6H_5$ | $NHSO_2C_6H_5$ | 0.5 | − 9(NS) | −0.30 | | |

a. dose in mg./kg.; b. p=0.01 except where noted; d. NS=not significant; † calculated $ID_{50}$

TABLE VIII

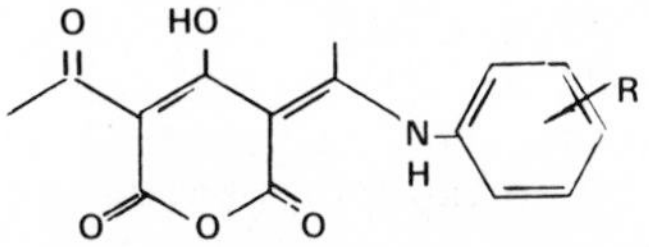

| CMPD. NO. | R | IV PCA DOSE[a] | IV PCA % INHIB.[b] | $pI_{50}$ | PO PCA DOSE[a] | PO PCA % INHIB.[b] |
|---|---|---|---|---|---|---|
| 98 | 2,6–$(Cl)_2$ | 10.0 | 3(NS)[c] | –1.50 | | |
| 99 | 2,6–$(OH)_2$ | 0.5 | –22(NS) | –0.50 | | |
| 100 | 3,4,5–$(OH)_3$ | 0.4† | 50 | 0.40 | 25 | –3(NS) |
| 101 | 2–OH–5–$NHCOCH_3$ | 0.5 | 40 | 1.70 | 25 | 4(NS) |
| 102 | 2–$NH_2$–5-OH | 5.0 | 47 | –0.50 | | |

a. dose in mg./kg.; b. p=0.01 except where noted; c. NS=not significant; † calculated $ID_{50}$

this test is the physical limitation of water solubility which the compound must have in order to be tested.

The results of _in vitro_ rat lung testing of some of our most promising candidates are shown in Table IX. As a point of reference, DSCG in this system has an $ID_{50}$ (that is the dose which causes an inhibition of 50% of the amount of histamine liberated by non-drug treated controls) of approximately $10^{-4}$ molar. Examination of the various derivatives tested, indicate that our PCA data correlate very well with the _in vitro_ data in the same species. For example, the rank order for increasing potency in the rat PCA test is _15_, _73_ and _82_ which have $ID_{50}$'s of 1.3, 0.7 and 0.2 mg/kg respectively. They also have the same rank order in the _in vitro_ assay with $ID_{50}$'s of $10^{-4}$, $3x10^{-6}$ and $10^{-8}$ respectively. These results are comforting from a theoretical viewpoint but they do not contribute any additional information to aid in the selection and evaluation of compounds and so we turned to the primate system.

In Table X are shown both the inhibition of histamine release and SRS-A release from Rhesus monkey lung tissue. Our observations with this system indicate that inhibition of both mediators does not usually follow the same dose related pattern and that frequently a compound will be more effective at inhibiting histamine release than it will be at inhibiting SRS-A release. For example, in this system DSCG has an $ID_{50}$ against histamine release of $10^{-3}$ molar while against SRS-A release it is somewhat greater than $3x10^{-3}$ molar (actually DSCG never quite accomplished a full 50% reduction of SRS-A release but rather plateaus in its dose response at approximately 42% inhibition).

In the primate lung system there appears to be no correlation between _in vivo_ rat PCA activity and this _in vitro_ activity. One of the most active compounds in this series was the 3-amino-4-hydroxy analog _73_ which we have labeled as SK&F 78729-A. It is nearly equipotent at inhibiting both histamine and SRS-A release, with an $ID_{50}$ of approximately $3x10^{-5}$ molar, nearly 2 orders of magnitude better than DSCG. Coupled with its favorable intravenous to oral potency ratio this compound then is our most interesting candidate and will be the subject of an extensive pharmacology review at the Federation Meeting in April.

In closing I would like to thank my numerous colleagues who compiled the formidable number of compounds and biological test data that was presented here today.

TABLE IX. Inhibition of Antigen-Induced Histamine Release in Passively Sensitized Fragmented Rat Lung

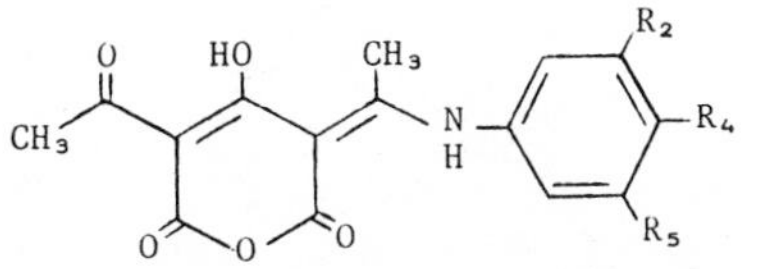

| Compound No. | $R_3$ | $R_4$ | $R_5$ | *In Vitro* Conc. (M) | % Inhib. Histamine |
|---|---|---|---|---|---|
| DSCG | | | | $1.3 \times 10^{-3}$ | 56 (10) |
| | | | | $2.7 \times 10^{-4}$ | 47 (4) |
| | | | | $5.3 \times 10^{-5}$ | 32 (3) |
| 15 | H | OH | H | $1.6 \times 10^{-4}$ | 45 (5)[a] |
| | | | | $6.6 \times 10^{-6}$ | 44 (7) |
| | | | | $6.6 \times 10^{-7}$ | 34 (4) |
| 48 | H | $NHCOCH(CH_3)_2$ | H | $1 \times 10^{-5}$ | 92 (1) |
| | | | | $1 \times 10^{-6}$ | 60 (1) |
| 73 | $NH_2$ | OH | H | $1 \times 10^{-5}$ | 47 (4) |
| | | | | $1 \times 10^{-6}$ | 61 (5) |
| | | | | $1 \times 10^{-7}$ | 42 (4) |
| | | | | $1 \times 10^{-8}$ | 26 (4) |
| 77 | $NHCOCH_3$ | OH | H | $1 \times 10^{-5}$ | 86 (5) |
| | | | | $1 \times 10^{-6}$ | 76 (5) |
| | | | | $1 \times 10^{-7}$ | 88 (5) |
| | | | | $1 \times 10^{-8}$ | 53 (1) |
| | | | | $1 \times 10^{-9}$ | 43 (1) |
| 81 | $NHCOCH_2CH_3$ | OH | H | $1 \times 10^{-5}$ | 65 (4) |
| | | | | $1 \times 10^{-6}$ | 66 (4) |
| | | | | $1 \times 10^{-7}$ | 70 (4) |
| | | | | $1 \times 10^{-8}$ | 41 (2) |
| 82 | $NHCOCH(CH_3)_2$ | OH | H | $1 \times 10^{-6}$ | 78 (1) |
| | | | | $1 \times 10^{-7}$ | 81 (1) |

a) ( ) is the number of different lung preparations

TABLE X. Inhibition of IgE - Antihuman IgE Release of Histamine and SRS-A from Passively Sensitized Fragmented Rhesus Monkey Lung Tissue

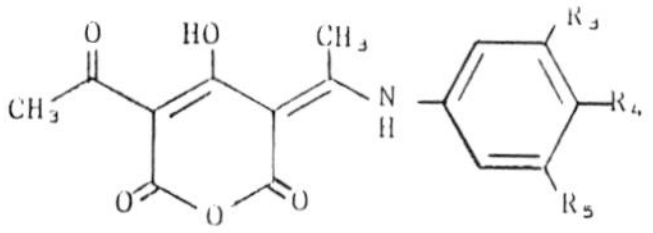

| Compound No. | $R_3$ | $R_4$ | $R_5$ | Conc. (M) | % Inhib. Histamine | % Inhib. SRS-A |
|---|---|---|---|---|---|---|
| DSCG | | | | $1.3 \times 10^{-3}$ | 54 (4) | 27 (4) |
| | | | | $2.7 \times 10^{-4}$ | 37 (4) | 36 (4) |
| | | | | $5.3 \times 10^{-5}$ | 11 (4) | 24 (4) |
| 15 | H | OH | H | $1.6 \times 10^{-4}$ | 59 (7)[a] | 51 (7)[a] |
| | | | | $3.3 \times 10^{-5}$ | 50 (10) | 33 (10) |
| | | | | $6.6 \times 10^{-6}$ | 18 (5) | 8.6 (5) |
| 73 | $NH_2$ | OH | H | $1 \times 10^{-4}$ | 66 (9) | 56 (7) |
| | | | | $5 \times 10^{-5}$ | 49 (5) | 40 (4) |
| | | | | $1 \times 10^{-5}$ | 22 (9) | 1 (7) |
| | | | | $1 \times 10^{-6}$ | 4 (7) | -24 (5) |
| 77 | $NHCOCH_3$ | OH | H | $5 \times 10^{-5}$ | 25 (4) | 33 (4) |
| | | | | $1 \times 10^{-5}$ | -31 (4) | 5 (4) |
| | | | | $5 \times 10^{-6}$ | -32 (4) | -11 (4) |
| 85 | OH | H | $NH_2$ | $1 \times 10^{-4}$ | 24 (3) | 18 (2) |
| | | | | $1 \times 10^{-5}$ | -0.7 (3) | 5 (2) |
| 86 | OH | H | $NHCOCH_3$ | $1 \times 10^{-4}$ | 57 (2) | 22 (2) |
| | | | | $1 \times 10^{-5}$ | 17 (2) | 6 (2) |
| 87 | $NH_2$ | H | $NHCOCH_3$ | $1 \times 10^{-4}$ | 17 (1) | 8 (1) |
| 95 | $NHCOCH(OH)CH_2OH$ | H | $NHCOCH(OH)CH_2OH$ | $1 \times 10^{-4}$ | 7 (2) | 7 (2) |
| | | | | $1 \times 10^{-5}$ | -20 (2) | -0.5 (2) |
| | | | | $1 \times 10^{-6}$ | -30 (2) | - 7 (2) |

a) ( ) is the number of different lung preparations

"Literature Cited"


1. Cox, J. S. G., Nature (London), (1967), 216, 1328; Cairns, H., et al., J. Med. Chem., (1972), 15, 583.
2. For a recent review of antiallergic compounds see Oronsky, A. L. and Wasky, J. W. F., in Annu. Rep. Med. Chem., (1977), 12, 70-79.
3. Willis, C. R., Snader, K. M., Miao, C. K., Mendelson, W. L. and Chakrin, L. W., 10th Middle Atlantic Regional Meeting, Philadelphia, PA, February 1976, Abstract No. J. 8.
4. Kiang, A. K., Tan, S. F. and Wong, W. S., J. Chem. Soc. (C), (1971), 2721.
5. Goose, J. and Blair, A. M. J. N., Immunol., (1969), 16, 749.
6. Chakrin, L. W., et al., Agents and Actions, (1974), 4/5, 297.


RECEIVED August 6, 1979.

# 9

# The Development of Antiallergic Pyranenamine Series: A QSAR Success Story

RICHARD D. CRAMER III, KENNETH M. SNADER, CHESTER R. WILLIS, LAWRENCE W. CHAKRIN, JEAN THOMAS, and BLAINE M. SUTTON

Research and Development Division, Smith Kline and French Laboratories, Philadelphia, PA 19101

Quantitative Structure-Activity Relationships (QSAR) express the biological potencies of a series of related compounds as a linear function of their physicochemical properties. A major reason for deriving a QSAR hypothesis is the hope that some aspect of the QSAR can be successfully extrapolated, to produce compounds of potency higher than any of those from which the QSAR was derived. Unfortunately, the QSAR literature does not contain many examples of successful extrapolation, or "predictive successes."(1) Even these few examples would be vulnerable to the following criticisms:

(1) The successful extrapolations are relatively small in magnitude, the potency enhancement in only one instance(2) being appreciably more than twofold.

(2) The actual number of superior compounds associated with each individual successful extrapolation is rather small.

(3) Alternative but simpler physicochemically based strategies, such as the "Topliss tree"(3), seem to point to superior compounds and require far less work.

(4) "Sooner or later" the compounds embodying the successful extrapolations would have been stumbled upon in any case. (Of course, actual medicinal chemistry programs have finite lifetimes, dependent in part on their own success, such that a "later" which is insufficiently "sooner" may become a "never"!)

In view of these criticisms, we suggest that the development of the pyranenamine series represents one of the more clearcut successes in the application of QSAR techniques. To provide substance for this claim, in this article we have elected to present the pyranenamine series development in a strictly chronological fashion.

Overall Considerations. As described in detail within the preceding article(4), the pyranenamines display Intal-like anti-

0-8412-0536-1/80/47-118-159$05.00/0

allergic properties in a well-established experimental animal model, the passive cutaneous anaphylactic (PCA) rat. In this study, we will be concerned only with the effects of changes in the aromatic substituents -X, -Y, and -Z upon potency in the PCA model.

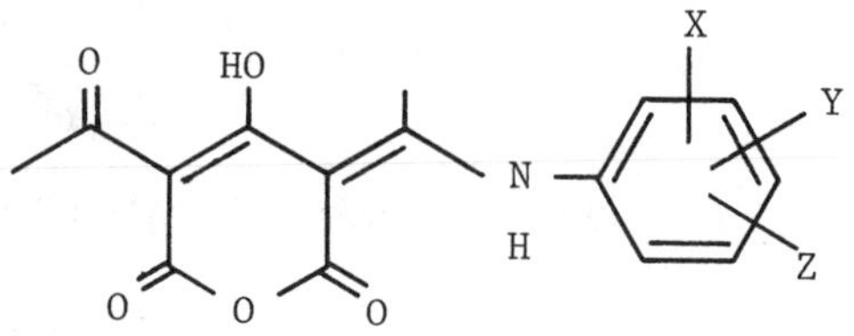

An unfavorable characteristic of these biological data is relatively high variability. The most serious variability occurs for a group of twenty compounds which displayed no activity at the testing dose. Such compounds were simply assigned a $pI_{50}$ one unit less than log (1/dose tested). The standard error for such an assignment is of course unknowable, if one assumes a value of $\pm.9$, the RMS error for the overall collection of 98 potency measurements would be roughly $\pm.48$. This value is to be compared with S, the standard error of a regression. If S is greater than .50, the still unexplained differences in compound potency are greater than those attributable to biological variability and thus additional structural explanations of the data may be sought. But once S has dropped below this estimated net biological variability of 0.5, there is an increasing danger that apparent structural trends may in fact only be artifacts originating in the biological variability.

The parameters and methods employed in regression studies of the pyranenamine series have been discussed elsewhere, along with complete results.(5)

"Pre-Qsar" Series Development. Potency (Log 1/c) values for the first nineteen pyranenamines to be synthesized and tested in the PCA assay, prior to the use of QSAR in this series, appear in part A of Table I. The majority of these derivatives were synthesized in response to a newly proposed (at that time) decision model, the Topliss operation scheme or "tree".(3). Based on the observation that physicochemically-based substituent constants are an aspect of the Hansch approach which is easier for synthetically oriented chemists to assimilate than is regression analysis, Topliss proposed specific sequences of substituted derivatives to be synthesized, with the next choice at each sequential step being governed by whether the preceding compound displayed either increased, decreased, or unaltered potency. Retrospective studies

Table I: Potencies of Pyranenamines Synthesized Before QSAR Had Been Established.

A. Pyranenamines Used in Derivation of the First QSAR

| Substituent | $pI_{50}$ |
|---|---|
| H | - .7 |
| 2-Cl | -1.2 |
| 3-Cl | - .7 |
| 4-Cl | - .6 |
| 4-F | -1.0 |
| 4-$NO_2$ | -2.0 |
| 4-COOMe | -1.7 |
| 4-Me | -1.2 |
| 2-OH | - .4 |
| 3-OH | - .2 |
| 4-OH | - .1 |
| 4-OMe | - .9 |
| 2-$NH_2$ | -1.4 |
| 4-N(Me)$_2$ | -2.0 |
| 4-pyridyl | - .9 |
| 3,4-Cl | -2.0 |
| 3,5-$CF_3$ | -1.1 |
| 2,6-Cl | -2.0 |
| 2,6-OH | - .7 |

B. Bioiosteres and Prodrugs of the 4-OH Derivative

| Substituent | $pI_{50}$ | Rationale[a] |
|---|---|---|
| 4-OCOMe | + .2 | 3 |
| 4-OCOEt | - .1 | 3 |
| 4-OCO(n)Pr | - .2 | 3 |
| 4-OCO(n)Bu | + .2 | 3 |
| 4-OCO(n)Am | -1.1 | 3 |
| 4-OCO(n)Hex | + .0 | 3 |
| 4-OCO(t)Bu | - .7 | 3 |
| 4-OCOPh | - .7 | 3 |
| 4-$OCONH_2$ | + .0 | 3 |
| 4-$OCONHCH_2Ph$ | + .0 | 3 |
| 4-$OCH_2COOH$ | + .3 | 3 |
| 4-SH | - .2 | 3 |
| 4-$NH_2$ | + .4 | 2 |
| 4-NHCHO | + .3 | 2 |

[a]Codes the rationale for synthesis: 1 = QSAR; 3 = classical medicinal chemistry; 2 = both. See Discussion.

indeed suggest that use of the "Topliss tree" might halve the number of derivatives needed to achieve an optimal potency.

In the pyranenamine series, choice among the "next" appropriate derivatives had been made difficult by experimental uncertainty surrounding the relative potency values, and as a result Table I contains information about most of the nodes in the "Topliss tree", not merely an individual branch. In fact, the 4-OH derivative, the most potent of the nineteen, can be reached *via* the tree only by taking the apparent "wrong turn" at two of three nodes. Strict adherence to the decision model would have produced nothing but derivatives less active than the starting unsubstituted compound.

As the most promising member of the pyranenamine series, by the oral as well as the intravenous route of administration, SK&F 64398 was selected for detailed biological evaluation. Meanwhile, following well-known precepts, a variety of derivatives and close congeners ("bioisosteres") of SK&F 64398 were prepared for testing in the PCA assay. The subsequent testing results, shown in Part B of Table I, might be summarized as suggesting that the traditional "close analogue" strategy yielded compounds which were equivalent, but not markedly superior, in potency to SK&F 64398. In the absence of the QSAR studies to be described it might well have been reasonable to conclude that SK&F 64398 is for practical purposes the "optimal" pyranenamine, and that the synthetic program which produced it had been successfully completed.

*Initial QSAR Studies.* The challenge posed for QSAR study was clearly, "Will analysis of the nineteen data shown in Part A of Table I produce any structure/activity trends whose extrapolation seems likely to suggest pyranenamines having potency significantly greater than that of SK&F 64398?" The nineteen compounds by virtue of their different substituents have differing physical properties. The observed differences in biological properties can ultimately be caused *only* by these differences in physical properties, according to all known facts of biochemistry and physiology. However, biochemistry and physiology also teach that the mechanisms through which these differences in physical properties might express themselves, including metabolism and distribution as well as the mechanics of interaction with the "receptor", may be so complex as to preclude the establishment of useful trends. These considerations of course have been more or less consciously recognized by every participant in medicinal chemistry research throughout its history. Reason demands an attempt to understand one's data but experience soon suggests that such an attempt will produce nothing more useful than *post hoc* rationalizations.

Initial analysis of the data in Table IA was carried out graphically, by plotting log (1/C) values for the nineteen compounds against measures of their physicochemical differences, specifically measures of size (molar refractivity), affinity for polar solvents ($\pi$), and intramolecular electronic effect ($\sigma$).

The most promising of the various graphs was the "three-dimensional" plot shown in Figure I. This plot portrays potency, plotted along the Cartesian axis perpendicular to the page as a joint function of π and σ, where as an aid in orientation the location in π/σ space of most common substituents also are indicated.(5) To help in communicating the dependence of potency on π and σ which was visualized as the graph was constructed, potency contour lines were also sketched in. Thus the completed graph shows potency as a hypothetical function of π and σ in the same manner that a conventional relief map shows ground elevation as a function of longitude and latitude.

The apparent "peak" in the potency/π/Δ map is located just below the center of its left-hand edge, corresponding to substituents possessing a combination of high hydrophilicity and negligible intramolecular electronic influence. If the relationships suggested by the graph are a correct model of the behavior of substituted pyranenamines in the PCA rat, substituents conferring even greater hydrophilicity should improve potency further, provided that the overall electronic character is not thereby disturbed. Unfortunately, the promising area of Figure I is very sparsely populated by actual substituents, only $-NHCONH_2$ and -NHOH being barely within the region of interest. To obtain substantially increased hydrophilicity without electronic effects, pyranenamines having particular combinations of substituents were proposed as synthetic targets.

Two of the twelve targets were synthesized immediately and found to be highly active, a 3-acetamide-4-hydroxyl derivative having a $pI_{50}$ of +0.8, or a potency 2-1/2 times greater than any of the other pyranenamines and the isomeric 2-hydroxy-5-acetamido derivative a $pI_{50}$ of +0.2, second only to the $4-NH_2$ congener. This striking confirmation of the "hydrophilicity hypothesis" led to a strong emphasis on hydrophilic substitution patterns in ensuing work.

Development of the Hydrophilicity Lead. Because of the ease of synthesizing and testing pyranenamines, it was possible to evaluate the effects of an unusually large variety of types and combinations of hydrophilic substituents. From a physicochemical point of view, while increased hydrophilicity was the primary objective it was also recognized that exploration of a broader class of substituents might uncover dependencies on parameters other than π and σ. From a more conservative point of view, whether or not the tenfold potency conferred upon the 4-OH derivative by adding a 3-acetamido substituent relates at all to increased hydrophilicity, the magnitude of the resulting increase mandates further exploration of a traditional nature, such as removal of the 4-OH, lengthening and shortening of the acylamido chain, transposing or altering the substituents, or introducing additional substituents. The actual compounds chosen for synthesis naturally tended to be constructive in terms of either

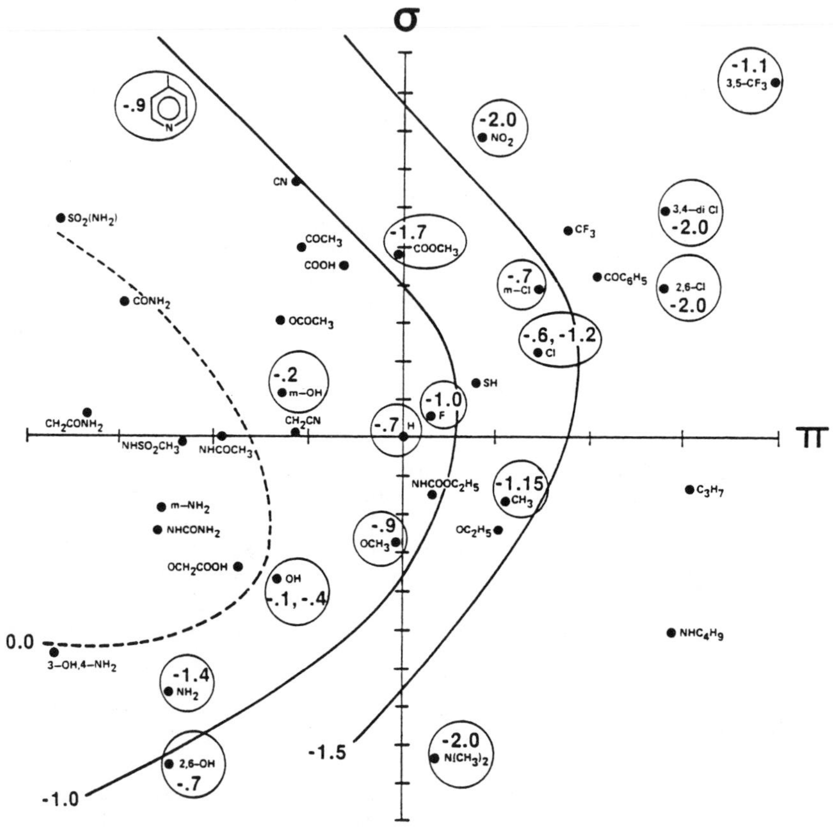


Journal of Medicinal Chemistry

*Figure 1. "Relief map" of the dependence of potency on the substituents σ and π for the pyranenamines of Table I (5)*

of these two points of view, and thus only a minority of the seventy-odd compounds remaining to be discussed bear unambiguously on the issue of whether the QSAR approach continued to enhance the efficiency of pyranenamine series development.

The Value of Regression Analysis. Once we had conceded the possibility that more than the two variables $\pi$ and $\sigma$ might be influencing PCA rat potency, the graphical approach exemplified in Figure I had to be abandoned, despite its ease of construction and clear portrayal of the postulated structure/activity relationship. In addition to the obvious impossibility of portraying more than three variables on a two-dimensional graph, the time required to construct graphs having more than, say, thirty points is much greater than that to perform equivalent regressions. A further bonus in using regression techniques is that the accompanying statistical indices (r, s, and F) allow an assessment of the probability that the SAR is "real", *i.e.*, not a chance ordering of information which in reality is unrelated. No objective response would have been possible to a critic who doubted the reality of the "hill" portrayed in Figure I.

A regression equation containing very much the same information as that contained in Figure I, and derived from the data in Table I, will be referred to subsequently as A:

$$pI_{50} = - .72 - .14(\pm.29) \times \Sigma\pi - 1.35(\pm.98) \times (\Sigma\sigma)^2$$

$$r^2 = .48 \quad s = .47 \quad F(2,16) = 7.3$$

The equation has two structurally-dependent terms, conforming to the two dimensions of the graph in Figure I. The negative coefficient of its $\pi$ term describes an increase in potency with decreasing lipophilicity equivalent to the right-to-left upward slope of the "hill" in Figure I. The negative coefficient of the $\sigma^2$ term connotes a potency which is maximal when $\sigma = 0$ and decreases as $\sigma$ deviates markedly above or below 0. This description of electronic effects differs slightly from that of Figure I where the apparent "optimal" $\sigma$ is less than 0. In a regression equation a non-zero, in this instance negative, value for the optimal $\sigma$ would require two terms for its expression ( $-a\sigma - b\,\sigma^2$). The additional term produced by entry of $\sigma$ into Equation A indeed possesses a negative coefficient but has very low statistical significance.

Parenthetically, it might be thought that this type of plot in principle offers the possibility of detecting non-linear or non-parabolic relationships between potency and $\pi$ or $\sigma$, relationships which might not be well-approximated by analytic functions of $\pi$ or $\sigma$ and hence would be undetectable by regression. The idea that a complex but continuous functional relationship might exist between $\pi$ or $\sigma$ and biological activity has also been cited in recommending optimization techniques such as the Simplex method for drug design problems(6). Nevertheless, we feel that an extensive search for such more mathematically complex relationships involving simple physicochemical properties is probably wasted effort. From a practical point of view it is almost exclusively the linear relationships between activity and a structural variable which seem likely to be extrapolable in a useful way. A structural dependency which already contains a well-defined optimum offers little hope and only negative guidance in the quest for improved potency!

The statistical quality of equations is indicated by their values for $r^2$, s, and F. To an excellent approximation, $r^2$ measures the <u>proportion</u> of the original differences in compound potency which <u>are</u> explained by the regression equation, whereas in contrast s measures the <u>absolute</u> differences in potency which <u>are not</u> explained by the regression equation. Thus $r^2$ and s are complementary indices, while F, a ratio of $r^2$ to s weighted by the number of degrees of freedom for each, allows an assessment of the likelihood of achieving a correlation as good or better by chance alone. Oddly, a concise statement of these principles seems absent from the QSAR literature, resulting in a certain amount of apparent confusion among some of its practitioners over what the statistical objective of a regression analysis should be. Since one should never expect s to be much less than the experimental variability of the biological measurements, the only way a high $r^2$ can realistically be expected is if the experimental variability is very low or if the range of biological potencies is very large. As will be seen, the regression equations herein illustrate these points rather well. In particular, the unusually poor value of $r^2$ for Equation A, .46, is actually about as high as one might hope to achieve with the data of Table I, since the estimated experimental variability of .5 for the overall data set is in fact somewhat greater than the s for Equation A. Despite the low $r^2$, comparison of the $F(2,16)=7.3$ with its tabulated values shows that the likelihood of obtaining a correlation even this poor by chance alone for two parameters actually unrelated to potency and nineteen compounds is less than 1%.

<u>Second Phase</u>: <u>Exploration of Other Hydrophilic Groups</u>: The large variety of hydrophilic groups explored in what might be regarded as the second phase of the QSAR development of the pyranenamine lead are listed in Table II. Several features of these data are particularly inconsistent with the hypothesis that biological potency depends solely on $\pi$ and on $\sigma$:

1) The exceptionally high potency of the 3,5-NHCOMe derivative, an order of magnitude greater than any other series member, despite unremarkable $\pi$ and $\sigma$ values, suggests that there must be other compound property(s) capable of enhancing potency.
2) The potencies of the increasingly lipophilic 3-NHCOMe, 3-NHCOEt, and 3-NHCOPr subseries would be expected to

Table II: Potencies of Compounds Synthesized After Development of the First QSAR (Equation A).

| Substituent | $pI_{50}$ | Rationale[a] |
|---|---|---|
| 3-$SO_2NH_2$ | + .3 | 1 |
| 4-$SO_2NH_2$ | - .1 | 1 |
| 3-$NH_2$ | + .5 | 2 |
| 2-NHCHO | + .3 | 2 |
| 3-NHCHO | - .7 | 2 |
| 2-NHCOMe | - .7 | 2 |
| 3-NHCOMe | + .7 | 2 |
| 4-NHCOMe | - .7 | 2 |
| 3-$NHCONH_2$ | + .3 | 1 |
| 4-$NHCONH_2$ | + .2 | 1 |
| 3-NHCOEt | + .7 | 2 |
| 4-NHCOEt | - .2 | 2 |
| 3-NHCO(i)Pr | + .5 | 2 |
| 4-NHCO(i)Pr | + .4 | 2 |
| 3-NHCO(n)Pr | + .4 | 2 |
| 3-N(COCH$_2$)(COCH$_2$) (cyclic imide: N bonded to two $COCH_2$ groups, which are bonded to each other) | + .0 | 2 |
| 3-$NHSO_2Me$ | + .1 | 2 |
| 4-$NHSO_2Me$ | - .7 | 2 |
| 3-$NHSO_2Ph$ | - .1 | 2 |
| 4-$NHSO_2Ph$ | - .7 | 2 |
| 3-$NH_2$-4-OH | + .15 | 2 |
| 3-NHCOMe-4-OH | + .7 | 1 |
| 3,4-N=CMe-O- | - .1 | 3 |
| 3-NHCOMe-4-OMe | + .1 | 3 |
| 3-NHCOEt-4-OH | + .4 | 2 |
| 3-NHCO(i)Pr-4-OH | + .7 | 2 |
| 3,5-NHCOMe | +1.9 | 2 |
| 3,5-$NHSO_2Me$ | + .5 | 2 |
| 3-NHCOMe-6-OH | + .2 | 1 |

[a]Codes the rationale for synthesis: 1 = QSAR; 3 = classical medicinal chemistry; 2 = both. See Discussion.

decline, rather than remain constant, in the absence of additional trends. Similarly, although less significantly because of a pro-drug possibility, the O-CO-R derivatives are equipotent despite representing a very large range of lipophilicities.

These observations appear to be satisfactorily explained by Equation B, derived from all data in Tables I and II except for exclusion of the 4-$OCH_2COOH$ substituent because of the structural ambiguity introduced by its two possible protomeric forms.

$$pI_{50} = -.75 \quad -.30(\pm.12) \times \Sigma\pi - 1.5(\pm.67) \times (\Sigma\sigma)^2 + 2.0(\pm2.0) \times F\text{-}5 + .39(\pm.22) \times \#345\text{-HBD} - .63(\pm.33) \times \#NHSO2 + .78(\pm.46) \times M\text{-}V + .72(\pm.31) \times 4\text{-OCO?}$$

$$r^2 = .77 \quad s = .40 \quad F(7,53) = 25.1$$

Lipophilicity, a statistically dubious causative factor in Equation A although apparently important in the logically equivalent Figure I, has with the additional data emerged as the dominant structural influence on potency.

At this point in series development, substituent lipophilicity spanned a range of four log units, potency doubling with each log unit increase in hydrophilicity. Many more log units of substituent hydrophilicity were still potentially accessible, most readily by employing charged substituents. Therefore a major question for subsequent resolution was, "As hydrophilicity is increased further, either with charged or uncharged substituents, will potency continue to increase indefinitely (unlikely)? Or will a substituent hydrophilicity be encountered which is optimal for potency in the PCA rat, further increases in hydrophilicity perhaps depressing potency?"

Electronic effects on potency are expressed by the second and third terms in Equation B. Strongly electron-donating or withdrawing effects upon the 1 position of the phenyl ring (the $(\Sigma\sigma)^2$ term) continue to be quite as deleterious to potency as was indicated by Equation A. However, the "F-5" term indicates tentatively than an inductively electron-withdrawing substituent (high value of the Swain-Lupton F) in the 5 position may very substantially enhance potency. A 5-substituent can exist only when there are at least equivalently bulky substituents at the 2 and/or 3 position, so there are only two examples, the 3,5-$CF_3$ (F-5=.38) and 3,5-NHCOMe (F-5=.28) derivatives. However, both of these were much more active than expected, 3,5-$CF_3$ being the most serious outlier for the series as a whole. Further exploration of a larger range of variation in F-5 was clearly indicated.

The next pair of terms in Equation B attributes desirability to certain types of hydrogen-bonding groups attached to the *meta* and *para* positions. The #345-HBD term implies that for every group of general type -HYR attached to the 3, 4, or 5 position, where Y may be N, O, or S and R may be anything including H or a lone pair, potency is enhanced by .42 log units. (At this point, the roster of -YHR listed OH, SH, $NH_2$, NHCOR', and $NHSO_2R'$, where R' = H, alkyl, $NH_2$, or aryl.) Although this trend is readily attributed to actual hydrogen bonding between pyranenamine and its receptor, it is a bit surprising that any number of hydrogen bond donors in any position have equivalent and additive effects. Since the trends in $PI and #345-HBD portrayed by Equation B would seem to parallel one another, it is worth noting that the colinearity between these variables for all 98 compounds is actually quite small (r = -.35). Thus these two trends in Equation B are clearly independent. The second hydrogen-bonding variable "$NHSO_2$" is substructural. Whatever the nature of the hydrogen-bonding interaction, the $-NHSO_2R$ group (which has the appropriate -YH-R substructure) apparently does not have suitable properties. This pair of QSAR trends raises the question "What types and arrangements of hydrogen-bonding groups will and will not enhance potency?" A range of possibilities was explored in the next roune of synthesis.

The M-V term implies a situation which is rather unusual in medicinal chemical experience; increase in the volume of meta (3- or 5-) substituents is stated to increase potency. One might further ask, in retrospect, whether it is reasonable to expect the sizes of these relatively varied substituent types to occupy the same region of "receptor space" and to have commensurable effects on potency, particularly when the existence of a hydrogen-bonding term suggests a probable specificity of orientation for maximal receptor binding. Previously published QSAR correlations involving size have been based mostly either on small and nearly symmetric groups or else on highly flexible groups such as higher alkyl, not on large, angular, semi-rigid groups such as many of the groups in this series must be. The validity of this trend now seems dubious, but in point of fact considerable QSAR effort was expended at this state of series development attempting to ascertain an "optimal group size."

Finally, the 4-OCO? term, the second most important to the overall correlation, is substructural and indicates that acyl derivatives of the 4-OH are five times as potent as would be implied by the physical properties of the esters themselves. This trend is consistent with the view that these acyl derivatives behave as biologically equivalent prodrugs, hydrolyzing in vivo to produce the 4-OH derivative itself.

"Second Generation" Pyranenamine (SK&F 78729). Insurmountable deficiencies were encountered in the secondary testing of the 4-OH derivative, and a new lead had to be chosen. Although not the most potent in the primary screen, the $3-NH_2-4-OH$ derivative (SK&F 78729) was found to possess the most desirable combination of properties in secondary tests. From the point of view of the "QSAR success story", we note that the initial QSAR study was clearly responsible for the type of structural modification which quickly led to SK&F 78729. Indeed, in the absence of the more potent pyranenamines resulting from QSAR, it is arguable that disappointment arising from the deficiencies of the 4-OH derivative would have led to abandonment of the series and even the research area itself. On the other hand, the particular virtues which distinguished SK&F 78729 in the secondary tests have little or nothing to do with the QSAR relationship, which is of course dependent on the primary test (PCA rat).

Final Phase of Pyranenamine Development. Most of the remaining pyranenamines, listed in Table III, were synthesized to answer specific QSAR or traditional SAR questions. As detailed above, the key QSAR questions raised in the intermediate series development concerned the possibility of a hydrophilicity optimum, the need to identify potency-enhancing hydrogen-bonding groups, and the reality of the F-5 and M-V terms. A considerable synthetic effort went into the preparation of particular exotic substituents, such as $-NHC(=NH)NH_2$, -CONH (Barbiturate), and $-NHCO(CHOH)_2H$, intended to help answer these questions.

The regression equation which seems to best describe the QSAR for all 98 pyranenamines is C. Compared with Equation B, additional terms relating to lipophilicity, electronic effects, and hydrogen bonding have appeared, while the volume-related term has disappeared.

$$\begin{aligned} pI_{50} = &- .59 - .33(\pm.11) \times \Sigma\pi - .034(\pm.016) \times (\Sigma\pi)^2 \\ &+ 4.3(\pm1.6) \times \text{F-5} + 1.3(\pm.85) \times \text{R-5} - 1.7(\pm.62) \times (\Sigma\sigma)^2 \\ &+ .73(\pm.22) \times \#\text{345-HBD} - .86(\pm.34) \times \#\text{HB-INTRA} \\ &- .69(\pm.28) \times \#\text{NHSO2} + .72(\pm.35) \times \text{4-OCO?} \end{aligned}$$

$$r^2 = .75 \quad s = .48 \quad F(9,88) = 28.7$$

The new lipophilicity term, $(\Sigma\pi)^2$, when taken with the $(\Sigma\pi)$ term constitutes the familiar definition of a parabolic relationship between potency and hydrophilicity. The unusual aspect of this parabolic relationship is the remarkably hydrophilic optimum, roughly -5, for the sum of substituent $\pi$ values. However, only one of the compounds has an estimated $\Sigma\pi$ less than -6 (3,5-$NHCOCOO^-$) and all of the $\pi$ estimates for the half-dozen of these groups between -6 and -2.5, being based on group additivity, must be regarded as probably too hydrophilic. It is also possible that negative charge, rather than extreme hydrophilicity, is the property deleterious to potency (although the necessarily concomitant hypothesis, that potency increases parallel hydrophilicity without limit, seems difficult to accept). Therefore this relationship between potency and hydrophilicity must be regarded as qualitatively correct only.

The electronic aspects of Equation C represent an extension of those discussed for Equation B. The $(\Sigma\sigma)^2$ term continues to indicate the desirability of an overall $\sigma$ near 0, while the F-5 term now strongly asserts the value of nevertheless attaching inductively withdrawing substituents to the 5 position. The R-5 term buttresses the F-5 term by its indication that resonance withdrawing effects as well as inductively withdrawing effects of a 5 substituent will promote potency.

Hydrogen bonding, or some other characteristic of the -YHR group as defined above, has become the most important influence on relative potencies (*i.e.*, the 345-HBD term has the largest F-test), provided that the constraints on hydrogen-bonding implied by the two terms #HB-INTRA and #NHSO2 are accepted. The #345-HBD term indicates that potency is enhanced fourfold for each -YHR substituent. However, the #HB-INTRA term in combination with the #345-HBD term indicates that a -YHR which is capable of forming an intramolecular hydrogen-bond (five or six-membered ring) with an *ortho* substituent will not enhance potency. As in Equation B, the effect of the NHSO2 term is to exclude $-NHSO_2R$ groups from this potency-enhancing -YHR class of substituents.

The remaining term, 4-OCO?, continues to ascribe special potency enhancement to acyl derivatives of the 4-OH pyranenamine, possibly by way of the pro-drug mechanism. However, the M-V effect within Equation B has not persisted strongly. Although a slightly favorable influence of substituent volume, particularly of *meta* substituents, would be the next term to enter Equation C, the associated increase in $r^2$ and decrease in s would be only .01 units.

The overall statistical qualities of Equations C, B, and A are much more alike than would be supposed from comparison of $r^2$ values alone. The variance not explained by the respective equations has remained stable as the range of potency spanded by the pyranenamine series expanded, the s values of .48, .40 and .48 being somewhat less than the estimated experimental variability and therefore unlikely to be improved upon in a meaningful way by adding more terms to the equations. The improvement in $r^2$ from .48 to .77 is the result of the increased spread in potency, in turn brought about by the success of the original QSAR itself!

The pyranenamine found to be the most potent of all, the $3,5-NHCO(CHOH)_2H$ derivative, exemplifies the traits that Equation C indicates as desirable: The two highly polar $-NHCO(CHOH)_2H$ groups give an estimated substituent total $\pi$ value of -6.2, not far from the presumed optimum $\pi$. There are two -YHR groups, which being *meta* are assumed not to form an intramolecular hydrogen bond. The 5- (or 3-) substituent has a positive F value of +.28, somewhat offset by a negative R value of -.25, producing an overall negligibly positive $\sigma$ of .37 or $\Sigma\ \sigma^2$ of .14. When inserted into Equation C, this combination of properties yields a predicted $pI_{50}$ of 2.3. The actual $pI_{50}$ of +3.0 corresponds to an $ID_{50}$ of $10^{-3}$ mg/kg, or effective biological activity at nano-molar administered blood levels.

Table III: Compounds Synthesized in Order to Establish a Final QSAR, and Miscellaneous.

| Substituent | $pI_{50}$ | Rationale[a] |
|---|---|---|
| 4-Br | - .7 | 3 |
| 2-COOEt | - .5 | 3 |
| 3-$OCH_2COOH$ | - .7 | 3 |
| 3-NHMe | - .7 | 2 |
| 3-$NHC{=}NHNH_2$ | + .1 | 1 |
| 3-$NHC{=}NHNHSO_2Ph(p)Me$ | - .7 | 3 |
| 3-$NHCOCH_2CH_2COOEt$ | + .3 | 2 |
| 3-$NHSO_2NH_2$ | + .5 | 1 |
| 4-$NHSO_2NH_2$ | + .5 | 1 |
| 3-NHCOOEt | + .4 | 2 |
| 3-$NHCOCOO^-$ | +1.5 | 2 |
| 3-$NHCO(CHOH)_2H$ | +1.3 | 1 |
| 3-$CH_2NHCOCH_3$ | - .7 | 3 |
| 3-$CONH_2$ | - .7 | 2 |
| 3-CONHMe | + .2 | 2 |
| 3-$CON(Me)_2$ | - .7 | 2 |
| 3-CONH-(2,4,6-trioxohexahydropyrimidin-5-yl; ring drawn with C=O, NH, C=O, NH, C=O) | + .2 | 1 |
| 3-OH-4-$NH_2$ | - .5 | 2 |

[a]Codes the rationale for synthesis: 1 = QSAR; 3 = classical medicinal chemistry; 2 = both. See Discussion.

Table III (Continued)

| Substituent | $pI_{50}$ | Rationale[a] |
|---|---|---|
| 3-NHMe-4-OH | - .7 | 2 |
| 3-$CH_2$NHMe-4-OH | - .7 | 2 |
| 3-CONHMe-4-OH | + .1 | 2 |
| 3-$NHSO_2$Me-4-OH | - .8 | 2 |
| 3-OH-5-$NH_2$ | + .2 | 2 |
| 3-NHCOMe-5-OH | +1.7 | 1 |
| 3-NHCOMe-5-$NH_2$ | +1.0 | 2 |
| 3,5-$NH_2$ | + .3 | 2 |
| 3,5-NHCOEt | +2.5 | 2 |
| 3,5-NHCO(n)Pr | +1.3 | 2 |
| 3,5-NHCOOEt | + .6 | 2 |
| 3,5-NHCOCOOEt | +1.7 | 2 |
| 3,5-$NHCOCOO^-$ | +1.5 | 2 |
| 3,5-NHCO$(CHOH)_2$H | +3.0 | 1 |
| 3,5-$NHSO_2$Me | + .5 | 2 |
| 3,5-$NHSO_2$Ph | - .7 | 2 |
| 3,4,5-OH | + .4 | 2 |
| 3-OH-6-$NH_2$ | - .5 | 2 |

[a]Codes the rationale for synthesis: 1 = QSAR; 3 = classical medicinal chemistry; 2 = both. See Discussion.

Drug/Receptor Binding. It is fashionable to derive a speculative physical model of drug/receptor binding from the physicochemical influences upon potency which are suggested by a QSAR. Certainly an unusual feature of the present QSAR is the tendency for potency to increase, rather than decrease, with increasing hydrophilicity (or decreasing lipophilicity). The assumption that this hydrophilicity dependence is related to receptor binding, rather than transport, is strongly supported by the additional potency introduced by specific -YHR groups, hydrogen-bonding of course being a property that tends to parallel hydrophilicity.

The special electronic influence of 5 substituents, electron withdrawing character particularly via an inductive mechanism being desirable, is easy to rationalize as being caused by an electrostatic attraction to some adjacent electropositive receptor moiety, perhaps $NH_3$+R. However, this rationalization raises a subsidiary question which is not usually given attention in QSAR studies. Whenever the aromatic ring is unsymmetrically substituted, it cannot automatically be assumed that all 3 or all 5 substituents interact with the receptor in the same way. The aromatic ring has the possibility of flipping, such that some 3 substituents may behave as 5 substituents and some 5 substituents as 3's, depending on the relative physical properties of the 3 and 5 substituents and the physical properties which dominate interaction between the receptor and the aromatic ring. In this treatmean of the pyranenamine series, unsymmetrical substitution patterns have been explicitly assumed to orient themselves on the basis of size, the more bulky group(s) being positioned 2 and/or 3. This is the usual if perhaps unconscious basis for assigning positions in QSAR work, because any unnamed substituent on an aromatic ring is H-, the smallest of all substituents. However, the electrostatic interaction which appears to exist between a 5-substituent and the receptor appears to be a second possible orienting influence, capable of competing with a steric influence. It is not obvious, for example, why a 3-Cl substituent, a small group with a strongly positive F value, could not be attracted to the electropositive moiety apparently adjacent to the 5-position, thereby being much more strongly bound and potent than might otherwise be expected.

The possible physical significance of the other electronic term, $SIG**, also merits some discussion. The general practice in QSAR work is to follow the precepts of physical organic chemistry and to use only the Hammett $\sigma$ as an overall measure of electronic effects. However, it should be recognized that the Hammett $\sigma$ is experimentally defined strictly as a measure of a particular class of intramolecular electronic effects...the predominantly through-ring effect of substituents ortho, meta, and/or para upon a center undergoing some sort of covalent change. In contrast, drug/receptor binding usually does not involve covalent bonding changes at all. When electrostatic attractions are important, as postulated above for the 5-position within the pyranenamine series, the effect of electronic changes elsewhere in the ring on this interaction would seem to be better expressed by summing the weighted F- and R-values of the substituents ortho, meta, and para with respect to the interacting position, not with respect to the 1 position. In the pyranenamine series, the finding that the Hammett σ (squared) itself $(\Sigma\sigma)^2$ is a useful correlate seems most reasonably attributable to an electronic effect specifically at the 1 position of the aromatic ring. A possible physical interpretation is that the electronic character of the ring influences electron distribution within the enamine moiety in a manner significant for receptor binding or action, with the ideal electronic distribution being that produced by the unsubstituted phenyl ring.

Discussion: The contributions of QSAR to the development of the pyranenamines were substantial at all stages of the program. As discussed above, an immediate potency enhancement of almost an order of magnitude was produced by the first graphical QSAR, specifically by the 3-NHAc-4-OH pyranenamine, whose de-N-acylated derivative became the clinical lead SK&F 78729. Continued pursuit of these and other trends ultimately led to the 3,5-NHCO$(CHOH)_2$H pyranenamine, a thousand times more active in the PCA rat assay than any member of the original series.

These successes were by no means isolated. Throughout the development of the series, intuition continued to play an important role in the selection of synthetic targets, and therefore it is possible to make a rough overall comparison of the performances of the QSAR equations with the performance of intuition. Of course, these two "rationale for synthesis" would not necessarily conflict and almost half of the series seemed reasonable synthetic targets from either point of view. However, there were compounds which, because of either synthetic difficulty or simple obscurity, would not have been prepared without a specific QSAR-based recommendation, and there were other compounds which were synthesized despite unfavorable QSAR auguries. Finally, the compounds in Table IA of course predated any possible QSAR rationale. These considerations allow the 98 pyranenamines to be divided into four classes, based on "rationale for synthesis" and the mean experimental potencies within each class to be computed:

| | | # of Examples | Mean $pI_{50}$ ($\pm$s.d.) |
|---|---|---|---|
| Class 1: | $QSAR^+$; traditional° | 13 | + .68 ($\pm$.86) |
| Class 2: | $QSAR^+$; $traditional^+$ | 47 | + .20 ($\pm$.80) |
| Class 3: | $QSAR^-$; $traditional^+$ | 19 | - .29 ($\pm$.41) |
| Class 4: | QSAR unavailable | 19 | -1.09 ($\pm$.91) |
| | | 98 | - .08 ($\pm$.91) |

The class of "synthetic rationale" which seemed to be most responsible for the synthesis of a particular pyranenamine can be seen in the last column of Tables I, II, and III.

The key comparison of mean $pI_{50}$, insofar as the relative performance of QSAR and medicinal chemistry rationale is concerned, is Class 1 vs. Class 3. Clearly the average $pI_{50}$ of compounds chosen solely on a QSAR basis (Class 1) is almost an order of magnitude higher than the average $pI_{50}$ of those synthesized despite QSAr considerations (Class 3). If one makes the usual statistical assumption about the normality of distribution of the individual compound potencies within Classes 1 and 3, the probability of encountering such a difference in mean $pI_{50}$'s if QSAR in fact has no relevance to predicting compound potency is less than .005, according to a T-test. One might also ask whether, given that in general the solely QSAR-based compounds (Class 1) were harder to make than those desirable from both traditional and QSAR considerations (Class 2), the extra effort produced compounds of significantly greater potency. This intra-class difference is also significant, but only at the .05 level. The final comparison possible, between Classes 2 and 3, might be taken as a measure of to what extent, ignoring the more exotic substituents of Class 1, the QSAR was a useful supplement to traditional considerations alone in picking targets once the fundamental desirability of increased hydrophilicity was recognized. This last difference in means is significant at the .01 level.

Encouraging as the preceding argument is to QSAR advocates, its improvement is still possible. A weakness in the argument is that membership in the four individual classes may also be biased with respect to their time of discovery. Since the average level of potency among pyranenamines generally increased with greater knowledge, might not the clearcut tendency for potency to increase with decreasing "class number" simply reflect a tendency for potency to increase with increasing experience? As a rough numerical indicator of experience, the SK&F# (accession number) can be used; its bias is anti-QSAR since Class 1 compounds usually took longer to make once their synthesis had been decided upon, and thus received a higher SK&F#, than did Class 2 or Class 3 compounds. Class 4 compounds, those on which the initial QSAR was based are irrelevant to this question and are not considered.

The colinearity of SK&F# and "rationale class" is in fact low, r=.4 when Class 4 compounds are excluded. Regression of $pI_{50}$ against SK&F# and "rationale class" together yields the following equation:

$$pI_{50} = -\ 2.79 \ +\ 4.8(\pm 5.9)\times 10^{-5} \times \text{SK\&F\#} - .40(\pm .28) \times \text{"rationale class \#"}$$

$$r^2 = .18 \qquad s = .72 \qquad F(2,76) = 8.6$$

Although the $r^2$ value is minuscule by QSAR standards, the correlation is significant at the .0005 level according to the F-test. From the ratio of 95% confidence interval to coefficient size in the two forms, it is evident that "rationale class" is a much more important indicator of potency than is SK&F#, and so the possibility that the apparent dependency of potency upon "rationale class" is actually an artifact of increasing experience can be excluded.

Conclusion: This QSAR success story comprises a very satisfactory rebuttal to the criticisms of previous QSAR "predictions" listed in the Introduction. Specifically:

1) The extent of the potency enhancement, from an original potency range spanning perhaps two orders of magnitude immediately to three orders and ultimately to five orders of magnitude, is hardly trivial.
2) As just discussed, the enhancements in potency produced by the use of QSAR are entirely too consistent, across the series and over time, to be attributed to chance.
3) A non-regression but physicochemically based strategy for developing an optimal compound, the Topliss tree, had not succeeded at all in identifying the "most potent compound". In order to better understand this failure to detect what, after all, was a $\pi/\sigma$ relationship of a type where the Topliss tree should have been productive, it is suggested that the interested reader connect the Topliss decision points in a "Craig plot" such as Figure I. It will be apparent that critical decisions about $\pi$ or $\sigma$ dependency will be made often as the result of two experimental points only. Nevertheless, the Topliss tree still appears to be, as its adherents claim, an excellent and rational basis for giving oneself a good chance to identify more active compounds at an early stage, before QSAR studies are possible. Furthermore, even an unsuccessful study such as this one did yield a satisfactory distribution of compounds for subsequent QSAR work.
4) Although many members of this series might, sooner or later, have been prepared without the influence of QSAR studies (if the project had survived the disappointing secondary tests of the 4-OH derivative), the compounds in Class 1 for the most part represent very unusual substituents which are almost never encountered in medicinal chemistry research programs.

## References and Footnotes

1. Reviewed in C. Hansch, M. Yoshimoto, and M. H. Doll, J. Med. Chem. 19, 1089 (1976), R. D. Cramer III in "Annual Reports in Medicinal Chemistry", Vol. 11, F. H. Clarke, Ed., Academic Press, 1976, p. 301, and J. G. Topliss and J. Y. Fukunaga, "Annual Reports in Medicinal Chemistry", 1978, Chapter 30, in press. Recent tests of predictions include C. Grieco, C. Silipo, A. Vittoria, and C. Hansch, J. Med. Chem. 20, 596 (1977); C. Hansch and J. Y. Fukunaga, ChemTech 7, 120 (1977); and J. T. Harrison, W. Kutch, J. J. Massey, and S. H. Unger, J. Med. Chem. 21, 588 (1978).

2. K. R. H. Wooldridge, Proc. 5th Int. Symp. Med. Chem., Paris, July 19-22, 1976, J. Matthieu (Ed.), p. 427. I thank J. G. Topliss for referring me to this work.

3. J. G. Topliss, J. Med. Chem. 15, 1006 (1972); Y. C. Martin and W. J. Dunn III, J. Med. Chem. 16, 578 (1973), J. G. Topliss and Y. C. Martin in "Drug Design", Vol. 5, E. J. Ariens, Ed., Academic Press, 1975, p. 1.

4. K. M. Snader, L. W. Chakrin, R. D. Cramer III, Y. M. Gelernt, C. K. Miao, D. H. Shah, J. W. Venslavsky, C. R. Willis, and B. M. Sutton, preceding paper.

5. R. D. Cramer III, K. M. Snader, C. R. Willis, L. W. Chakrin, J. Thomas, and B. M. Sutton, J. Med Chem., in press.

6. T. M. Bustard, J. Med. Chem. 17, 777 (1974); N. J. Santora and K. Auyang, J. Med. Chem. 18, 959 (1975); F. Darvas, J. Med. Chem. 17, 799 (1974).

RECEIVED August 14, 1979.

10

# Oxatomide: The Prototype of a Chemical Series of Compounds Inhibiting Both the Release and the Effects of Allergic Mediators

F. AWOUTERS, C. J. E. NIEMEGEERS, and P. A. JANSSEN

Department of Pharmacology, Janssen Research Laboratories, B-2340 Beerse, Belgium

M. JANSSEN, J. VANDENBERK, L. KENNIS, M. VAN DER AA, and A. VAN HEERTUM

Department of Chemical Research, Janssen Research Laboratories, B-2340 Beerse, Belgium

In our laboratories the interest in compounds with anti-allergic activity goes back to 1955, when cinnarizine (R 516) was synthesized. Cinnarizine, or trans 1-cinnamyl-4-(diphenylmethyl)-piperazine, proved to be a potent antagonist of many smooth muscle activators and spasmogens, including calcium and histamine. The antihistaminic and antianaphylactic properties of cinnarizine were studied in detail by Halpern et al. (1), who concluded that this compound was a potent antihistaminic *in vivo*, but only moderately effective in preventing anaphylactic shock in guinea-pigs, passively sensitized with rabbit anti-ovalbumin antibodies.

The cinnarizine-analogue, flunarizine was synthesized in 1967. Van Nueten and Janssen (2) described the particular way cinnarizine and flunarizine antagonize histamine. The type of interaction was partly competitive and partly non-competitive, with the result of a much more effective blockade of the higher histamine concentrations than obtained with pyrilamine, a pure competitive antagonist.

Several studies during 1974-1978 revived the interest in the antianaphylactic component of the activity of these drugs. A clinical trial demonstrated the efficacy of cinnarizine in preventing exercise-induced asthma in children. Also in adults with chronic asthma a controlled study demonstrated the therapeutic benefit of orally administered cinnarizine, respiratory peak flow rate being particularly improved (3). Anaphylactic bronchoconstriction in rabbits could strongly be inhibited by administration of cinnarizine. In guinea-pigs the antianaphylactic activity of cinnarizine and flunarizine was surprisingly pronounced (4).

Oxatomide, synthesized in 1975, proved to be a compound with unusual antiallergic properties. In this chapter the synthesis of oxatomide and 69 analogues is described. The test systems

0-8412-0536-1/80/47-118-179$07.50/0

for suppression of hypersensitivity reactions, for antagonism of mediators and for inhibition of mediator release are also described. The results obtained with oxatomide are presented in detail, together with the screening results of some analogues. For comparative purposes selected reference compounds have also been studied. Parts of this experimental work have been presented previously (5, 6).

## Chemistry

Introduction. Oxatomide and analogous structures were synthesized as a part of an extensive chemical research project. A detailed study revealed that introduction of 1-alkyl-1, 3-dihydro-2H-benzimidazol-2-ones on known pharmacophores is compatible with neuroleptic (milenperone), antiemetic (domperidone, 7) and also with antihistaminic-antiallergic activity (oxatomide).

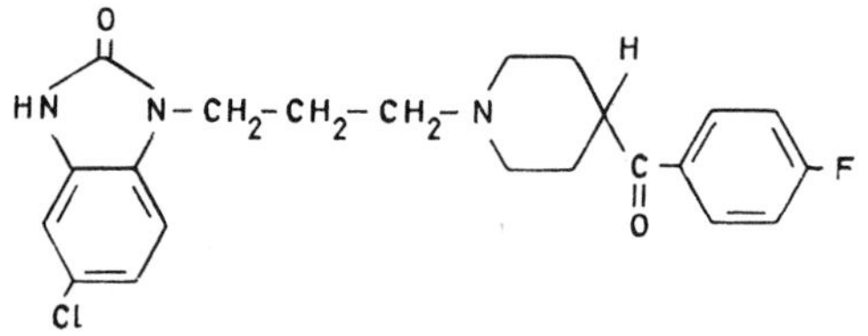

MILENPERONE
(R 34009)

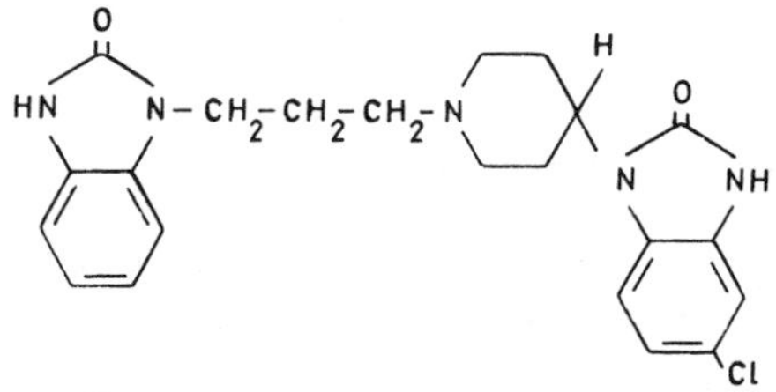

DOMPERIDONE
(R 33812)

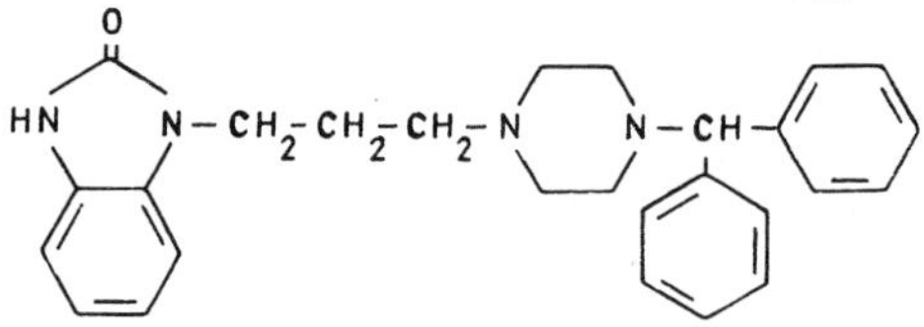

OXATOMIDE
(R 35443)

Benzimidazolones. The general procedure consists of alkylation of 1-(α, α-diarylmethyl)piperazines (II) with 1-haloalkyl-1, 3-dihydro-3R-2H-benzimidazol-2-ones (I) in the presence of an HCl acceptor (Scheme 1).

Oxatomide (III, $R = X_1 = X_2 = X_3 = H$), the selected compound of the series, is currently prepared according to Scheme 2. Alkylation of 1, 3-dihydro-1-(1-methylethenyl)-2H-benzimidazol-2-one (IV) (8) with 1-bromo-3-chloropropane afforded V, which reacted with 1-(α,α-diphenylmethyl)-piperazine to yield VI. Finally, acidic deprotection of the benzimidazolone nitrogen atom gave oxatomide.

Scheme 1

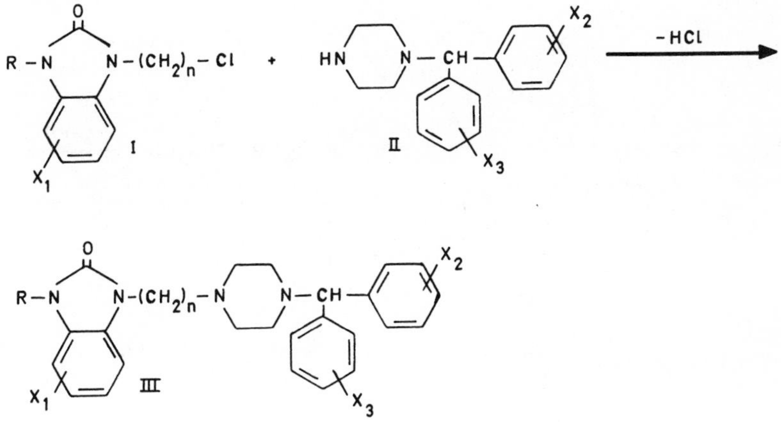

Scheme 2

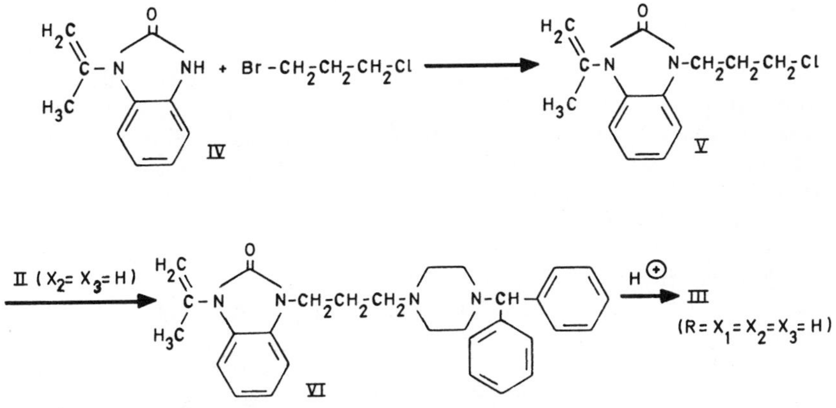

The synthesis of substituted benzimidazolone analogues ($X_1 \neq H$) was started from appropriate 2-chloronitrobenzenes (VII) as outlined in Scheme 3. The reaction of VII with aminoalkanols in an inert solvent afforded N-hydroxy-alkyl-2-nitroanilines (VIII). Catalytic hydrogenation of the nitro group resulted in o-phenylenediamines (IX) which reacted with urea to give the N-hydroxyalkylbenzimidazol-2-ones (X). After treatment of X with thionylchloride, the desired chloroalkylbenzimidazol-2-ones (I) could be isolated.

Scheme 3

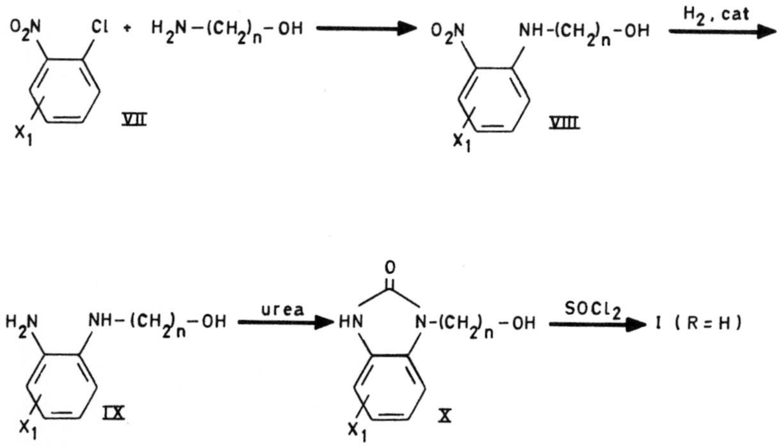

$O_2N$, Cl, $X_1$ (VII) + $H_2N-(CH_2)_n-OH$ → $O_2N$, $NH-(CH_2)_n-OH$, $X_1$ (VIII) $\xrightarrow{H_2,\ cat}$

$H_2N$, $NH-(CH_2)_n-OH$, $X_1$ (IX) $\xrightarrow{urea}$ O, HN, $N-(CH_2)_n-OH$, $X_1$ (X) $\xrightarrow{SOCl_2}$ I (R = H)

Introduction of different substituents on the benzimidazol-2-on nitrogen atom was achieved by different chemical pathways.

1. Treatment of oxatomide with formaldehyde gave the hydroxymethylderivative (R = $-CH_2OH$).
2. Acylation with acid anhydrides gave the N-acylderivatives (e.g. R = $-COCH_3$).
3. Addition of isocyanates afforded the ureido derivatives (e.g. R = $CONHCH_3$).
4. Addition of acrylates gave the carboxyethyl derivative (e.g. R = $-CH_2CH_2COOC_2H_5$).
5. The synthesis of N-alkyl and N-aryl derivatives started from N-substituted o-phenylenediamines which reacted with urea to the benzimidazolones and were then alkylated with 1-bromo-3-chloropropane as described in Scheme 2.

The compounds of type III are summarized in Table I.

Table I. Benzimidazolones

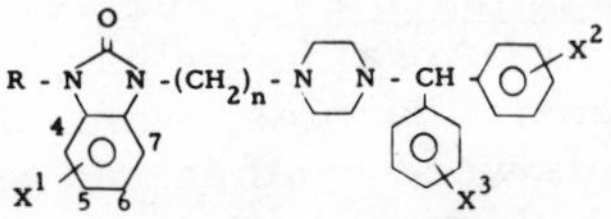

| Compound nr. | R | n | $X^1$ | $X^2$ | $X^3$ | mp °C | Formula | Seq. number |
|---|---|---|---|---|---|---|---|---|
| 1 | H | 2 | H | H | H | 218.0 | $C_{26}H_{28}N_4O$ | 35 449 |
| 2 | H | 2 | H | 4F | H | 172.4 | $C_{26}H_{27}FN_4O$ | 35 802 |
| 3 | H | 2 | H | 4F | 4F | 132.0 | $C_{26}H_{26}F_2N_4O.1/2H_2O$ | 35 603 |
| 4 | H | 2 | $5CH_3$ | H | H | 214.6 | $C_{27}H_{30}N_4O$ | 36 785 |
| 5 | H | 2 | $5CF_3$ | H | H | 163.7 | $C_{27}H_{27}F_3N_4O$ | 36 753 |
| 6 | H | 2 | 5Cl | H | H | 203.6 | $C_{26}H_{27}ClN_4O$ | 36 531 |
| 7 | H | 2 | 6Cl | H | H | 204.1 | $C_{26}H_{27}ClN_4O$ | 36 597 |
| 8 | H | 3 | H | H | H | 153.6 | $C_{27}H_{30}N_4O$ | 35 443 |
| 9 | H | 3 | H | 4F | H | 153.6 | $C_{27}H_{29}FN_4O$ | 35 392 |
| 10 | H | 3 | H | 4F | 4F | 203 | $C_{27}H_{28}F_2N_4O$ | 34 058 |
| 11 | H | 3 | H | 3Cl | H | 112.7 | $C_{27}H_{29}ClN_4O$ | 35 496 |
| 12 | H | 3 | H | 4Cl | H | 180.2 | $C_{27}H_{29}ClN_4O$ | 35 511 |
| 13 | H | 3 | H | 4Cl | 2F | 136 | $C_{27}H_{28}ClFN_4O$ | 35 519 |
| 14 | H | 3 | $5CH_3$ | H | H | 167.4 | $C_{28}H_{32}N_4O$ | 36 460 |
| 15 | H | 3 | $5CF_3$ | H | H | 152.8 | $C_{28}H_{29}F_3N_4O$ | 36 840 |
| 16 | H | 3 | 5Cl | H | H | 175.0 | $C_{28}H_{29}ClN_4O$ | 36 415 |
| 17 | H | 3 | 6Cl | H | H | 206.1 | $C_{28}H_{29}ClN_4O$ | 36 599 |
| 18 | H | 3 | $6CH_3$ | H | H | 195.7 | $C_{28}H_{32}N_4O$ | 36 799 |
| 19 | H | 3 | 7Cl | H | H | 196.9 | $C_{27}H_{29}ClN_4O$ | 36 810 |
| 20 | H | 3 | $5,6Cl_2$ | H | H | 214.7 | $C_{27}H_{28}Cl_2N_4O$ | 36 910 |
| 21 | H | 3 | 5Cl | 4F | 4F | 205.8 | $C_{27}H_{27}ClF_2N_4O$ | 35 546 |
| 22 | H | 3 | 6Cl | 4F | 4F | 132.9 | $C_{27}H_{27}ClF_2N_4O.H_2O$ | 35 588 |
| 23 | H | 4 | H | H | H | 198.2 | $C_{28}H_{32}N_4O$ | 35 918 |
| 24 | H | 4 | H | 4F | H | 172.3 | $C_{28}H_{31}FN_4O$ | 37 907 |
| 25 | H | 4 | H | 4F | 4F | 184.4 | $C_{28}H_{30}F_2N_4O.2HCl.H_2O$ | 37 281 |
| 26 | H | 5 | H | H | H | 215.3 | $C_{29}H_{34}N_4O.2HCl.H_2O$ | 37 477 |
| 27 | H | 5 | H | 4F | 4F | 203.7 | $C_{29}H_{32}F_2N_4O.2HCl.H_2O$ | 37 486 |
| 28 | H | 6 | H | H | H | 189.7 | $C_{30}H_{36}N_4O$ | 37 685 |
| 29 | H | 6 | H | 4F | 4F | 204.5 | $C_{30}H_{34}F_2N_4O.2HCl$ | 37 900 |
| 30 | H | a | H | 4F | 4F | 176.0 | $C_{28}H_{30}F_2N_4O$ | 35 873 |
| 31 | $CH_3-C(=CH_2)-$ | 3 | H | H | H | 103.0 | $C_{30}H_{34}N_4O$ | 36 262 |
| 32 | $-CH_2OH$ | 3 | H | H | H | 102.5 | $C_{28}H_{32}N_4O_2$ | 36 885 |
| 33 | $-COCH_3$ | 3 | H | H | H | 124.4 | $C_{29}H_{32}N_4O_2$ | 36 767 |
| 34 | $-CONHCH_3$ | 3 | H | H | H | 153.1 | $C_{29}H_{33}N_5O_2$ | 36 794 |
| 35 | $-CH_2CH_2COOC_2H_5$ | 3 | H | H | H | 204.0 | $C_{32}H_{38}N_4O_3.2HCl.H_2O$ | 36 757 |
| 36 | $-CH_3$ | 3 | H | H | H | 201.8 | $C_{28}H_{32}N_4O.2HCl.H_2O$ | 36 865 |
| 37 | $-CH_2-C_6H_5$ | 3 | H | H | H | 199.6 | $C_{34}H_{36}N_4O.2HCl$ | 36 762 |
| 38 | $C_6H_5$ | 3 | H | H | H | 184.2 | $C_{33}H_{33}ClN_4O.2HCl.H_2O$ | 37 162 |

a: $(CH_2)_n \equiv -CH_2-CH(CH_3)-CH_2-$

Benzimidazoles. Further modification of the benzimidazol-one-moiety of oxatomide has led to the synthesis of a large number of benzimidazoles, which are summarized in Table II. These compounds were synthesized as outlined in Scheme 4. Cyclization of IX with the appropriate carboxylic acids or with the bisulphite complexes of the aldehydes gave benzimidazoles XI (9). Successive chlorination with thionylchloride and coupling with 1-(α, α-diaryl-methyl)-piperazines (II) afforded the benzimidazoles XIII (R = H, alkyl, aryl, cycloalkyl, aralkyl).

Scheme 4

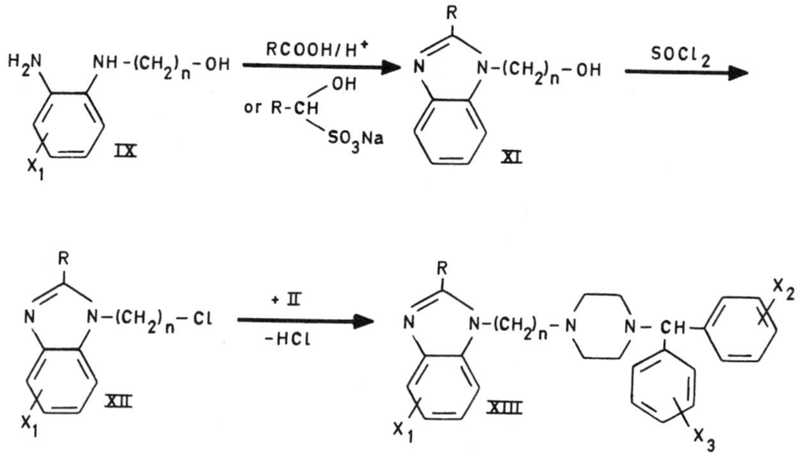

An alternative pathway started with N-hydroxyalkyl-o-nitro-anilines (VIII), which were successively chlorinated with thionyl-choride and coupled with 1-(α, α-diarylmethyl)-piperazine (II) to give the intermediates XV. Catalytic hydrogenation of the nitro group afforded o-phenylenediamines XVI, which could be used to synthesize either III or XIII. Cyclisation of XVI with $CS_2$ in ethanol gave the 2-mercaptoimidazole (XVII) (10), which was methylated to XVIII with dimethylsulphate. On the other hand, ring closure, with methyl (α-imino-α-methoxymethyl)carbamate, gave the 2-methoxy carbonylamino derivative XIX (11), which was further hydrolyzed and then reacylated affording 2-amino (XX) and 2-acetylamino (XXI) derivatives (Scheme 5). These compounds are also summarized in Table II.

Table II. Benzimidazoles

| Compound nr. | R | n | $X^1$ | $X^2$ | $X^3$ | mp °C | Formula | Seq. number |
|---|---|---|---|---|---|---|---|---|
| 39 | H | 2 | H | H | H | 192.3 | $C_{26}H_{28}N_4$ | 36 951 |
| 40 | $C_2H_5$- | 2 | H | H | H | 208.5 | $C_{28}H_{32}N_4 \cdot 3HCl \cdot H_2O$ | 37 425 |
| 41 | ⟨◯⟩- | 2 | H | H | H | 198.3 | $C_{32}H_{32}N_4 \cdot 3HCl \cdot H_2O$ | 37 145 |
| 42 | H | 3 | H | H | H | 132.3 | $C_{27}H_{30}N_4$ | 36 636 |
| 43 | H | 3 | H | 4F | H | 102.5 | $C_{27}H_{29}FN_4$ | 37 259 |
| 44 | H | 3 | H | 4F | 4F | 108.0 | $C_{27}H_{28}F_2N_4 \cdot H_2O$ | 37 268 |
| 45 | H | 3 | H | 2Cl | H | 182.9 | $C_{27}H_{29}ClN_4 \cdot 3HCl \cdot 2H_2O$ | 37 427 |
| 46 | H | 3 | H | 3Cl | H | 191.1 | $C_{27}H_{29}ClN_4 \cdot 3HCl \cdot H_2O \cdot 1/2C_3H_8O$ | 37 390 |
| 47 | H | 3 | H | 4Cl | H | 90.8 | $C_{27}H_{29}ClN_4$ | 37 352 |
| 48 | $CH_3$- | 3 | H | H | H | 121.2 | $C_{28}H_{32}N_4$ | 36 882 |
| 49 | $C_2H_5$- | 3 | H | H | H | 224.5 | $C_{29}H_{34}N_4 \cdot 3HCl \cdot H_2O$ | 37 163 |
| 50 | ⟨H⟩- | 3 | H | H | H | 106.5 | $C_{33}H_{40}N_4$ | 36 984 |
| 51 | ⟨◯⟩-$CH_2$- | 3 | H | H | H | 187.9 | $C_{34}H_{36}N_4 \cdot 3HCl \cdot H_2O$ | 37 415 |
| 52 | ⟨◯⟩- | 3 | H | H | H | 130.5 | $C_{33}H_{34}N_4$ | 36 912 |
| 53 | $CH_3$- | 3 | 5Cl | H | H | 226.4 | $C_{28}H_{31}ClN_4 \cdot 3HCl \cdot H_2O$ | 37 171 |
| 54 | $C_2H_5$- | 3 | 5Cl | H | H | 233.1 | $C_{29}H_{33}ClN_4 \cdot 3HCl \cdot H_2O$ | 37 135 |
| 55 | ⟨H⟩- | 3 | 5Cl | H | H | 114.9 | $C_{33}H_{39}ClN_4$ | 37 072 |
| 56 | ⟨H⟩- | 3 | 6Cl | H | H | 173.6 | $C_{33}H_{39}ClN_4$ | 37 203 |
| 57 | ⟨◯⟩-$CH_2$- | 3 | 5Cl | H | H | 198.2 | $C_{34}H_{36}N_4 \cdot 3HCl \cdot H_2O$ | 37 341 |
| 58 | ⟨◯⟩- | 3 | 5Cl | H | H | 127.8 | $C_{33}H_{33}ClN_4$ | 37 148 |
| 59 | ⟨◯⟩- | 3 | 6Cl | H | H | 143.9 | $C_{33}H_{33}ClN_4$ | 37 143 |
| 60 | H | 4 | H | H | H | 106.0 | $C_{28}H_{32}N_4$ | 37 029 |
| 61 | H | 4 | H | 4F | H | 114.9 | $C_{28}H_{31}FN_4$ | 37 280 |
| 62 | H | 4 | H | 4F | 4F | 86.3 | $C_{28}H_{30}F_2N_4$ | 37 382 |
| 63 | $CH_3$- | 4 | H | H | H | 118.7 | $C_{29}H_{34}N_4$ | 37 113 |
| 64 | H | a | H | H | H | 237.3 | $C_{28}H_{32}N_4 \cdot 3HCl \cdot 1/2H_2O$ | 37 563 |
| 65 | H | a | H | 4F | 4F | 223.4 | $C_{28}H_{30}F_2N_4 \cdot 3HCl \cdot 1/2H_2O$ | 37 286 |
| 66 | -$NH_2$ | 3 | H | H | H | 228.7 | $C_{27}H_{31}N_5$ | 37 419 |
| 67 | -$NHCOOCH_3$ | 3 | H | H | H | 137.8 | $C_{29}H_{33}N_5O_2$ | 37 418 |
| 68 | -$NHCOCH_3$ | 3 | H | H | H | 143.3 | $C_{29}H_{33}N_5O$ | 37 436 |
| 69 | -SH | 3 | H | H | H | 181.8 | $C_{27}H_{30}N_4S$ | 36 967 |
| 70 | -$SCH_3$ | 3 | H | H | H | 203.4 | $C_{28}H_{32}N_4S \cdot 3HCl \cdot H_2O$ | 36 541 |

a: $(CH_2)_n \equiv -CH_2-CH(CH_3)-CH_2-$

$C_3H_8O \equiv$ 2 - propanol.

Scheme 5

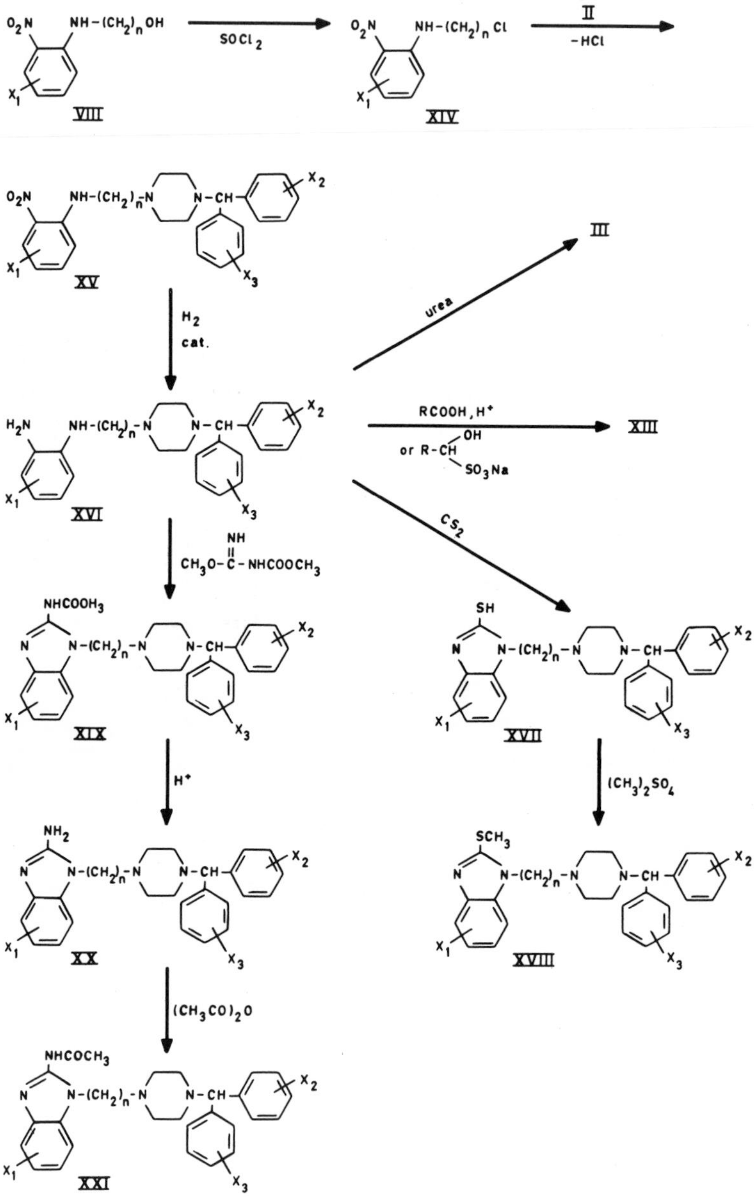
O2N
NH-(CH2)n OH
SOCl2
X1
VIII
NH-(CH2)n Cl
XIV
II
-HCl
NH-(CH2)n-N
N-CH
X2
X3
XV
H2
cat.
urea
III
H2N
XVI
RCOOH, H+
or R-CH
OH
SO3Na
XIII
CS2
NH
CH3O-C-NHCOOCH3
NHCOOH3
N-(CH2)n-N
XIX
SH
XVII
H+
(CH3)2SO4
NH2
XX
SCH3
XVIII
(CH3CO)2O
NHCOCH3
XXI

## Studies in Guinea-Pigs

Introduction. The guinea-pig has long been known for its rather uniform anaphylactic response and its high sensitivity to the prominent allergic mediator, histamine. The origin of histamine, as well as of most other mediators of immediate hypersensitivity, has been traced to mast cells which in human lung are found at two distinct anatomical sites, the surface of the bronchial mucosa and around the venules in the deeper connective tissue. Mast cell activation by immunologic and other stimuli in this double location may be responsible for the distinct acute and subacute phases of respiratory distress (12).

Histamine, when released from human or guinea-pig lung in hypersensitivity reactions, increases bronchiolar resistance to air flow and decreases pulmonary compliance (13). Slow reacting substance of anaphylaxis (SRS-A) primarily affects pulmonary compliance (14). Prostaglandin $F_{2\alpha}$, a bronchoconstrictor in guinea-pigs, is a very potent lung spasmogen in some patients with asthma, but the contribution of endogenous prostaglandins and of other described mediators to anaphylaxis and allergy is less well defined than that of histamine and SRS-A (12).

Guinea-pigs can be easily sensitized to foreign proteins. A single parenteral injection of an antigen without the use of an immunologic adjuvant can be sufficient to induce hypersensitivity. Even the substitution of milk for drinking water leads to fairly uniform, but transient, hypersensitivity to milk or its proteins (15). The type of antibody responsible for this anaphylactic sensitization has been characterized as $IgG_1$, a homocytotropic subgroup of the classical gamma-globulins. Animals injected with serum which contains antibodies of this class are sensitive to the corresponding antigen for at least seven days (16), presumably because of relatively tight binding of these antibodies to lung mast cells.

### Materials, Methods and Results.

Systemic Anaphylaxis and Histamine Oedema. The induction of anaphylactic shock and of histamine oedema in guinea-pigs has been described in detail (4). The majority (283 out of 345; 82 %) of the sensitized guinea-pigs receiving solvent orally died between 1 and 6 min after the intravenous challenge with ovalbumin. Very few animals (4.9 %) died during the remainder of the observation period, i.e. between 6 and 120 min, and in a considerable number of animals (13 %) the challenge was not lethal. In accordance with the distribution of death from acute bronchospasm and with the frequency of false positives in the control group, protection from anaphylactic shock in guinea-pigs after compound administration was defined as survival for at least 15 min after challenge and in the calculation of $ED_{50}$'s as 16 % correction was applied for false positives (19).

The median histamine oedema, 10 min after the injection of 50 μg of histamine, was 16 units (= 1.6 mm). The paw diameter increase followed an approximately normal distribution, values higher than 21 or lower than 10 units being very rare (less than 5 %). Inhibition of the histamine oedema in animals after oral administration of a test compound was therefore considered significant for all values below 10 units. $ED_{50}$-values were calculated on the number of guinea-pigs with significantly inhibited histamine oedema (19).

The results obtained in the guinea-pig anaphylaxis test after oral oxatomide administration are presented in Fig. 1. A dose-dependent increase in the number of animals protected from the acute anaphylactic shock was observed and the histamine-induced paw oedema was similarly reduced by increasing doses of oxatomide. As previously found with cinnarizine, protection from anaphylactic shock was a more sensitive measure of the activity of oxatomide than was the reduction of paw oedema. In comparison with cinnarizine, however, oxatomide was considerably more potent. The calculated $ED_{50}$'s, 2 h after oral administration, were 0.16(0.081 - 0.31) mg/kg for protection from anaphylactic shock and 0.30(0.18 - 0.50) mg/kg for inhibition of histamine oedema.

Oxatomide has a relatively long duration of action. When challenged 6 h after oral administration of the compound, the guinea-pigs were protected from lethal anaphylaxis at about the same dose as found in the standard procedure. The calculated $ED_{50}$ for the 6 h-interval was 0.14(0.075 - 0.28) mg/kg. Inhibition of the paw oedema induced by exogenous histamine in the same animals required a dose of 0.56(0.27 - 1.14) mg/kg.

For the oxatomide-analogues the results of histamine antagonism in vitro, together with the $ED_{50}$'s for protection from anaphylactic shock and the values of histamine oedema at a standard dose of 2.5 mg/kg are summarized in Table III a and b.

From the results in Table III a, the following conclusions can be drawn:

a) In vitro, optimal activity is obtained when n = 3 or 4 (compounds 8, 9, 10, 23, 24, 31, 32). Introduction of substituents on the benzhydryl group ($X^2$ and $X^3$) generally results in a decrease of activity (compounds 9, 10, 11, 12, 13, 24, 25). Substituents on the phenyl ring ($X^1$) of the benzimidazolone group have little or no effect when n = 2 and reduce activity when n = 3. Replacement of the acidic proton of the benzimidazolone in all cases, except for 2-methylethenyl (compound 31) and hydroxymethyl (compound 32), lowers activity.

b) In vivo, both for anaphylactic shock and histamine oedema,

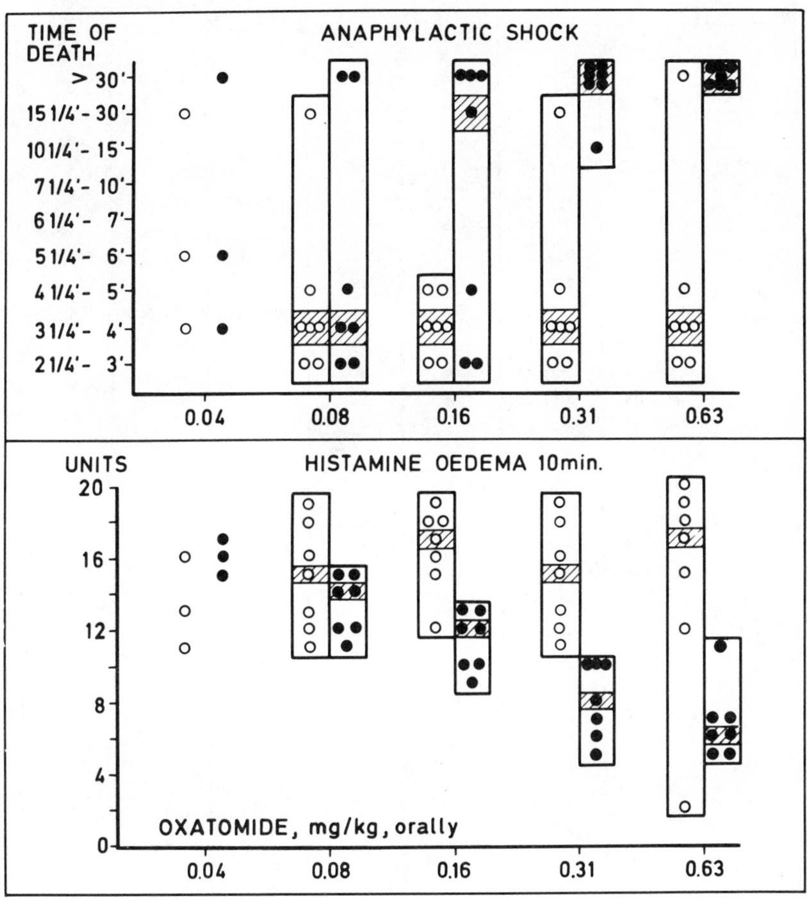


*Figure 1. Individual survival time and histamine oedema after oral oxatomide administration* (t = *2 hr) in the guinea pig anaphylaxis test*

TABLE III

Histamine antagonism in vitro ($A_{10}$), protection from anaphylactic schock ($ED_{50}$) and histamine oedema values.

| Compound nr. | Hist. Vitro a | Guinea-pigs | | Compound nr. | Hist. Vitro a | Guinea-pigs | |
|---|---|---|---|---|---|---|---|
| | | $ED_{50}$ Anaphylaxis (mg/kg) | Histamine oedema values at 2.5 mg/kg | | | $ED_{50}$ Anaphylaxis (mg/kg) | Histamine oedema values at 2.5 mg/kg |
| a. Benzimidazolones | | | | | | | |
| 1 | > 0.04 | ~ 1.25 | 6 | 21 | > 0.04 | ~ 2.5 | 3 |
| 2 | ≥ 0.04 | ~ 0.31 | 4 | 22 | > 0.04 | ~ 0.63 | 7 |
| 3 | > 0.04 | ~ 0.63 | 4 | 23 | 0.026 | ~ 0.31 | 5 |
| 4 | ≥ 0.04 | ~ 1.25 | 5 | 24 | ≤ 0.04 | ~ 0.63 | 5 |
| 5 | > 0.04 | ~ 0.31 | 4 | 25 | 0.085 | ~ 0.31 | 5 |
| 6 | ~ 0.04 | ~ 1.25 | 5 | 26 | > 0.04 | ~ 0.63 | 8 |
| 7 | ~ 0.1 | ~ 2.5 | 6 | 27 | ~ 0.04 | < 2.5 | 9 |
| 8 | 0.014 | ~ 0.16 | 2 | 28 | ~ 0.04 | ~ 1.25 | 7 |
| 9 | ~ 0.03 | ~ 0.31 | 5 | 29 | ≥ 0.04 | > 2.5 | 8 |
| 10 | 0.028 | ~ 0.31 | 4 | 30 | > 0.16 | ~ 1.25 | 7 |
| 11 | > 0.04 | ~ 0.63 | 6 | 31 | ≤ 0.04 | ~ 0.16 | 2 |
| 12 | ≥ 0.04 | ~ 1.25 | 4 | 32 | ~ 0.03 | ~ 0.31 | 5 |
| 13 | > 0.04 | ~ 0.31 | 6 | 33 | ~ 0.04 | - | - |
| 14 | ~ 0.04 | ≤ 0.16 | 3 | 34 | ~ 0.04 | > 2.5 | 11.5 |
| 15 | > 0.04 | ~ 0.31 | 4 | 35 | ~ 0.04 | ~ 0.63 | 6 |
| 16 | ~ 0.04 | ~ 1.25 | 4 | 36 | ~ 0.04 | ~ 2.5 | 9 |
| 17 | ~ 0.12 | ~ 0.63 | 5 | 37 | > 0.16 | ~ 2.5 | 5 |
| 18 | ~ 0.04 | ~ 0.31 | 3 | 38 | ~ 0.08 | > 2.5 | 9.5 |
| 19 | > 0.04 | > 2.5 | 10 | | | | |
| 20 | > 0.16 | ~ 2.5 | 7 | | | | |
| b. Benzimidazoles | | | | | | | |
| 39 | ~ 0.04 | ~ 1.25 | 4 | 55 | > 0.16 | ~ 0.63 | 7 |
| 40 | > 0.16 | > 2.5 | 17 | 56 | > 0.16 | ~ 2.5 | 11 |
| 41 | > 0.16 | > 2.5 | 15.5 | 57 | > 0.16 | ~ 2.5 | 14 |
| 42 | ~ 0.01 | ~ 0.08 | 4.5 | 58 | > 0.16 | > 2.5 | 11.5 |
| 43 | ≤ 0.01 | ~ 0.31 | 4 | 59 | > 0.16 | ~ 2.5 | 12 |
| 44 | ~ 0.02 | ~ 0.63 | 6 | 60 | ~ 0.01 | ~ 0.31 | 4 |
| 45 | ~ 0.08 | ~ 1.25 | 4 | 61 | ~ 0.01 | ~ 0.08 | 3 |
| 46 | ~ 0.04 | ~ 1.25 | 6 | 62 | ~ 0.02 | ~ 0.31 | 2 |
| 47 | ~ 0.01 | ~ 0.08 | 3 | 63 | ~ 0.04 | ~ 2.5 | 5 |
| 48 | ~ 0.04 | ~ 2.5 | 8 | 64 | ~ 0.03 | ~ 1.25 | 4 |
| 49 | ~ 0.04 | ~ 2.5 | 6 | 65 | ~ 0.04 | ~ 0.63 | 6 |
| 50 | > 0.16 | ~ 2.5 | 5 | 66 | ~ 0.08 | > 2.5 | 9 |
| 51 | > 0.16 | > 2.5 | 14 | 67 | ~ 0.08 | ~ 2.5 | 5 |
| 52 | ≤ 0.16 | > 2.5 | 16 | 68 | > 0.16 | ~ 2.5 | 11 |
| 53 | ~ 0.03 | > 2.5 | 11 | 69 | ~ 0.04 | ~ 0.63 | 3 |
| 54 | ~ 0.04 | > 2.5 | 15 | 70 | > 0.16 | ~ 1.25 | 5 |

a: $A_{10}$ value in mg/l.

generally a parallelism is found with in vitro results. In this series of compounds 2, 5, 8, 9, 10, 15, 18, 23, 25, 31 and 32 are the most potent ones.

Analysis of the results in Table III b demonstrates:

a) In vitro, optimal activity for compounds with n = 3 or 4 (42, 43, 44, 47, 60, 61, 62). Substituents either on the benzhydryl group or on the phenyl ring of the benzimidazole have little or no effect on activity, while introduction of a substituent (R) in the 2-position of the benzimidazole nucleus results in a decrease in activity.

b) In vivo: optimal chain length is n = 3 or 4. In this series fluoro or chloro substituents on the benzhydrylgroup either enhance or at least retain activity (compounds 47, 61, 62). Any substituent (R), except the SH group (compound 69), in the 2-position of benzimidazol destroys activity. The latter compound represents the sulphur isostere of oxatomide.

In no case total protection from anaphylactic shock was found at 0.16 mg/kg and the $ED_{50}$ values for oxatomide (compound 8) and some of the most active compounds, namely R 35 918, R 37 280 and R 37 281 (compounds 23, 61, 25) are presented in Table IV. These compounds were not superior to oxatomide in affording protection from anaphylactic shock, whereas their antihistamine activity tended to be somewhat more pronounced.

The results obtained with reference compounds are also presented in Table IV. The selectivity of the procedure is illustrated by the lack of activity of high doses of a potent inhibitor of prostaglandin biosynthesis (suprofen), of a $H_2$-histamine antagonist (cimetidine) and of the orally active anti-allergic agent doxanthrazole. Doxanthrazole is an agent of the cromolyn-type and its lack of activity confirms many experimental studies, in which this type of compounds was found not to inhibit $IgG_1$-mediated hypersensitivity reactions.

Qualitatively oxatomide shared with cinnarizine and flunarizine the property of being at least as active in preventing lethal anaphylaxis as in reducing histamine oedema, quantitatively oxatomide was several times more potent than the cinnamyl-derivatives, with a duration of action intermediate between the short-acting cinnarizine and its long-acting fluoro-derivative. Several classical antihistaminics, such as pyrilamine and diphenhydramine, were not maximally active at 40 mg/kg, probably because of their poor resorption after oral administration to rodents. Clemastine, however, was active within the usual test dose range. In comparison to its inhibitory effect on histamine-induced oedema, the activity of clemastine for protection from anaphylactic shock was relatively weak and irregular, as reflected in the wide confidence limits.

TABLE IV $ED_{50}$-values of various orally administered compounds in the guinea-pig anaphylaxis test

| Compound | Time interval to challenge (h) | Oral $ED_{50}$ (with confidence limits) in mg/kg | |
|---|---|---|---|
| | | Protection from Anaphylactic shock | Inhibition of Histamine Oedema |
| Oxatomide | 2 | 0.16 (0.081 - 0.31) | 0.30 (0.18 - 0.50) |
| | 6 | 0.14 (0.075 - 0.28) | 0.56 (0.27 - 1.14) |
| R 35 918 (Compound 23) | 2 | 0.21 (0.099 - 0.46) | 0.15 (0.082 - 0.26) |
| R 37 280 (Compound 61) | 2 | 0.14 (0.083 - 0.22) | 0.16 (0.13 -0.21) |
| R 37 281 (Compound 25) | 2 | 0.23 (0.13 - 0.43) | 0.22 (0.14 - 0.34) |
| Cinnarizine | 1 | 0.79 (0.39 - 1.59) | 1.19 (0.58 - 2.44) |
| | 2 | 2.01 (1.18 - 3.43) | 1.06 (0.55 - 2.06) |
| Flunarizine | 2 | 0.72 (0.41 - 1.27) | 0.97 (0.61 - 1.55) |
| | 6 | 0.38 (0.16 - 0.90) | 0.53 (0.35 - 0.82) |
| Clemastine | 2 | 2.33 (0.68 - 8.01) | 1.12 (0.86 - 1.46) |
| Doxanthrazole | 2 | > 40 | > 40 |
| Cimetidine | 2 | > 40 | > 40 |
| Suprofen | 2 | > 40 | > 40 |

TABLE V Protection of actively sensitized guinea-pigs from acute bronchospasm and from protracted shock by orally administered oxatomide

| Dose of oxatomide mg/kg | Surviving animals at 15 min | Surviving animals at 4 h | Median survival time in min (limits) |
|---|---|---|---|
| 0 | 0/25 | 0/25 | 4 (3 3/4 - 5) |
| 0.04 | 0/5 | 0/5 | 4 1/2 (4 - 5 1/4) |
| 0.08 | 2/7 | 1/7 | 5 (3 1/2 - >240) |
| 0.16 | 5/7 | 3/7 | 29 (4 3/4 ->240) |
| 0.31 | 7/7 | 5/7 | >240 (24 - >240) |
| 0.63 | 11/11 | 8/11 | >240 (39 - >240) |
| $ED_{50}$ | 0.11 | 0.24 | |
| L.L. | 0.067 | 0.11 | |
| U.L. | 0.19 | 0.56 | |

Active Anaphylaxis. Guinea-pigs were injected with an emulsion of ovalbumin in saline and Mycobacterium butyricum in oil in the hind-paws and skin, as described for the preparation of anti-ovalbumin serum (4). A dose of a compound or solvent was administered orally, 13 to 16 days after these injections. Two hours after the oral administration ovalbumin (0.4 ml of a 0.25 % solution in saline) was injected intravenously. Survival time was recorded up to 4 h after the challenge.

Because of the frequent occurrence of a less violent, protracted shock phase, despite protection of the animals from the acute bronchospasm, $ED_{50}$'s were calculated for protection from both the acute anaphylactic shock (survival at 15 min) and the delayed phase (survival for at least 4 h).

The results obtained in actively sensitized guinea-pigs are presented in Table V. All control animals died from acute bronchospasm, with symptoms identical to those observed in passive anaphylaxis. Dose-dependent protection from early death by orally administered oxatomide, two hours before the intravenous challenge with ovalbumin, was virtually the same in actively and passively sensitized animals. As expected from literature descriptions of protracted shock, some animals which were totally free of respiratory distress in the first minutes after ovalbumin challenge, showed a gradually developing, less violent form of shock, which eventually resulted in delayed death. Slightly higher doses of oxatomide were required to prevent the protracted shock.

Morphological Studies. The methods used to study peribronchiolar mast cells at the ultrastructural level have been fully described (17, 18). Specimens were obtained from sensitized non-challenged guinea-pigs, and from control or oxatomide-treated animals 3 min after the injection of ovalbumin.

Oral administration of oxatomide to sensitized guinea-pigs prevented the anaphylactic symptoms following ovalbumin challenge and at the same time the characteristic changes in peribronchiolar mast cells, including those of the nucleus and of the mitochondria (18).

Acute Toxicity. The acute intravenous toxicity of oxatomide was determined in 30 adult male (375 - 525 g) and 30 adult female (400 to 600 g) guinea-pigs. Solutions of the compound were prepared by adding an equivalent amount of lactic acid and aqueous dilutions of cremophor EL, from 5 to 20 %, in proportion to the required oxatomide concentration. A volume of 0.2 ml per 100 g body weight was injected. The $LD_{50}$ with 95 % confidence limits (19) in male guinea-pigs was 23.2(17.7 - 30.3) mg/kg and in female guinea-pigs 22.2(17.0 - 29.0) mg/kg.

The acute oral toxicity of oxatomide was studied in 35 adult male (350 to 500 g) and 45 adult female (350 - 550 g) guinea-pigs. The compound was given as an aqueous suspension in a volume of 1 ml per 100 g body weight. The animals were individually housed and observed during seven consecutive days. Gross behavioural effects and mortality were recorded 1, 3, 6, 24, 72 and 168 h after drug administration. The oral $LD_{50}$ in male guinea-pigs was 332(254-434) mg/kg and in female guinea-pigs 313(209 - 469) mg/kg.

With respect to the lowest $ED_{50}$ for protection from anaphylactic shock (0.11 mg/kg) the safety margin ($LD_{50}/ED_{50}$) for orally administered oxatomide is 3,000.

Comments. From these studies in guinea-pigs it can be concluded that oxatomide is a potent anti-anaphylactic agent. Part of this activity can be attributed to histamine antagonism, since histamine induced paw oedema is reduced by oral doses of oxatomide only slightly higher than those affording protection from anaphylactic shock and since the role of endogenous histamine in guinea-pig anaphylaxis is prominent (13). Throughout the various experimental studies, including comparison with classical antihistaminics and the protection from active anaphylaxis, it appeared unlikely that histamine antagonism was the only basis for the antianaphylactic activity of oxatomide. The morphologic studies on the lung mast cells, which demonstrate the virtual absence of the extremely rapid degranulation of mast cells in challenged animals, after oxatomide administration, strongly suggest that the new compound also acts by reducing the amount of released endogenous histamine.

## Studies in Rats

Introduction. As in guinea-pigs $IgG_1$-antibodies can mediate human hypersensitivity (20), but the major class of sensitizing antibodies in man is the reaginic or IgE-type (21). Serum levels of IgE are low when compared to other antibody classes, but the affinity of mast cell receptors is extremely high for the binding portion of IgE molecules. Although the tight binding is reversible, mast cells remain sensitized for a long time, i.e. contact with the corresponding antigen results in histamine release, which is now thought to require bridging of the IgE receptors in the mast cell membrane (22).

The sensitizing capacity of the serum from allergic subjects has been known since the classical transfer experiments of Prausnitz-Küstner. Passive cutaneous anaphylaxis in the rat is essentially identical to the reaction of Prausnitz-Küstner. A skin area of normal rats is sensitized to an allergen by the local injection of serum containing specific IgE-antibodies and appropriate challenge of the animals induces an allergic reaction which is restricted to the sensitized area.

Mast cell degranulation and mediator discharge can also be induced by chemicals of low molecular weight (23). Compound 48/80, a mixture of oligomers obtained by condensation of p-methoxy phenetylmethylamine with formaldehyde, is potent and specific in this respect: its administration produces effects which can be ascribed exclusively to the action of mast cell-derived mediators. An appropriate intravenous dose of compound 48/80 (0.5 mg/kg) induces lethal shock in rats; dose-dependent protection from the lethal shock is possible by administration of any compound possessing histamine $H_1$-antagonistic activity but other pharmacological properties can contribute to the protective effect (24).

## Materials, Methods and Results.

*The Rat PCA-Test.* The procedure of the PCA-test was in agreement with the recommendations for optimal induction of PCA-reactions (25). IgE-containing anti-ovalbumin serum was obtained according to Mota (26). On the back of male Wistar rats four reactions were induced: two PCA reactions due to interaction of intravenously injected ovalbumin with a sensitized skin area and two skin reactions due to intradermally injected histamine. The intensity of the blue areas on the dissected skin was scored by two independent observers in comparison to standard sets of 5 PCA and histamine reactions with increasing intensity from 0 to 4. The results were expressed in terms of a total score (varying from 0 to 16) obtained by summing the 4 scores for the same reaction type in an individual rat.

Results in control animals indicated that inhibition of PCA-reactions in compound treated animals was significant on one of the following conditions: either a total score below 3, or a difference of more than 8 in comparison to the control rat of the same experimental session. Inhibition of the histamine reactions was significant for a total score below 7, which occurred in 2.0 % of the control animals.

The individual intensities of PCA and histamine-induced reactions in rats after oral administration of oxatomide are presented in Fig. 2. A progressive dose-dependent inhibitory effect of oxatomide was obtained on both PCA and histamine reactions. In Table VI a and b the results of 56 oxatomide analogues (36 benzimidazolones and 20 benzimidazoles) are summarized. All compounds were tested at a standard dose of 10 mg/kg. In particular those compounds are active which showed the highest activity in guinea-pig anaphylaxis and histamine oedema, e.g. the benzimidazolones 8, 9, 10, 13, 14, 23, 24 and 25 and the benzimidazoles 48, 61 and 62. However, no linear correlation was found.

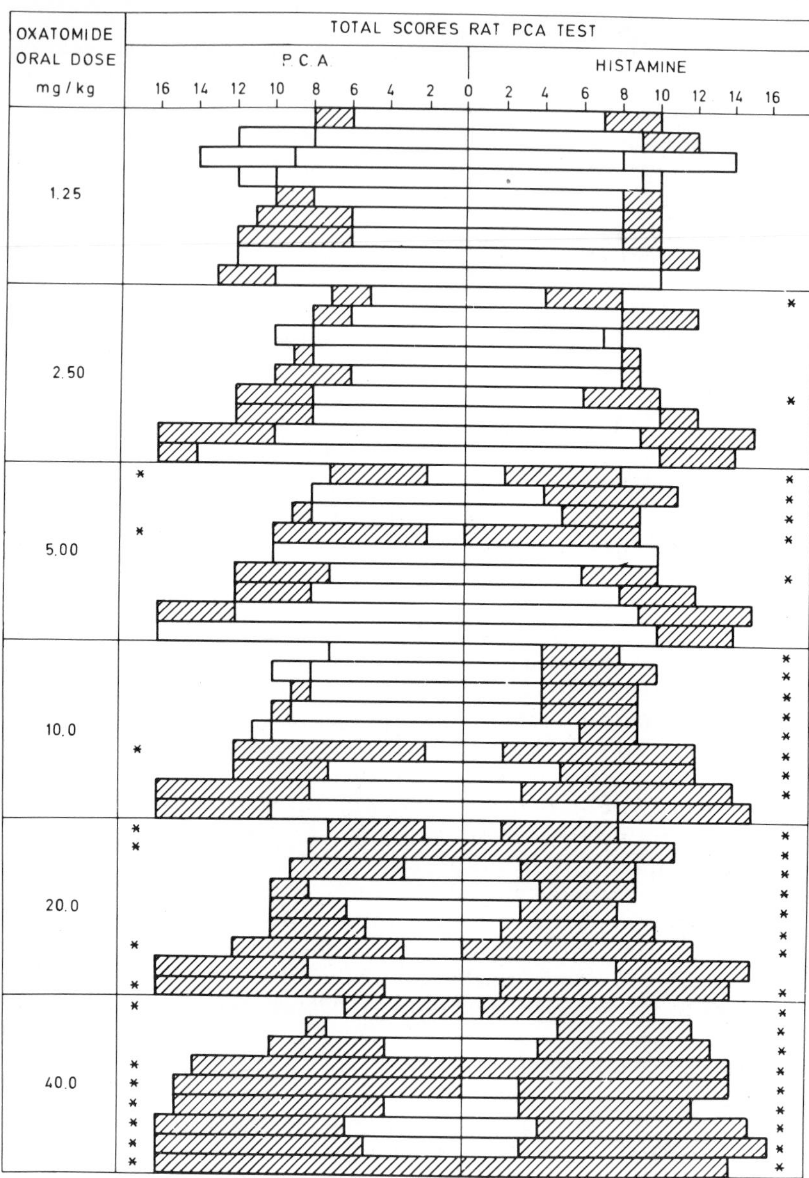


*Figure 2. The rat PCA test. Each horizontal bar indicates the total score for the reactions induced by ovalbumin (intravenously; PCA reaction) and by histamine (intradermally) in the control rat and in the oxatomide-treated rat (p.o., t = 2 hr) of the same daily session. Hatched areas represent the reduction observed with oxatomide and the asterisks indicate significant reduction of the total score.*

TABLE VI

Inhibitory effect on PCA and histamine reactions in the rat.

| Compound nr. | PCA $ED_{50}$ (mg/kg) | Histamine $ED_{50}$ (mg/kg) | Compound nr. | PCA $ED_{50}$ (mg/kg) | Histamine $ED_{50}$ (mg/kg) |
|---|---|---|---|---|---|
| a. Benzimidazolones | | | | | |
| 1 | > 10 | > 10 | 17 | > 10 | > 10 |
| 2 | > 10 | > 10 | 18 | > 10 | > 10 |
| 3 | > 10 | > 10 | 20 | > 10 | > 10 |
| 4 | > 10 | > 10 | 21 | > 10 | > 10 |
| 5 | > 10 | > 10 | 22 | > 10 | > 10 |
| 6 | > 10 | > 10 | 23 | ~ 10 | ~ 7.5 |
| 7 | > 10 | > 10 | 24 | ~ 2.5 | ~ 1.25 |
| 8 | ~ 20 | ~ 5 | 25 | ~ 2.5 | ~ 5 |
| 9 | ~ 10 | ~ 5 | 26 | > 10 | > 10 |
| 10 | ≥ 10 | ~ 5 | 30 | > 10 | > 10 |
| 11 | > 10 | > 10 | 31 | > 10 | > 10 |
| 12 | > 10 | > 10 | 32 | > 10 | > 10 |
| 13 | ~ 10 | ~ 5 | 35 | > 10 | > 10 |
| 14 | > 10 | ≤ 10 | 37 | > 10 | > 10 |
| 15 | > 10 | > 10 | | | |
| 16 | > 10 | > 10 | | | |
| b. Benzimidazoles | | | | | |
| 39 | > 10 | > 10 | 55 | > 10 | > 10 |
| 42 | > 10 | > 10 | 60 | > 10 | > 10 |
| 43 | > 10 | > 10 | 61 | ~ 10 | ~ 5 |
| 44 | > 10 | > 10 | 62 | > 10 | < 10 |
| 45 | > 10 | > 10 | 63 | > 10 | > 10 |
| 46 | > 10 | > 10 | 64 | > 10 | > 10 |
| 47 | > 10 | > 10 | 65 | > 10 | > 10 |
| 48 | ~ 10 | ~ 10 | 67 | > 10 | > 10 |
| 49 | > 10 | > 10 | 69 | > 10 | > 10 |
| 50 | > 10 | > 10 | 70 | > 10 | > 10 |

In Table VII the calculated $ED_{50}$'s with confidence limits are summarized for oxatomide and various reference compounds. Higher doses of oxatomide (19.6 mg/kg) were required to practically abolish the vascular permeability changes, which occur upon ovalbumin injection, than to reduce the acute histamine-induced changes (4.8 mg/kg). Pyrilamine, diphenhydramine and doxanthrazole were inactive against either reaction type at orally administered doses of 40 mg/kg. Cinnarizine and flunarizine were virtually as active against the histamine reaction as was oxatomide, but were definitely less effective inhibitors of the PCA-reaction. Azatadine, known to be a potent antihistaminic, was very effective in reducing the intensity of the histamine reactions. Inhibition of PCA-reactions, however, did not regularly increase with increasing dose and the calculated $ED_{50}$ showed wide confidence limits. Cromolyn sodium and bufrolin were tested intravenously at a single dose, expected to be active according to literature data. Both compounds were effective on the PCA-reactions, but did not reduce the intensity of the histamine reactions.

*The Compound 48/80 Lethality Test*. Control data and the protection obtained after oxatomide administration have fully been described (24). The oral $ED_{50}$ of oxatomide, with an interval of 2 h between its administration and the intravenous challenge with compound 48/80, was 4.82(3.69 - 6.80) mg/kg.

Comparison with numerous reference compounds in this test indicated that histamine antagonism at the level of the so-called $H_1$-histamine receptors was sufficient to prevent the lethal shock, but other effects in relation to the release and action of mast cell mediators may promote the protective activity of a compound.

*M. Butyricum-Induced Arthritis*. Rats of a sensitive breed (27) were injected with *M. butyricum* in oil and used for the oxatomide experiment after development of arthritis, according to fully described procedures (28). The increase in diameter of hind-paws and tibiotarsal joints on day 14 was 8.8, 10.7 and 11.9 mm in the rats at the time food, mixed with sufficient oxatomide to give an approximate daily dose of 40 mg/kg, was provided. On day 28 the increases in diameters were 10.9, 12.0 and 12.4 mm, respectively. Changes in body weight over the same period ranged between 0 and + 10 g.

*Acute Toxicity of Oxatomide in Rats*. Upon intravenous injection the $LD_{50}$ of oxatomide in male Wistar rats was 34.4 (26.3 - 45.0) mg/kg and in female Wistar rats 28.2(21.6 - 36.8) mg/kg. Upon oral administration the $LD_{50}$ in male rats was higher than 2,560 mg/kg; in female rats there was no linear increase in mortality with dose and the estimated $LD_{50}$ was 1,670 mg/kg. The safety margin of oxatomide with respect to the lowest $ED_{50}$ for protection from mast cell-mediated effects was more than 530($LD_{50}/ED_{50}$ = > 2 560/4.82).

Comments on the Studies in Rats. Passive cutaneous anaphylaxis in rats has been used extensively in the study of cromoglycate-like compounds. Upon intravenous administration these compounds can abolish the vascular permeability changes, which follow mediator release from sensitized mast cells. This activity appears at doses which do not inhibit the effects of exogenous mediators. The oral activity of this type of compounds is generally nil and this holds also for doxanthrazole, which was inactive in the standard conditions of our test.

Oxatomide, by contrast, is capable of completely suppressing PCA-reactions after oral administration. At active doses, complete suppression of histamine-induced reactions is also observed. Moreover antagonism of compound 48/80-induced lethality is observed in the same dose-range. This raises questions about the relative importance of the contribution of endogenous histamine to PCA-reactions. In our experience all potent $H_1$-histamine antagonists attenuate PCA-reactions, but even in the case of azatadine (29), the observed irregular activity may result from complex antagonism, including serotonin.

Mast cells and their mediators may play a role in various reactions of inflammatory type. In the experiment with M. butyricum-induced arthritis a daily dose of 40 mg/kg of oxatomide was totally ineffective in improving the prominent symptoms of the arthritis, i.e. the diameter increase of the hind-paws and the impaired growth. The observed lack of activity indicates at least that oxatomide does not interfere with the synthesis nor the action of prostaglandins.

Oxatomide thus appears in the rat studies to be a specific and orally active antagonist of mast cell-mediated reactions.

## Studies in Dogs

Introduction. The anti-allergic activity of compounds has only rarely been studied in dogs, even though systemic anaphylaxis was first properly recognized in this species (30). Spontaneous immediate hypersensitivity in dogs to allergens of clinical importance has now repeatedly been reported and the sensitizing antibody type has all the characteristics of IgE (31-36). The most common condition which leads to pronounced symptoms upon appropriate challenge with allergen preparations is nematode infection. An aerosol challenge, which induces pronounced changes in pulmonary resistance and breathing frequency, has now been described as a useful model of human asthma (37-39).

TABLE VII

Rat PCA test
Oral $ED_{50}$ - values (mg/kg, t - 2 h) of various compounds for protection from PCA and histamine reactions

| Compound (dose) | PCA | Histamine |
|---|---|---|
| Oxatomide | 19.6 (9.48 - 40.5) | 4.78 (2.90 - 7.86) |
| Cinnarizine | $>$40.0 | 5.14 (2.65 - 9.95) |
| Flunarizine | $\geqslant$40.0 | 7.75 (3.84 - 15.7) |
| Pyrilamine | $>$40.0 | $>$40.0 |
| Diphenhydramine | $>$40.0 | $>$40.0 |
| Hydroxyzine | $\geqslant$40.0 | 14.7 (6.2 - 35.0) |
| Azatadine | 13.6 (1.45 - 127) | 1.53 (0.61 - 3.85) |
| Doxanthrazole | $>$40.0 | $>$40.0 |
| I.V. t- 1 min | (Positive animals/total) | |
| Cromolyn Sodium (40 mg/kg) | 4/5 | 0/5 |
| Bufrolin (0.16 mg/kg) | 3/5 | 0/5 |

TABLE VIII

Inhibition (4 hr) of ACF (1/100) and histamine reactions in dog

| Compound nr. | $ED_{50}$ ACF (1/100) mg/kg | $ED_{50}$ histamine mg/kg |
|---|---|---|
| 8 | 1.25 | 1.22 |
| 23 | $\sim$ 1.25 | $\sim$ 5 |
| 25 | $\sim$ 2.5 | $\geqslant$ 2.5 |

Materials, Methods and Results.

The Dog Ascaris Allergy Test. *Ascaris*-sensitive Beagle dogs were used. On the clipped abdomen two intradermal injections of 0.05 ml were given, one of diluted *Ascaris coeloma* fluid (ACF, 1:100 in saline) and one of histamine (10 μg/ml saline). The oedema index, i.e. the difference between oedematous and normal skin thickness was measured 15 min after the injections.

In control conditions the median oedema index was 25 (= 2.5 mm) for ACF reactions and 20 (= 2.0 mm) for histamine reactions. On the basis of the distribution of the oedema indices, inhibition of ACF-reactions was significant for values below 14 and of histamine reactions for values below 11.

In preliminary experiments oxatomide was administered at a relatively high dose of 10 mg/kg. This dose had no effect on gross behaviour of the animals, but virtually totally abolished the skin responses both to ACF (1:100) and to histamine (0.5 μg), 4 h after its oral administration.

The time course of the effectiveness of different oxatomide doses in reducing the reactions is presented in Fig. 3. The reactions in solvent-treated dogs (dose 0) remained stable throughout the 24 h-test period, whereas increasing doses of oxatomide, from 0.16 up to 10.0 mg/kg had an increasingly pronounced and lasting inhibitory effect. In Table VIII the results are summarized for oxatomide, R 35 918 and R 37 281 (compounds 8, 23 and 25). It appears that, 4 h after administration, there is no significant difference between the three compounds.

Inhibition of Cremophor-Induced Histamine Release. Intravenous challenge of dogs with Cremophor EL®, a wetting agent, releases histamine (40). The effect of Cremophor is pronounced in this species. Although the mechanism of this release is not fully understood, it is clearly not a general property of detergents (41).

In our experiments 30 adult Beagle dogs of either sex were used. Four hours after the oral administration of oxatomide or solvent 5 ml blood was sampled. This was followed by intravenous injection of Cremophor EL (BASF) 25 %, in a volume of 0.1 ml/kg and further blood samples were collected 5, 15 and 30 min after the Cremophor injection. During this period behavioural changes were recorded.

The blood samples were cooled in ice and centrifuged for 10 min at 2,000 rpm; 2 ml plasma was mixed with 50 μl 12N perchloric acid. The supernatant, obtained after centrifugation for 10 min at 4,000 rpm, was deep frozen until automatic fluorometric histamine analysis according to Siraganian (42, 43).

After intravenous injection of Cremophor repeated head

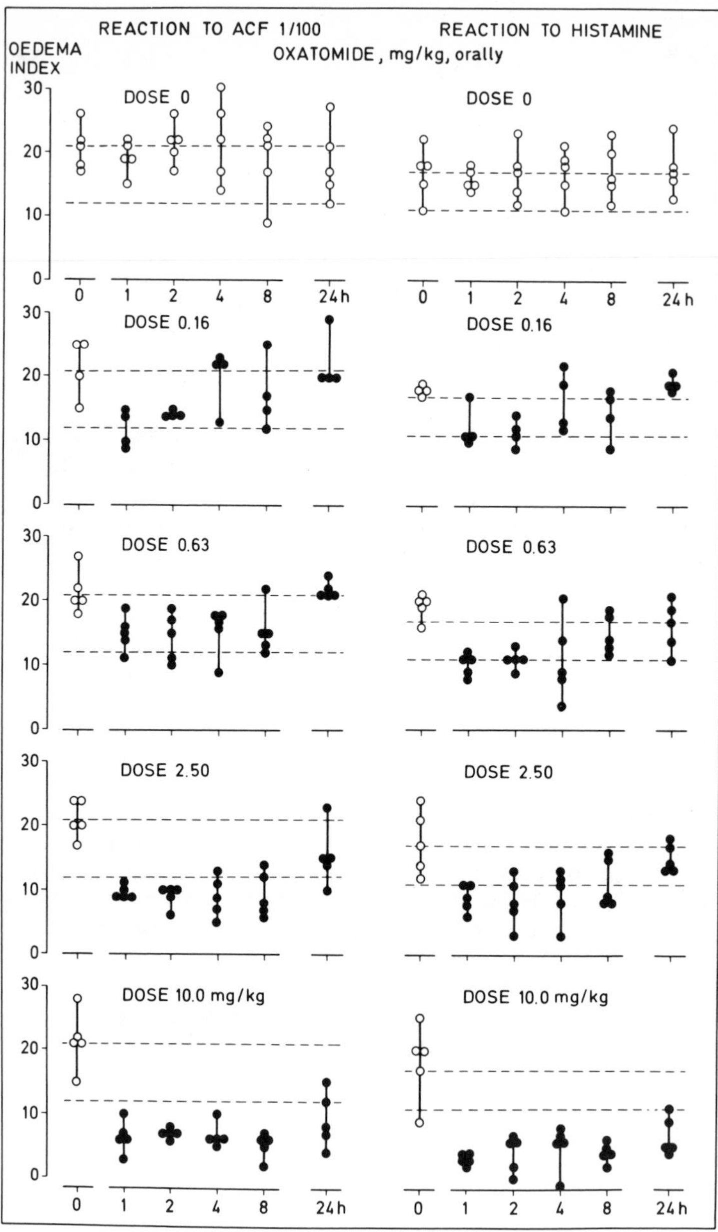


*Figure 3. Individual oedema indices for* Ascaris coeloma *fluid (ACF 1:100) and histamine reactions at various times after oral administration of oxatomide in the dog* Ascaris *allergy test*

shakes, licking and scratching were observed in all animals. In most dogs blood sampling was difficult, especially at the 5 and 15-min interval, presumably as a consequence of hypotension. Hypotonia and ataxia occurred in some dogs and vomiting was recorded for two dogs. The administration of oxatomide had no pronounced effect on these behavioural changes, except at the dose of 10 mg/kg, which afforded partial protection. The frequency of head shakes and scratching movements was low as compared to the records of the same dogs in their control session.

The median normal histamine concentration in the 30 control plasmas was 5.0(4.8 - 6.1) ng/ml (confidence limits according to Owen, 44). Four hours after oral administration of oxatomide the median of the treated groups stayed within the control limits, except for the group treated with 10 mg/kg, in which the median plasma histamine concentration was 3.0 ng/ml.

The effect of intravenously injected Cremophor on the circulating histamine concentration is illustrated in Table IX. The median histamine levels in the control group were highest at the 5 min interval and decreased at the later sampling times. For the 30 control values the overall median was 181(147 - 261) ng/ml plasma 5 min after Cremophor injection, 97(71 - 130) ng/ml at the 15 min interval and 53.5(36 - 73) ng/ml at the 30 min interval. At the end of the experiment about 10 times more histamine was still circulating than before the Cremophor injection.

The lowest dose of oxatomide, 0.63 mg/kg, had no effect on the histamine levels, but from the dose of 1.25 mg/kg and above significantly less histamine was found in comparison with the corresponding control data. Half an hour after Cremophor injection the plasma histamine concentration was virtually normal in dogs treated with 2.50 mg/kg or more of oxatomide. A reduction to half of the control histamine levels was obtained with the dose of 2.75 mg/kg at the 5 min-interval; 15 and 30 min after Cremophor injection the same reduction was obtained with doses of 1.90 and 0.88 mg/kg respectively.

Histamine Clearance in Dogs. It has previously been reported that mepyramine increases the rate of histamine elimination from the circulation of guinea-pigs (45). It is conceivable that a similar effect played a role in the reduction of plasma histamine by oxatomide in the Cremophor experiments, especially since the reduction was more pronounced with time. An additional experiment was arranged to determine whether oxatomide changes the rate of histamine elimination.

Three Beagle dogs were injected intravenously with histamine (1 mg/ml saline; 1 ml/kg body weight). Before and 1, 3 and 9 min after the injection a 5 ml blood sample was drawn. One week later oxatomide, 10 mg/kg was administered orally to the

TABLE IX

Cremophor-induced histamine release in dogs. Individual data (ng/ml histamine) obtained in 30 dogs, treated orally with solvent (S) or with different doses of R 35 443 (D) 4 h before the cremophor injection.

| Dose mg/kg | Time in minutes after cremophor injection | | | | | |
|---|---|---|---|---|---|---|
| | 5' | | 15' | | 30' | |
| | S | D | S | D | S | D |
| 0.63 | 126<br>287<br>151<br>251<br>60<br>519 | 158<br>242<br>214<br>357<br>141<br>204 | 98<br>102<br>147<br>256<br>71<br>200 | 158<br>73<br>339<br>235<br>128<br>69 | 34<br>53<br>131<br>144<br>63<br>52 | 39<br>13<br>144<br>76<br>43<br>44 |
| 1.25 * | 81<br>161<br>174<br>359<br>200<br>248 | 137<br>133<br>76<br>307<br>98<br>308 | 43<br>127<br>56<br>216<br>57<br>264 | 20<br>71<br>36<br>80<br>47<br>168 | 12<br>80<br>54<br>279<br>44<br>139 | 9<br>26<br>13<br>13<br>19<br>142 |
| 2.5 * | 294<br>188<br>147<br>318<br>200<br>68 | 487<br>149<br>29<br>156<br>50<br>17 | 96<br>131<br>147<br>71<br>57<br>27 | 125<br>37<br>13<br>98<br>41<br>7 | 59<br>46<br>49<br>98<br>22<br>21 | 13<br>10<br>7<br>31<br>8<br>6 |
| 5. * | 187<br>65<br>174<br>318<br>110<br>364 | 24<br>9<br>40<br>75<br>72<br>279 | 87<br>10<br>69<br>91<br>85<br>129 | 15<br>7<br>13<br>51<br>12<br>20 | 17<br>4<br>17<br>187<br>59<br>24 | 7<br>7<br>15<br>9<br>7<br>3 |
| 10. * | 146<br>132<br>112<br>160<br>340<br>270 | 54<br>26<br>35<br>30<br>70<br>85 | 100<br>120<br>60<br>87<br>140<br>230 | 13<br>7<br>8<br>17<br>102<br>60 | 77<br>67<br>38<br>9<br>160<br>69 | 7<br>5<br>5<br>3<br>12<br>7 |

* Significantly different from controls ($P < 0.05$), Wilcoxon one-tailed Matched-pairs signed ranks test.

same dogs followed 4 h later by the same sequence of histamine injection and blood samples. In the deproteinized plasma samples histamine was measured as described.

The results are presented in Fig. 4. The clearance of injected histamine from the circulating blood was very rapid in the control session and oral administration of a high dose of oxatomide did not change the elimination curve.

Comments on the Dog Experiments. A procedure similar to the presently described dog Ascaris allergy test has been used to study the anti-allergic activity of BM 06.001 (46). Apparently oxatomide is a much more potent inhibitor of both the allergic and the histamine-induced skin reactions, when compared to BM 06.001. Furthermore oxatomide virtually abolished the skin oedemas at doses below those inducing behavioural changes in the animals.

Active doses of oxatomide with respect to ACF-reactions, histamine reactions and Cremophor-induced histamine release are of the same order. It appears therefore likely that the anti-allergic activity of oxatomide is the result of two simultaneously occurring actions, a reduction of the amount of mediators set free from sensitized mast cells and an effective antagonism of whatever released histamine is going to act on smooth muscle.

## General Conclusions

Oxatomide has been selected from a new chemical series of benzimidazolones and benzimidazoles on th basis of its activity on hypersensitivity and histamine-induced reactions in three species, the guinea-pig, the rat and the dog. In a well-known model, the guinea-pig anaphylaxis, oxatomide was at least as effective on the anaphylactic shock as on the histamine oedema induced in the same animals. In the rat, the new compound was an orally active inhibitor of PCA-reactions. Compound 48/80-induced lethal shock was prevented at doses of the same order as those required to inhibit histamine skin reactions. In the dog inhibition of allergic reactions, induced by Ascaris allergens in the skin of hypersensitive dogs, inhibition of histamine skin reactions and reduction of circulating histamine released by Cremophor EL were obtained by virtually the same oral doses.

From these studies it is concluded that oxatomide is a safe, orally active compound with pronounced anti-allergic activity, which appears to be based on both the reduction of the amount of released allergic mediators and antagonism of their action on target smooth muscle.

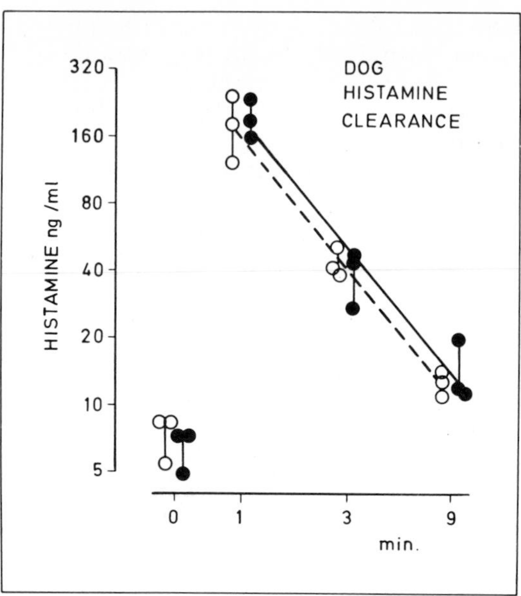


*Figure 4. Histamine levels in the circulating blood of three dogs after iv injection of 0.1 mg/kg histamine in the control experiment (○) and 4 hr after the oral administration of 10 mg/kg oxatomide (●)*

Acknowledgement

Part of this work has been supported by the I. W. O. N. L. (Instituut tot Aanmoediging van het Wetenschappelijk Onderzoek in Nijverheid en Landbouw).

## Literature Cited

1. Halpern, B.N., Stiffel, C., Liacopoulos-Briot, M., and Conovici, L., Arch. Int. Pharmacodyn. (1963) 142, 170-184.
2. Van Nueten, J.M., and Janssen, P.A.J., Arch. Int. Pharmacodyn. (1973) 204, 37-55.
3. Emanuel, M.B., Chamberlain, J.A., Whiting, S., Rigden, B.G., and Craven, A.H., Brit. J. Clin. Pharmacol. (1978) in press.
4. Awouters, F., Niemegeers, C.J.E., and Janssen, P.A.J., Arch. Int. Pharmacodyn. Ther. (1975) 217, 38-43.
5. Awouters, F., Niemegeers, C.J.E., Vandenberk, J., Van Nueten, J.M., Lenaerts, F.M., Borgers, M., Schellekens, K.H.L., Broeckaert, A., De Cree, J., and Janssen, P.A.J., Experienta (1977) 33, 1657-1659.

6. Awouters, F., Borgers, M., De Clerck, F., and Niemegeers, C.J.E., International Meeting of Medical Therapy "Recent advances on asthma" Campione d'Italia, June 1978. Biomedical Series of Bioscience, Roma (1978) in press.
7. Reyntjens, A.J., Niemegeers, C.J.E., Van Nueten, J.M., Laduron, P., Heykants, J., Schellekens, K.H.L., Marsboom, R., Jagenau, A., Broeckaert, A., and Janssen, P.A.J., Arzneim. Forsch. (1978) 28, 1194-1196.
8. Davoll, J., J. Chem. Soc. (1960) 308-314.
9. Preston, P.N., Chem. Rev. (1974) 74, 279-314.
10. Van Allen, J.A., and Deacon, B.D., Org. Synthesis (1950) 30, 56-57.
11. Raeymaekers, A.H.M., and Van Gelder, J.H.L., U.S. Patent n° 4.032.536 (1977).
12. Lewis, R.A., and Austen, K.F., Fed. Proc. (1977) 36, 2676-2683.
13. Piper, P.J., Pharmacol. Ther. (B) (1977) 3, 75-98.
14. Drazen, J.M., and Austen, K.F., J. Clin. Invest. (1974) 53, 1679-1685.
15. Devey, M.E., Anderson, K.J., Coombs, R.R.A., Henschel, M.J., and Coates, M.E., Clin. Exp. Immunol. (1976) 26, 542-548.
16. Broder, I., Rogers, S., Chamberlain, D.W., and Milne, E.N.C., Clin. Immunol. Immunopathol. (1978) 9, 1-15.
17. Borgers, M., De Brabander, M., Van Reempts, J., Awouters, F., and Jacob, W.A., Lab. Invest. (1977) 37, 1-8.
18. Borgers, M., De Brabander, M., Van Reempts, J., Awouters, F., and Janssen, P.A.J., Int. Arch. Allergy Appl. Immunol. (1978) 56, 507-516.
19. Finney, D.J., Probit Analysis. Cambridge University Press, Cambridge (1962) 236-254.
20. Bryant, D.H., Burns, M.W., and Lazarus, L., J. Allergy Clin. Immunol. (1975) 56, 417-428.
21. Ishizaka, T., Hosp. Practice (1977) 57-66.
22. Ishizaka, T., Ishizaka, K., Conrad, D.H., and Froese, A., J. Allergy Clin. Immunol. (1978) 61, 320-330.
23. Goth, A., Adv. Pharmacol. (1967) 5, 47-78.
24. Niemegeers, C.J.E., Awouters, F., Van Nueten, J.M., De Nollin, S., and Janssen, P.A.J., Arch. Int. Pharmacodyn. Ther. (1978) 234, 164-176.
25. Watanabe, N., and Ovary, Z., J. Immunol. Methods (1977) 14, 381-390.
26. Mota, I., Immunology (1964) 7, 681-699.

27. Awouters, F., Niemegeers, C.J.E., Lenaerts, F.M., and Janssen, P.A.J., Arzneim. Forsch. (1975) 25, 1526-1537.
28. Awouters, F., Lenaerts, P.M.H., and Niemegeers, C.J.E., Arzneim. Forsch. (1976) 26, 40-43.
29. Tozzi, S., Roth, F.E., and Tabachnick, I.I.A., Agents Actions (1974) 4, 264-270.
30. Portier, M.M., and Richet, C., C.R. Soc. Biol. (1902) 54, 170-172.
31. Booth, B.H., Patterson, R., and Talbot, C.H., J. Lab. Clin. Med. (1970) 76, 181-189.
32. Kessler, G.F., Frick, O.L., and Gold, W.M., Int. Arch. Allergy (1974) 47, 313-328.
33. Patterson, R., and Sparks, D.B., J. Immunol. (1962) 88, 262-268.
34. Rockey, J.H., and Schwarzman, R.M., J. Immunol. (1967) 98, 1143-1151.
35. Rocha e Silva, M., and Graña, A., Arch. Surg. (1946 a) 52, 523-537.
36. Rocha e Silva, M., and Graña, A., Arch. Surg. (1946 b) 52, 713-728.
37. Gold, W.M., Meyers, G.C., Dain, D.S., Miller, R.L., and Bourne, H.R., J. Appl. Physiol. (1977) 43, 271-275.
38. Krell, R.D., Br. J. Pharmac. (1978) 62, 519-528.
39. Yamatake, Y., Sasagawa, S., Yanaura, S., and Kobayashi, N., Jpn. J. Pharmacol. (1977) 27, 791-797.
40. Lorenz, W., Agents Actions (1975) 5, 402-416.
41. Lorenz, W., Reimann, H.-J., Schmal, A., Dormann, P., Schwarz, B., Neugebauer, E., and Doenicke, A., Agents Actions (1977) 7, 63-67.
42. Siraganian, R.P., Anal. Biochem. (1974) 57, 383-394.
43. Siraganian, R.P., J. Immunol. Methods (1975) 7, 283-290.
44. Owen, D.B., in: Handbook of Statistical Tables. p. 362-365. Addison Wesley, Reading (1962).
45. Hahn, F., Kretzschmar, R., Teschendorf, H.J., and Mitze, R., Int. Arch. Allergy (1970) 39, 449-458.
46. Zimmerman, I., Ulmer, W.T., and Roesch, A., Arzneim. Forsch. (1977) 27, 1999-2002.

RECEIVED August 6, 1979.

# BRONCHODILATORS AND OTHER PHARMACODYNAMIC AGENTS

# 11

# Introduction: Bronchodilators and Other Pharmacodynamic Agents

DAVIS L. TEMPLE, JR.

Mead Johnson Pharmaceuticals, Evansville, IN 47721

The first section of this book deals with drugs which inhibit the immunologically-induced release of mediators of anaphylaxis from certain target cells such as mast cells and polymorphonuclear neutrophils. Such drugs thus would be expected to be useful for the treatment of asthma and related atopic disease in a purely prophylactic sense. Since asthma is a multipartite disease, or even a family of diseases of varied etiology, simple inhibition of immunologically-induced mediator release may not be sufficient to prevent clinical manifestations. Thus it is necessary to consider other pharmacodynamic agents as useful antiasthma drugs. The second section of this book deals with such drugs, which may block mediator release, but also act to inhibit the consequences of mediator release or other bronchospastic stimulation. Such drugs could then provide therapeutic utility beyond the often incomplete prophylactic actions of mediator release inhibitors.

Figure 1 shows proposed interrelationships between the various anaphylactic substances and control of smooth muscle tone and secretory processes. Although somewhat oversimplified, this diagram provides a framework for determining sites for drug interaction as well as for proposing mechanisms of action. According to this scheme, histamine, ECF-A, SRS-A, kallikrein, and PAF are the primary mediators of anaphylaxis released from mast cells, whereas the prostaglandins (which are sensitized *de novo* following an appropriate stimulus) and bradykinin are secondary mediators of anaphylaxis. Likewise, leukocytes release other constrictive, chemotactic, and proteolytic substances which play crucial roles in asthma, bronchitis, emphysema, and other respiratory disease. Patients with chronic obstructive pulmonary disease (COPD) such as chronic bronchitis and emphysema may possess excessive proteolytic enzyme activity which have a part in tissue destruction. The esterolytic enzyme elastase, which is a lysosomal enzyme derived from neutrophilic polymorphonuclear leukocytes, has been shown to be the primary proteolytic enzyme involved in the progressive alveolar wall destruction characteristic of emphysema. The effects of elastase are normally held in check by the

0-8412-0536-1/80/47-118-211$05.00/0

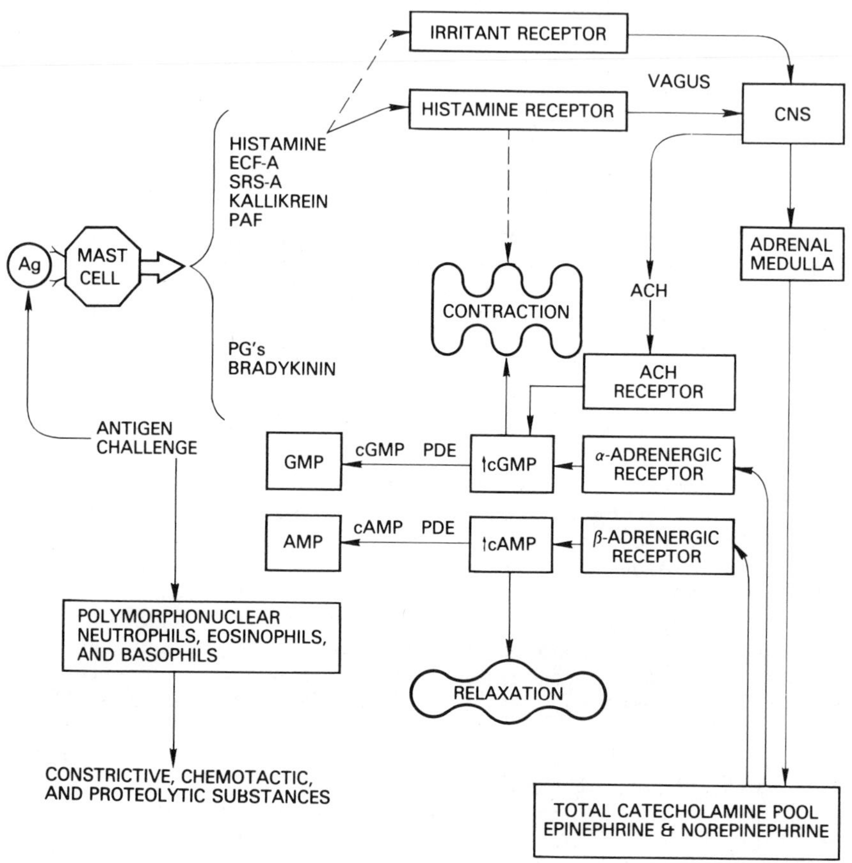


*Figure 1. Interrelationships between the various anaphylactic substances and control of smooth muscle tone and secretory processes*

presence of protease inhibitor enzymes, of which $\alpha_1$-antitrypsin is the most important. Local alveolar protease-antiprotease imbalances due to cigarette smoke or genetic $\alpha_1$-antitrypsin deficiency may develop and relate to the pathogenesis of COPD. Thus, an effective, nontoxic elastase inhibitor would potentially represent a useful drug for the treatment of COPD.

Accretion of a viscid mucus is the hallmark of the more chronic forms of obstructive pulmonary disease. The presence of the mucus exacerbates the pathology both by providing a mechanical block to the inspiration and expiration of air and by preventing topical drugs from reaching the distal bronchi. Although not universally accepted, therapy which will liquify the mucus so that it can be expectorated should have a place in the treatment of COPD. Sulfhydryl drugs such as N-acetylcysteine are available for this use.

For the purposes of this discussion, we will consider histamine as the mediator of anaphylaxis. The importance of this substance in asthma and respiratory disease is well documented. As shown in Figure 1, histamine may act at either a histamine or a nonspecific receptor site to produce direct smooth muscle contraction or more importantly vagal reflex smooth muscle contraction. Although the classical antihistamines have long been known to be of value in the treatment of the symptoms of various allergic conditions, they are generally considered ineffective in the treatment of bronchial asthma. We do note, however, that some of the new "second generation" antihistamines such as ketotifen and oxatomide are not only classical histamine antagonists but are also reported to be effective inhibitors of mediator release, although the mechanism of the latter activity remains undefined for this group of drugs.

Histamine-induced vagal reflex bronchoconstriction is mediated *via* acetylcholine release at nerve endings in bronchi. Acetylcholine leads to increased levels of cGMP in bronchial smooth muscle and then sequentially to constriction. Thus the parasympathetic system is important in the airways, playing a modulating role in bronchomotor tone and in responses to irritants. Various workers have, however, shown that parasympathetic reflexes are not invariably a major component of human bronchial responses to inhaled antigen. Hence anticholinergic bronchodilator drugs may be more useful in chronic congestive states which lead to a high degree of reflex cholinergic stimulation as seen in chronic bronchitis. Until recent years anticholinergic bronchodilator drugs were not of great interest for use in the treatment of chronic obstructive airway disease - primarily because of uncontrolled, often inappropriate, use in the past as well as a high incidence of the overt systemic anticholinergic side effects seen with atropine usage. Renewed interest in anticholinergic bronchodilator drugs was precipitated by the introduction of Sch-1000, a topically-effective anticholinergic bronchodilator drug characterized by a low incidence of side effects when administered by the topical route. Current work in this area is directed at "non-classical" agents which show selectivity for the bronchi over the salivary receptor site.

Stimulation of the α-adrenergic receptor, like cholinergic stimulation, leads to a concomitant increase in cGMP, and hence to increased contractility of smooth muscle. The presence of α-adrenergic receptors in tracheal smooth muscle has been a matter of controversy. Various workers have however demonstrated that sympathomimetic agents will contract human tracheal smooth muscle *in vitro* in the presence of β-adrenergic blocking agents. These observations lend validity to the concept of α-adrenergic receptors playing a role in the maintenance of airway tone. Clinical experience with phentolamine, thymoxamine, indoramine and others has shown mixed results; the consensus however is that these drugs may be useful in some severe cases of asthma where the activity of α-receptors is enhanced.

Anaphylactic conditions in the bronchi induce a CNS-mediated release of catecholamines from the adrenal medulla. These catecholamines contribute to the total catecholamine pool of stored and circulating epinephrine and norepinephrine. Stimulation of the β-adrenergic receptor (adenylate cyclase) leads to an increase in cAMP levels in both bronchial smooth muscle and mast cells to give smooth muscle relaxation and lessened mediator release. This β-adrenergic receptor site has proven sensitive to synthetic compounds which show marked advantages in terms of oral activity, selectivity ($\beta_2$ over $\beta_1$), and duration of action over epinephrine and isoproterenol as drugs. These newer agents which are discussed in detail in a following chapter may not yet represent optimal agents as they are reported to possess a variety of deficits such as tumorigenicity and tremorigenicity.

Just as cAMP levels are enchanced by adenylate cyclase stimulation, they are decreased through metabolism of cAMP by cAMP phosphodiesterase. Correspondingly, inhibition of this enzyme leads to increased smooth muscle and mast cell intracellular cAMP levels and hence bronchodilation and inhibition of mediator release. cAMP phosphodiesterase is inhibited by drugs such as theophylline which is useful in the treatment and prophylaxis of asthma. Theophylline has seen a recent resurgence in interest for use in the treatment of asthma partly due to the development of improved pharmaceutical preparations and to the availability of convenient methods for measuring blood and salivary levels. Theophylline is in fact now the drug of choice for maintenance therapy in chronic asthma. Theophylline unfortunately remains an unpredictable and erratic drug with severe toxicologic consequences following inappropriate or incorrect clinical use. Therefore, current research is aimed at new drugs possessing similar profiles of activity, but with lessened toxicologic and metabolic disadvantages.

Even though many new developments are being made in the area of classical bronchodilator drugs, extensive efforts are also being directed at more recent innovations such as synthetic prostaglandins. Prostaglandins and the lungs seem to have a close interrelation - bronchial tissue contains some of the highest prostaglandin levels in the body, of the PGE's which relax bronchial smooth muscle, of the PGFα's which constrict bronchial smooth muscle, as well as the various products of arachidonic acid cascade. Although both classes of prostaglandins have been shown to increase cAMP levels *in vitro, in vivo* biologic effects (bronchodilation) are apparently mediated by direct stimulation of adenyl cyclase. It was demonstrated some time ago that topical application of either $PGE_1$ or $PGE_2$ produced marked bronchodilation, with the latter compound being more potent. These natural PGE's are not useful bronchodilator drugs even though they are more potent bronchodilators than isoproterenol due to upper airway irritation, reflex bronchoconstriction, potent cough induction, and a very short duration of action. These considerations have led various groups to synthesize prostaglandin analogs with modifications aimed at preventing these problems.

A variety of pharmacodynamic agents are thus useful for the treatment of respiratory disease. Agents which affect cyclic nucleotide systems are important in the maintenance of airway smooth muscle tone and in the inhibition of mediator release from mast cells, while other agents act directly on specific enzymes, cells, or secretions involved in respiratory disease. The purpose of all of these agents that we have discussed is to increase or restore the ability of the lung to act as a blood oxygenating organ. Progress has been made in the area of bronchodilator and other respiratory pharmacodynamic agents in recent years, some of which is discussed in the following chapters.

RECEIVED August 6, 1979.

# Pathophysiologic Derangements in the Chronic Obstructive Pulmonary Diseases and Pharmacologic Regulation of Airway Function

SANFORD CHODOSH

Thorndike Memorial Laboratory, Pulmonary Section, Department of Medicine, Boston City Hospital and Boston University School of Medicine, Boston, MA 02118

Effective pharmacologic modification of abnormal airway function is dependent on an understanding of the specific underlying pathophysiologic derangements. Of the variety of lung diseases, it is the group characterized by the physiologic abnormality of chronic airways obstruction which relates to the content of this symposium. Although interest has considerably increased, the factual base of information pertinent to the pathophysiology of this group of diseases is still rather meager. A significant part of what we do know has been derived by investigating mechanisms of action of successful pharmacologic therapies that often were empirically developed. Newer therapeutic agents have emerged from such knowledge. Models which attempt to mimic the actual human disease state have become common tools in drug development research. Unfortunately, with the exception of bronchodilators, the models developed for chronic obstructive lung diseases have not been as predictive as desired. Indeed, the diseased human is usually the best model. In this chapter I will attempt to present a clinically oriented background from which pharmacologic therapy can be considered. There will be no pretense of completeness, and personal bias will be evident.

## Chronic Obstructive Lung Disease

Precise scientific communication has been hindered by the indiscriminate use of the physiologically descriptive terms of chronic obstructive lung disease (COLD) or chronic obstructive pulmonary disease (COPD). Although clinically useful for describing the patient with combinations of the obstructive diseases, the terms are not helpful in understanding the underlying pathophysiologic mechanisms of the specific disease entities that result in chronic airways obstruction. Chronic bronchitis and emphysema are generally considered to be the main diseases which comprise COLD, but chronic forms of intrinsic and extrinsic asthma are commonly included. On the other hand, other diseases,

0-8412-0536-1/80/47-118-217$08.25/0

such as cystic fibrosis, are considered to be outside the perimeter of the definition. Unfortunately, COLD or COPD are likely to remain part of medical terminology. One would hope for the development of diagnostic descriptions similar to those used in cardiology so that chronic airways obstruction would be one possible description of the physiologic defect. This would avoid the current confusion caused by the difficulty in the categorization of those chronic bronchitics, asthmatics and emphysematous patients who do not have chronic and/or even demonstrable airways obstruction. Even the early clinical manifestations of each of these diseases often reflect their basic pathologies, whereas the physiologic changes may not be demonstrable until the pathologic change is well advanced. The pathophysiologic process is the same whether the obstructive component is or is not present. Therefore, a diagnostic classification primarily based on obstruction of airways is less helpful than one which is primarily related to the pathophysiologic mechanisms.

Chronic bronchitis (CB), chronic pulmonary emphysema (CPE) and chronic bronchial asthma (CBA) are common diseases. The concurrence in individual patients of CB and CPE is frequent and of CBA and CB is not unusual. In the United States, the incidence of CB with or without CPE is about 15-30% of all adults (1). The estimates for CBA are around 3% (2). These diseases account for a significant proportion of the morbidity and mortality from all causes. Preventive measures and the use of therapeutic modalities aimed at reversing the pathologic change would be expected to have a significant impact in decreasing the incidence of disability and premature death.

## Common Physiologic Abnormalities

It is the similarity of some of the physiologic abnormalities which can develop in the evolution of each of these diseases that had led to the regressive diagnostic terminology of COLD or COPD. Although the abnormalities of airways obstruction and air trapping are common to all three diseases, they are often not helpful in the differential diagnosis among CB, CPE and CBA. Other measures of the physiologic state of the lung can be useful differentiators, although these may be manifestations of relatively late stages of disease. The airways obstruction can be demonstrated by a variety of tests, the most common being the timed forced expiratory spirogram. The degree of reversibility with a standard aerosol bronchodilator such as isoproterenol often is considered in the description of the nature of the obstruction. The air trapping is more difficult to document objectively since its assessment requires measurement of lung volume parameters. The compartment of the total lung volume most easily measured is the vital capacity (VC). In these obstructive airway diseases the VC is often reduced, but this is usually associated with an increase of the residual volume of air left in the lung after the full expiration of the VC.

## Potential Causes of Airways Obstruction

Although the obstructive phenomenon is quite similar in these diseases when characterized physiologically, the underlying pathologic changes of the bronchopulmonary system are significantly different in each of the diseases. Indeed, the combination and degree of the various abnormalities leading to obstruction are likely to be different for each patient and may vary from time to time in the same individual. The documented and possible reasons for airways obstruction in each of the three diseases is outlined in Table I. CBA is separated into extrinsic and intrinsic types, although hard data about intrinsic asthma is scant. In CB, the main causes of airways obstruction are bronchial secretions and constriction of the bronchial smooth muscle due to increased bronchomotor tone secondary to vagal influence. In CPE, collapse of the bronchial wall during expiration is the main problem although anatomic distortion from scarring must play a role. The reversible obstruction in extrinsic CBA is due to a number of factors including smooth muscle constriction relating to mast cell mediators and vagal activity, bronchial secretions and mucosal edema. In the more chronic phases of CBA, the bronchial smooth muscle hypertrophy and mucus plugs are important factors in the irreversible obstructive aspects of this disease. Factors common to both CB and extrinsic CBA play a role in the obstruction seen in instrinsic CBA.

It is also likely that changes common in CB and CBA are due to different pathophysiologic mechanisms. It is known that the inflammatory cell infiltrate in the mucosa is different in CB as opposed to CBA. The hypersecretion of mucus and vagal bronchomotor tone seen in both CB and CBA may also have different mechanisms. The little that is known about the basic pathophysiologic mechanisms at the human level is often soft data because the specific pathologic process of the subjects studied was not clearly identified. Often these mechanisms are proposed from studies of normal humans or arbitrary animal models. The transference of facts obtained by these methods to the interpretation of the pathophysiology of specific disease states should be undertaken cautiously.

## Chronic Bronchitis

Definition. The definition of CB is based on the clinical symptoms of chronic productive cough for at least three months of the year for two successive years. Other etiologies for these symptoms must be excluded before the diagnosis can be accepted (3). Among the diseases with which CB can be confused are tuberculosis,

Table I
Probable Causes of Airways Obstruction in CB, CPE and CBA

| Bronchial Pathophysiologic Abnormality | Chronic Bronchitis | | Chronic Pulmonary Emphysema | | Chronic Bronchial Asthma Extrinsic | | Chronic Bronchial Asthma Intrinsic | |
|---|---|---|---|---|---|---|---|---|
| | Role* | Nature+ | Role | Nature | Role | Nature | Role | Nature |
| Smooth Muscle | | | | | | | | |
| Reversible Constriction(cAMP) | ? | -- | 0 | --- | 4 | AR | 2-3 | AR |
| Reversible Constriction(Vagal) | 3 | AR | 0 | --- | 3 | AR | 3 | ? |
| Hypertrophy | 0 | -- | 0 | --- | 2 | SR | 1 | SR |
| Secretions | 4 | SR | 0 | --- | 3 | SR | 4 | SR |
| Wall Collapse | 0 | -- | 4 | N | 0 | -- | 0 | -- |
| Architectural Distortion | | | | | | | | |
| Anatomic (Scarring) | 1 | N | 2 | N | 0 | -- | 1 | N |
| Functional (Dynamic) | 2 | ? | ? | --- | ? | -- | 2 | ? |
| Mucosal and Submucosa | | | | | | | | |
| Edema | 1 | SR | 0 | --- | 3 | AR | 1-2 | AR |
| Metaplasia | 1 | SR | 0 | --- | 0 | -- | 1 | SR |
| Inflammatory Cellular Infiltrate | 1 | SR | 0 | --- | 1 | AR | 1 | SR |
| Mucus Gland Hypertrophy | 1 | SR | 0 | --- | 1 | SR | 1 | SR |

*Relative importance in obstruction: 0-4, 0=not important, 4=very important, ?=unknown importance

+Reversible nature of abnormality: AR=acutely reversible, SR=slowly reversible, N=not reversible

fungal infection, CBA, cystic fibrosis, chronic heart failure, etc. However, CB can also coexist with any of these. The lack of more definitive or acceptable criteria for establishing the diagnosis of CB indicates the limitations of our knowledge of this common disease.

Pathology. There are remarkably few critical descriptions of the pathology of CB (4). The disease appears to be limited to the bronchial wall. The inflammatory response in the mucosa and submucosa is characterized by an increase of monocytes in the submucosa with a spotty increase of polymorphonuclear neutrophils throughout the wall with some noted sticking to the walls of the capillaries. This small increase of neutrophils is surprising since the cellular composition of the intrabronchial exudate (sputum) is predominantly neutrophilic with lesser numbers of mononuclear phagocytes (monocytes and macrophages), suggesting that neutrophils are the major cell of the inflammatory response in CB. This predominance of neutrophils suggests that CB is likely a series of overlapping recurrent acute inflammatory episodes since chronic inflammation is usually characterized by mononuclear cells. Friable and denuded bronchial mucosal epithelium suggests that this tissue damage results in the reticulo-endothelial cell response. Repeated insults and regeneration of epithelium lead to the development of metaplasia. Goblet cells increase in numbers. All of these changes result in the loss of ciliated pseudo-columnar cells in the epithelial lining of the bronchial lumen. Associated with these changes is a hypertrophy and hyperplasia of the submucosal mucus glands with dilation of their ducts. These changes, along with the increase of mucus producing goblet cells in the epithelium, lead to an increased production of what also is likely an abnormal mucus. This increased production of mucus adds volume to the inflammatory exudate and accounts for the excess of secretions found in the bronchial lumen. There is evidence that viable bacteria are present in the mucosa of established chronic bronchitics (5), suggesting that bacterial infection of the epithelium may become an important component of the pathologic process. It has also been noted that lymphocytes accumulate in the tissues around the respiratory bronchioles. The significance of this finding is unknown, but it is possible that this may be related to the pathogenesis of emphysema.

Comparable findings have been noted in experimental bronchitis produced in rats exposed by inhalation to sulfur dioxide (6). In that setting, the progression of the pathology is noxious inhalant, inflammatory cellular response, hypersecretion, and lastly, lymphocytic accumulations with or without bacterial pneumonitis. Comparable studies in man do not exist. Consequently there is still controversy relative to the initial pathology in human bronchitis which must occur at a stage before it can be called "chronic".

Pathophysiology. The etiology of CB is not known. One suspects that there is an individual susceptibility which may predispose to the development of CB which is likely dependent on inherited and acquired host defense capability. A classification of host defense factors would include cellular, immune, non-immune humoral and mucociliary functions (7). Acquired host defense problems may be related to the patient's concomitant disease(s) such as CBA, tuberculosis, sickle cell disease, etc.

A postulated schema of the pathophysiologic mechanisms which may lead to CB is noted in Figure 1. A number of stimuli can be implicated and it appears likely that many different insults, alone or in combination, may precipitate the disease when superimposed on an enhanced host susceptibility. The inflammation producing stimuli, virtually all of which would affect the bronchi via their inhalation, can be divided into gases, particles and infectious agents. Examples of gases would be sulfur dioxide, oxidant air pollutants, cyanide, anesthetic agents, etc. The commonest implicated particle load comes from inhaled cigarette smoke, but "dusty" work conditions such as seen in coal mines and the hydrocarbon particles in air pollution are also likely noxious stimuli. Acute viral or bacterial bronchial infections are also possible initiating stimuli which may persist into the chronic phase. The concurrence of infection with some other inflammation-producing stimuli appears to increase the risk.

These stimuli probably trigger at least three types of bronchial response: 1) inflammation; 2) hypersecretion; and 3) increased vagal discharge. It is likely that the inflammatory response and the vagal stimulation may induce further hypersecretion. The death or injury of bronchial epithelial cells is the logical pathologic event which results in a typical acute inflammatory response. Each bronchial area of damaged epithelium elicits its own acute inflammatory response characterized by an initial predominance of neutrophils. With resolution in each area, monocytes, macrophages and other cells become predominant. The ratio of neutrophils to monocytic cells seen in the expectorated sputum reflects the balance between the number of areas with acute inflammation versus the number of areas undergoing recovery. With repeated injury, metaplasia replaces the normal epithelium in localized areas contributing to inadequate ciliary clearance of secretions. The cellular and non-cellular components of the inflammatory response contribute to the increase of intraluminal secretions. Acute hypersecretion by mucus producing glands and goblet cells is a normal response to noxious stimuli. Whether the persistent hypersecretion in CB is due to chronic exposure to stimuli and/or dysfunction of regulatory mechanisms is unclear. This chronic hypersecretion supplies additional obstructing material to the bronchial lumina. Ciliary function is compromised by the pathologic loss of ciliated cells and the inhibition of activity resulting from inhaled toxins. Mucociliary clearance is hindered by problems relating to both the

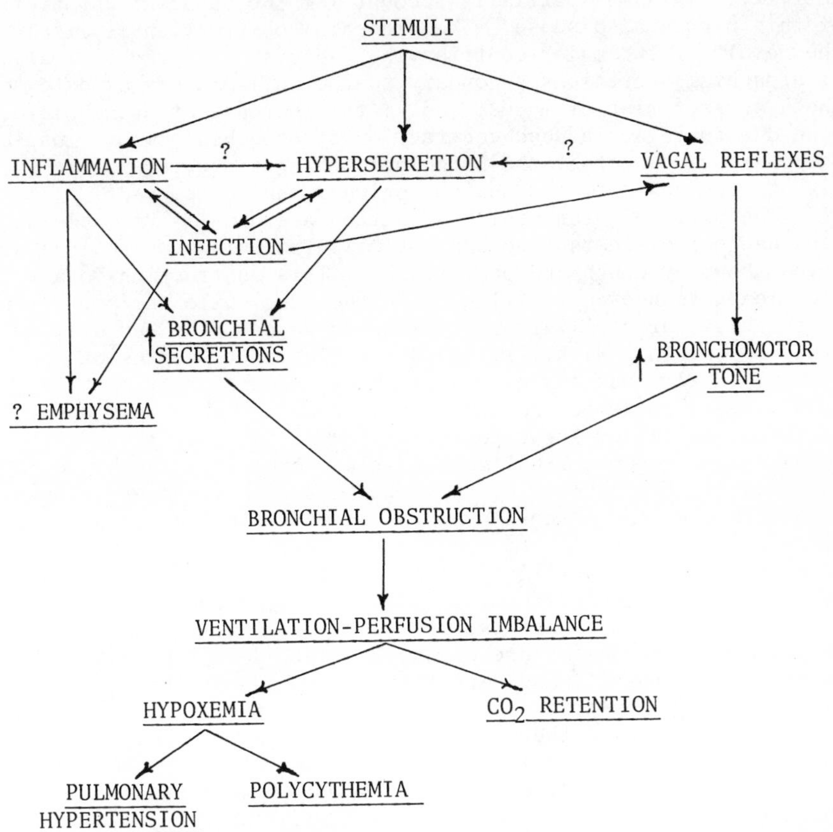


*Figure 1. Postulated pathophysiologic mechanisms in chronic bronchitis*

cilia and the secretions. With the stasis of secretions in the bronchi, inhaled microorganisms colonize the airways and may then invade the epithelium. These infections are usually bacterial in etiology and result in an indolent process which provides a built-in stimulus for more inflammation, hypersecretion and vagal activity. This may partially account for the apparent chronicity of this bronchial disease. The bronchial obstruction is likely the result of two major contributing factors: 1) the increase of bronchial secretions secondary to the inflammatory exudate and the hypersecretion of mucus, and 2) the increase of bronchomotor tone due to vagal induced contraction of bronchial smooth muscle. There is evidence that the pathologic changes are reversible in five to ten years if the noxious stimuli can be removed.

The sites of bronchial obstruction are usually variable and can change from instant to instant as intraluminal secretions are moved about by cough and positioning. This obstruction to air-flow leads to uneven ventilation in the lung while the perfusion of the alveolar capillaries remains unchanged. The sum of the areas in the lung with mismatched ventilation to perfusion probably determines the degree of shunt and when sufficiently imbalanced, hypoxemia and hypercarbia result. When this occurs acutely, the latter leads to respiratory acidosis. When chronically present, renal compensation normalizes the hydrogen ion content of the blood by the retention of bicarbonate. Severe hypoxemia can lead to cell hypoxia and death in many organ systems. Since hypoxemia usually develops gradually, compensatory changes first lead to hyperventilation and eventually to an increase of hemoglobin mass (polycythemia), pulmonary hypertension and chronic right-sided heart failure (cor pulmonale). These compensatory mechanisms are eventually self-defeating and cause significant morbidity and mortality. Reversal of the bronchial obstruction at any point short of death can reverse the hypoxemia and hypercarbia, and there is always the potential for a return to a normal functioning lung. The irreversible component which may remain can often be attributed to the emphysematous damage which seems to be a by-product of CB. Unfortunately, the noxious stimuli cannot always be identified and removed. It is fortunate that the majority of chronic bronchitics do not progress beyond the level of uncomplicated bronchial obstruction as noted in Figure 1.

Clinical Manifestations. The clinical manifestations of the majority of chronic bronchitics is limited to the basic symptoms of chronic cough productive of sputum. The typical patient is usually described as being a cigarette smoking male over the age of 40 years. However, this is misleading since a significant number of patients of both sexes often date the onset of symptoms to their 30's, or 20's or even teenage. Males do predominate but this difference is less apparent as the sex difference in smoking habits has changed and pollution affects all urban dwellers. The epidemiologically determined incidence is likely underestimated since a significant percentage of mild to moderately severe chronic bronchitics deny the symptoms, either because they are unaware or because they consider their chronic productive cough to be normal. It is also not known how to predict which of these bronchitics will spontaneously get better, will not progress or will go on to disabling disease. It is clear that the patient with even the mildest degree of chronic sputum production already has pathologic bronchial changes (8). In the early stages of the disease the patient often has a normal physical examination of the chest, a normal x-ray and pulmonary physiologic tests may, at worst, be equivocally abnormal. These early CB patients often get more chest colds which take longer than usual to resolve. However, a few severe chronic bronchitics will deny ever having a chest cold or pneumonia. The patient may first seek medical care because of such an acute bronchial infection, but even then the underlying CB may be denied or missed.

Shortness of breath during exertion, with or without wheezing, is the main reason that the chronic bronchitic first seeks help. The degree of measured physiologic abnormality may vary tremendously at this time. Careful questioning of the patient often reveals a subtle and gradual decrease of exercise tolerance prior to the overt awareness of this loss of function. The patient may also notice that shortness of breath is precipitated by exposure to cold and windy weather, irritating fumes, dusty environments and other stimuli which previously did not affect breathing. Examination of the chest at this time may still be within normal limits, but now one is more apt to hear rales, rhonchi, wheezes and a prolonged expiratory phase of respiration. It is common to hear abnormal adventitious sounds in one area of the lung, only to have them clear or change in quality or type after the patient coughs or breaths deeply. When these abnormal physical findings are present, they are indicative of the obstructive component of the chronic bronchitic's disease process.

The degree of disability noted by the chronic bronchitic is often not explained by the abnormalities of pulmonary function. Morbidity may be related to the recurrent exacerbations of bronchial infection or the lassitude associated with chronic inflammation in general while persistent and/or severe cough may also be contributory. This decreased ability to perform can be subtle and progressive if the disease is untreated and usually precedes the more serious physiologic consequences of hypoxia, hypercarbia, right heart failure and polycythemia. Even when the patient is aware that something is seriously wrong, these secondary complications may not be related to his chronic productive cough. Breathing becomes more labored and complaints of malaise, insomnia, irritability and indigestion are common. Family and associates may be the first to tell him he looks blue, and a dusky cyanosis of peripheral body areas can be detected. Dependent edema, increased problems with digestion and abdominal distention are often the first indications that right heart failure is present, although these are relatively late manifestations of this complication. Inappropriate somnolence suggests increasing retention of carbon dioxide. Bronchitics with these advanced problems are frequently admitted to the hospital, and many physicians only see them in these circumstances. However, in the full spectrum of this disease, such severely disabled patients represent only a small fraction of all chronic bronchitics.

Treatment--General Considerations. There are a number of therapeutic interventions useful in CB. Choices for the individual patient are dependent on the variety and severity of the problems and require modification as symptoms change. As is true for all chronic disease, planned long-term care with periodic observations is essential to achieve successful therapy. The goal of treatment in CB should always be the elimination of the disease. Cure can be achieved in some, and significant clinical improvement should be expected in most chronic bronchitics. The patient and the family should be educated about the nature of the disease as well as the specific purposes of the therapeutic regimen. Pharmacologic therapy prescribed without the background of a close physician-patient relationship is unlikely to be successful in achieving long-term benefits. The general areas in which therapy can be useful are infections, secretions, bronchodilatation, cough suppression and the avoidance of noxious stimuli.

Treatment--Avoidance of Stimuli. It is self-evident that decreasing or eliminating stimuli responsible for the bronchial damage will significantly help the chronic bronchitic. A major offending stimulus is inhalation of cigarette smoke, and a prime effort must be to stop or at least decrease this insult. Elimination of this problem may lead to a complete remission in some bronchitics and improvement in most. Avoidance of dusty environments and air pollution will also contribute to improvement. Bronchitics should be instructed to avoid situations where they may be subject to viral infections. The use of anti-viral vaccines is advocated, the prime immunization being against influenza. Since a significant number of acute bronchitis exacerbations are due to the pneumococcus, the use of pneumococcal vaccine is being recommended for bronchitics. However, there is no specific evidence that immunity to the few serotypes in the available vaccine will decrease bacterial exacerbations in CB.

Treatment--Bacterial Infection. Perhaps the most significant pharmacologic therapy in CB is the effective use of antimicrobials in the treatment of bacterial infections. These infections most commonly present as acute chest colds but may be subacute, chronic or even subclinical. Bronchial infection can be identified in the patient's sputum by a significant increase of bacterial flora associated with an increase of inflammation. The usual bacteria associated with these infections are Hemophilus influenzae and Streptococcus pneumoniae although other bacteria usually considered to be non-pathogens are probably also etiologic. Fortunately, these bacteria are effectively treated with a number of broad spectrum antimicrobials when given in adequate doses. These antimicrobials and their total daily doses include ampicillin (2g), amoxicillin (1.5g), doxycycline (200 mg), methacycline (600 mg), minocycline (200 mg), tetracycline (2-4g), trimethoprim (160 mg) with sulfamethoxazole (800 mg), and chloramphenicol (2g). They are all comparable in efficacy, but consideration of toxicity affects the choice for individual patients. The duration of therapy for acute, sub-acute and sub-clinical infections is generally around 14 days. For chronic or relapsing infections, therapy for months to years may be required. In most instances antimicrobial therapy does not eradicate the bacteria but seems to significantly decrease the bacterial load and consequent inflammation in the bronchial mucosa.

Treatment--Secretions. Clearance of the excessive secretions in the tracheobronchial tree is of great therapeutic importance in CB, as well as to patients with CBA. Unfortunately little is known about how to control the production of these secretions. Pharmacologic agents useful for secretion problems are used empirically and are often less than ideal. Some may modify the production, and others clearly act on the excreted and secreted material. Maintaining adequate environmental humidification often makes patients more comfortable with their secretions. Adequate hydration is advocated as the cornerstone of secretion therapy. Evidence for the efficacy or mechanism of action of oral or parenteral water on bronchial secretions is very limited. One study suggests that extra oral water increases the water content and decreases the apparent viscosity of the sputum of CB patients (9). Other evidence suggests that inhaled normal saline does not have a favorable action on bronchial secretions (10). However, hydration by various routes often does produce subjective improvement of the patient's secretion problems. Expectorant drugs may be useful when these simple measures are inadequate. The desired outcome is to make it easier for the patient to clear secretions. Again, as with water, there is much controversy and little evidence to support their efficacy. Commonly used expectorants are guaifenisen (glyceryl guaiacolate) iodides and ammonium chloride. Guaifenisen in relatively large doses (1.2 to 2.4g per day) increases mucociliary clearance (11), decreases the sticky nature of the sputum, changes the water binding capacity of the sputum gel, but does not affect apparent viscosity (9). Subjectively, chronic bronchitics volunteer that their secretions are easier to clear when guaifenisen is used. The mechanism of action is unknown. Other guaiacol derivatives are said to have similar activity. Iodides, as potassium iodide or iodinated glycerol by mouth or sodium iodide intravenously, are widely used expectorants. There is even less evidence of iodide's efficacy or mechanism of action. Again, chronic bronchial disease patients, particularly asthmatics, will attest to their efficacy in clearing secretions. Ammonium chloride is infrequently used as an expectorant because of the risks of abuse which can lead to acid-base problems. The least is known about this compound's expectorant properties. With all of the available expectorants subjective benefit is rarely dramatic.

When secretions remain difficult to clear despite the aforementioned therapy, mucolytic therapy is indicated. N-acetylcysteine is the only mucolytic available in America. Efficacy in reduction of sputum viscosity has only been demonstrated with topical application, although there are claims of benefit from oral and intravenous administration. Acetylcysteine *in vitro* will decrease the apparent viscosity of the majority of sputum specimens. When a 5 to 10% solution is directly applied to secretions in the tracheobronchial tree a similar response can be achieved. The action as an inhaled aerosol is less dramatic since the amount of drug reaching the widespread secretions is not great with a single treatment. Persistence of therapy will usually lead to a decrease of apparent viscosity and clinical benefit (12). Because of its hyperosmolarity, it is best administered with an adrenergic bronchodilator, such as isoproterenol, to offset potential increases of airways obstruction. There are claims that S-carboxymethylcysteine is an orally active bronchial mucolytic, but studies to support this contention are not entirely convincing. Besides these pharmacologic measures, physical therapy to facilitate clearance of secretions and mechanical aspiration of secretions is employed in resistant cases. Clearly the management of secretions in both CB and CBA is not optimal with our currently available therapies. The best therapy for secretions in both diseases remains those measures which alleviate the primary disease process, since this usually decreases the volume and normalizes the characteristics of the secretions.

*Treatment--Bronchodilators*. The methylxanthine theophylline and its analogues are widely used in the treatment of CB. However, the bronchodilation which is easily demonstrated in the asthmatic is not evident in CB. Nevertheless, the bronchitic with airways obstruction will report improvement of exercise capability with effective theophylline therapy. Theophylline is a phosphodiesterase inhibitor and results in a decreased breakdown of cAMP. This action in the bronchial tree has not been shown to be of benefit in the pathophysiologic mechanisms of CB. Although the mechanism of action in CB is not clear, benefit may be related to central nervous system stimulation, cardiac action, its modest diuretic activity, or to actions not yet discovered. Oral administration is adequate for maintenance therapy, but rectal and intravenous use may be required in advanced cases, although clearly less convenient. Individualization of dosage schedules is essential since the adult oral dose needed to achieve therapeutic blood levels may vary from 300 to 2500 mg. In most cases, the gastrointestinal and minor central nervous system side effects correlate with the blood level and can be used in adults as guides to regulate the dosage schedule. Blood level determinations are essential in patients with altered consciousness or who are receiving multiple therapeutic manipulations. The use of time-release theophylline preparations helps to eliminate some of the side effects associated with the peak blood levels noted with regular fast acting theophylline dosage forms.

The beta-receptor stimulating adrenergic drugs (sympathomimetic amines) have little, if any, activity in CB. When bronchodilation is demonstrated in CB, it is often minimal and of short duration. Considering the cardiogenic toxicity of even the more specific $\beta_2$ drugs in this group, their use in this generally older-aged group of patients should be justified by demonstration of beneficial action. Rather than bronchodilation, their potential efficacy in CB may be related to the increase of ciliary activity seen with this group of drugs.

Anticholinergic agents may represent the first true bronchodilators for the CB patients. Ipratropium by inhalation has been demonstrated to provide 5-6 hours of bronchodilation in CB as was similarly seen earlier with atropine (13). The mechanism of action is thought to be a blocking of the vagal efferent discharge which is responsible for the increased bronchomotor tone of the bronchial smooth muscle in CB as well as in CBA. Parenteral or inhaled atropine appears to have the deleterious effect of drying bronchial secretions and has not been useful for protracted therapy, whereas inhaled ipratropium does not appear to have this unwanted effect.

Treatment--Antitussives. An occasional patient with CB will be seriously bothered by cough. Often, most of their coughing is non-productive and can have debilitating effects on the patient. Disturbed sleep, vomiting with severe cough, rib fractures, syncope or even simple fatigue may become incapacitating. The oft written axiom that the cough of a patient with secretions should not be suppressed cannot have been derived from real life. Many antitussive agents are useful for the occasional periods of increased coughing to which CB patients are prone. When cough remains a persistent daily problem, the ideal agent for continued use may be difficult to find for the individual bronchitic. Dextromethorphan is helpful in some of these patients. Codeine itself often has troublesome side effects in CB, and these counteract the potential antitussive activity. Codeine derivatives have been effective, but there is a hesitancy to use them daily. Chlophedianol hydrochloride is an effective agent, but when used in therapeutic dosages the alterations of proprioception can be a limiting factor. So little is known about the pathophysiology of cough itself and the difficulty in objectively proving efficacy in patients that the lack of advances in antitussive therapy is not surprising.

Remaining Problems. Basic to the problem of developing more definitive therapy for CB is our inadequate knowledge of the underlying pathophysiology of the disease. We do not know why certain individuals develop CB while others do not despite similar stimuli exposures. One must suspect a variability of individual susceptibility. An attractive hypothesis to pursue is that CB patients have some subtle derangement of their host defense system. This may be inherited and/or acquired. Detection of such factors could define the individuals at risk and preventative and/or corrective measures might then be more precise.

Despite our lack of knowledge of its pathophysiology, significant therapy has been empirically developed to treat CB. However, no "curative" agents are available and many of the drugs that we use empirically are less than ideal. There is a need for better topical and orally active mucolytics. Pharmacologic agents which could normalize the secretion production or affect the inflammatory process itself could be of great advantage for the CB patient. Considering the burden that this prevalent disease imposes on society, it is unfortunate that there is so little interest in finding solutions.

## Chronic Bronchial Asthma

Definition. There are many definitions of asthma, some of which would even propose to discard the name "asthma" and replace it with a physiologic description, e.g., reversible airways obstruction. This would then be compatible with the regressive term COLD. Perhaps it would be better to more carefully define chronic bronchial asthma (CBA) as, for example, airways obstruction secondary to hyperreactive bronchi which is often manifested episodically, is usually reversible, and in which allergic phenomena are implicated. The clinical recognition of two major types of asthma: extrinsic asthma which most closely is described by the above definition, and intrinsic asthma which has often been called asthmatic bronchitis, adds additional confusion to the definition. Our knowledge about extrinsic CBA has been increasing rapidly, whereas our understanding of intrinsic CBA remains mostly at a clinical level.

Pathology. Pathologic descriptions of CBA are largely based on examination of patients who died during status asthmaticus (14). The pathology can be considered under the three major types of responses seen in the bronchial system, i.e., inflammation, changes of the mucus producing elements, and changes of the bronchial smooth muscle.

A striking feature of the inflammatory reaction is edema of the bronchial wall. This edema involves the epithelial cells as well as the interstitial tissues. In the extreme, this edema can result in folding and polypoid deformations of the bronchial epithelium. With this hydropic degeneration the cells themselves may have altered staining characteristics. The cilia are usually retained in the pseudocolumnar ciliated bronchial epithelial cells. Denudation of epithelium can be found, representing areas from which the tissue has been sloughed down to the edematous basement membrane. When coughed out in the sputum, the individual cells may be three to four times their normal size, and the tissue fragments, called Creola bodies, are generally rounded together in clusters which may contain up to several hundred epithelial cells (15). The epithelium and the submucosa are usually infiltrated with polymorphonuclear eosinophils, the characteristic inflammatory cell type in CBA. Compared to CB, there is a paucity of mast cells seen in the tissue (16). The numbers of plasma cells may be increased in the submucosa. These bronchial epithelial cell changes and the inflammatory cell response are reflected in the sputum and the intrabronchial mucus plugs (17). Eosinophils account for 10 to 90% of the inflammatory cells, although neutrophils may be predominant when the asthmatic is stable. Mast cells are plentiful during stable phases of asthma but are difficult to find during an attack. Macrophages or histiocytes follow this same pattern. Plasma cells, however, are always difficult to identify.

The changes of the mucus producing elements are somewhat similar to those seen in CB. Both hypertrophy and hyperplasia of the submucosal mucus glands and some proliferation of goblet cells in the epithelium are seen. Distinct differences between changes in CBA as opposed to CB have not been described. The abnormality of the secretions produced by these elements is demonstrated in the presence of mucus plugs in the bronchial lumina of almost all patients who died of their asthma. Trapped in these plugs are the same inflammatory cells eventually seen in the expectorated sputum. Also, one may find Charcot-Leyden crystals which are likely the product of lysed eosinophils and mast cells. The Curschmann spirals seen in the sputum of asthmatics represent these expelled mucus plugs.

It is common to find that the bronchial smooth muscle is hypertrophied. The degree of hypertrophy may be a measure of the chronicity and severity of the disease. However, smooth muscle hypertrophy may be minimal or absent in patients with intrinsic CBA. The acute constriction of the smooth muscle cannot, of course, be noted pathologically.

CBA does not appear to involve the alveolar areas of the lung. When such involvement is noted, the clinical manifestations are somewhat different, and they are classified as various types of allergic alveolitis. It is possible that many of these allergic bronchopulmonary diseases have similar pathophysiologic mechanisms.

Allergic changes in other organs may be noted but are insufficient in themselves to make the diagnosis of CBA. Also, although not well described, it is possible that many of the features typical of CBA might not be found in the asthmatic who dies after receiving intensive corticosteroid therapy.

Pathophysiology. Considerably more is known about the pathophysiology of CBA than is the case with CB (18). There often appears to be more factual data on the molecular aspects of asthma than of the clinical manifestations. A simplified schema of the patholophysiology is noted in Figure 2. Not shown in the diagram is the clear evidence that host susceptibility to extrinsic CBA is generally inherited, whereas this is not the case in intrinsic CBA. One might hypothesize that intrinsic asthma may be an acquired immunological abnormality without the noted hyperreactivity manifested in extrinsic asthma. Another possibility is that these two types of asthma are different because of the predominant trigger stimulus, in the case of pure extrinsic CBA the stimulus being specific antigen(s), and in pure intrinsic CBA being of non-specific nature somewhat similar to what may occur in CB. Others postulate that the induction of the disease may be by viral infection of the bronchial system. Indeed, the pathology of viral tracheobronchitis, short of eosinophilia, is very similar to that seen in CBA. There is no conclusive evidence for any of these hypotheses.

There appear to be two major groups of stimuli which can produce asthmatic manifestations: discrete antigens and non-specific stimuli. Numerous specific antigens are known. These may be inhaled or ingested, and their specificity in the individual patient can be demonstrated by an increase of airways obstruction after exposure to such agents. Ragweed, dust, molds, aspirin, and fish are a few examples. The other type of stimulus is relatively non-specific and can adversely affect CB patients as well. These stimuli include cold air, exercise, dusty environments, etc. The mechanisms by which these two types of stimuli lead to airways obstruction are different, although there is some overlap in their ultimate physical effect.

The antigenic stimulus pathway appears to involve an interaction with specific immunoglobulin E (IgE) at the cell membrane of mast cells resulting in the release of a variety of mediators from their intracytoplasmic granules. These mediators are responsible for a large part of the inflammatory reaction which

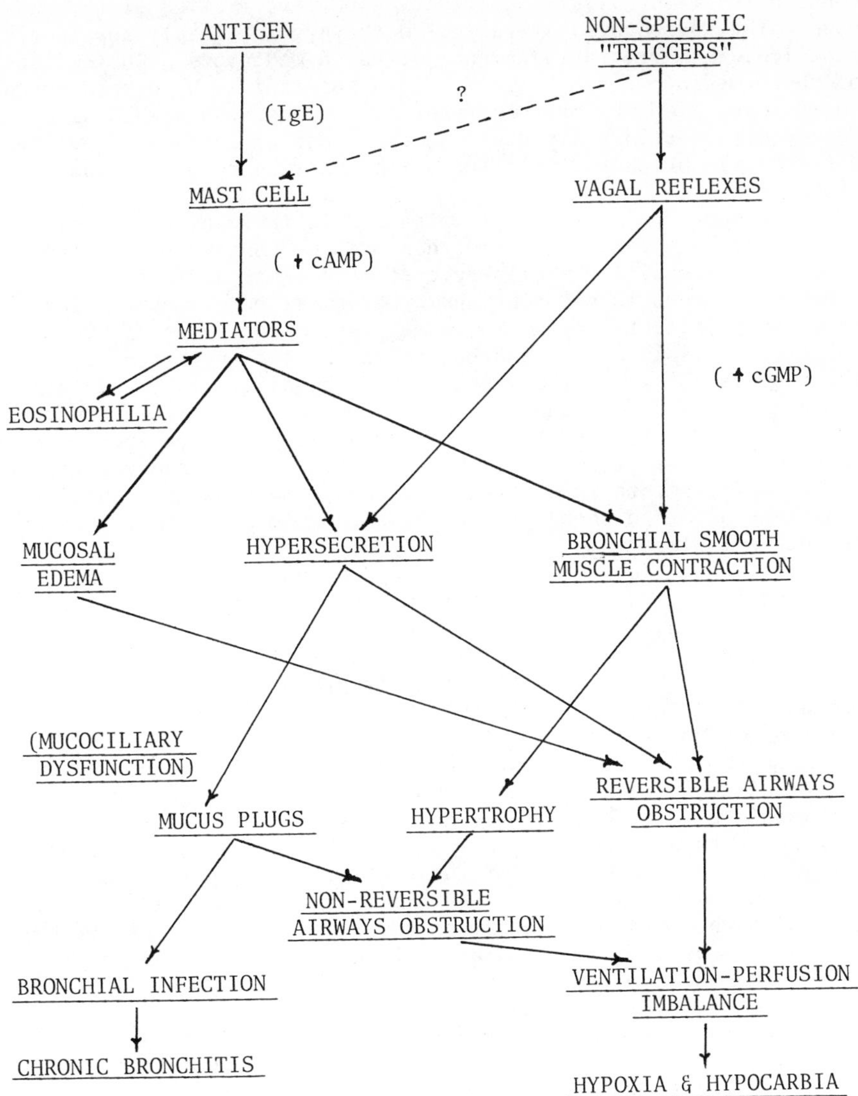


*Figure 2. Postulated pathophysiologic mechanisms in bronchial asthma*

seems to be potentiated in the asthmatic. Among the responses to these mediators of significance in the pathophysiology of asthma are the tissue edema, bronchial smooth muscle constriction, hypersecretion of mucus, and eosinophilia. The first three can all contribute to the airways obstruction characteristics of the disease. The eosinophils attracted to the area of insult apparently function, in part, to inactivate released mediators. The actions of these mediators can be reversed rather rapidly by agents which increase cyclic AMP, or this reversal can occur spontaneously. The resultant clinical picture in this case of antigen stimulated asthma fits the characteristics of the extrinsic form of the disease.

Non-specific stimuli or "triggers" in these hyperreactive individuals act primarily through neural mechanisms via the vagus nerve. The resulting cholinergic effects cause an increase of bronchial smooth muscle tone and hypersecretion of mucus. These cholinergic effects appear to be related to increases of cyclic GMP. It is possible that there also may be some direct effect on the mast cell, since otherwise it would be difficult to explain the eosinophilia that can accompany such non-specifically induced attacks. It is clear that in both the antigen and non-specifically induced attacks, it is still the asthmatic's increased reactivity of bronchial smooth muscle, mucus glands, and other bronchial tissues that distinguishes between the asthmatic and normal response to such stimuli.

It is not clear where prostaglandins and related products of arachidonic cascade fit into this pathophysiologic schema. The bronchodilating and bronchoconstricting prostaglandins may act through the cyclic AMP route.

Although the reversibility of airways obstruction is an important characteristic of asthma, those asthmatics with chronic symptoms do not reverse completely. The chronic airways obstruction is probably related to mucus plugging of bronchi and hypertrophy of the bronchial smooth muscle. These changes are not reversible by bronchodilators, and it is not clear that they can be reversed with any specific therapy. Both types of obstruction contribute to an imbalance of the ventilation to perfusion ratio in the lung and can result in hypoxemia and hypocarbia. The decreased carbon dioxide content of the blood is the result of the asthmatic's hyperventilation and will persist until the respiratory muscles fatigue and hypoventilation becomes prominent. Asthmatics can die quite quickly when this occurs.

A common complication of persistent hypersecretion and mucus plugging is a less effective mucociliary clearance mechanism. Inhaled bacteria which are normally quickly cleared from the bronchial system have greater opportunity for tissue invasion. Chronically affected asthmatics are more likely to develop bacterial bronchitis. It is not unusual for CB to become superimposed on the asthma as a consequence of these infections. Interestingly asthmatics who get an acute bacterial bronchitis will often note an improvement of their asthmatic symptoms.

The pathophysiologic mechanisms behind this are not understood.

Clinical Manifestations. The initial manifestations of bronchial asthma can occur at any age. However, the vast majority of extrinsic asthmatics first note symptoms as children or young adults, and those who appear in later decades often have had some earlier manifestation of atopy or allergy. On the other hand, intrinsic asthma generally occurs after the age of 30. Other differences between these two types of asthmatics are noted in Table II. Any individual patient may demonstrate some overlap of these features. For example, the extrinsic asthmatic may be continuously exposed to the specific antigen(s) and, therefore, have symptoms chronically.

Table II
Clinical Differences Between Extrinsic and Intrinsic Asthma

| | Extrinsic | Intrinsic |
|---|---|---|
| Allergen | external to host | ? internal to host |
| Other allergies (atopy) | usual | incidental |
| Allergies in family | usual | incidental |
| Symptoms | usually episodic | usually chronic |
| Eosinophilia | marked | moderate |
| Pathophysiology | fairly clear | obscure |
| Synonyms | bronchial asthma | asthmatic bronchitis |

The first symptom usually noted by the extrinsic asthmatic is shortness of breath with or after effort which may or may not be associated with wheezing. The more dramatic presentation is the abrupt onset of wheezing dyspnea. Cough, with or without sputum production, may precede or occur concomitantly with the wheezing dyspnea, but it is certainly not uniformly present. Occasional patients present with productive cough as the major complaint, and the difficulty with breathing may be quite minor. The clearance of secretions by coughing often marks the beginning of improvement of the attack. Classically, the attacks are episodic in the extrinsic asthmatic with the patient feeling relatively well between attacks. When between attacks, the physical examination of the patient may be within normal limits. During attacks, the chest is found to have an increased size with low diaphragms. There is a prolonged expiratory phase, and rather uniform wheezing is heard predominantly during the expiratory phase. Rhonchi may be heard. Peripheral cyanosis can be observed, and there is often a paradox in the blood pressure between inspiration and expiration of the respiratory cycyle. The chest roentgenograph will reflect the hyper-inflation. Any sputum produced should have the characteristics described previously under pathology, and peripheral blood eosinophilia is present. The blood gases would characteristically show a low oxygen and carbon dioxide tension. If the carbon dioxide tension is normal or elevated in the presence of low oxygen levels, then one suspects that the asthmatic cannot physically hyperventilate and is in serious trouble. The pulmonary physiology would reveal increased lung volumes at the expense of the vital capacity, an increase of airways resistance, a decrease of flow parameters, and a normal or elevated diffusing capacity. Most of these abnormalities can be reversed with appropriate therapy, or reversal can occur spontaneously.

The clinical picture of intrinsic asthma is less well characterized. Classically, wheezing dyspnea first presents during a bronchopulmonary infection and improves as the infection clears. However, these patients often have symptoms between such infectious episodes. Their symptoms of chronic productive cough associated with wheezing dyspnea do not readily distinguish them from chronic bronchitics. The striking difference is that intrinsic asthmatics will have more than 5% eosinophils in their sputum when stable and during infectious episodes, whereas the bronchitic will not have this in either case, and the extrinsic asthmatic rarely will have sputum eosinophilia during infections. The course in intrinsic asthma is much more like that of bronchitis, and these diseases are often confused.

The prognosis in extrinsic asthma is generally excellent, but deaths do occur in otherwise uncomplicated cases. Those who die are usually the more chronic asthmatics. Over 90% will have extensive mucus plugs at autopsy, and hypertrophy of the bronchial smooth muscle is common. Sudden death in young asthmatics also occurs without a good explanation. The prognosis in intrinsic asthma is not as good and is likely similar to that for moderately severe chronic bronchitics.

Treatment. A realistic goal of therapy is to minimize the manifestations of the disease (19, 20). One must assume that the atopic patient who has demonstrated asthmatic manifestations must thereafter be considered susceptible to more of the same. Therefore, asthma must be treated like any chronic disease with planned long-term care with periodic observations to document stability or to alter therapy aimed at returning patients to stability. A trusting physician-patient relationship is essential to the success of the therapy. In this setting, the general plan of therapy should be designed to avoid triggering stimuli, block or reverse stimulus effects, block or reverse mediator effects, and provide psychologic support.

Avoidance of Stimuli. This can be the most important aspect of the therapy of asthma. The identification of such stimuli must be individualized, and this usually requires careful detective work. Critical history taking is essential since this most often leads to meaningful relationships between exposure to some allergen or non-specific stimulus and the asthmatic's symptoms. Sometimes the patient is well aware of such relationships, but more often this is not the case. Seasonal, geographical or diurnal patterns frequently provide important clues. Suspected stimuli can be tested in a controlled laboratory setting, but this is usually not necessary. Once identified, the offending stimulus should be eliminated from the patient's environment or specific treatment planned to alleviate the consequences of exposure. If only a limited number of such stimuli are important in triggering a patient's attacks, it may be possible to completely control the asthma. In this approach to therapy one must always consider the financial and/or emotional cost of eliminating implicated stimuli. Occasional patients may prefer to take medication to block the effects of the stimulus. Of course, when the stimuli cannot be identified or eliminated, then pharmacologic therapy is required. The type, amount, and continuity of use of such available agents must be tailored to the individual needs of each patient.

Hyposensitization. When an antigenic stimulus can be identified but cannot be removed from the environment, it would seem reasonable to protect against the effects of such antigens by desensitizing the patient to that specific antigen via blocking antibodies. There is evidence that such protection can be achieved against a few specific antigens in patients with allergic rhinitis. The evidence for efficacy in bronchial asthma is not scientifically nor clinically convincing. Nevertheless, this empirical therapy may be worthy of trial in selected patients.

Bronchodilators. These agents constitute the backbone of therapy for the asthmatic. All asthmatics who are symptomatic or are demonstrated to have airways obstruction on physiologic testing should receive continuous bronchodilator therapy during the periods of such abnormality. The goal should be to eliminate or minimize the airways obstruction with the least drug toxicity. Therapy should be modified as that patient's needs change. This is best accomplished by periodic monitoring with simple pulmonary function tests and assessment of symptoms.

There are three major groups of bronchodilators: two of these, the methylxanthines and the sympathomimetic amines are available, while the third, anticholinergics, is still experimental. Available routes of administration include oral, inhalation, rectal, subcutaneous, and intravenous. The choice of types of agent and routes of administration depends on individual patient need and tolerance. Long-term maintenance is usually achieved with oral bronchodilators with occasional supplementation with rectal or inhalation agents. Rectal, subcutaneous and intravenous therapy is indicated in acute attacks of asthma, and the need for such intervention is another measure of the adequacy of the patient's long-term therapy.

The methylxanthine and sympathomimetic amine drugs may work by both reversing the effects of mediators and blocking the effects of new stimuli since both groups result in an increase of cyclic AMP. Methylxanthines block the degradation of cyclic AMP and sympathomimetic amines stimulate cyclic AMP production. Because of these different mechanisms the concomitant use of both types of drugs is often beneficial to the patient. The theophyllines are the most therapeutically useful of the methylxanthines. Theophylline is well suited to provide continuous protection since its regular use can result in relatively stable therapeutic blood levels. Since the half-life of theophylline varies from patient to patient, appropriate dosage schedules must be developed for each patient. The schedule for the oral route of administration will also depend on whether the theophylline is a delayed or rapidly absorbed formulation. At least in adults, therapy can be maximized by starting with a low oral daily dose and gradually increasing this until the patient's airways obstruction is eliminated or mild toxicity (e.g., nausea, jitteriness, insomnia, etc.) occurs. If the latter occurs, then the dose should be slightly decreased to avoid the adverse effects. Therapeutic blood levels are almost certainly attained by this method. When in doubt, or if the patient is incompetent to note such side effects, theophylline blood levels can be used for dosage adjustment. During an asthmatic attack, aminophylline by the intravenous route of administration can quickly achieve therapeutic blood levels. This is best accomplished by giving an intravenous bolus as a loading dose and then titrating the level using a continuous infusion. The rectal administration of aminophylline solution can also rapidly achieve therapeutic blood levels. Asthmatics who are prone to attacks of asthma can successfully utilize this route of administration instead of intravenous therapy. This route is also useful when fluid restriction is essential for the hospitalized patient who needs theophylline. Bronchodilation may be achieved with total daily doses of as little as 300 mg in some asthmatics, whereas the other extreme may require 2 to 3 g.

When adequate bronchodilation is not achieved with therapeutic levels of theophylline, or if adverse effects preclude reaching therapeutic levels, then sympathomimetic amines should be added to the bronchodilator regimen (21). In some asthmatics these agents alone may provide adequate bronchodilation. The trend in the development of more specific sympathomimetic amine bronchodilators has been to eliminate or decrease the $\alpha$-receptor and $\beta_1$-receptor (cardiogenic) activities so that the $\beta_2$-receptor (bronchial smooth muscle) activity is predominant. Unfortunately peripheral muscle tremor is also accentuated with the $\beta_2$ agents and may be sufficiently annoying to the patient to prompt stopping therapy.

Ephedrine sulfate was the first sympathomimetic amine available for oral therapy. It is still commonly used in most combination asthma preparations. Alone, it has a short duration of action and a fair incidence of annoying central nervous system effects, even at the usually prescribed dosage of 25 mg four times a day. However, when given with theophylline, the duration of action is comparable to terbutaline or higher doses of theophylline. Although they continue to be useful in mild asthmatics, marketed fixed combinations of theophylline and ephedrine usually preclude optimizing the bronchodilator therapy. Other sympathomimetic agents became available (protokylol, ethylnorepinephrine hydrochloride and methoxyphenamine hydrochloride) but offered little, if any, advantage over ephedrine. Metaproterenol sulfate was the first clearly superior agent which possessed improved $\beta_2$-receptor selectivity. Duration and degree of bronchodilation were much better than ephedrine, although more tremorgenic activity was noted. Although the duration of effective bronchodilation is rarely more than five hours, the recommended dosage is 20 mg every six hours. An introductory course of 10 mg four times a day is advisable as this seems to decrease the ultimate tremorgenic activity. Terbutaline sulfate has the least $\beta_1$-and the most $\beta_2$-receptor action of the oral sympathomimetic amines. Other $\beta_2$-receptor stimulating drugs have been developed (albuterol, carbuterol hydrochloride, soterenol, fenoterol and the like) but are not available for use in the United States. All are quite similar in action and provide bronchodilation for around four to six hours. Although the recommended dosage of terbutaline is 5 mg three times a day, some adverse effects can be avoided by starting at lower doses and increasing gradually to maximal efficacy or minimal toxicity in two to three weeks. The common side effect with this generation of sympathomimetic drugs is annoying peripheral muscle tremor. Tachycardia and decrease of diastolic blood pressure can occur since some $\beta_1$-receptor stimulating activity remains. The same efficacy with fewer adverse effects can be obtained with much smaller dosages of these agents administered by aerosol inhalation, but none of these aerosols is approved for use in the United States. They should replace their oral counterparts in maintenance therapy when they become available. In the determination of the best oral sympathomimetic amine for the individual patient, the choice often depends on the tolerance of the patient to the tremorgenic side effects.

Although the majority of asthmatics will be well controlled with the regular use of oral bronchodilators, some may still experience periods of increased asthma. These episodes can usually be managed with additional or increased doses of their oral bronchodilators. In addition, such asthmatics should be carefully instructed in the use of a sympathomimetic aerosol for such attacks. The prompt response to these may abort the attack, or at least provide some relief before the oral medication becomes effective (one-half to two hours). The risk of abuse of inhaled bronchodilators is real, but the incidence of abusers is small, and the benefits generally far outweigh such risks. The sympathomimetics that are available for aerosol inhalation are epinephrine, isoproterenol hydrochloride, isoetharine hydrochloride, and metaproterenol. Epinephrine is the least active of these agents and has $\alpha$, $\beta_1$ and $\beta_2$ activity. Isoproterenol has mixed $\beta$-receptor stimulant activity, while isoetharine is more $\beta_2$ selective. Both isoproterenol hydrochloride and isoetharine hydrochloride are rapidly metabolized,and the duration of action is usually less than three hours. Metaproterenol sulfate is less rapidly metabolized so that efficacy may last for up to five hours. It has somewhat fewer $\beta_1$ effects. These agents are available in metered-dose canisters and (all but metaproterenol) as solutions usable in nebulizers. The regular use of solution nebulized by an air compressor for maintenance bronchodilator therapy is useful for some, but the regular use of oral terbutaline or metaproterenol is more convenient for many asthmatics.

The use of subcutaneous sympathomimetic bronchodilator is indicated for the severe asthma attack that requires emergency treatment. Epinephrine and terbutaline are available for subcutaneous therapy and, in usual doses, are comparable in efficacy. By this route, terbutaline appears to be no more $\beta_2$ selective than epinephrine and is reported to have more adverse effects (22). Aqueous suspension of epinephrine provides a longer duration of action. In status asthmaticus sympathomimetics are often not helpful. Intravenous aminophylline is the basic therapy in this setting. The acute therapy should be instituted with a loading dose, but this should be proportionally reduced if the patient has been on regular theophylline therapy. A constant infusion should maintain the serum level. If serum theophylline levels are quickly available, these should be used as a guide to dosing. Concomitant oxygen therapy should be given for the hypoxemia that is usually present.

As with CB, anticholinergic agents are also rational bronchodilators for use in asthma. Their use would be expected to contribute additional bronchodilation to that provided by methylxanthines and sympathomimetic amines since the mechanism of action is directed at the effects of the non-specific stimuli. The concomitant use of all three types could also permit a more precise assessment of the non-reversible component of the patient's airways obstruction. Since many antihistamines have anticholinergic activity, it is possible that patients who take such therapy for other reasons may already have some benefit of this kind of bronchodilation.

Antiallergic Agents. The available and experimental agents in this category probably work by blocking the effect of the stimulus on the hyperreactive tissue elements. These agents could logically have been discussed in conjunction with the avoidance of stimuli since safe and effective therapy which blocks stimulus effects could be as effective a primary therapy as avoidance. Experimental work suggests that the major blocking effect is at the mast cell level. This does not adequately explain why some of these agents are capable of blocking exercise-induced asthma which is likely vagus nerve mediated. Available drugs which could be considered to be antiallergic are cromolyn sodium, antihistamines, and corticosteroids, although it is clear that methylxanthines and sympathomimetics can provide similar protection.

The introduction of cromolyn sodium for the therapy of asthma in the last decade has stimulated extensive research in antiallergic agents. The exact mechanisms of action in man are not clearly known, but the prevention of the release of mast cell mediators is likely. Cromolyn appears to decrease the severity of symptoms and the need for other antiasthma therapy. Objectively demonstrable effect in man is the protection against obstruction of airways which is induced by specific inhaled antigen and exercise. The importance of these factors in the individual asthmatic may determine its efficacy. Cromolyn in regular dosages of 20 mg four times a day by inhalation is indicated in asthmatics not readily controlled with bronchodilators or who are steroid dependent. Cromolyn used just prior to exposure to specific antigen or exercise may be useful for the asthmatic susceptible to these occasional stimuli. Although worthy of a trial, the success rate for longterm use in adult asthmatics has not been as dramatic as preliminary studies suggested. Administration after an inhaled bronchodilator assures the best distribution of the powder. However, cromolyn powder can induce throat irritation, coughing and wheezing, and may, in itself, be allergenic (23, 24, 25).

There is some anecdotal clinical experience to suggest that antihistamines may also block the stimulus effect. Experimental evidence to support this is meager, but it has been demonstrated that prolonged promethazine therapy leads to the gradual degranulation of basophils. This suggests that although the mast cell could be triggered, there would not be any mediator to release. This hypothesis has not been tested in asthmatics; however, the use of antihistamines in asthmatics not adequately responding to other therapy has been occasionally successful. The experimental drug ketotifen may prove to be a useful antiallergic agent (26).

Corticosteroids. These potent antiasthma agents may also act to block stimulus effects, perhaps by stabilizing mast cell (and other cell) membranes and making degranulation more difficult.

Although all of the mechanisms of action of corticosteroids in asthma are not fully understood, they are potent agents for reducing mucosal edema. Corticosteroids are indicated for the asthmatic with troublesome symptoms despite full therapy. The duration of therapy required varies depending on the individual subject's clinical course.

Beclomethasone dipropionate by inhalation is the agent of choice when long-term corticosteroid therapy appears inevitable since only a small proportion is systemically absorbed. Adrenal suppression is unlikely at the usual daily dosage of 100μg to 200μg four times a day. Toxicity is usually limited to local irritation from the spray. However, since long-term effects are not yet determined, indications for such use should be as cautious as for orally administered corticosteroids. Beclomethasone is also indicated for asthmatics already on long-term oral corticosteroids so that the oral therapy can be reduced or eliminated. Gradual dosage reduction of the oral agent is mandatory to allow return of adrenal function. During or after this tapering it is essential that the asthmatic be alerted that systemic steroids may be necessary during periods of physiologic stress since the adrenal response may not yet be adequate. Extra-bronchial manifestations of allergy may appear as oral corticosteroids are withdrawn. Oral or pharyngeal candidiasis may occur in steroid dependent asthmatics and require treatment with topical antifungal agents.

Oral corticosteroids may be required in asthmatics not adequately controlled with bronchodilators, cromolyn and/or beclomethasone therapy. When indicated, alternate-day therapy with a prednisone-like steroid should be used. Reduction of either the oral or inhaled corticosteroid dose should be frequently attempted. Although less frequent with alternate-day dosing, monitoring for the undesirable effects of oral corticosteroids should be routine.

Most acute asthmatic attacks not controlled by lesser therapy can often be managed at home with a three- or four-day course of oral corticosteroids in dosages equivalent to 60 to 100 mg of prednisone per day, although as much as 200 mg/day may be needed. Tapering of dosages is unnecessary as long as background therapy is continued through the attack. Initial improvement should occur after six hours with considerable change in 12 to 24 hours. Complicating factors such as infection, mucus plugs, etc. should be suspected if reasonable response is not noted in 24 hours. Sputum eosinophilia should be suppressed if the corticosteroid dosage is adequate.

Status asthmaticus not responsive to intravenous aminophylline and sympathomimetic therapy is an indication for hospitalization. Intravenous aminophylline should be continued, and intravenous corticosteroids may be required in doses equivalent to that described for orally administered prednisone. The intravenous steroid should be limited to five to seven days, and therapy switched to beclomethasone or an alternate-day oral regimen with a prednisone-like drug as soon as practical. There is evidence that corticosteroids may affect β-receptor sites to abolish the apparent tachyphylaxis to sympathomimetic amines common in status asthma.

Agents classified as anti-inflammatory or immunosuppressive have some theoretical basis for consideration in the therapy of asthma. Anecdotal clinical observations suggest that acetylsalicylic acid can alleviate the asthmatic's symptoms. Perhaps this is related to the effects of this agent on prostaglandins. On the other hand, there is a subgroup of asthmatics who clearly are made worse by acetylsalicylic acid. There have been investigations of the use of immunosuppressive agents in asthma, but the risks of these drugs likely preclude any widespread trial to ascertain possible benefits.

Secretion Therapy. Airways obstruction in asthma is almost always partially due to often clinically unsuspected excessive secretions and mucus plugs. The therapeutic regimen described to this point may decrease this problem. Unfortunately, the treatment of the asthmatic's secretions is often neglected. When secretions remain a problem, the therapy as previously noted for the chronic bronchitic should be employed. Anecdotal clinical experience suggests that iodides are superior to guaifenesin as expectorants for the asthmatic.

Ancillary Therapy. Recurrent or chronic bronchopulmonary bacterial infection requires appropriate antibiotic therapy. However, antibiotic use during attacks of asthma is justified only when bacterial infection is demonstrated. Psychotropic drugs for the ambulatory asthmatic may be clinically indicated. Barbiturates, particularly phenobarbital, should be avoided since they can affect the metabolism of drugs used to treat asthma. Central nervous system depressants are contraindicated when hypoventilation or severe asthma is present unless ventilation can be controlled. In steroid-dependent asthmatics, therapy is often required to treat the consequences of the hyperadrenocorticalism. The inherent problems of the drugs required for this often present a major therapeutic dilemma. It is important to balance the problems engendered by the corticosteroid therapy against the problem that the patient's asthma would be without steroids. Indeed, this concept should be kept in mind with all therapy given the asthmatic so that a more balanced therapeutic regimen can result. The ultimate goal of asthma therapy should always be to permit the asthmatic to have as normal a life style as possible.

Remaining Problems. The most profound advance in asthma therapy would be a means for definitively altering the inherited molecular abnormality which predisposes one to become an asthmatic. Lacking this, other advances could clearly make asthma a more bearable problem. More efficient mechanisms for blocking the effects of specific allergens on the target tissues could make the necessity for avoiding such allergens less important. The availability of safe anticholinergic bronchodilators could decrease the residual bronchial obstruction noted by many asthmatics despite full use of other therapeutic agents. Investigations of the effect of various antihistamines could uncover immediately available therapy of benefit for some asthmatics. Much work will be needed to determine how best to manage the secretion problems unique to asthma. The deciphering of how to manipulate the physiologic effects of prostalandins should provide important information on pathophysiologic mechanisms in asthma, as well as novel approaches to therapy. Although we appear to know a great deal about asthma, there is much more to be learned.

Pulmonary Emphysema.

Definition. The definition of pulmonary emphysema is based on the pathologic changes characteristic of the disease; e.g., destruction of air spaces beyond the terminal bronchioles with resulting loss of gas exchange membrane. These changes occur in most humans and are related to increasing age. By the time clinical manifestations of emphysema appear, there is a considerable loss of alveolar tissue. It is unclear how much loss must be present to justify making the clinical diagnosis. This, of course, is a moot point since it is unlikely that routine lung biopsy will ever become part of the annual physical examination. For the purposes of this overview of COLD, I will limit the discussion to cases where clinical, physiologic or roentgenographic evidence of the disease exists.

Pathology. There is an abundance of descriptions of the pathology of pulmonary emphysema (4). Indeed, there are numerous classifications of the various types of pulmonary emphysema, an aspect of this disease that will not be dealt with here. In terms of COLD, the important common feature of all types of emphysema is the destruction of the alveolar wall which concomitantly destroys both the alveolar membrane and the capillary. As this destruction procedes, the residual airspaces become progressively larger. Very large airspaces are called bullae. With the loss of the alveolar structure which serves as a support for maintaining bronchial integrity, the bronchi are easily collapsed by external, intrapulmonary pressure. Such collapsibility of the bronchi on expiration can lead to air-trapping in the remaining air spaces, distending them even more. The whole lung becomes hyper-inflated with increase of the anterior-posterior diameter of the chest and a lowering of the diaphragm. The remaining larger elements of the vasculature and bronchial tree become stretched out. In the extreme forms of the disease, the accessory muscles of respiration are found to be hypertrophied because of their regular use in trying to increase the thoracic cage during inspiration from the already increased position due to the large lung volume. At any of these stages of the development of the common forms of emphysema, inflammatory changes are rarely evident. Exceptions to this are found in some of the forms of localized emphysema which may occur secondary to pneumonitis, tuberculosis, etc.

Pathophysiology. Intensive research is ongoing to discover the underlying etiology of this devastating disease. Emphysema can be reproduced in experimental animals by the intratracheal administration of proteolytic enzymes, cadmium, etc. Perhaps the most promising lead is that enzymes derived from inflammatory cells can cause emphysema. On the other hand, in the inherited alpha-1-antitrypsin deficiency emphysema, it is suggested that the inability to appropriately stop the proteolytic action of these intrinsic enzymes leads to the tissue destruction. Although the vast majority of cases of emphysema do not have alpha-1-antitrypsin deficiency, it is possible that an overwhelming local concentration of proteases may be beyond the body's capability to counter with anti-proteases. There is evidence that elastases are important in this process.

A simple diagram of the possible events in the pathophysiology of emphysema is presented in Figure 3. It seems likely that inflammation is key to the development of the disease. The imbalance between proteases and antiproteases leads to the proteolytic destruction of alveoli. Clinically, there is a high degree of association between a long-standing CB preceding the development of emphysema. The recurring inflammation which is an integral aspect of CB may be the principal etiology. The fact that some individuals with decades of clinical CB do not have significant emphysema at death speaks for some inherited or acquired host susceptibility. The loss of alveolar structures leads to a decrease of diffusing membrane for the respiratory gases, an increase of the airspaces, a loss of lung elasticity, and a loss of the bronchial supporting structures. The changes of the airspaces and lung elasticity result in an increase of the lung volume which necessitates that the patient breathe from a less efficient expiratory position. The loss of bronchial wall support results in the collapse of such affected airways during expiration because of pressure differences between the low pressures quickly reached in the bronchus being opposed by the high pressures retained in the surrounding parenchyma due to air trapping. With the diminution of the total alveolar-capillary interface, the patient must increase the work of breathing to maintain gas exchange. Because alveoli and capillaries are concomitantly destroyed, hypoxemia does not develop until the area of membrane left is insufficient to provide gas exchange. When hypoxemia does develop in emphysema, the patient has a very poor prognosis. When large bullae develop because of air trapping, an additional compromising of ventilatory

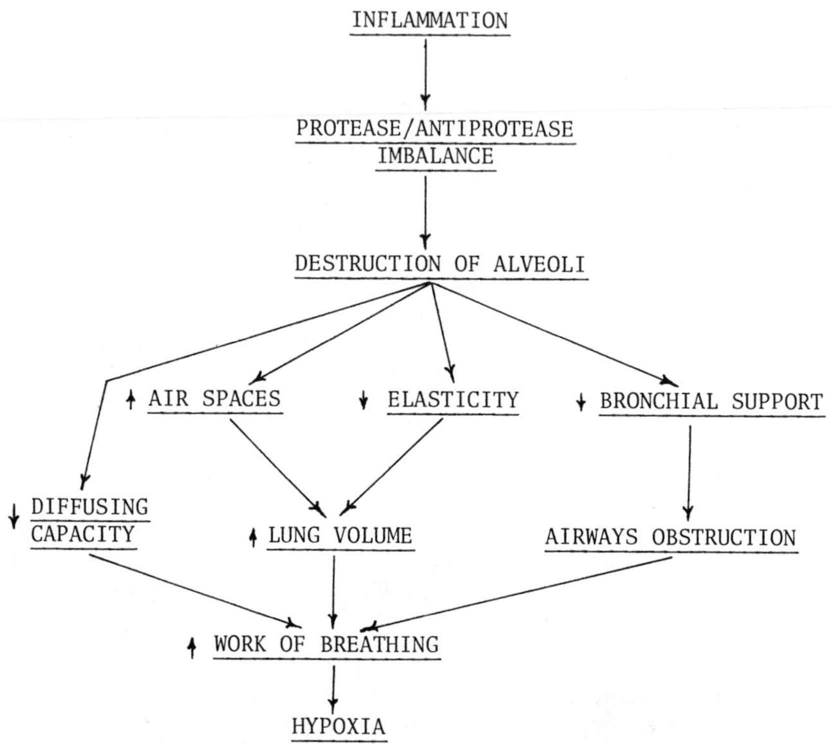


*Figure 3. Postulated schema of the pathophysiology of pulmonary emphysema*

function may be due to compression of surrounding parenchyma which may otherwise be functional. This can be reversed by removal or decompression of the bullous lesion, whereas the loss of alveoli is irreversible.

Clinical Manifestations. Pulmonary emphysema usually becomes clinically apparent after the age of 40. It typically occurs in patients with long-standing CB. Patients with alpha-1-antitrypsin deficiency emphysema are the exception in that the disease usually is evident before the age of 40. The classical symptoms are progressive exertional dyspnea usually associated with expiratory wheezing. Chronic dry cough may be present, but sputum production is not part of the syndrome. The airways obstruction in emphysema is not reversible by bronchodilators since it is due to tissue destruction. Because of the increased work of breathing, these patients often complain of fatigue and tend to be thin. Cyanosis is not noted until the very last stages of the disease. Respiratory failure is often the terminal event. It is unfortunate that clinical manifestations are not evident until the pathologic process is moderately advanced. In the later stages of the disease one may note an increase of the chest diameter, a flattened and fixed low diaphragm, a prolonged expiratory phase of respiration often associated with a tight wheezing and the use of accessory muscles of respiration. The most inexperienced medical student can detect these abnormalities, but even the most sophisticated physician can miss the earlier stages of emphysema. Laboratory findings can be more sensitive in that physiologic testing can detect the increasing lung volumes, the irreversible airways obstruction, and the progressive loss of diffusing capacity. The roentgenogram of the chest may most closely reflect the pathologic changes. The earliest changes may be an attenuation of the vasculature with a splaying-out of the branches of the vessels. When bullae are present, they are diagnostic of the disease. When the disease is clinically evident, then the hyperinflation is readily demonstrated roentgenographically. The blood gases may be remarkably normal until the terminal stage of the disease.

Treatment. No pharmacologic therapy exists for the treatment of emphysema. The major emphasis in therapy is to prevent additional destruction. These preventive measures are identical to those detailed for chronic bronchitis with emphasis on avoidance of inhaled inflammation-producing stimuli and the treatment of bronchopulmonary infections. When CB is present, the treatment of this disease must be aggressive. When the work of breathing becomes significantly increased, the emphysematous patient should be taught how to breathe most efficiently. Supplemental oxygen can be helpful in decreasing the work of breathing and, when hypoxemia develops, can prolong life. When large bullae are compromising good lung parenchyma surgery to remove or compress these air sacs can significantly improve the respiratory status of the patient. Some feel that the methylxanthines can be of benefit, but I have never seen improvement in a purely emphysematous patient.

Despite the bleak picture portrayed here, it is essential to make every possible effort to stop the progression of the emphysematous process. The almost invariable presence of CB in these patients provides a component whose reversal can encourage the patient to a more sensible way of life.

Remaining Problems. There are almost too many problems remaining in the therapy of emphysema to reasonably enumerate here. At the present time it is important to develop a sound understanding of what causes the tissue destruction. When this is known, then therapy may be developed which may be capable of reducing or eliminating the irreversible damage. Until our basic knowledge improves, it remains important to educate physicians and patients on the necessity of the early treatment of CB, before emphysema has significantly developed.

## Conclusions

COLD does not describe any specific disease entity. If progress is going to be made in our basic understanding of the chronic lung diseases, it is essential that each of the diseases, chronic bronchitis, bronchial asthma and emphysema, be dealt with as separate pathophysiologic entities even though they may have some common physiologic characteristics. The development of new, rational treatments depends on a more complete knowledge of the mechanisms of these diseases. Despite our currently inadequate knowledge, there is worthwhile therapy for the bronchitic and the asthmatic, but virtually none for the emphysema patient.

## Literature Cited


1. Ferris, B.G. and Anderson, D.O.: Am Rev Respir Dis, 86, (1962) 165.
2. U. S. Department of Health, Education and Welfare: PHS Health Resources Administration. Vital and Health Statistics Series 10, 84 (1973).
3. American Thoracic Society: Am Rev Respir Dis, 85 (1961) 762.
4. Thurlbeck, W. M.: "Chronic Airflow Obstruction in Lung Disease", W.B.Saunders Company, Philadelphia, London, Toronto, (1976) 31.
5. Hers, J.F.PH.: The pathology of chronic relapsing mucopurulent bronchitis with and without bronchiectasis. In "Bronchitis", edited by N.G.M.Orie and H.J.Sluiter, Charles C.Thomas, Royal Vangorcum, Assen, Netherlands, (1961) 149.

6. Knauss, H. J., Robinson, W.E., Medici, T.C. and Chodosh, S.: Arch Environ Health, 31, (1976) 241.
7. Medici, T.C. and Bürgi, H.: Am Rev Respir Dis, 103 (1971)784.
8. Reid, L.: Thorax, 15 (1960) 132.
9. Chodosh, S., Medici, T.C. and Enslein, K.: Bull Physio-Pathol Resp, 9, (1973) 453.
10. Chodosh, S.: Am Rev Respir Dis, 103 (1971) 904.
11. Thomson, M.L., Pavia, D, and McNicol, M.W.: Thorax, 28 (1973) 724.
12. Chodosh, S., Baigelman, W., Medici, T.C.and Enslein, K.: Curr Ther Res, 17 (1975) 319.
13. Baigelman, W. and Chodosh, S.: Chest, 3 (1977) 324.
14. Dunhill, M.S.: J Clin Pathol, 13 (1960) 27
15. Naylor, B.: Thorax, 17 (1962) 69.
16. Salvato, T.: Thorax, 23 (1968) 168.
17. Chodosh, S.: Advances in Asthma and Allergy, 4 (1977) 8.
18. Weiss, E.B. and Segal, M.S.: "Bronchial Asthma, Mechanisms and Therapeutics", Little, Brown and Company, Boston (1976).
19. Chodosh, S.: Arch Intern Med, 138 (1978) 1394.
20. Webb-Johnson, D.C. and Andrews, J.L.: N Engl J Med, 297 (1977) 476, 758.
21. Chodosh, S. and Baigelman, W.: Chest, 73(Suppl) (1978) 1014.
22. Smith, P., Heurich, A., Leffler, C., Henis, M., and Lyons, H: Chest, 71 (1977) 129.
23. Repo, U.K. and Nieminen, P.: Scand J respir Dis, 57 (1976) 1.
24. Lopez, H., Machtry, I., and Eldor, M.Y.: Lancet : November 11, 1972 (letter).
25. Paterson, I.C., Grant, I.W.B., and Crompton, G.K.: Brit Med J, 2, (1976) 916
26. Girard, J.P. and Cuevas, M.: Acta Allergol, 32 (1977) 27.

RECEIVED August 6, 1979.

# 13

# New Aspects of β-Adrenergic Bronchodilator Drugs

CARL KAISER

Research and Development Division, Smith Kline and French Laboratories, Philadelphia, PA 19101

Although bronchoconstriction caused by contraction of bronchiolar muscles is only one of several factors involved in asthma, drugs that induce relaxation of these muscles are frequently used in therapy. Agents that cause bronchiolar muscle relaxation may act by several different modes as suggested by the biochemical mechanism of smooth muscle relaxation (1). Such agents include a group of adrenergic receptor agonists. In mild and occasional episodic asthma, bronchoconstriction and its resultant symptoms are easily reversed by administration of effective β-adrenoreceptor activators. Such agents also find some utility in alleviation of respiratory distress in emphysema and bronchitis. Some more recent aspects of such adrenergic bronchodilators, i.e., compounds that are structurally related to the natural hormones and neurotransmitters norepinephrine (**1a**) and epinephrine (**1b**), are the subject of this review.

Classification of adrenergic receptors into α and β subtypes (2) is now generally accepted. On the basis of differences in response to selective agonists (3, 4, 5) and antagonists (6, 7), Lands and his associates (3, 4, 5, 8) further subdivided the β receptors into two groups, i.e., $\beta_1$ and $\beta_2$-adrenoreceptors. Activation of $\beta_2$-adrenoreceptors causes relaxation of smooth muscle in bronchi, uterus and vasculature, decreases tension in some skeletal muscle, and mediates glycolysis and glycogenolysis. Responses mediated by interaction with $\beta_1$-adrenoreceptors are increased force and rate of contraction of cardiac muscle, dilation of coronary blood vessels (9, 10), relaxation of smooth muscle in the alimentary tract, and lipolysis.

Epinephrine, administered either by injection or inhalation, is still employed to relieve bronchoconstriction in bronchial asthma. Isoproterenol (**1c**), the prototype of β-adrenergic receptor agonists, because of its greater potency and selectivity has largely replaced epinephrine as an inhaled bronchodilator. This synthetic analog of epinephrine also lacks selectivity. It is almost equally effective in activating both $\beta_1$ and $\beta_2$-adrenergic receptors. Thus, it not only produces a powerful bronchodilating

0-8412-0536-1/80/47-118-251$08.25/0

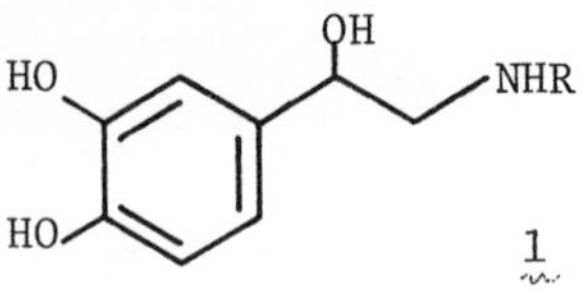

OH

HO NHR

HO

1

a, R=H

b, $R=CH_3$

c, $R=CH(CH_3)_2$

d, $R=C(CH_3)_3$

action by activating $\beta_2$-adrenoreceptors in bronchial smooth muscle, but it also induces a multiplicity of unwanted side effects by interaction with various other β-adrenoreceptors. Isoproterenol causes significant cardiovascular side effects including marked positive inotropic and chronotropic effects on the heart, an increase in pulse pressure and reduction in mean arterial pressure. Physiological tremor, presumably the consequence of stimulation of $\beta_2$-adrenoreceptors in skeletal muscle, is another disturbing side effect of β-adrenergic bronchodilators in man (11, 12). The most severe side effect of isoproterenol is its cardiac stimulant effect.

Other limitations to the therapeutic utility of isoproterenol are its short duration of action and its lack of oral efficacy. The brief duration of bronchodilation is a result of facile metabolic inactivation. Upon reaching systemic circulation isoproterenol is rapidly accumulated into extraneuronal cells, perhaps by an uptake-2 process (13), where, except in the gut, it is inactivated in a reaction catalyzed by catechol O-methyltransferase (COMT) which methylates the meta-OH group (14). Isoproterenol's lack of activity following oral administration is a consequence of its metabolic conversion into readily excreted meta- or para-ethereal sulfates by sulfokinases in the intestine (15).

Another, albeit difficultly defined, problem is that several β-adrenoreceptor agonists upon chronic administration cause benign mesovarial leiomyomas in certain strains of rats (16, 17, 18). Sufficient data are unavailable to determine if this tumorigenicity, which appears to be species specific, is related to β-adrenoreceptor agonists in general. Whether the observed tumorigenicity warrants discontinuation of clinical trials of β-adrenergic bronchodilators is controversial (18, 19).

Recognizing these limitations of isoproterenol, a search for new selective β-adrenergic bronchodilator drugs was initiated. Incentive for this undertaking was provided by the suggestion that some $\beta_2$-adrenergic agonist effects, e.g., those on tracheobronchial and vascular smooth muscle may be separable (20, 21). Previously described structure-activity relationships of sympathomimetics (e.g., 8, 22-28), including those in the classic investigations of Barger and Dale (29), provided an excellent foundation for additional study. The objective of this study was the development of new agents with (a) improved separation of bronchodilating and cardiac stimulating effects, (b) a longer duration of action, (c) oral efficacy, and (d) no seriously limiting side effects. In the course of this investigation (30-40) more than 500 compounds were examined. In the present review will be described the primary biological test systems employed in this study, significant recent structure-activity relationships derived in our laboratories and elsewhere, with reference to clinical results where appropriate, and finally to examine conformational and configurational preferences of active agents and consider how this might provide information about their interaction with adrenergic receptors.

Pharmacology Methods (30)

As a measure of potential bronchodilating ($\beta_2$-adrenoreceptor) activity, test compounds were examined *in vitro* for their ability to relax a spontaneously-contracted guinea pig tracheal chain preparation (41). Cardiac stimulant ($\beta_1$-adrenoreceptor) potential was evaluated *in vitro* by changes induced in the rate of contraction of spontaneously beating guinea pig right atria (42). Comparison of the $ED_{50}$ for tracheal relaxation with the $ED_{25}$ for atrial stimulation provides an indication of selectivity for tracheobronchial *vs*. cardiac muscle; i.e., for $\beta_2$- *vs*. $\beta_1$-adrenoreceptors. Compounds that showed selectivity were examined in secondary pharmacological tests (43, 44) to confirm *in vivo* bronchodilator activity, duration of oral activity and lack of side effects. These included i.v. cat pulmonary resistance (45) and dog cardiovascular tests (30), p.o. tests for inhibition of acetylcholine-induced bronchospasm (30) and increase in heart rate in guinea pigs, and an i.v. cat soleus muscle contractility test.

Guinea Pig Tracheal Chain Test (30). A guinea pig tracheal chain prepared by modification of previously described methods (46, 47) was suspended in pH 7.3 Krebs buffer (48) aerated (95% $O_2$ - 5% $CO_2$) at 37.5°C. After a period of equilibration to allow the chain to attain spontaneous contraction, isotonic relaxations of the tracheal chain (under a tension of 250 mg) produced by cumulative dosing with the test compound were recorded using a linear motion transducer. Responses were expressed as the percent relaxation induced by a concentration of 10 μg/ml of papaverine hydrochloride - a concentration that produces the same degree of relaxation as does a supramaximal dose of isoproterenol. Generally, one compound was tested per tissue over the entire cumulative dose-response range. The best fitting log dose-response line was determined for each chain and the $ED_{50}$, defined as the concentration producing 50% of the maximum papaverine-induced relaxation, was estimated from the plot. Mean $ED_{50}$s (usually from five tissues) were obtained by the direct assay method (49).

Guinea Pig Right Atria Test (30). Isolated guinea pig right atria were suspended in an aerated (95% $O_2$ - 5% $CO_2$) bath of Krebs solution (47) at 37.5°C. The rate of contraction of a spontaneously beating atrium under a diastolic tension of 0.5 g was recorded with a force transducer. After a period of equilibration, increases in rate of contraction in response to cumulative dosing were measured. Increases were expressed as percent of the previously determined maximum isoproterenol-induced increase in rate (324±10 beats per minute - the average of 22 control experiments). Usually one compound per atrium was tested over the entire cumulative dose-response range. The best fitting log dose-response line was drawn for each atrium and the $ED_{25}$, i.e., the molar concentration of test compound producing 25% of the maximum isoproterenol-induced rate increase, was estimated from the plot. Mean $ED_{50}$s (usually from five atria) were obtained by the direct assay method (49).

## Structure-Activity Relationships

In considering the influence of alterations in the chemical structure of catecholamines and related compounds on their β-adrenergic activity, potencies will be related to those of isoproterenol which will be employed as a reference standard. For the sake of uniformity, primary biological test data derived in the guinea pig tracheal chain and right atria tests in our laboratories will be implied unless otherwise indicated. Isoproterenol is a potent agonist in both of these tests which offer a measure of potential bronchodilator ($\beta_2$-adrenoreceptor agonism) and cardiac stimulant ($\beta_1$-adrenoreceptor agonism) activities. It has an $ED_{50}$ of $7.1 \times 10^{-9}$ M in the guinea pig tracheal chain test and an $ED_{25}$ of $3.4 \times 10^{-9}$ M in the right atria test. Where possible, potency relative to isoproterenol in both *in vitro* tests, as well as a ratio of these potencies, will be presented. Data not derived in our laboratories will be indicated by an asterisk.

Definition of Terms (50). Derivation of the relative potency of N-*tert*-butylnorepinephrine (**1d**) will be described to illustrate the terms and symbols used in considering structure-activity relationships among β-adrenergic bronchodilators. This compound is an appropriate secondary standard because many of the more recent agents of this class bear a *tert*-butylamino substituent. In the guinea pig tracheal chain test, **1d** has an $ED_{50}$ of $1.3 \times 10^{-9}$ M. In the atrial test, **1d** has an $ED_{25}$ of $7.1 \times 10^{-9}$ M. Relative potency (*T*) in the tracheal test is defined as the molar $ED_{50}$ for isoproterenol divided by the comparable value for the investigational compound in the same test. On this basis the value T for N-*tert*-butylnorepinephrine (**1d**) is $7.1 \times 10^{-9}$ M ÷ $1.3 \times 10^{-9}$ M = 5.5. Similarly, the relative potency (*A*) in the atrial test is $3.4 \times 10^{-9}$ M ÷ $7.1 \times 10^{-9}$ M = 0.48. As an index of bronchodilator *vs*. cardiac stimulant selectivity, the T/A value (separation ratio) will be presented. For **1d** this is 5.5 ÷ 0.48 = 11.5. In those instances in which data in these tests are unavailable similar potencies relative to isoproterenol in stated test systems will be given.

Modification of the Catechol System. Stepwise elimination of the phenolic-OH groups of isoproterenol demonstrates that the meta-OH is more important than the para-OH for the activation of adrenergic receptors (51, 52, 53). Thus, in the guinea pig tracheal chain and right atria tests 2, in which the meta-OH of isoproterenol is retained and the para-OH is removed, is more effective than its isomer 3 in which the para-OH is retained. Elimination of both of the catecholic OH groups decreases intrinsic activity on β-adrenoreceptors (25). The analog 4 of isoproterenol antagonizes the tachycardia induced by β-adrenergic agonists (24, 51) and is only very weakly effective in the guinea pig tracheal chain and right atria tests, as well as in other tests for bronchodilator activity (54).

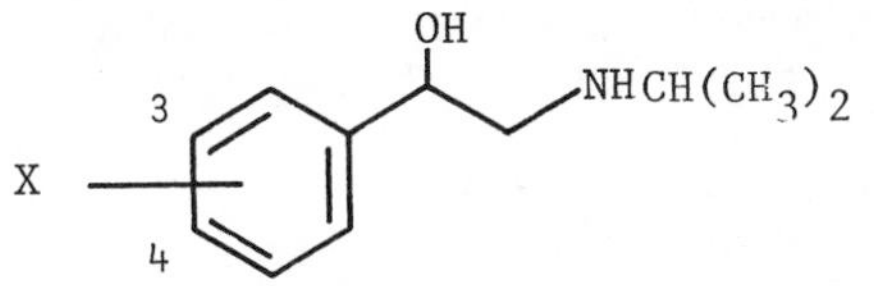

OH
NHCH$(CH_3)_2$
3
X
4

2, X = 3-OH : T = ca. 0.16, A = ca. 0.092, T/A = ca. 1.74
3, X = 4-OH : T = ca. 0.065, A = ca. 0.044, T/A = ca. 1.48
4, X = H : T = ca. 0.003, A = ca. 0.006, T/A = ca. 0.5

More recent studies have demonstrated that the meta-phenolic function may be replaced with various groups to afford compounds with improved selectivity for bronchial vs. cardiac musculature. The structural requirements for groups that can simulate the meta-phenolic moiety are not clearly defined. For example, strongly acidic groups, e.g., the methanesulfonamide group of soterenol (5a) and mesuprene [2-hydroxy-5-(1-hydroxy-2-(4-methoxyphenyl)ethylaminopropyl)methanesulfanilide] (26, 55, 56, 57), weakly acidic groupings, e.g., the $HOCH_2$ group of salbutamol (5b) and salmefamol (5c) (27, 58), homologous moieties, e.g., 5d and 5e (22), and even basic substituents, e.g. 5f (59), and 5g (60), can replace the meta-OH of isoproterenol to give β-adrenergic receptor agonists. The resorcinol terbutaline (6a) (61, 62) is also an effective β-adrenoreceptor stimulant. Even the presence of a mobile proton (63) in the meta substituent is not an absolute requirement for β-adrenergic activity of an analog of isoproterenol. Thus, quinterenol (7), which incorporates an 8-hydroxyquinoline metal-chelating system, is a potent β-adrenoreceptor agonist; however, unlike many other catecholamine analogs, quinterenol is selective for bronchial vs. cardiac muscle in vitro, but not in vivo (64). In addition to improving bronchodilator selectivity, alteration of the meta-OH group also affords compounds that are resistant to metabolic inactivation by COMT.

Many of these so-called "second generation" bronchodilators, e.g., salbutamol (65, 66, 67, 68), salmefamol (69, 70) and terbutaline (71, 72, 73, 74), are clinically effective bronchodilators with prolonged activity following various routes of administration. Higher serum levels of terbutaline are obtained after administration of its diisobutyryl ester, ibuterol (**6b**) (75).

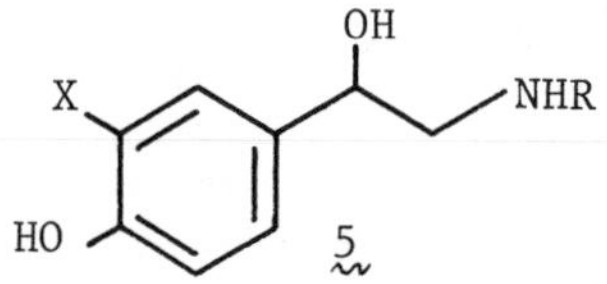

**5**

**a**, X = $CH_3SO_2NH$; R = $CH(CH_3)_2$ : T = 0.27, A = 0.045
T/A = 6.0

**b**, X = $HOCH_2$; R = $C(CH_3)_3$ : T = 0.65, A = 0.011, T/A = 59.1

**c**, X = $HOCH_2$; R = $CH(CH_3)CH_2$-$C_6H_4$-$OCH_3$ : T* (27) = 1.5,
A* (27) = 0.00075, T*/A* (27) = 2000

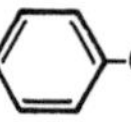

**d**, X = $HO(CH_2)_2$; R = $C(CH_3)_3$ : T* = 0.09, A* $<$ 0.00007,
T*/A* $>$ 1285 (63)

**e**, X = $CH_3SO_2NHCH_2$; R = $C(CH_3)_3$ : T* = 0.18, A* = 0.001,
T*/A* = 180 (63)

**f**, X = $H_2N$; R = $C(CH_3)_3$ : T = 0.34, A = 0.031, T/A = 10.9

**g**, X = $C_6H_5NH$; R = $C(CH_3)_3$ : T* = 10 x **5b** (60).

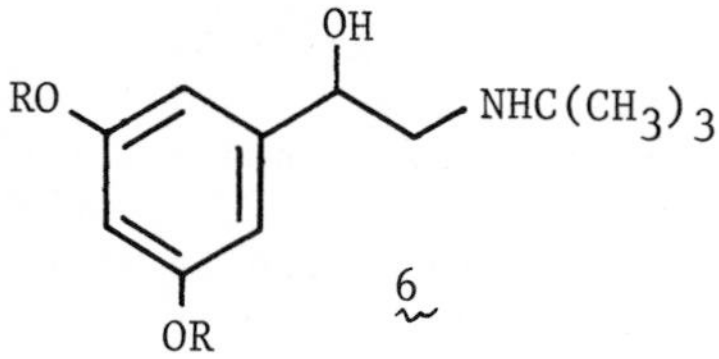

**6**

**a**, R = H : T = 0.059,
A = 0.01, T/A = 5.9

**b**, R = $(CH_3)_2CHCO$ (75)

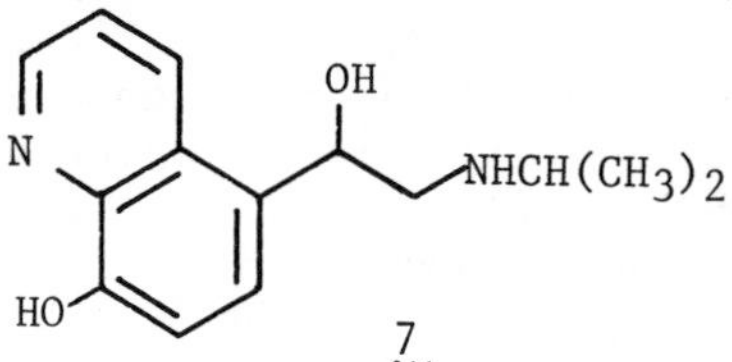

**7**

T = 0.053, A $<$ 0.00008,
T/A $>$ 633

As a general rule, isoproterenol analogs in which the meta-OH is retained and the para-OH is replaced by a "OH-simulating" group are β-adrenoreceptor antagonists or they are only very weak agonists (26, 27). On the basis of these results, it has been suggested (27) that the para-OH is critically important in the receptor interaction. The meta substituent may initiate formation of an ordered water crust that interacts with adenylate cyclase to induce a specific and highly favored conformational perturbation of this enzyme that may be involved in β-adrenergic receptor actions (76, 77, 78). In fact, structure-activity relationships based on measurement of the ability of catecholamines to bind to the β-receptor and activate or inhibit adenylate cyclase in membranes of turkey erythrocytes corresponds closely with those derived using guinea pig tissue (79, 80).

In a search for new selective β-adrenergic bronchodilators a series of catecholamine analogs bearing a substituted amino functionality in the meta position was investigated (30). Some results of this study are presented in Table I. The secondary methylamino analog **8** was the most potent and selective $\beta_2$-adrenergic receptor agonist in the series. By contrast, the tertiary dimethylamino derivative **9** was much less potent and although it was selective for tracheobronchial *vs.* cardiac muscle *in vitro*, as noted with a similar tertiary amine quinterenol (**7**) this selectivity was not observed *in vivo*. Among amide, urea, carbanilate and sulfamide derivatives, **10**-**20**, only few generalizations can be made. Potency usually increased with decreasing size of the acyl substituent. Thus, the formanilide **10**, a very potent relaxant of the guinea pig tracheal chain preparation, was more effective than the acetanilide **11**. Similarly, the urea **12** (carbuterol) is a potent and selective $\beta_2$-adrenergic receptor agonist; however, methylation of the terminal nitrogen of the urea moiety (**13**) produces a ten-fold decrease in potency whereas substitution with larger groups **14**, multiple substitution **15**, or methylation of the anilino nitrogen **16** very significantly decreases β-adrenoreceptor agonist activity. A similar decrease in potency with increase in size of the alkyl group is noted for the alkyl carbanilates **17** > **18** > **19**. The sulfamide **20** has β-adrenoreceptor stimulant potency intermediate between the ethyl (**18**) and isopropyl (**19**) carbanilates.

Secondary pharmacological tests revealed an extremely promising profile of selective bronchodilator activity for carbuterol (**12**) (43, 44). In a double-blind study carbuterol, which is marketed in several countries, produced safe and effective bronchodilation both orally and upon inhalation (81, 82). Extensive testing of the formanilide **21** by various routes in guinea pigs indicates it is a more potent, but less selective bronchodilator, than salbutamol (83). A series of isoproterenol analogs with a $FCH_2SO_2NH$ group in the meta position generally had $\beta_2$-adrenoreceptor agonist potency less than their $CH_3SO_2NH$ counterparts (84).

Table I. Catecholamine Analogs with a Substituted Amino Group in the Meta Position (30)

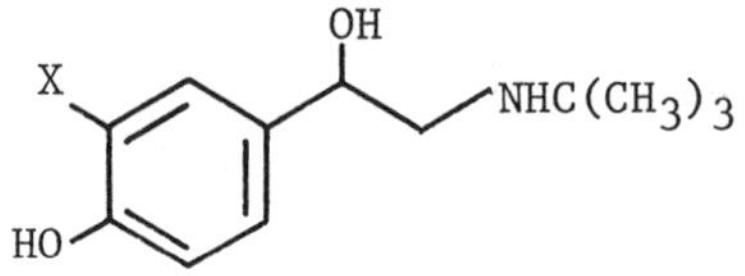

| No. | X | T | A | T/A |
|---|---|---|---|---|
| 8 | $CH_3NH$ | 71 | 0.37 | 192 |
| 9 | $(CH_3)_2N$ | 0.06 | 0.0001 | 600 |
| 10 | HCONH | 6.45 | 0.20 | 32.3 |
| 11 | $CH_3CONH$ | 0.25 | 0.0024 | 104.2 |
| 12 | $H_2NCONH$ | 0.37 | 0.005 | 74.0 |
| 13 | $CH_3NHCONH$ | 0.039 | 0.00052 | 75.0 |
| 14 | $(CH_3)_2CHNHCONH$ | <0.00015 | - | - |
| 15 | $(CH_3)_2NCONH$ | <0.0004 | - | - |
| 16 | $H_2NCON(CH_3)$ | ca. 0.00004 | <0.00006 | >0.67 |
| 17 | $CH_3OCONH$ | 0.74 | 0.028 | 26.4 |
| 18 | $C_2H_5OCONH$ | 0.106 | 0.01 | 10.6 |
| 19 | $(CH_3)_2CHOCONH$ | 0.028 | 0.002 | 14.0 |
| 20 | $(CH_3)_2NSO_2NH$ | 0.065 | 0.003 | 21.7 |

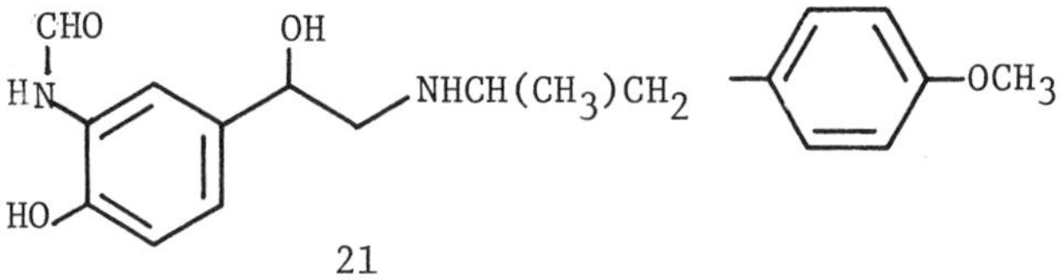

21

Recently, an extremely potent series of meta NH analogs of isoproterenol, some 8-hydroxycarbostyrils, has shown exceptionally potent β-adrenoreceptor agonist activity (85). One of these compounds 22a is 23,650 times more potent than isoproterenol in a modification of the guinea pig tracheal chain test employed in our laboratories. It is also selective for $β_2$-adrenergic receptors as it is significantly less potent in a guinea pig right atria test that differs somewhat from that used in our studies; the separation ratio in these tests is 537,500. A related N-(phenyl-*tert*-butyl) derivative 22b is also a potent β-adrenoreceptor agonist. It is remarkably potent in the modified guinea pig right atria test having an $ED_{25} = 3.05 \times 10^{-14}$ M. An α-ethyl-N-isopropyl relative, procaterol (22c) has potency, selectivity and a long duration of *in vivo* activity suggesting potential utility in the treatment of asthma (86, 87). Another modification involving a meta N-substituted analog is the benzimidazole

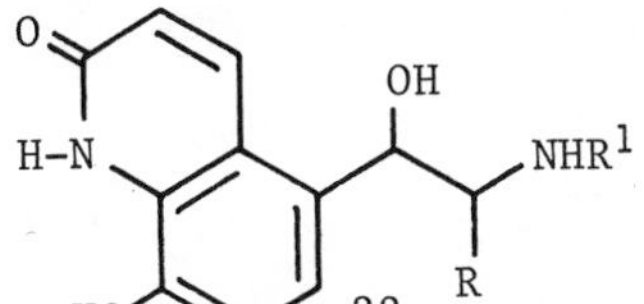

22

a, R = H, $R^1 = C(CH_3)_3$ :
T* = 23,650, A* = 0.044,
T*/A* = 537,500

b, R = H, $R^1 = C(CH_3)_2CH_2C_6H_5$ :
T* = 7200, A* = 813,
T*/A* = 8.9

c, R = $C_2H_5$, $R^1 = CH(CH_3)_2$ :
T* = 7.95, A* = 0.0054
T*/A* = 1472

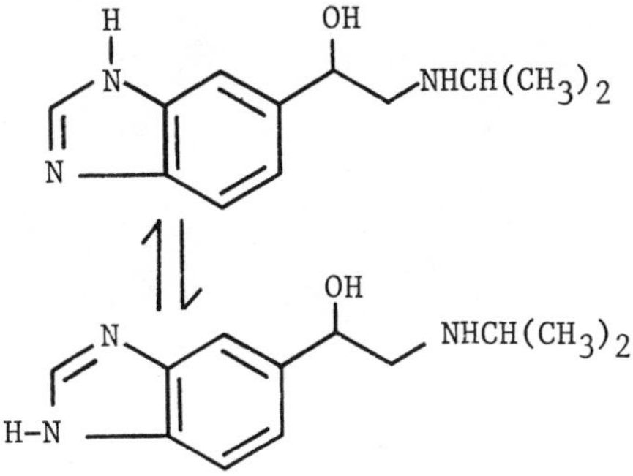

23

T* = 0.048, A* = 0.0035
T*/A* = 13.7

bioisosteric tautomer 23 of isoproterenol. Although less potent than isoproterenol as a $β_2$-adrenoreceptor agonist it is more selective in modified *in vitro* guinea pig tracheal chain and atria tests and is chemically more stable than the catechol (88).

Thus, many meta-substituted analogs of catecholamines bearing labile protons of significantly different acidities attached to an O or N have marked β-adrenoreceptor agonist activity. It, therefore, seemed pertinent to examine some catecholamine analogs having an acidic proton attached to a carbon atom. For this reason, some analogs having a substituted sulfonyl or sulfonylalkyl group in the meta position were examined for β-adrenergic receptor agonist activity (32). Some of the results of this study are presented in Table II.

Table II. Catecholamine Analogs with a Substituted Sulfonyl or Sulfonylalkyl Group in the Meta Position (32)

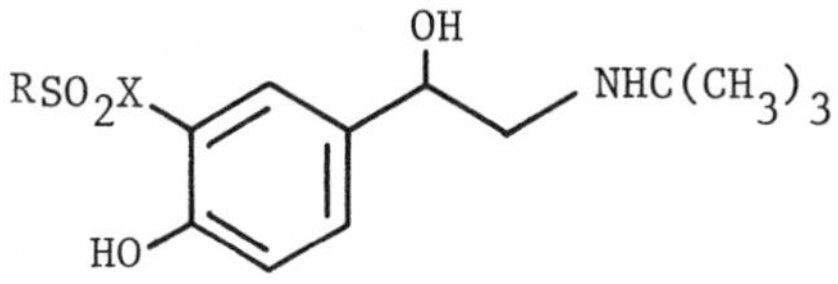

$$\mathrm{RSO_2X}\text{-}\mathrm{C_6H_3(OH)}\text{-}\mathrm{CH(OH)CH_2NHC(CH_3)_3}$$

| No. | R | X | T | A | T/A |
|---|---|---|---|---|---|
| 24 | $CH_3$ | - | β-Adrenergic Antagonist | | |
| 25 | $H_2N$ | - | β-Adrenergic Antagonist | | |
| 26 | $CH_3$ | $CH_2$ | 0.42 | 0.00012 | 3500 |
| 27 | $CH_3$ | $(CH_2)_2$ | 0.01 | <0.00067 | >14.9 |
| 28 | $CH_3$ | $(CH_2)_3$ | <0.00016 | <0.00007 | - |
| 29 | $CH_3$ | $CHCH_3$ | <0.00044 | 0 | - |
| 30 | $C_2H_5$ | $CH_2$ | 0.12 | 0 | ∞ |
| 31 | n-$C_3H_7$ | $CH_2$ | ca.0.00014 | <0.00007 | > 2.0 |
| 32 | i-$C_3H_7$ | $CH_2$ | <0.00048 | <0.00023 | - |
| 33 | 4-$CH_3C_6H_4$ | $CH_2$ | β-Adrenergic Antagonist | | |

Both length and branching of the alkylene bridge between the substituted sulfonyl group and the aromatic ring had a marked effect on adrenergic activity. The order of $\beta_2$-adrenoreceptor agonist potency as measured in the guinea pig tracheal chain test was $CH_2$ (26) > $(CH_2)_2$ (27) >> $(CH_2)_3$ (28) ≈ $CH(CH_3)$ (29) >> no alkylene bridge (24). In fact, 24 and 25, which lack an alkylene bridge have β-adrenergic receptor blocking activity. This action is consistent with the observation that several other catecholamine analogs having an electron-withdrawing moiety in place of the meta-OH are antagonists. For example, the meta-$H_2NCO$ congener (AH 3474) related to 25 is a β-adrenoreceptor blocker (89) as is its N-phenylisopropyl derivative, AH 5158 (90, 91). The salicylic acid derivative, i.e. a congener bearing a meta-COOH group, is described as "inactive" (27). Clearly, a methylene bridge between the ring and sulfonyl group affords maximum β-adrenergic agonist potency. Additionally, sulfonterol (26) demonstrates a striking selectivity for tracheal *vs*. cardiac muscle; it has a separation ratio of 3500.

Substitution of the sulfonyl group also affects adrenergic activity. In general, as noted in related series (Table I), β-adrenoreceptor agonist potency decreases as the size of the sulfonyl-substituent is increased. Thus, in the guinea pig tracheal test the methyl derivative sulfonterol (26) is three to four times more potent than the ethyl derivative 30 and about 300 times more potent than the n-propyl homolog 31. The bulkier i-propyl congener 32 is even less effective and the p-tolyl derivative 33 produces pharmacological actions suggestive of β-adrenergic receptor blockade (32).

Table III. Catecholamine Analogs With a Bridge Between the Meta-OH or OH-Simulating Group

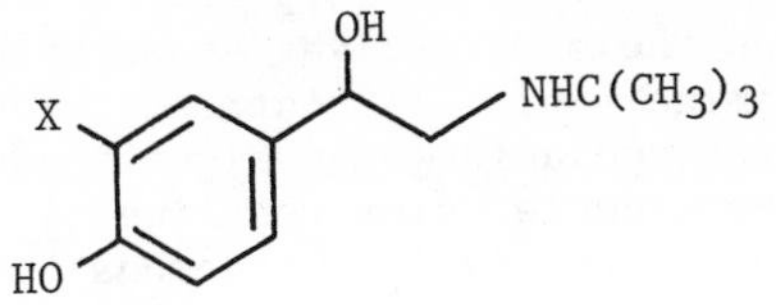

OH, X, HO, $NHC(CH_3)_3$

| No. | X | T | A | T/A |
|---|---|---|---|---|
| 34 (63) | $CH_3SO_2NHCH_2$ | 0.18 | 0.001 | 180 |
| 35 (63) | $HO(CH_2)_2$ | 0.09 | <0.00007 | >1285 |
| 36 (63) | $H_2NCONHCH_2$ | 0.31 | 0.015 | 20.7 |
| 37 (63) | $HCONHCH_2$ | 0.046 | 0 | ∞ |
| 38 (35) | $CH_3CH(OH)$ | 0.39 | ca. 0.00065 | ca. 600 |
| 39 (35) | $HOCH_2CH(OH)$ | 0.072 | ca. 0.00011 | ca. 654 |
| 40 (35) | $CH_3OCH_2CH(OH)$ | 0.013 | <0.00003 | >433 |
| 41 (35) | $CH_3SO_2CH_2CH(OH)$ | <0.0006 | 0 | - |
| 42 (27) | $(CH_3)_2C(OH)$ | "Weak β-adrenergic antagonist" | | |

It is particularly noteworthy that the ethylene bridged congener 27 of sulfonterol (26) retains significant, albeit weak, $β_2$-adrenoreceptor agonist activity. Studies in several series of meta-modified catecholamine analogs indicate that the mobile proton in this position need not be attached directly to the atom joined to the phenyl ring. A methylene or even an ethylene bridge may be interspersed between the "HO-simulating group" and the aromatic ring with retention of significant β-adrenoreceptor agonist activity. Several examples, 34-37, of this general structure-activity relationship are presented in Table III. Branching of the methylene bridge of salbutamol (5b) with a methyl (38), hydroxymethyl (39), methoxymethyl (40) or methylsulfonylmethyl (41) group permits the retention of a high order of $\beta_2$-adrenoreceptor agonist potency which decreases as the size of the branching group is increased. Branching with two methyl groups, as in 42 changes activity from β-adrenergic agonist to antagonist (35).

The effect of additional substitution of the aromatic ring of adrenergic catecholamines has been the subject of relatively little study. Various 2-alkyl-, cycloalkyl-, and alkoxy-substituted derivatives of isoproterenol are claimed (92, 93, 94) to possess sympathomimetic and broncholytic actions. In a test for norepinephrine-releasing ability in mouse heart, the 2-, 5-, and 6-methyl and methoxy derivatives of isoproterenol are only weakly effective (95), whereas the 6-OH derivative of epinephrine induces release of the amine (96). In contrast, a number of halogen-substituted phenylethanolamines have significant β-adrenergic receptor activity. For example, clorprenaline (43a) is a clinically effective bronchodilator (97). It demonstrates $\beta_2$-adrenoreceptor agonist selectivity in the guinea pig tracheal chain and right atria tests. Both β-adrenoreceptor agonist (98) and antagonist (99) activity have been reported for clorprenaline. Dichlorisoproterenol (43b) is the prototype of β-adrenoreceptor antagonists, however, it is also a weak agonist (100). Several 4-amino-3,5-dichlorophenylethanolamines, e.g., clenbuterol (44), are potent β-adrenoreceptor agonists (101). A double-blind study has shown clenbuterol orally effective in the treatment of moderately severe asthma (102). Interestingly, the (-)-isomer of clenbuterol is a potent $\beta_2$-adrenoreceptor agonist whereas the (+)-enantiomer is an antagonist (103).

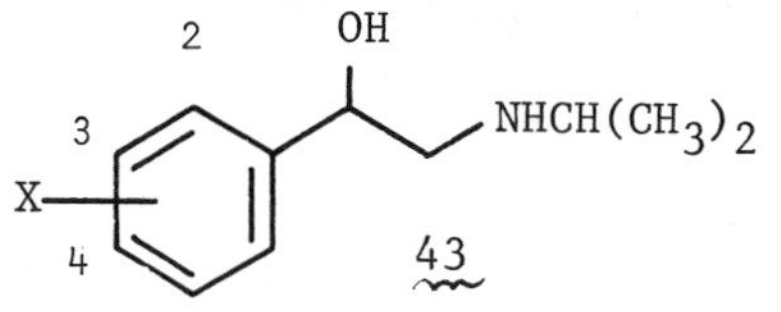

2 OH
3 X 4 NHCH($CH_3$)$_2$
43

a, X = 2-Cl : T = 0.065, A = 0.0017, T/A = 38.2

b, X = 3,4-$Cl_2$: β-adrenergic antagonist (100)

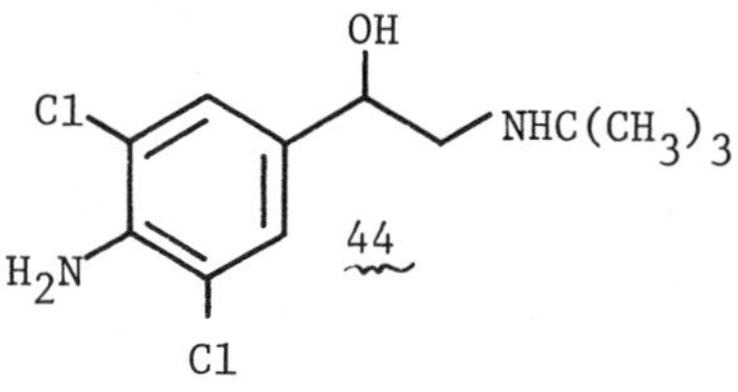

OH
Cl $H_2N$ Cl NHC($CH_3$)$_3$
44

T = 6.5, A = 0.13
T/A = 50

A series of chloro-substituted analogs of isoproterenol and related compounds was studied. Some of the results of this investigation are tabulated in Table IV. These data indicate that substitution of position 2 of isoproterenol and several N-substituted derivatives generally affords compounds that are more potent than their nonchlorinated relatives; however, chlorination of either position 5 or 6 decreases β-adrenergic potency as determined in the guinea pig tracheal chain and right atria tests. No significant trend relative to tissue selectivity is noted, and *in vivo* tests did not indicate that the 2-Cl derivatives had an enhanced duration of action (31).

Table IV. Ring-Chlorinated Derivatives of Adrenergic Catecholamines (31)

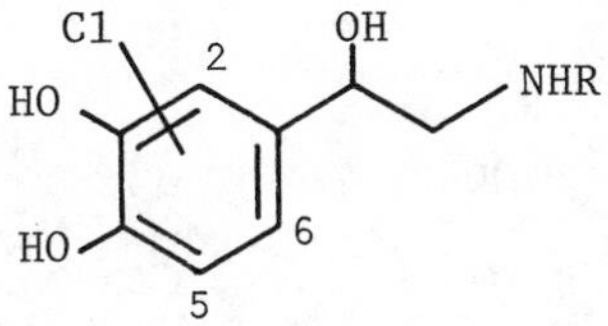

| No. | Cl position | R | T | A | T/A |
|---|---|---|---|---|---|
| 45 | 2 | $CH(CH_3)_2$ | 4.73 | 0.83 | 5.70 |
| 46 | 2 | $C(CH_3)_3$ | 15.43 | 38.20 | 0.40 |
| 47 | 2 | *c*-$C_5H_9$ | 1.78 | 0.26 | 6.85 |
| 48 | 5 | $CH(CH_3)_2$ | 0.055 | 0.14 | 0.39 |
| 49 | 5 | *c*-$C_5H_9$ | *ca.* 0.033 | *ca.* 0.013 | *ca.* 2.54 |
| 50 | 6 | $CH(CH_3)_2$ | *ca.* 0.031 | *ca.* 0.031 | *ca.* 1.00 |
| 51 | 6 | *c*-$C_5H_9$ | 0.019 | 0.0065 | 2.92 |

Several heterocyclic ethanolamine relatives of β-adrenergic catecholamines have been investigated. Pyrbuterol (52a), a 2-pyridyl analog of salbutamol (5b) is a potent and selective $\beta_2$-adrenoreceptor agonist (104); it is a clinically effective bronchodilator (105). Several other 2-pyridylethanolamines, e.g. 52b, which places an acidic α-picoline group in a position meta to the side chain, 52c, a sulfonterol (26) analog, and 52d are weak but selective $\beta_2$-adrenoreceptor agonists as measured in the guinea pig tracheal chain and right atria tests (36). Only a few other pyridylethanolamines have been reported. Several chloro-substituted pyridylethanolamines are claimed to be potent β-adrenoreceptor antagonists (106). A series of 4-pyridylethanolamines had similar activity (107); however, subsequent studies indicated that N-isopropyl-4-pyridylethanolamine has mixed agonist-antagonist actions

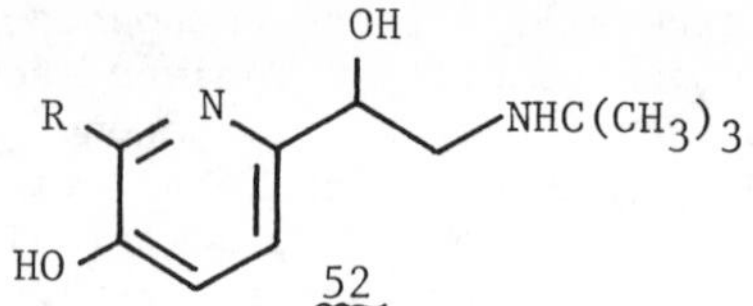

52

a, R = $HOCH_2$ : T = 2.54, A = 0.028, T/A = 90.7

b, R = $CH_3$ : T = 0.025, A = ca. 0.00034, T/A = ca. 73.5

c, R = $CH_3SO_2CH_2$ : T = 0.24, A = <0.00003, T/A = >8000

d, R = H : T = 0.023, A = <0.0002, T/A = >115

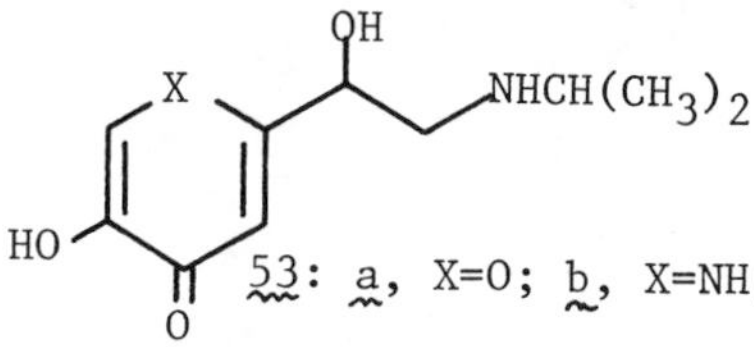

53: a, X=O; b, X=NH; c, X=$NCH_3$

on β-adrenoreceptors and that the 2- and 3- pyridyl counterparts are weak agonists (108). Various other heterocyclic ethanolamines, e.g., pyrrole (109), furan (110, 111), thiophene (112), indole (113, 114), benzofuran (113, 115, 116, 117), benzothiophene (118, 119), chromone (114, 116, 120), quinoline (121), isoquinoline (114) and phenanthridine (121) derivatives, are primarily β-adrenergic receptor antagonists. Potent, but non-specific β-adrenergic potency is described for the 4-pyranone 53a; however, the related pyridines 53b and 53c have a much lower order of activity (122).

Effect of N-Substitution on β-Adrenoreceptor Activity of Catecholamines. This subject has been carefully reviewed (e.g., 8, 22, 25, 28, 53, 63). For this reason, it will not be reviewed in detail here. Generally, the influence of N-substitution on adrenergic activity is similar for catecholamines and various derivatives in which the catechol system is modified (cf. 26, 27, 32). Potent β-adrenergic receptor activity, either agonistic or antagonistic, is usually confined to secondary amines. The primary amines, e.g., norepinephrine (1a) generally activate both α- and β-receptors, but their main effect is on the former. In a test for inhibition of acetylcholine-induced bronchoconstriction in guinea pigs 1a was only 1/50th as potent as isoproterenol (123) and in a test that measures the increase in rate of contraction of isolated perfused rabbit hearts it was one-tenth as potent as the prototype (3). Tertiary amines usually have only weak actions on adrenergic receptors (54). Thus, N-methylepinephrine has weak vasopressor action of short duration in anesthetized dogs (3). Apparently, this tertiary amine has direct α-adrenoreceptor agonist, but only weak β-agonist, activity (96, 124, 125). A morpholinyl relative of norepinephrine is somewhat of an exception. This tertiary amine has both α and β-adrenoreceptor agonist activity. In a guinea pig tracheal chain test it has a T* value of 0.059 (126). As indicated in Table V, epinephrine is a potent agonist of both $\beta_1$ and $\beta_2$-adrenergic receptors. Adrenergic actions generally decrease with increasing length of straight chain alkyl substitution. Thus, in the test for inhibition of acetylcholine-induced bronchoconstriction in guinea pigs, N-alkylation of norepinephrine (1a) decreases potency as follows: $C_2H_5$ (T* = 0.33) > n-$C_3H_7$ (T* = 0.02) ≈ n-$C_4H_9$ (T* = 0.02) (123). In contrast, branching of the N-substituent often increases β-adrenoreceptor potency and, in some instances $\beta_2$ selectivity. Thus, isoproterenol (1c) and N-tert-butylnorepinephrine (1d) are more potent β-agonists than epinephrine. Certain aralkyl groups, notably ones that are branched at the carbon attached to the N, e.g. 54 (protokylol) - 58, have enhanced potency and selectivity as relaxants of tracheobronchial muscle (3, 22, 63, 127 128, 129). It has been suggested that the phenyl group of N-(4-hydroxyphenyl)alkyl derivatives contributes to specific binding with the receptor and that the phenolic OH reinforces this by hydrogen bonding with the receptor (22, 123). The β-adrenoreceptor actions of selected N-substituted derivatives of norepinephrine are presented in Table V.

A unique class of N-substituted catecholamines is represented by some "bis" compounds. A hexamethylene bridge appears to afford maximum β-adrenoreceptor agonist potency. Thus, hexoprenaline (59a) (130, 131) is a potent and selective $\beta_2$-adrenoreceptor agonist. It has been tested extensively in the clinic and produces selective bronchodilation of prolonged duration following various routes of administration (132, 133, 134, 135). A related series of meta-modified "bis" hexamethylene bridged catecholamines, e.g., 59b (40) also have selective $\beta_2$-adrenoreceptor agonist activity as measured in the guinea pig tracheal chain and right atria tests.

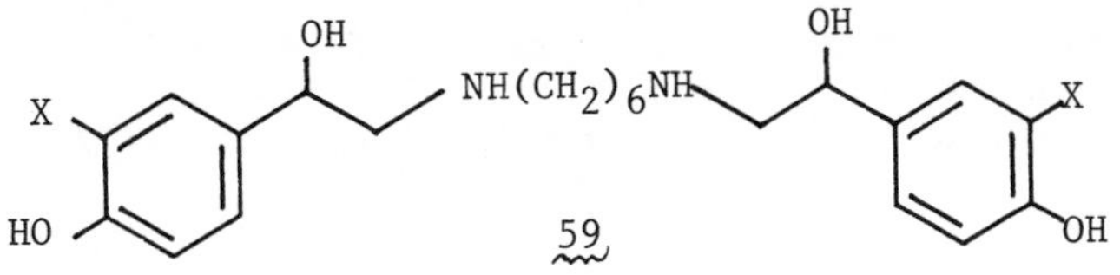

OH OH

X NH$(CH_2)_6$NH X

HO OH

59

a, X = HO : T = 7.9, A = 0.21, T/A = 37.6

b, X = $CH_3SO_2NH$ : T = 2.9, A = 0.047, T/A = 61.7.

Table V. N-Substituted Derivatives of Norepinephrine

| No. | R | T | A | T/A |
|---|---|---|---|---|
| 1b | $CH_3$ | 0.26 | 0.035 | 7.4 |
| 1c | $CH(CH_3)_2$ | 1.0 | 1.0 | 1.0 |
| 1d | $C(CH_3)_3$ | 5.5 | 0.48 | 11.5 |
| 54 | $CH(CH_3)CH_2$-(3,4-methylenedioxyphenyl) | 5.6 | 0.8 | 7.0 |
| 55 | $CH(CH_3)CH_2$-(4-hydroxyphenyl)-OH | 4.3 | 2.0 | 2.1 |
| 56 | $C(CH_3)_2CH_2$-(4-hydroxyphenyl)-OH | 10.0[a] | 1.7[b] | 5.9 |
| 57 | $CH(CH_3)CH_2$-(4-methoxyphenyl)-$OCH_3$ | 2.0[c] | - | - |
| 58 | $CH(CH_3)CH_2$-(indol-3-yl, N-H) | 10.0[d] | - | - |

[a] Determined in a guinea pig tracheal chain test (128).
[b] Determined in a guinea pig right atria test (128).
[c] Determined in a test for relaxation of perfused guinea pig lung constriction induced by histamine (127).
[d] Determined in a guinea pig tracheal chain test (129).

Another example of marked β-adrenoreceptor potency enhancement by N-substitution is illustrated by fenoterol (60a), which is strikingly more potent than its N-*tert*-butyl counterpart, terbutaline (6a). Fenoterol is a clinically effective bronchodilator by either oral or aerosol administration; however, some cardiac stimulation and tremors are noted (136, 137). Cat soleus muscle, bronchial and heart rate experiments indicate selective $\beta_2$-adrenoreceptor potency for 60b (138). Another resorcinol, one of a series of xanthine derivatives, is reproterol (60c). Reproterol is clinically effective in bronchial asthma; it causes minimum CNS and cardiovascular side effects upon administration orally or by inhalation, and tachyphylaxis is not observed (139).

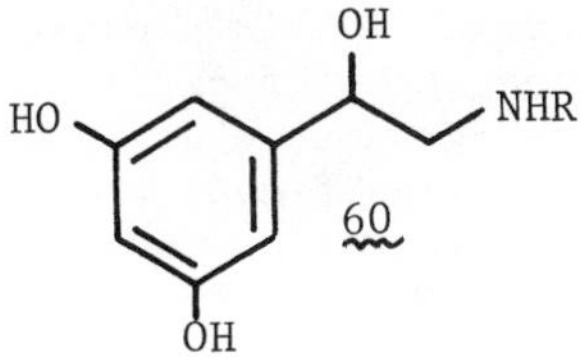

60

a, R = $CH(CH_3)CH_2$-(4-hydroxyphenyl)

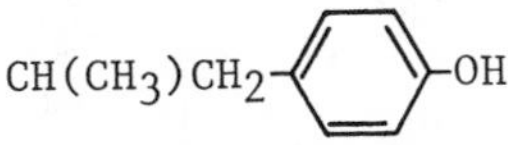

T = 2.34, A = 0.31, T/A = 7.55

b, R = $C(CH_3)_2CH_2$-(4-hydroxyphenyl)

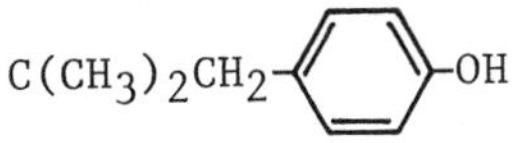

c, R = $(CH_2)_3$-N (theophylline-7-yl)

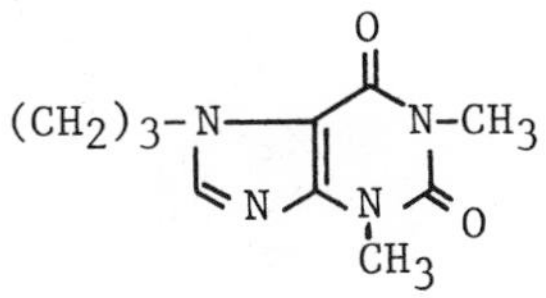

Side Chain Alteration of Adrenergic Catecholamines and Related Compounds. The benzylic hydroxyl of adrenergic phenylethanolamines has been implicated in the interaction of these compounds with postulated adrenoreceptors involving adenylate cyclase (22, 76, 77, 78) as well as other proposed models (26, 140). Its presence in the absolute R stereochemistry at the benzylic position is essential for potent β-adrenoreceptor activity. In all known instances, these are the levorotatory (-)-isomers (22, 25, 30, 32, 63, 141). Generally, the S (+)-enantiomers have only weak β-adrenergic receptor activity. Interestingly, α-adrenergic receptor agonist activity is described for R-isoproterenol whereas the S-isomer is an antagonist (51, 142, 143).

Removal of the benzylic OH, i.e., to give a dopamine derivative markedly reduces β-adrenergic agonist activity (144, 145) to a level comparable to that of the less potent phenylethanolamine enantiomer, an observation that has been rationalized at the receptor level (146). Replacement of the benzylic OH with a carbonyl group (123) results in a marked decrease in effectiveness in various tests for adrenoreceptor activity (8, 147). In the guinea pig tracheal chain test N-*tert*-butylnoradrenalone had a relative potency T < 0.0001 (37). Methylation of the benzylic OH of isoproterenol, i.e., to give a methyl ether (148) also reduces $\beta$-adrenergic receptor agonist potency, T = *ca.* 0.004, A = *ca.* 0.01 (37). Addition of a methyl group to the benzylic position of isoproterenol (1c) provides a tertiary alcohol (149) which also has significantly decreased $\beta$-adrenergic agonist potency, T = *ca.* 0.002, A < 0.00005 (37).

In some instances alteration of the benzylic OH affords compounds with significant adrenoreceptor activity. For example, substitution of an amino group for epinephrine's benzylic OH gives a pressor agent (150) having a positive inotropic effect on isolated frog heart (151). Also, the hydroxymethyl homologue 61 of N-*tert*-butylnorepinephrine (1d) is a potent $\beta$-adrenoreceptor agonist (152). Several congeners of 61 in which the meta-OH was replaced by "OH simulating" groups, e.g., $HOCH_2$, $H_2NCONH$, $H_2N$ and $CH_3SO_2NH$, also retained significant and selective $\beta_2$ *vs.* $\beta_1$-adrenoreceptor agonist activity as measured in the guinea pig tracheal chain and right atria tests (37).

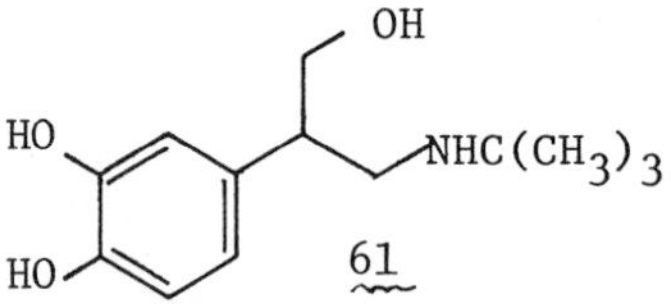

61

T = 0.22, A = 0.035
T/A = 6.3

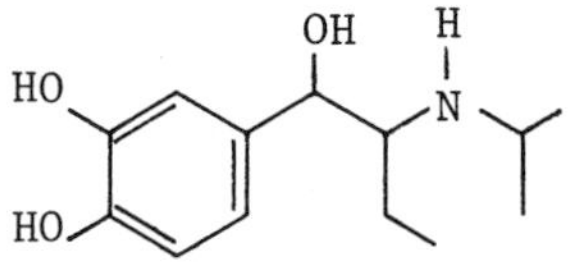

62

T = 1.1, A = 0.051
T/A = 21.6

Introduction of $\alpha$-alkyl groups into the ethanolamine side chain of adrenergic phenylethanolamines generally reduces effectiveness; however, in compounds with erythro stereochemistry (153) and a methyl or ethyl substituent a high degree of potency and increased $\beta_2$ selectivity may result. Thus, erythro-$\alpha$-ethylisoproterenol (isoetharine, 62) (154) retains the $\beta_2$-adrenoreceptor agonist potency of isoproterenol whereas selectivity is enhanced. Substitution of the $\alpha$-position with groups larger than ethyl markedly decreases adrenergic activity. The $\alpha$-propyl and $\alpha$-isopropyl derivatives, for example, are at least 1000 times less potent than isoproterenol as bronchodilators in anesthetized guinea pigs (8, 54). Several $\alpha$-substituted catecholamines and related compounds in which the substituent is incorporated into a ring system are potent and selective $\beta_2$-adrenergic receptor agonists. For example, rimiterol (erythro- 63) (155, 156), which might be envisioned as congener of isoetharine (62) in which the $\alpha$-ethyl group is joined to the N-substituent to form a piperidine ring, is a potent and selective relaxant of tracheobronchial muscle (38). As in the case of isoetharine, activity is greater for the erythro than the threo isomer. Rimiterol is a clinically effective bronchodilator (157, 158). The trans-aminotetralin 64

(159), a congener of isoetharine (62) in which the α-substituent is joined to position 2 of the catechol ring, as well as several derivatives (160, 161, 162), is a potent and selective relaxant of tracheobronchial muscle, in a modification of the *in vitro* guinea pig tracheal chain and right atria tests. It is of

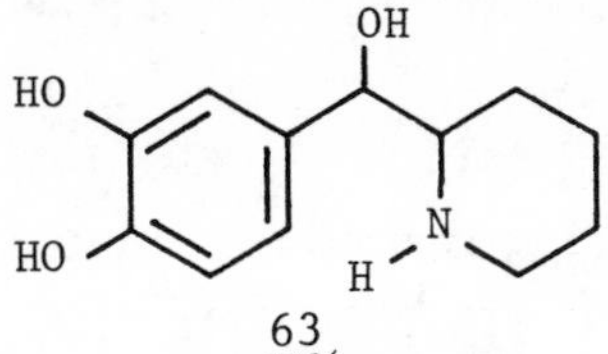

63

T = 0.44, A = 0.022
T/A = 20

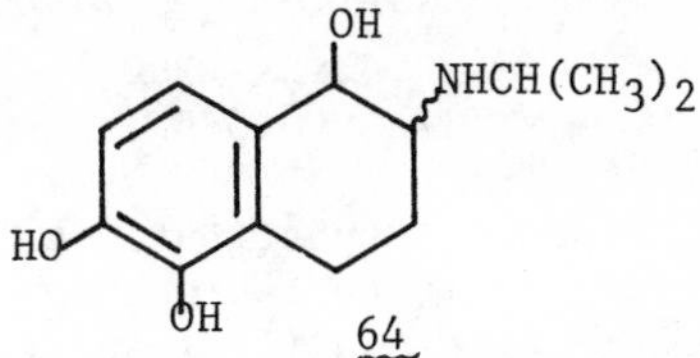

64

T* = 1.62, A* = 0.087,
T*/A* = 18.6

interest to note that the related 6,7-dihydroxytetralin, which might be viewed as arising from joining of isoetharine's α-ethyl group into position 6 of the catechol ring, apparently is considerably less effective than isoproterenol in antagonizing the bronchoconstrictor effect of acetylcholine on guinea pig lung (163). A homolog, *cis*-2,3-dihydroxy-6-amino-6,7,8,9-tetrahydro-5H-benzocyclohepten-5-ol, is virtually without β-adrenergic agonist activity (164).

Several other catechols and related compounds with β-adrenergic agonist activity involve a more profound structural modification of the phenylethanolamine skeleton. The catecholoxypropanolamine 65, which might be viewed as a congener of N-*tert*-butylnorepinephrine in which a $OCH_2$ group is inserted between the catechol nucleus and the ethanolamine side chain, is a very potent β-adrenoreceptor agonist; however, it has a marked selectivity for cardiac rather than tracheobronchial muscle (33). In a series of ring-hydroxylated phenoxypropanolamines, several showed marked β-adrenoreceptor agonist properties on guinea pig cardiac muscle (165, 166), although mixed agonist-antagonist actions were seen in other tests (167). Modification of the catechol substitution in this series seems quite similar to that observed with phenylethanolamines, i.e., the meta-OH may be replaced by a "OH-simulating" group with retention of β-adrenergic agonist activity (33). The thiazoloxypropanolamine tazolol (66) also demonstrates selective myocardial stimulant activity of prolonged duration (168, 169). Thus, oxypropanolamines have potent $\beta_1$-adrenoreceptor agonist or antagonist (168, 169) selectivity provided they have the absolute stereochemistry S (33, 169). This is the same relative spacial orientation of the aromatic ring, hydroxyl and amino groups found in the active adrenergic R-phenylethanolamines.

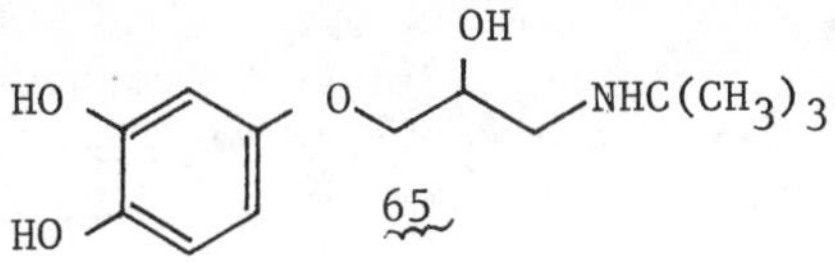

65

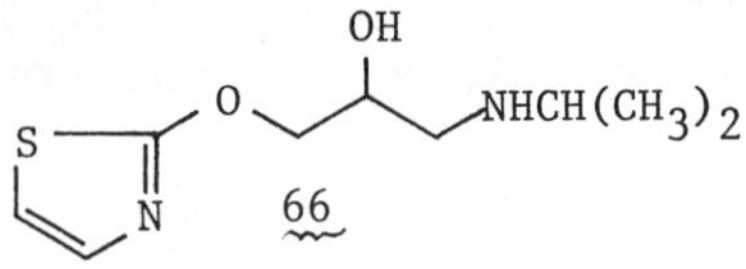

66

T = 22.4, A = 300
T/A = 0.075

Some 1-substituted-6,7-dihydroxy-1,2,3,4-tetrahydroisoquinolines are potent bronchodilators. For example, the 1-isopropyl derivative 67a (170) and tetrahydropapaveroline (67b) (171, 172, 173) have significant $\beta_2$-adrenergic receptor agonist activity. Among a large series of compounds, however, by far the most potent bronchodilator was trimetoquinol (67c) (174, 175). Orally, trimetoquinol has clinical bronchodilator activity similar to that of isoproterenol (176, 177). Structure-activity relationships in the tetrahydroisoquinoline series of bronchodilators seem quite different from other series, e.g., introduction of a "OH-simulating" group into position 6 or 7 of trimetoquinol results in loss of activity (178), apparently a benzylic OH is not required, and the absolute stereochemistry S at position 1 is essential (174). Nevertheless, trimetoquinol and related tetrahydroisoquinolines apparently react with β-adrenergic receptors in order to produce their effects. In an _in vitro_ test for relaxation of isolated guinea pig tracheal tissue pronethalol, a β-adrenergic receptor antagonist, induced a dose related shift of trimetoquinol's dose-response curve to the right (175).

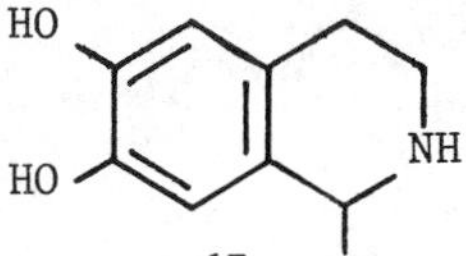

67

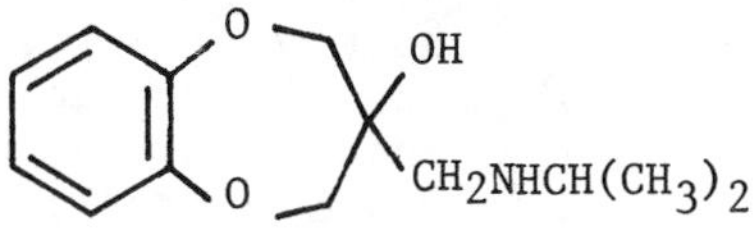

68

a, R = $CH(CH_3)_2$ : T = 0.043,
A = 0.001, T/A = 43

b, R = $CH_2$-(3,4-dihydroxyphenyl) : T = 0.089;
A = 0.057, T/A = 1.6

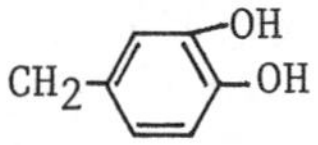

c, R = $CH_2$-(3,4,5-trimethoxyphenyl) : T = 8.5,
A = 2.0, T/A = 4.2

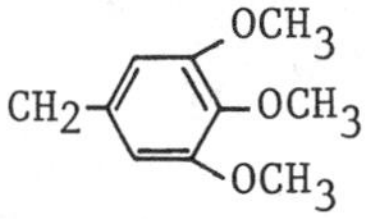

Another class of β-adrenoreceptor agonists is illustrated by the 1,5-benzodioxepin 68 which is 0.0057 times as potent as isoproterenol as an inhibitor of histamine-induced bronchoconstriction in dogs (179).

## Conformational Analysis of β-Adrenergic Receptor Agonists (50)

Comparison of the conformations of semi-rigid β-adrenoreceptor agonists with that of isoproterenol sulfate determined by X-ray diffractometric analysis (180) permits the rationalization that the crystal conformation might actually be the one preferred for receptor interaction. In this conformation of R-isoproterenol sulfate, as illustrated in the Newman projection 69, the α-ammonium group is gauche to the β-OH and trans to the catechol ring, the benzylic C-to-OH bond makes an acute angle of about 15° with the plane of the aromatic ring (the rotomer in which the edge of the ring is almost directly toward the viewer) and is oriented opposite the meta-OH group. This conformation of isoproterenol, also suggested by NMR analysis in solution (181), a situation more comparable to that in vivo, permits almost exact superimposition of all functional groups with those of the potent β-adrenoreceptor agonist trans-1,5,6-trihydroxy-2-isopropylaminotetralin (64), illustrated in the Newman projection 70, in which the OH and ammonium groups are in a trans diequatorial orientation and the tetralin ring is in its preferred half boat-half-chair form (159). The tetralin system not only holds the 5(meta)-OH opposite from the 1(benzylic)-OH, but it also introduces a 2-substituent into the catechol ring, a substitution pattern beneficial for β-adrenergic receptor interaction (31).

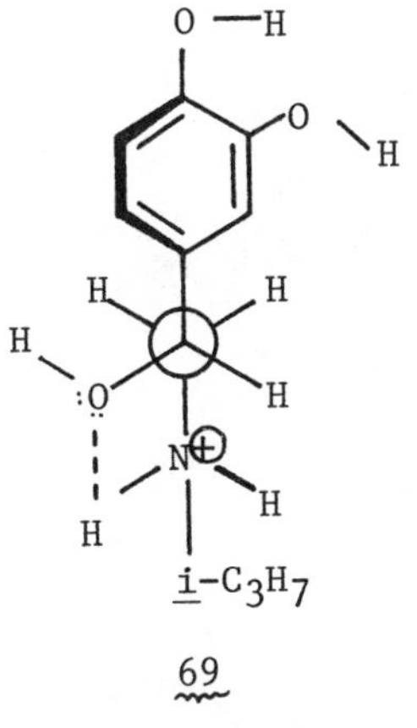

O—H O H H H H :O H N⊕ H H i-C₃H₇

69

O—H O H H H :O H N⊕ H H i-C₃H₇

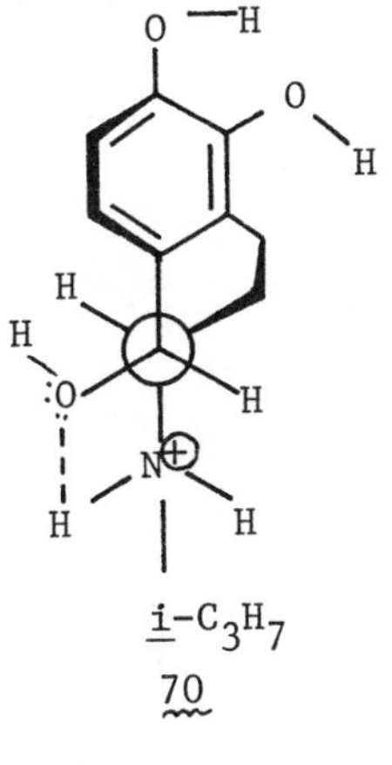

70

Two configurations may be considered for the related cis-1, 5,6-trihydroxy-2-methylaminotetralin which is only one-tenth as potent as its trans isomer in guinea pig tracheal and right atria tests (159). Placement of the β-OH in an axial position, i.e., the cis-$\alpha_e$, $\beta_a$ isomer illustrated in the Newman projection 71, affords the inactive S configuration at the benzylic position 1. Alternatively, location of the ammonium group in the axial position, i.e., the cis $\alpha_a$, $\beta_e$ isomer, profoundly modifies its relationship to the ring. The related trans-$\alpha_e$, $\beta_e$-2-amino-1,6,7-trihydroxytetralin, shown in the Newman projection 72, may owe its weak bronchodilator activity (163) to the orientation of the 7(meta)-OH toward, rather than away from, the benzylic OH in position 1. Also, in this structure the tetralin system introduces a 6-substituent which is detrimental to β-adrenergic agonist potency of chlorinated catecholamines (31).

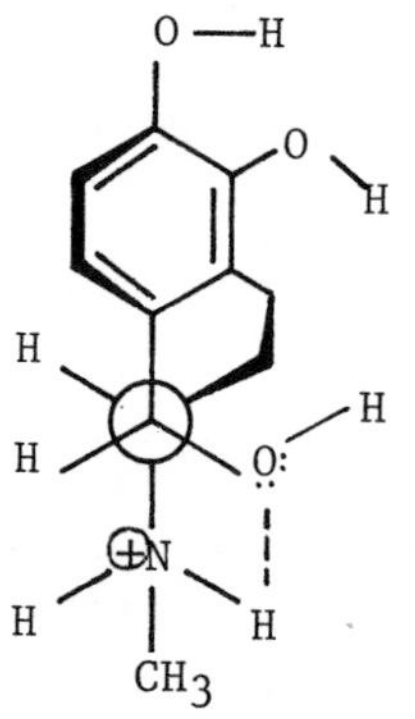

71

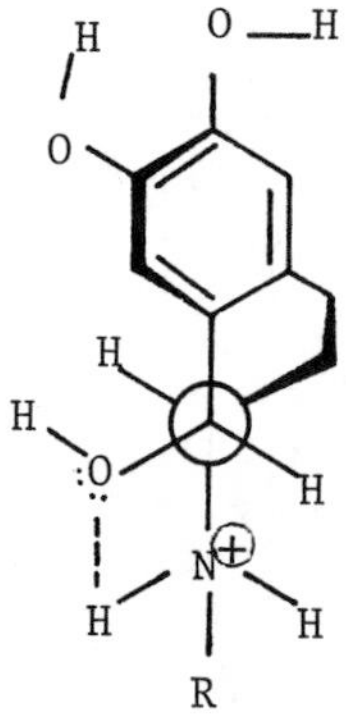

72

Considering the preferred crystal conformation 69 of isoproterenol as the one which may interact with β-adrenergic receptors also permits rationalization of the considerably greater potency of erythro-iosetharine (62) relative to its trans isomer. As illustrated in the Newman projection 73 of the erythro isomer, the catechol ring in a rotameric conformation with the 5,6-edge toward the viewer (it forms an acute angle of 15° with the benzylic C-OH bond) there is limited steric interaction with the α-ethyl substituent. In contrast, in the threo isomer shown in the Newman projection 74 interactions of the catechol ring with the α-ethyl group appear sufficiently great that the rotomeric conformation of the ring in the preferred crystal conformation of isoproterenol sulfate is probably disfavored. Thus, the threo isomer would be anticipated to attain a preferred conformation with greater difficulty and consequently be a less effective β-adrenergic receptor reagent.

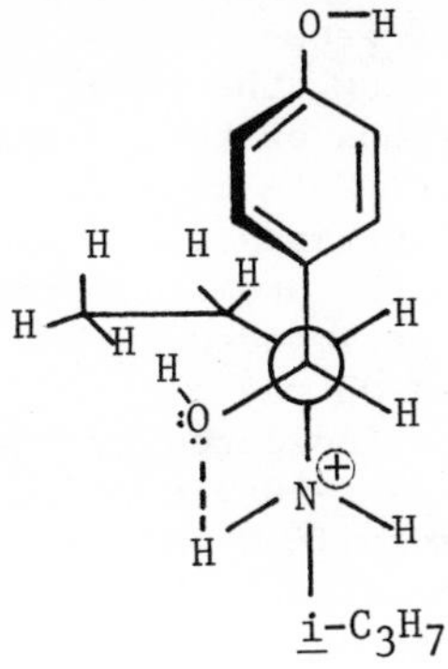

73 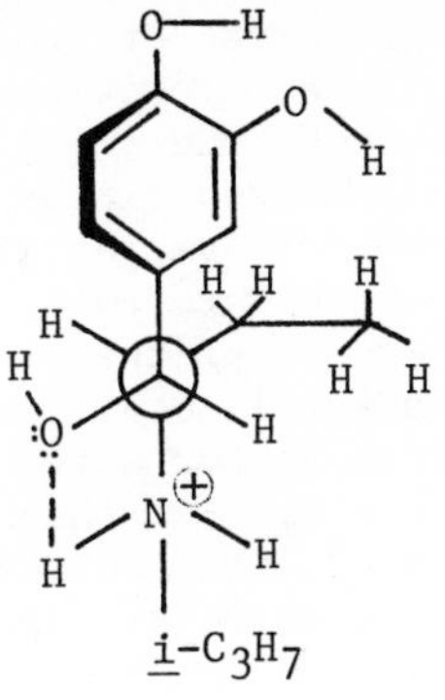 74

A more challenging problem involves the mode of interaction of β-adrenergic receptor agonists, e.g., 65, and antagonists, e.g., propranolol, bearing an oxypropanolamine side chain with β-receptors. Several suggestions have been advanced. For example, it has been speculated (182, 183) that aryloxypropanolamines may interact with β-adrenergic receptors by assuming an orientation that permits superimposition of the aromatic ring and the ethanolamine side chain with those of adrenergic phenylethanolamines. Others (25, 184) suggest, on the basis of investigation of X-ray crystal sturctures of a number of adrenergic aryloxypropanolamines, that the interposed $OCH_2$ unit may simulate a portion of the aromatic ring and thus take the place of the aryl group of phenylethanolamine adrenergic agents in their reaction with the receptor (184) or that accessory receptor areas may be involved in the action of the oxypropanolamines (25). Further, quantum mechanical calculations indicate that the conformations of these classes of adrenergic agents obtained by X-ray diffraction are actually privileged ones (185). These suggestions, however, fail to rationalize the observation that similar modifications of the catechol ring of phenylethanolamines and phenoxypropanolamines induce a comparable change in β-adrenoreceptor activity (33). To explore the possibility that these two different classes might share a common ground-state conformation as an essential structural feature that satisfies the specific steric requirements for the receptor loci of interaction an NMR conformational analysis of some aryloxypropanolamines was performed (34). This study of salts of 1-alkylamino-3-aryloxy-2-propanols in a non-polar solution suggested a stable "rigid" conformation involving two intramolecular hydrogen bonds to form a 6-5 bicyclic chelated structure 75. Comparison of this conformer, illustrated in the Newman projection 76 for the catecholoxypropanolamine 65, with the preferred crystal conformation of isoproterenol (69) indicates that all positions of the phenyl ring, the phenyl to O or phenyl to C bonds, and the ammonium groups of both chemical classes may be superimposed almost perfectly. A major difference between the two species is the relative location of the alcoholic OH groups which are about 2Å removed when the aromatic rings and ammonium groups of the two species are superimposed. That a specific spacial location of the alcoholic OH may not be a critical requirement for adrenergic activity is indicated by the significant activity of the homolog 61 of N-tert-butylnorepinephrine in which a $CH_2$ is inserted between the benzylic C and the OH. Possibly the different spacial position of the alcoholic OH group may be involved in the difference in $\beta_1$ and $\beta_2$-adrenergic receptor selectivity of phenylethanolamines and phenoxyproprropanolamines. A possible alternative explanation is that the $OCH_2$ unit in the aryloxypropanolamines may be involved in accessory binding accessible only in the $\beta_1$-receptors.

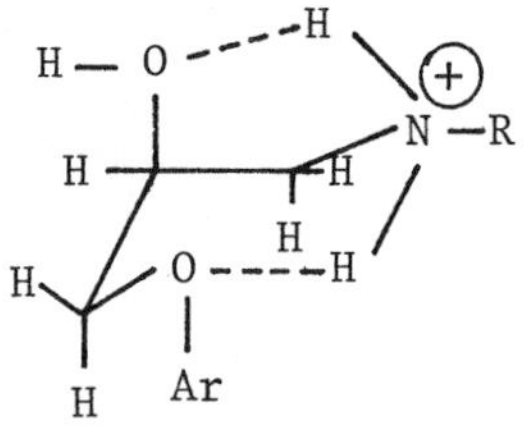

75

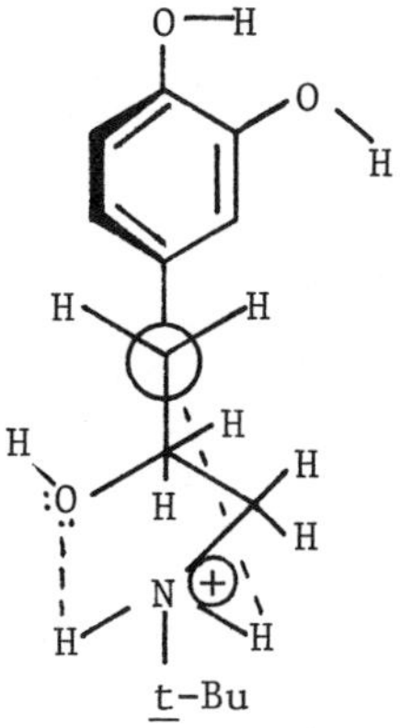

76

Another perplexing problem is how to relate the structure of tetrahydroisoquinolines, e.g. trimetoquinol (67c), with that of other β-adrenergic agents. As a consequence of the requirement of the 1-trimethoxybenzyl substituent in the S configuration it has been speculated (22, 159) that the isoquinoline N in the conformation shown in the Newman projection 77 might play the role of the benzylic OH of other adrenergic agents in the interaction of this class of compounds with the adrenergic receptor. In this case the tetrahydroisoquinolines with β-adrenergic activity would not bear a N group that interacts with receptors in the same manner that the NH of catecholamines does.

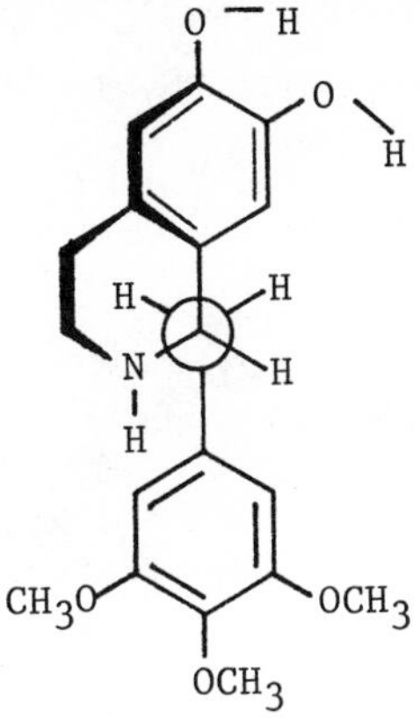

77

As structure-activity relationships of tetrahydroisoquinolines differ from those of other classes of β-adrenergic receptor agents the possibility that these compounds may interact with the same receptors in a different manner must be considered. It has been proposed that various analgetics may interact with the same opioid receptor by different modes (186).

In summary, the interaction of various β-adrenergic bronchodilator drugs with a receptor can be rationalized without involving allosteric interactions or conformational changes of the receptor. In all instances, with the possible exception of the tetrahydroisoquinolines, a similar mode of interaction with the β-adrenergic receptors may be advanced. Various changes involving the catechol ring, the N-substitution and the ethanolamine side chain of catecholamines may provide agents with enhanced bronchodilator selectivity.

## Acknowledgments

The author is very grateful to his colleagues who contributed substantially to the described research. Pharmacological studies were conducted by Donald F. Colella and Dr. Joe R. Wardell. Dr. Timothy Jen, Dr. Stephen T. Ross, Wayne D. Bowen, Karl F.

Erhard, James S. Frazee, Eleanor Garvey, Alex M. Pavloff and Mark S. Schwartz contributed significantly to the chemistry. I am grateful to all of these scientists, as well as to Dr. Richard D. Foggio and Dr. James W. Wilson, for their ideas, enthusiasm and encouragement.

## Literature Cited

1. van den Brink, F.G., Bull. Physio.-path. resp. (1972) 8, 475.
2. Ahlquist, R.P., Am. J. Physiol. (1948) 153, 586.
3. Lands, A.M. and Brown, T.G., Jr., Proc. Soc. Exp. Biol. Med. (1964) 116, 331.
4. Lands, A.M., Arnold, A., McAuliff, J.P., Luduena, F.P. and Brown, T.G., Jr., Nature (London) (1967) 214, 597.
5. Lands, A.M., Luduena, F.P. and Buzzo, H.J., Life Sci. (1967) 6, 2241.
6. Furchgott, R.F., Ann. N.Y. Acad. Sci. (1967) 139, 553.
7. Dunlop, D. and Shanks, R.G., Brit. J. Pharmacol. (1968) 32, 201.
8. Lands, A.M. and Brown, T.G., Jr., "Drugs Affecting the Peripheral Nervous System," Vol. 1, Burger, A., Ed., p. 399 Marcel Dekker, New York, N.Y., 1967.
9. Drew, G.M. and Levy, G.P., Brit. J. Pharmacol. (1972) 46, 348.
10. Baron, G.D., Speden, R.N. and Bohr, D.F., Am. J. Physiol. (1972) 223, 878.
11. Bowman, W.C. and Nott, M.W., Pharmacol. Rev. (1969) 21, 27.
12. Bowman, W.C. and Nott, M.W., Brit. J. Pharmacol. (1970) 38, 37.
13. Gryglewski, R. and Vane, J.R., Brit. J. Pharmacol. (1970) 39, 573.
14. Blackwell, E.W., Briant, R.H., Conolly, M.E., Davies, D.S. and Dollery, C.T., Brit. J. Pharmacol. (1974) 50, 587.
15. George, C.F., Blackwell, E.W. and Davies, D.S., J. Pharm. Pharmacol. (1974) 26, 265.
16. Nelson, L.W. and Kelly, W.A., Vet. Pathol. (1971) 8, 452.
17. Nelson, L.W., Kelly, W.A. and Weikel, J.H., Jr., Toxicol. Appl. Pharmacol. (1972) 23, 731.
18. Poynter, D., Harris, D.M. and Jack, D., Brit. Med. J. (1978) January 7, p. 46.
19. Finkel, M.J., Brit. Med. J. (1978) March 11, p. 649.
20. Bristow, M., Sherrod, T.R. and Green, R.D., J. Pharmacol. Exp. Ther. (1970) 171, 52.
21. Wasserman, M.A. and Levy, B., Fed. Proc., Fed. Am. Soc. Exp. Biol. (1973) 32, 723.
22. Brittain, R.T., Jack, D. and Ritchie, A.C., "Advances in Drug Research," Vol. 5, Harper, N.J. and Simmonds, A.B., Eds., pp. 197-253, Academic Press, New York-London, 1970.

23. Barlow, R.B., "Introduction to Chemical Pharmacology," p. 282, Methuen, London, 1964.
24. Pratesi, P. and Grana, E., "Advances in Drug Research," Vol. 2, Harper, N.J. and Simmonds, A.B., Eds., p. 127, Academic Press, New York-London, 1965.
25. Ariëns, E.J., Ann. N.Y. Acad. Sci. (1967) 139, 606.
26. Larsen, A.A., Gould, W.A., Roth, H.R., Comer, W.T., Uloth, R.H., Dungan, K.W. and Lish, P., J. Med. Chem. (1967) 10, 462.
27. Collin, D.T., Hartley, D., Jack, D., Lunts, L.H.C., Press, J.C., Ritchie, A.C. and Toon, P., J. Med. Chem. (1970) 13, 674.
28. Triggle, D.J., "Medicinal Chemistry," 3rd Ed., Burger, A., Ed. pp. 1235-1295, Wiley Interscience, New York-London, 1970.
29. Barger, G. and Dale, H.H., J. Physiol. (London) (1911) 41, 19.
30. Kaiser, C., Colella, D.F., Schwartz, M.S., Garvey, E. and Wardell, J.R., Jr., J. Med. Chem. (1974) 17, 49.
31. Kaiser, C., Colella, D.F., Pavloff, A.M. and Wardell, J.R., Jr., J. Med. Chem. (1974) 17, 1071.
32. Kaiser, C., Schwartz, M.S., Colella, D.F. and Wardell, J.R., Jr., J. Med. Chem. (1975) 18, 674.
33. Kaiser, C., Jen, T., Garvey, E., Bowen, W.D., Colella, D.F. and Wardell, J.R., Jr., J. Med. Chem. (1977) 20, 687.
34. Jen, T. and Kaiser, C., J. Med. Chem. (1977) 20, 693.
35. Jen, T., Frazee, J.S., Kaiser, C., Colella, D.F. and Wardell, J.R., Jr., J. Med. Chem. (1977) 20, 1029.
36. Jen, T., Frazee, J.S., Schwartz, M.S., Kaiser, C., Colella, D.F. and Wardell, J.R., Jr., J. Med. Chem. (1977) 20, 1258.
37. Jen, T., Frazee, J.S., Schwartz, M.S., Erhard, K.F., Kaiser, C., Colella, D.F. and Wardell, J.R., Jr., J. Med. Chem. (1977) 20, 1263.
38. Colella, D., Wardell, J.R., Jr., Kaiser, C. and Ross, S., Pharmacologist (1971) 13, 273.
39. Kaiser, C. and Ross, S.T., U.S. Patent 3,705,169 (1972).
40. Colella, D.F. and Kaiser, C., U.S. Patent 3,933,913 (1976).
41. Foster, R.W., J. Pharm. Pharmacol. (1966) 18, 1.
42. Blinko, J.R., Ann. N.Y. Acad. Sci. (1967) 139, 673.
43. Wardell, J.R., Jr., Colella, D.F., Shetzline, A. and Fowler, P.J., J. Pharmacol. Exp. Ther. (1974) 189, 167.
44. Colella, D.F., Chakrin, L.W., Shetzline, A. and Wardell, J.R., Jr., Eur. J. Pharmacol. (1977) 46, 229.
45. Familiar, R.G., Wardell, J.R., Jr. and Greene, L.C., J. Pharm. Sci. (1967) 56, 768.
46. Akcasu, A., Arch. Int. Pharmacodyn. Ther. (1959) 122, 201.
47. Castillo, J.C. and de Beer, E.J., J. Pharmacol. Exp. Ther. (1947) 90, 104.
48. Chahl, L.A. and O'Donnell, S.R., Eur. J. Pharmacol. (1967) 2, 77.

49. Finney, D.J., "Statistical Methods in Biological Assay," Hafner Publishing Co., New York, N.Y., 1952.
50. Kaiser, C., "Recent Advances in Receptor Chemistry," Gualtieri, F., Giannelli, M. and Melchiorre, C., Eds., pp. 189-206, Elsevier/North-Holland, 1979.
51. Ariëns, E.J., "Proceedings First Int. Pharmacol. Meeting," Stockholm, Vol. 7, pp. 247-264, Pergamon Press, Oxford, 1961.
52. Corrodi, H., Persson, H., Carlsson, A. and Roberts, J., J. Med. Chem. (1963) 6, 751.
53. Bovet, D. and Bovet-Nitti, F., "Structure et Activité Pharmacodynamique des Médicaments des Système Nerveux Végétatif," pp. 13-217, S. Karger, S.A. Bale, New York, 1948.
54. Lands, A.M. and Tainter, M.L., Arch. Exp. Pathol. Pharmakol. (1953) 219, 76.
55. Larsen, A.A. and Lish, P.M., Nature (London) (1964) 203, 1283.
56. Uloth, R.H., Kirk, J.R., Gould, W.A. and Larsen, A.A., J. Med. Chem. (1966) 9, 88.
57. Lish, P.M., Weikel, J.H. and Dungan, K.W., J. Pharmacol. Exp. Ther. (1965) 149, 161.
58. Brittain, R.T., Farmer, J.B., Jack, D., Martin, L.E. and Simpson, W.T., Nature (London) (1968) 219, 862.
59. N. V. Philips' Gloeilampenfabrieken, Dutch Patent 85,197 (May 15, 1957); Chem. Abstr. (1958) 52, 11121d.
60. Hermansen, K., Hedegaard, K., Larsen, J.J. and Weis, J., Acta Physiol. Scand. (1976) Suppl. 440, 143.
61. Shanks, R.G., Brick, I., Hutchison, K. and Roddie, I.C., Brit. Med. J. (1967) 1, 610.
62. Offermeier, J., Dreyer, A.C., Brandt, H.D. and Steinberg, S., C. Afr. Med. J. (1972) 46, 5.
63. Brittain, R.T., Dean, C.M. and Jack, D., Pharmacol. Ther. B. (1976) 2, 423.
64. Scriabine, A., Moore, P.F., Iorio, L.C., Goldman, I.M., McShane, W.K. and Booher, K.D., J. Pharmacol. Exp. Ther. (1968) 162, 60.
65. Kamburoff, P.L. and Prime, F.J., J. Dis. Chest (1970) 64, 46.
66. Prime, F.J., Postgrad. Med. J. Suppl. (1971) 47, 88.
67. Anderson, S.D., Seale, J.P., Rozea, P., Bandler, L., Theobald, G. and Lindsay, D.A., Am. Rev. Respir. Dis. (1976) 114, 493.
68. Grant, I.W.B., Brit. J. Clin. Pharmacol. (1976) 3, 509.
69. Campbell, I.A., Dash, C.H., McHardy, G.J.R. and Shotter, M.V., Brit. J. Clin. Pharmacol. (1976) 3, 151.
70. Sillett, R.W., Dash, C.H. and McNicol, M.W., Eur. J. Clin. Pharmacol. (1976) 9, 277, 281.
71. Morse, J.L.C., Jones, N.L. and Anderson, G.D., Am. Rev. Respir. Dis. (1976) 113, 89.
72. Allegra, J., Field, J., Trautlein, J., Gillin, M. and Zelis, R., J. Clin. Pharmacol. (1976) 16, 367.

73. Schwartz, H.J., Trautlein, J.J. and Goldstein, A.R., J. Allergy Clin. Immunol. (1976) 58, 516.
74. Formgren, H., Scand. J. Respir. Dis. (1975) 56, 321.
75. Hörnblad, Y., Ripe, E., Magnusson, P.O. and Tegner, K., Eur. J. Clin. Pharmacol. (1976) 10, 9.
76. Belleau, B., "Ciba Foundation Symposium on Adrenergic Mechanisms," Vane, J.R., Wolstenholme, G.E. and O'Connor, M., Eds., p. 223, Churchill, London, 1960.
77. Bloom, B.M. and Goldman, I.M., "Advances in Drug Research," Vol. 3, Harper, N.J. and Simmonds, A.B., Eds., pp. 121-169, Academic Press, New York-London, 1966.
78. Belleau, B., Ann. N.Y. Acad. Sci. (1967) 139, 580.
79. Bilezikian, J.P., Dornfeld, A.M. and Gammon, D.E., Biochem. Pharmacol. (1978) 27, 1445.
80. Bilezikian, J.P., Dornfeld, A.M. and Gammon, D.E., Biochem. Pharmacol. (1978) 27, 1455.
81. Cockcroft, D.W., Donevan, R.E. and Copland, G.M., Curr. Ther. Res., Clin. Exp. (1976) 19, 170.
82. Funahashi, A. and Hamilton, L.H., Am. Rev. Respir. Dis. (1976) 113, 398.
83. Ida, H., Arzneim.-Forsch. (1976) 26, 1337.
84. Banitt, E.H., Coyne, W.E., McGurran, K.T. and Robertson, J.E., J. Med. Chem. (1974) 17, 116.
85. Yoshizaki, S., Tanimura, K., Tamada, S., Yabuuchi, Y. and Nakagawa, K., J. Med. Chem. (1976) 19, 1138.
86. Yamashita, S., Takai, M. and Yabuuchi, Y., J. Pharm. Pharmacol. (1978) 30, 273.
87. Castañer, J. and Weetman, D.F., Drugs of Future (1978) 3, 135.
88. Arnett, C.D., Wright, J. and Zenker, N., J. Med. Chem. (1978) 21, 72.
89. Blackburn, C.H., Byrne, L.J., Cullum, V.A., Farmer, J.B. and Levy, G.P., J. Pharm. Pharmacol. (1969) 21, 488.
90. Boakes, A.J., Knight, E.J. and Prichard, B.N.C., Clin. Sci. (1971) 40, 18P.
91. Farmer, J.B., Kennedy, I., Levy, G.P. and Marshall, R.J., Brit. J. Pharmacol. (1972) 45, 660.
92. C. H. Boehringer Sohn (1968) French Patent 1,541,394; Chem. Abstr. (1970) 72, 31420c.
93. C. H. Boehringer Sohn (1966) Netherlands Appl. 6,607,489; Chem. Abstr. (1967) 67, 11339b.
94. Mentrup, A., Schromm, K., Zeile, K. and Thoma, O. (1972) U.S. Patent 3,657,244.
95. Creveling, C.R., Daly, J.W. and Witkop, B., J. Med. Chem. (1968) 11, 595.
96. Daly, J.W., Creveling, C.R. and Witkop, B., J. Med. Chem. (1966) 9, 273.
97. Johnston, R.E. and Shipley, R.E., Am. J. Med. Sci. (1957) 233, 303.

98. Igarashi, T., Wakabayashi, T., Shoji, T. and Tomiuga, T., Arzneim.-Forsch. (1970) 20, 1738.
99. Watanabe, M., Ohwaki, A., Nemoto, N. and Kasuya, Y., Arch. Int. Pharmacodyn. Ther. (1970) 184, 343.
100. Powell, C.E. and Slater, I.H., J. Pharmacol. Exp. Ther. (1958) 122, 480.
101. Engelhardt, G., Arzneim.-Forsch. (1972) 22, 869.
102. Salorinne, Y., Stenius, B., Tukiainen, P. and Poppius, H., Eur. J. Clin. Pharmacol. (1975) 8, 189.
103. Thomae Gesellschaft GmbH K., Netherlands Patent 7,303,612, March 16, 1972.
104. Barth, W.E., German Offen. 2,204,195 (1972); Chem. Abstr. (1972) 77, 151968n.
105. Steen, S.N., Ziment, I. and Thomas, J.S., Curr. Ther. Res., Clin. Exp. (1974) 16, 1077.
106. Hartley, D., Lunts, L.H.C. and Toon, P., U.S. Patent 3,558,642 (1971).
107. Schultz, O.-E. and Weber, H., Arch. Pharm. (Weinheim, Ger.) (1972) 305, 248.
108. Gnewuch, C.T. and Friedman, H.L., J. Med. Chem. (1972) 15, 1321.
109. Teotino, U.M. and Della Bella, D., U.S. Patent 3,558,652 (1971).
110. Novitskii, K. Yu., Oleinik, A.F., Naidenova, N.M. and Yur'ev, Yu. K., Zh. Org. Khim. (1965) 1, 541; Chem. Abstr. (1965) 63, 1761h.
111. Oleinik, A.F., Vozyakova, T.I., Modnikova, G.A. and Novitskii, K. Yu., Khim. Geterotsikl. Soedin. (1972) 1148; Chem. Abstr. (1973) 78, 43169q.
112. Corral, C., Darias, V., Fernández-Tomé, M.P., Madroñero, R. and del Río, J., J. Med. Chem. (1973) 16, 882.
113. Preobrazhenshaya, M.N., Orlova, L.M., Starostina, Z.G., Liberman, S.S., Sukhinina, G.P. and Suvorov, N.N., Khim.-Farm. Zh. (1970) 4, 5; Chem. Abstr. (1971) 74, 42248v.
114. Chodnekar, M.S., Crowther, A.F., Hepworth, W., Howe, R., McLoughlin, B.J., Mitchell, A., Rao, B.S., Slatcher, R.P., Smith, L.H. and Stevens, M.A., J. Med. Chem. (1972) 15, 49.
115. Hill, R.C. and Turner, P., Brit. J. Pharmacol. Chemother. (1968) 32, 663.
116. Howe, R., U.S. Patent 3,371,100 (1968).
117. F. Hoffmann-La Roche & Co., A.-G., Netherlands Appl. 6,606,441 (1966); Chem. Abstr. (1967) 67, 21808t.
118. Kaiser, C. and Zirkle, C.L., U.S. Patent 3,326,935 (1967).
119. Campaigne, E. and Rogers, R.B., J. Heterocyclic Chem. (1973) 10, 297.
120. Da Re, P., Valenti, P., Borraccini, A., and Primofiore, G.P., J. Med. Chem. (1972) 15, 198.
121. Meyer, R.F., Stratton, C.D., Hastings, S.G. and Corey, R.M., J. Med. Chem. (1973) 16, 1113.
122. Williams, H.W.R., Can. J. Chem. (1976) 54, 3377.

123. Moed, H.D., Van Dijk, J. and Niewand, H., Recl. Trav. Chim. Pays-Bas Belg. (1955) 74, 919.
124. Grana, E. and Lilla, L., Farmaco, Ed. Sci. (1965) 20, 817.
125. Berry, D.G. and Miller, J.W., Eur. J. Pharmacol. (1974) 28, 164.
126. Buist, R.A., Williams, L.R. and Cairncross, K.D., Arch. Int. Pharmacodyn. Ther. (1974) 209, 227.
127. Biel, J.H., Schwarz, E.G., Sprengeler, E.P., Leiser, H.A. and Friedman, H.L., J. Am. Chem. Soc. (1954) 76, 3149.
128. O'Donnell, S.R. and Wanstall, J.C., Brit. J. Pharmacol. (1974) 52, 407.
129. Van Arman, C.G., Miller, L.M. and O'Malley, M.P., J. Pharmacol. Exp. Ther. (1961) 133, 90.
130. Stormann, H. and Turnheim, K., Arzneim.-Forsch. (1973) 23, 30.
131. Schindl, R., Arzneim.-Forsch. (1970) 20, 1755.
132. Witek, F., Wein. Klin. Wochenschr. (1971) 83, 114.
133. Wilk, F., Wein. Klin. Wochenschr. (1971) 83, 98.
134. Thiede, D., Stempel, G. and Ulmer, W.T., Arzneim.-Forsch. (1971) 21, 416.
135. Pall, H. and Schlick, W., Wein. Klin. Wochenschr. (1971) 83, 117.
136. Blackhall, M.I., Dauth, M., Mahoney, M. and O'Donnell, S.R., Med. J. Austr. (1976) 2, 439.
137. Geumei, A.M., Miller, W.F., Miller, J. and Gast, L.R., Chest (1976) 70, 460.
138. Malta, E. and Raper, C., Clin. Exp. Pharmacol. Physiol. (1976) 3, 49.
139. Klingler, K.H., Arzneim.-Forsch. (1977) 27 (1a), 4 and following articles.
140. Larsen, A.A., Nature (London) (1969) 224, 25.
141. Beale, J.P. and Stephenson, N.C., J. Pharm. Pharmacol. (1972) 24, 277.
142. Lands, A.M., Luduena, F.P. and Tullar, B.F., J. Pharmacol. Exp. Ther. (1954) 111, 469.
143. Luduena, F.P., Arch. Int. Pharmacodyn. Ther. (1962) 137, 155.
144. Lands, A.M., Nash, V.L., McCarthy, H.M., Granger, H.R. and Dertinger, B.L., J. Pharmacol. Exp. Ther. (1947) 90, 110.
145. Lands, A.M., Nash, V.L., Dertinger, B.L., Granger, H.R. and McCarthy, H.M., J. Pharmacol. Exp. Ther. (1948) 92, 369.
146. Easson, H.L. and Stedman, E., Biochem. J. (1933) 27 1257.
147. Langecker, H. and Friebel, H., Arch. Exp. Pathol. Pharmakol. (1955) 226, 493.
148. Heacock, R.A., Hutzinger, O. and Scott, B.D., Can. J. Chem. (1965) 43, 2437.
149. Bettinetti, G.P., Conte, U., LaManna, A. and Pratesi, P., Farmaco, Ed. Sci. (1968) 23, 1011; Chem. Abstr. (1969) 70, 28525u.
150. Lehmann, G. and Randall, L.O., J. Pharmacol. Exp. Ther. (1948) 93, 144.

151. Ellis, S., J. Pharmacol. Exp. Ther. (1949) 96, 365.
152. Ebnother, A. and Hasspacher, K., U.S. Patent 3,804,899 (1974).
153. Mardle, M.J., Smith, H., Spicer, B.A. and Poyser, R.H., J. Med. Chem. (1974) 17, 513.
154. Lands, A.M., Groblewski, G.E. and Brown, T.G., Jr., Arch. Int. Pharmacodyn. Ther. (1966) 161, 68.
155. Sankey, G.H. and Whiting, K.D.E., J. Heterocyclic Chem. (1972) 9, 1049.
156. Kaiser, C. and Ross, S.T., U.S. Patent 3,705,169 (1972).
157. Griffin, J.P. and Turner, P., J. Clin. Pharmacol. (1971) 11 (4), 280.
158. Carney, I., Daly, M.J., Lightowler, J.E. and Pickering, R.W., Arch. Int. Pharmacodyn. Ther. (1971) 194, 334.
159. Nishikawa, M., Kanno, M., Kuriki, H., Sugihara, H., Motohashi, M., Itoh, K., Miyashita, O., Oka, Y. and Sanno, Y., Life Sci. (1975) 16, 305.
160. Itoh, K., Motohashi, M., Kuriki, H., Sugihara, H., Inatomi, N., Nishikawa, M. and Oka, Y., Chem. Pharm. Bull. (Tokyo) (1977) 25, 2917.
161. Sugihara, H., Ukawa, K., Kuriki, H., Nishikawa, M. and Sanno, Y., Chem. Pharm. Bull. (Tokyo) (1977) 25, 2988.
162. Miyake, A., Kuriki, H., Itoh, K., Nishikawa, M. and Oka, Y., Chem. Pharm. Bull. (Tokyo) (1977) 25, 3289.
163. Thrift, R.I., J. Chem. Soc. (C) (1967) 288.
164. Singh, G.B., Srimal, R.C. and Dhawan, B.N., Japan. J. Pharmacol. (1974) 24, 5.
165. Smejkal, V., Trcka, V., Vanecek, M., Weichet, J. and Blaha, L., Thérapie (1967) 22, 1343.
166. Åblad, B., Brogärd, M. and Corrodi, A., Acta Pharm. Suec. (1970) 7, 551.
167. Casagrande, C., Ferrini, R., Miragoli, G. and Ferrini, G., Boll. Chim. Farm. (1973) 112, 445.
168. Roszkowski, A.P., Strosberg, A.M., Miller, L.M., Edwards, J.A., Berkoz, B., Lewis, G.S., Halpern, O. and Fried, J.H., Experientia (1972) 28, 1336.
169. Edwards, J.A., Berkoz, B., Lewis, G.S., Halpern, O., Fried, J.H., Strosberg, A.M., Miller, L.M., Urich, S., Liu, F. and Roszkowski, A.P., J. Med. Chem. (1974) 17, 200.
170. Craig, P.N., Nabenhauer, F.P., Williams, P.M., Macko, E. and Toner, J., J. Am. Chem. Soc. (1952) 74, 1316.
171. Holtz, P., Stock, K. and Westermann, E., Arch. Exp. Pathol. Pharmakol. (1964) 246, 133.
172. Holtz, P., Pharmacol. Rev. (1966) 18, 85.
173. Santi, R., Ferrari, M., Tóth, C.E., Contessa, A.R., Fassina, G., Bruni, A. and Luciani, S., J. Pharm. Pharmacol. (1967) 19, 45.
174. Yamato, E., Hirakura, M. and Sugasawa, S., Tetrahedron Suppl. (1966) 8, 129.

175. Iwasawa, Y. and Kiyomoto, A., Japan J. Pharmacol. (1967) 17, 143.
176. Kiyomoto, A., Iwasawa, Y. and Harigaya, S., Arzneim.-Forsch. (1970) 20, 46.
177. Yamamura, Y. and Kishimoto, S., Ann. Allergy (1968) 26, 504.
178. Dyke, S.F., White, A.W.C. and Hartley, D., Tetrahedron (1973) 29, 857.
179. Rooney, C.S., Stuart, R.S., Wasson, B.K. and Williams, H.W.R., Can. J. Chem. (1975) 53, 2279.
180. Mathew, M. and Palenik, G.J., J. Am. Chem. Soc. (1971) 93, 497.
181. Ison, R.R., Partington, P. and Roberts, G.C.K., Mol. Pharmacol. (1973) 9, 756.
182. Barrett, A.M., "Drug Design," Vol. III, Ariëns, E.J., Ed. pp. 205-228, Academic Press, New York, 1972.
183. Comer, W.T., Am. Chem. Soc., Med. Chem. Symposium Abstr. (1970), 14a.
184. Ammon, H.L., Balsamo, A., Macchia, B., Macchia, F., Howe, D.-B. and Keefe, W.E., Experientia (1975) 31, 644.
185. Gadret, M., Léger, J.-M., Carpy, A. and Berthod, H., Eur. J. Med. Chem. (1978) 13, 367.
186. Portoghese, P.S., Mikhail, A.A. and Kupferberg, H.J., J. Med. Chem. (1968) 11, 219.

RECEIVED August 6, 1979.

14

# Recent Innovations in Theophylline-Like Bronchodilator Drugs

RICHARD J. SEIDEHAMEL and DAVIS L. TEMPLE, JR.
Mead Johnson Pharmaceuticals, Evansville, IN 47721

Theophylline is recognized as a primary or first-line drug in the treatment of chronic asthma and is especially valuable in moderate-to-severe asthma where maintenance therapy is essential. It is generally more effective than cromolyn in preventing the symptoms of asthma (1) and, when used on a continued basis, is not associated with tolerance or tachyphylaxis. There are other observations which attest to the popularity of this drug. In 1977 some 26 million prescriptions were written for bronchodilators; 11 million of these or 42%, were for theophylline products, and sales for these theophylline products totaled 60 million dollars, up 30% over the previous year. Furthermore, more pharmaceutical houses are getting involved in the theophylline business, and there have been numerous publications concerning all aspects of theophylline.

Theophylline, from the time of its entry into bronchopulmonary medicine in the 1930's (2) has not always been so popular. Clinical results with the drug over the years have been erratic, mainly because of a remarkable patient-to-patient and sometimes within-patient variability in response to generally recommended doses. It is now recognized, through the help of pharmacokinetic and metabolic studies, that individuals can vary greatly in their serum theophylline levels following a standard oral dose of the drug. Figure 1 shows what the clinician might expect when he gives an equal mg/kg oral dose. These patients (i.e., six) may fall into one of four categories according to peak-serum theophylline levels. While the majority may fall into the 10 to 20 μg/ml or supposedly optimal therapeutic range (3) at a recommended dose level and receive maximal bronchodilator benefits with little or no side effects, others may fall into a higher and toxic range and exhibit side effects like CNS and cardiovascular stimulation <u>or</u> into the lower and subtherapeutic range and get no benefits at all from the drug. This figure serves to illustrate the narrow optimal

0-8412-0536-1/80/47-118-285$05.00/0

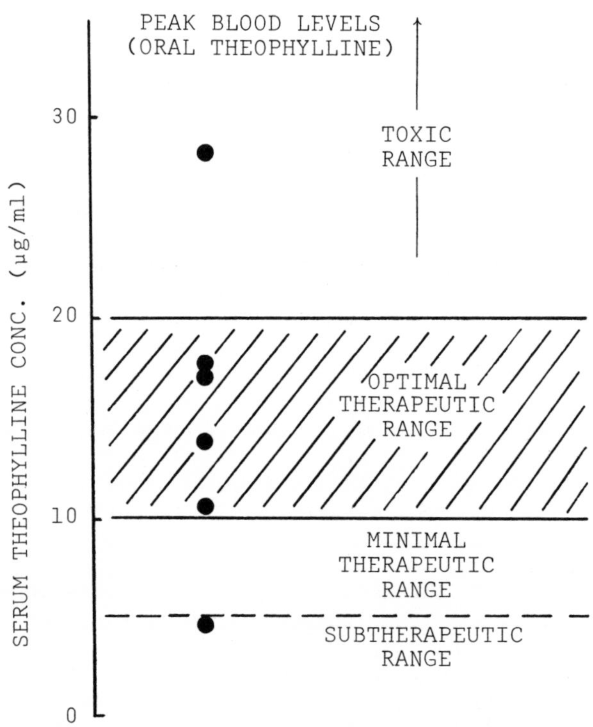


*Figure 1. Blood levels of theophylline showing the potential interpatient variability following an equal mg/kg oral dose of a theophylline product*

serum theophylline range. Yet, there is sufficient potency separation between desirable and undesirable effects so that side effects do not necessarily have to accompany effective bronchodilation. In order to place a patient in the optimal range the dose of theophylline must be individualized, and this is best done by adjusting dose to optimal serum levels. Even though advanced technology with HPLC and UV spectrophotometry has facilitated serum determinations in the clinical laboratory as well as the office, the procedure is still costly and inconvenient and considered a drawback to the use of the drug.

Individuals vary in their serum theophylline levels because their rates of metabolism differ. Theophylline undergoes extensive metabolism (Figure 2) by liver microsomal enzymes (4). Less than 10% is excreted unchanged. The other 90% plus is metabolized through demethylation in the 1- and 3- positions and oxidation in the 8- position to be excreted as a mixture of 3-methylxanthine, 1-methyluric acid, and 1,3-dimethyluric acid. While the average serum half-life in the adult may be approximately five hours, the range may vary from one hour in some individuals to 10 hours in others; hence, there is variability in serum levels. Factors such as age, health, body weight, diet, concurrent drug (including theophylline) tobacco, and alcohol use, can cause considerable variance in theophylline half-life. This metabolic scheme provides a starting basis for appreciating what needs to be done synthetically to make a more biologically stable form of bronchodilator drug. Later, attention will turn to some structures that might not be susceptible to the same metabolic routes.

There are other factors besides metabolism which govern the length of stay of an oral dose of drug in the body--namely, rate and extent of absorption and elimination. As regards the former, sustained-release formulation can prolong the effective life of a dose of theophylline by prolonging its absorption from the intestinal tract. This technology avoids the many peaks and valleys in serum levels that occur in the course of frequent dosing with immediate-release products and also lengthens the dosing interval. There are now several sustained-release theophylline products on the market. Some of these, however, may not offer substantial benefit over the standard theophylline products.

Illustrated in Figure 3 is a likely over-all mechanistic role of theophylline in asthma. Extrinsic or immediate hypersensitivity-type asthma begins with an antigen - antibody complex at mast cells and results in the release of chemical mediators which affect cells in airways. Smooth muscle cells contract, capillaries leak, and secretory cells hypersecrete to give a triad of bronchospasm, edema and increased mucous, respectively. Shown is the two-enzyme

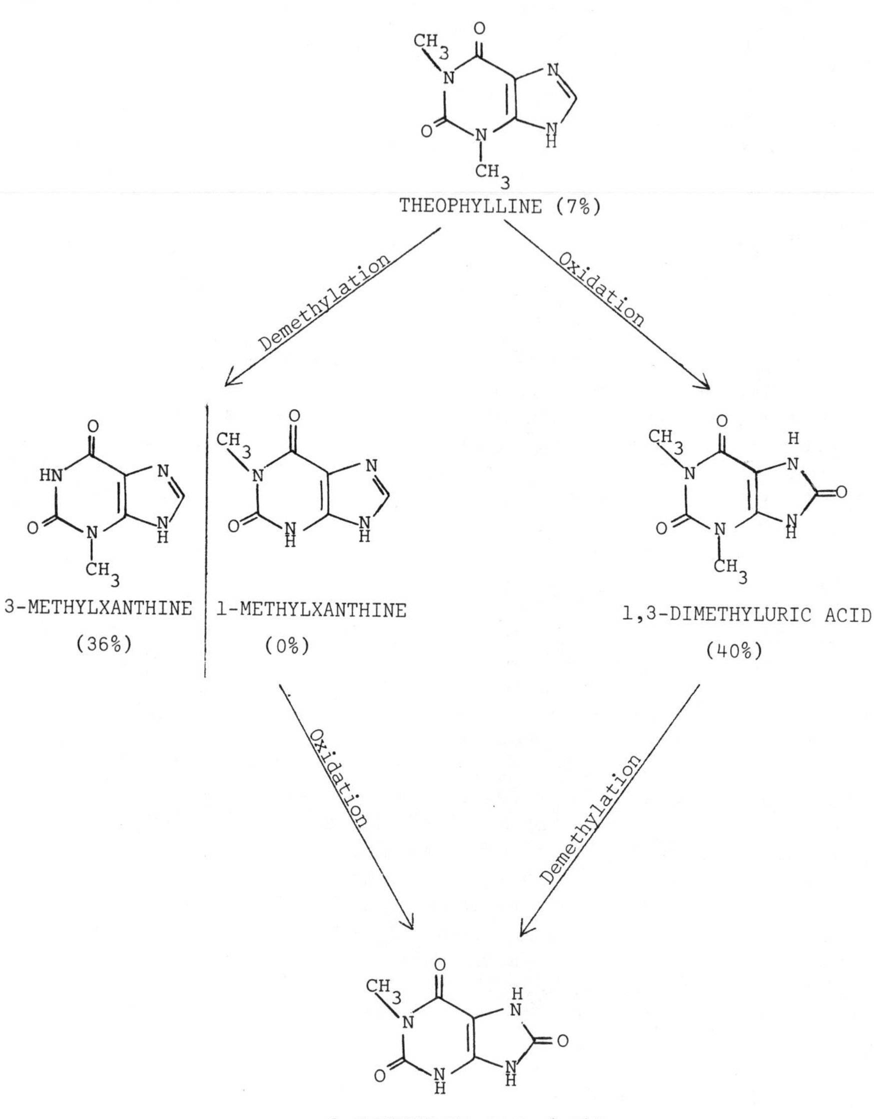


*Figure 2. Qualitative and quantitative aspects of the metabolic conversion of theophylline by liver microsomal enzymes*

system that governs the intracellular steady state level of cyclic AMP. Theophylline inhibits phosphodiesterase causing the accumulation of cyclic AMP. In the smooth muscle cell this nucleotide promotes relaxation giving rise to bronchodilation which opposes any bronchospasm. There is growing evidence (3,5) to support a second site of action of theophylline, in the mast cells. By causing elevation of cyclic AMP in these cells, theophylline can inhibit the release of mediators as does cromolyn sodium and prevent or attenuate the entire triad of events for an overall greater benefit to the patients than through bronchodilation alone.

Observations with theophylline over the past 10 to 15 years have led to a better understanding of the underlying problems and features of the drug and hence its more rational use within the last few years. Today, theophylline is a much harder drug to surpass than it was several years ago. Certainly, the following features are in its favor: effectiveness in acute and chronic asthma; safety when dosed properly; long action and twice-daily dosing when given in sustained-release form; low cost. In its disfavor are: patient-to-patient variability in its metabolism; need to individualize dosage; narrow serum level range between bronchodilator effects and side effects; gastrointestinal irritation.

For years there have been synthetic efforts to make new and better theophylline-like bronchodilator drugs. There have been many attempts to modify the basic theophylline molecule with various functional group substitutions. Dyphylline or 7-dihydroxypropyl theophylline (see Figure 4) was synthesized in the 1940's (6). It has been receiving more attention in the U.S. as a drug (7,8,9). Often confused as a theophylline salt, dyphylline is a distinct chemical entity. Typical of many 7-alkyl substituted theophyllines, it has a low incidence of side effects but also a low level of activity and short duration of action.

Reproterol is a *beta*-phenethylaminoalkylxanthine recently marketed abroad. It represents a chemical hybrid of theophylline and either terbutaline or metaproterenol (Figure 4). This agent has a preferential impact on beta-adrenergic receptors and can be classified as a $beta_2$-adrenergic stimulant (10). Reproterol is claimed not to exhibit the CNS and cardiovascular effects typical of other beta-adrenergic stimulants, suggesting that the theophylline moiety may be important to this molecule.

Many compounds have resulted from the substitution of thio, amino and large alkyl groups on the theophylline molecule. But for the most part, these have shown good *in vitro* bronchodilator potency which does not carry over into *in vivo* tests (11). (For this class of drugs, experience dictates that *in vitro* testing should not alone be the guide

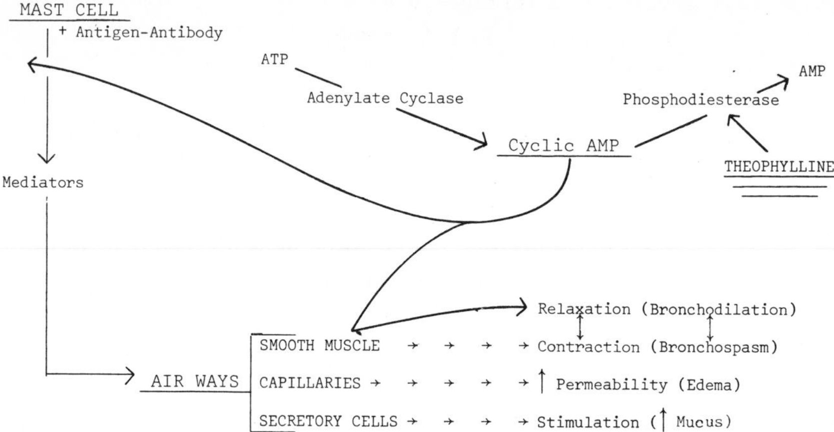


*Figure 3. Likely mechanistic role of theophylline in asthma. By inhibition of phosphodiesterase and subsequent elevation of cyclic AMP in mast cells and airway smooth muscle, theophylline is shown to have an overall beneficial effect on airways in asthma.*

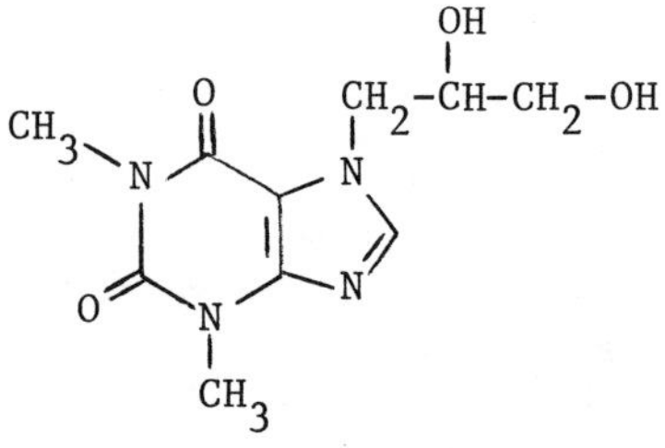

DYPHYLLINE

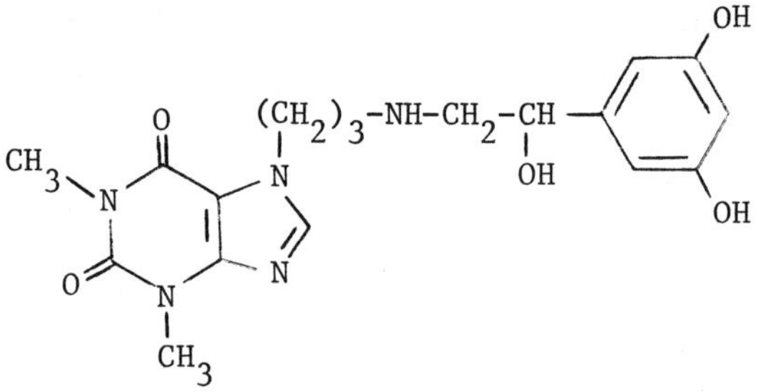

REPROTEROL

*Figure 4.*

to synthesis.) One multi-substituted theophylline molecule with promise will be discussed later.

Some major innovations in theophylline-like agents, especially in terms of new chemical structure, are found in several new heterocyclic types of compounds. These include purines, pyrimidines, benzopyranopyridines, quinazolines and pyridobenzodiazepines (Compounds I - XI, Figure 5). Showing varying degrees of structural resemblance to theophylline, many of these compounds are potent bronchodilator agents in man and/or animals. Some, through inhibition of phosphodiesterase and subsequent elevation of cyclic AMP, relax bronchial smooth muscle. A few, however, have other potentially useful antiasthma properties.

Compounds I and II, respectively, are some 15 and 10 times as potent as theophylline as bronchodilators when administered to guinea pigs by the oral route (12,13,14). They do not exhibit the cardiac stimulatory properties of theophylline. In addition, to bronchodilator action, compound II possesses, as predicted from its tricyclic structure, antihistaminic and possibly even some mediator release inhibitor properties which could compliment its overall utility in allergic airways disease.

Compound III has a remarkably greater oral bronchodilator potency in animals than does theophylline (15). Not only does this agent inhibit phosphodiesterase, but it also appears to stimulate beta-adrenergic receptors, the end result of both actions being a complimentary cyclic AMP induced bronchial smooth muscle relaxation.

Compound IV, which represents perhaps one of the simplest bronchodilator structures, is somewhat more potent as a bronchodilator in guinea pigs than is theophylline (16,17). Like the other agents described thus far, it too inhibits phosphodiesterase. The cardiovascular and CNS profiles of this compound have not been described.

Compound V has advanced to the stage of investigation in man (18). In spite of its encouraging pharmacologic profile in animals, however, it was found in asthmatics to have no potency advantage over theophylline. Furthermore, the compound caused considerable drowsiness, an action most likely attributed to its known antihistaminic effects.

Compound VI has bronchodilator activity when administered by the intravenous route (19). Its potency relative to theophylline has not been reported. This compound does not appear to possess cardiac stimulatory action but it does have an expectorant action which could prove to be of value when the airways are obstructed with tenacious mucous.

Interest in the xanthine moiety has, for the most part, centered on bronchodilator activity. As described earlier, theophylline has a mixture of bronchodilator and antiallergy components. By progressive modifications of methylxanthines,

Bronchodilator Compounds

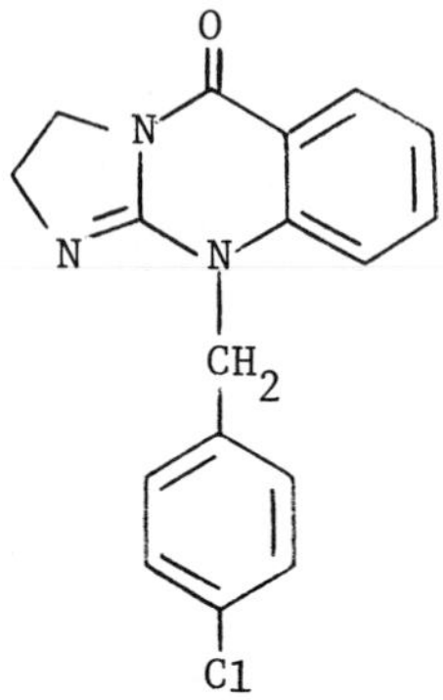

I SANDOZ

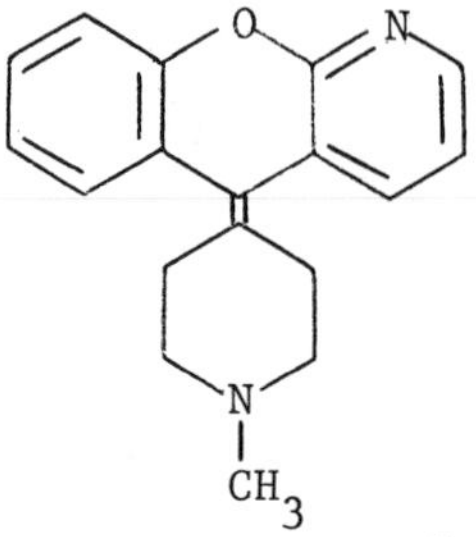

II SCHERING 15280

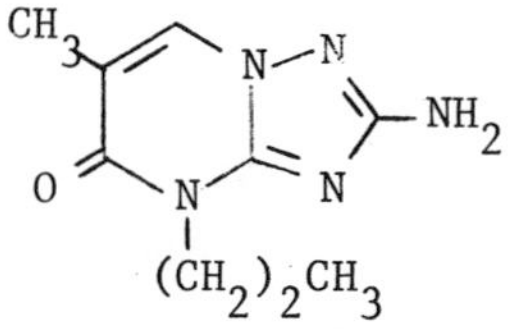

III ICI 63,197

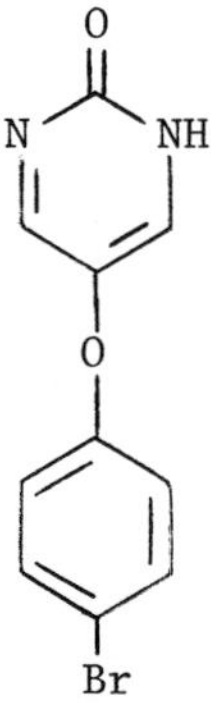

IV PFIZER

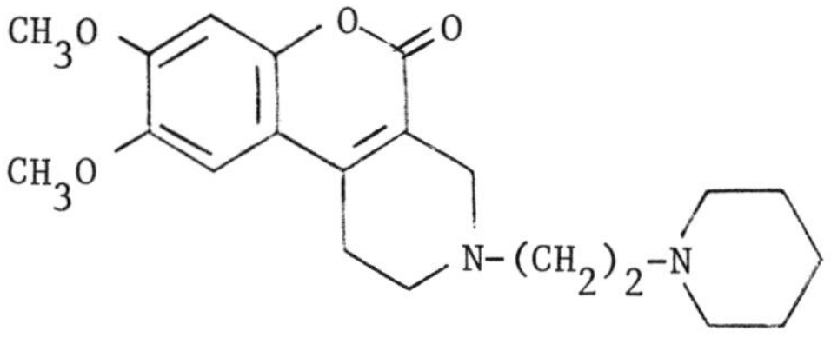

V WARNER-LAMBERT 10294 A

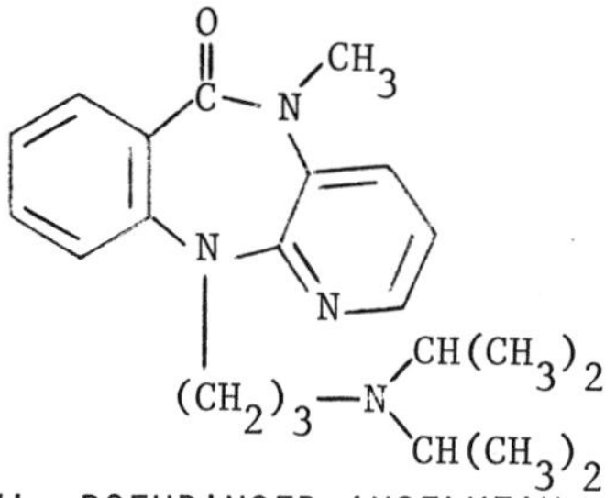

VI BOEHRINGER INGELHEIM

*Figure 5.*

Antiallergic Compounds

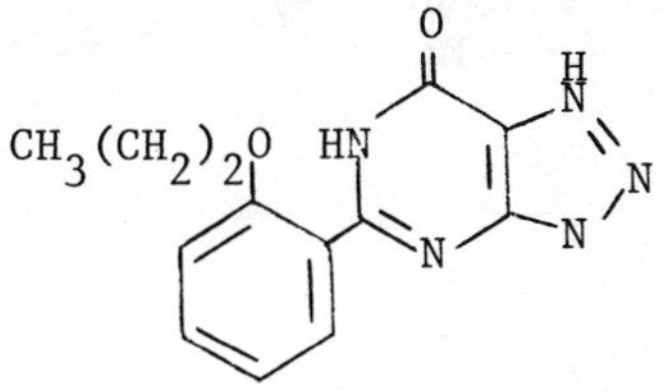

VII MAY & BAKER 22,948

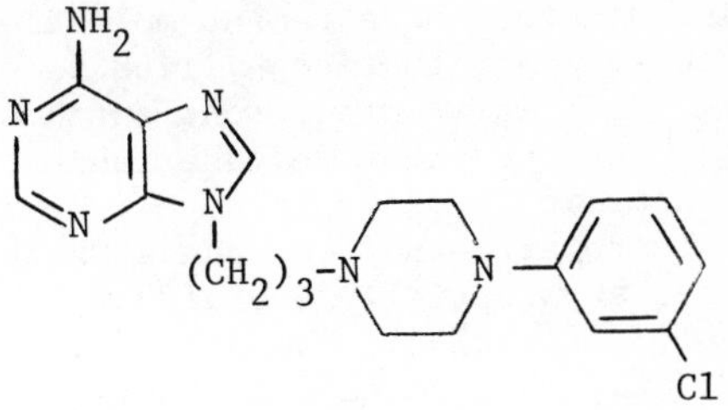

VIII BOEHRINGER MANNHEIM 06.001

Antiallergic (Bronchodilator) Compounds

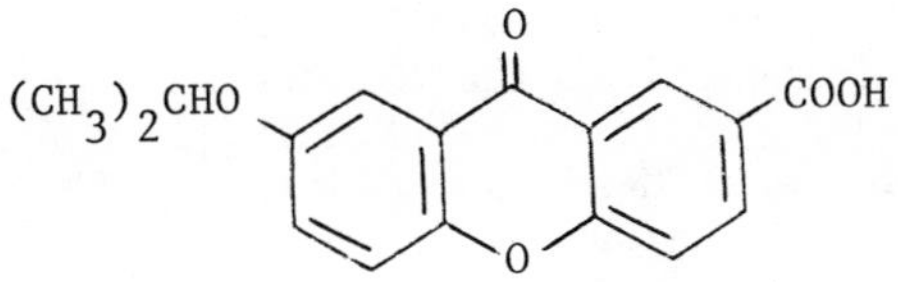

IX SYNTEX (IXC)

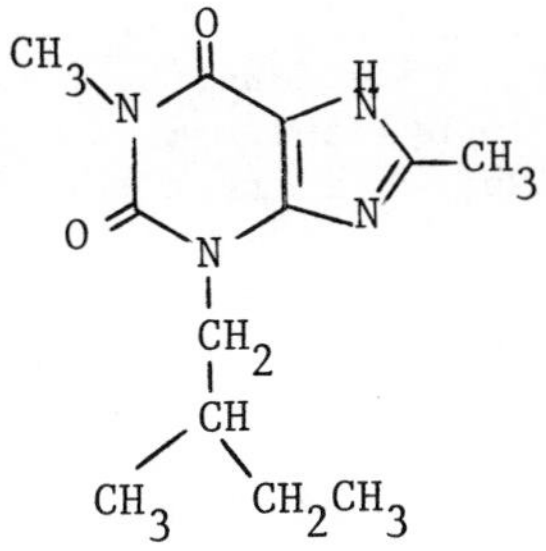

X COOPER CK-0383

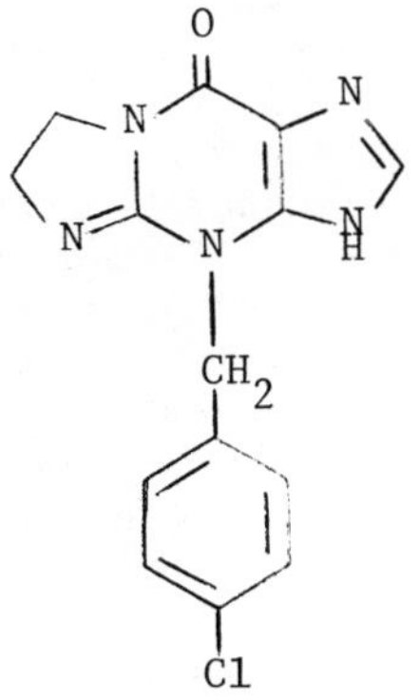

XI MEAD JOHNSON 12504

*Figure 5. (Continued).*

compound VII evolved. It possesses strong antiallergic effects *via* mediator release inhibition but essentially no bronchodilator effects (20). This compound represents an early example of a potent orally active cromolyn-like compound. Another more recent molecule with this same profile and resemblance to theophylline is compound VIII which, unlike VII, is also a potent antihistaminic agent (21). These "pure mediator release inhibitors" are discussed elsewhere in this symposium.

There are other compounds in the literature which seem to have a potentially useful blend of bronchodilator and antiallergy action. Compound IX, having a cromolyn-type structure, is effective in the passive cutaneous anaphylaxis test in rats as well as in the histamine aerosol test in guinea pigs (22). It has less cardiovascular effects than theophylline but causes some CNS stimulation. Compound X is a recent compound which in animals appears to be more potent than theophylline in its bronchodilator/antiallergic actions and also appears to have greater broncho-selectivity (23, 24). It seems to be somewhat more acutely toxic than theophylline. Compound X could, as a result of the substituents in positions otherwise vulnerable to demethylation and oxidation metabolic reactions, be a more biologically stable molecule than theophylline. It is now undergoing clinical trials.

Research in respiratory disease at Mead Johnson has centered on heterocyclic molecules having a mixture of bronchodilator and antiallergic actions. One of these, an imidazopurinone (compound XI), recently emerged with particularly interesting pharmacologic features. Illustrated in Figure 6 are dose-response curves for intraduodenally administered compound XI in three appropriate tests in rats. The compound inhibits the passive cutaneous anaphylaxis (PCA) reaction, methacholine-induced bronchospasm and allergen-induced bronchospasm indicative of both bronchodilator and antiallergic activity. Of these three tests, the first is probably the least predictive and the last the most predictive of antiasthma activity in man. Interestingly, it is in the allergen-induced bronchospasm test (see Table 1) that compound XI shows a 15-fold greater potency over aminophylline (theophylline ethylenediamine). The duration of action of compound XI is at least half-again as long as that of aminophylline, suggesting greater biologic stability. It appears to be non-tachyphylactic upon repeated administration, and does not exhibit antihistamine or antiserotonin activity. Bronchodilator action has been confirmed in dogs. Under *in vitro* conditions, compound XI is more potent than aminophylline in relaxing airway smooth muscle and in inhibiting phosphodiesterase and histamine release from mast cells. At bronchodilator doses there are no appreciable differences between compound XI and aminophylline

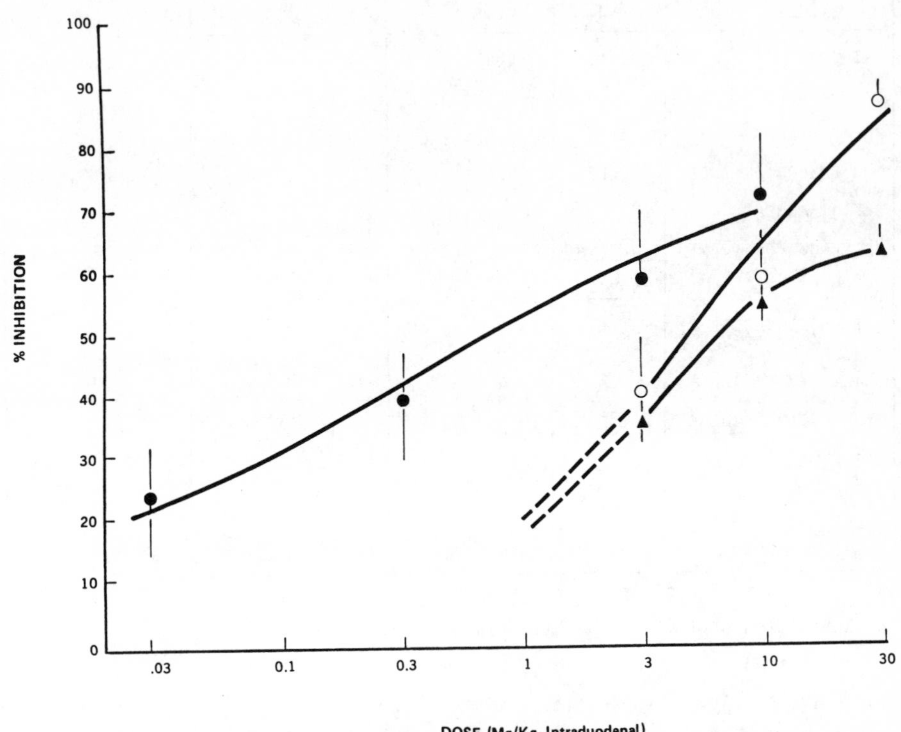


*Figure 6. Dose vs. antiallergic and/or bronchodilator effects of MJ 12504 in three appropriate tests in rats. Points represent mean values from 4 to 14 animals per dose level. Vertical bars represent SE of the means. (●) allergen-induced bronchospasm; (○) methacholine-induced bronchospasm; (▲) PCA reaction.*

TABLE I

SUMMARY OF PHARMACOLOGIC ACTIONS OF MJ 12504

| TEST | ROUTE | POTENCY | | RELATIVE DURATION (Aminophylline=1) |
|---|---|---|---|---|
| | | $ED_{50}\pm$S.E. (mg/kg) | RELATIVE (Aminophylline=1) | |
| RAT PCA[a] | I.D. | 8.4±1.1 | 2 | ≥1.5 |
| RAT BRONCHODILATOR[b] | I.D. | 5.2±1.3 | 3 | ≥1 |
| RAT "ASTHMA"[c] | I.D. | 0.90±0.5 | 15 | - |
| DOG BRONCHODILATOR[d] | I.D. | 3.1±1.5 | 3 | ≥1 |
| G.P. TRACHEA[e] | *IN VITRO* | $IC_{50}$=14 μg/ml[i] | 2 | - |
| RAT LUNG PDE (cAMP)[f] | *IN VITRO* | Ki=0.7X10$^{-4}$M[i] | 8 | - |
| RAT MAST CELL[g] | *IN VITRO* | $IC_{50}$=490μM[i] | 5 | - |
| RAT CARDIOVASCULAR | I.D. | | | |
| HR | | -[j] | 1 | - |
| BP | | - | <1 | - |
| DOG CARDIOVASCULAR | I.D. | | | |
| HR | | - | 1 | - |
| CF | | - | ≤0.5 | - |
| BP | | - | 2 | - |
| RAT CNS[h] | P.O. | MJ 12504 - No Effect<br>Aminophylline - Stimulation | | |

a) Inhibition of passive cutaneous anaphylaxis (25,26).

b) Inhibition of i.v. methacholine-induced bronchospasm.

c) Inhibition of allergen-induced bronchospasm (27,28).

d) Inhibition of serotonin-induced bronchospasm (29).

e) Intrinsic relaxant effect on spontaneous tonus of spirally cut guinea-pig trachea *in vitro*.

f) Inhibition of whole lung homogenate cyclic AMP phosphodiesterase (PDE) assayed by method reported (30).

g) Inhibition of histamine release form isolated peritoneal mast cells (31,32).

h) Effect on spontaneous motor activity as measured by an annular cage method.

i) Standard error (S.E.) not determined.

j) Value not determined.

on the cardiovascular system in rats. In the dog, compound XI causes less increase in myocardial contractile force but more reduction in mean arterial blood pressure. At bronchodilator doses, compound XI shows no CNS stimulation or depression while aminophylline shows marked stimulation. Compound XI is undergoing extensive toxicologic evaluation.

## Conclusion

There is no question that the resurgence of theophylline has had a major impact on the development of new theophylline-like agents. On one hand, there has been a general dampening of enthusiasm because of the impression that theophylline has such a strong "hold" in bronchopulmonary medicine that it can never be displaced by another agent in this category. On the other hand, there has been a sense of renewed interest in this category because, with theophylline as the "ground-breaker", the potential for a new agent without theophylline's shortcomings has been realized. Desirable features are achievable, at least in the laboratory. Whether theophylline will be replaced by one of the types of innovations presented here remains to be seen.

## Literature Cited

1. Hambleton, G., Weinberger, M., Taylor, J., Cavanaugh, M., Ginchansky, E., Godfrey, S., Tooley, M., Bell, T. and Greenberg, S.: Lancet (1977) 1, 381.

2. Herrmann, G. and Aynesworth, M. B.: J. Lab. Clin. Med. (1937) 23, 135.

3. Brandon, M. L.: Ann. Allergy (1977) 39, 117.

4. Jenne, J. W.: "New Directions in Asthma", M. Stein, ed., p.398, American College of Chest Physicians, Park Ridge, 1975.

5. Lichtenstein, L. M.: Ann. N.Y. Acad. Sci. (1971) 185, 403.

6. Maney, P. V., Jones, J. W., Gross, E. G. and Korns, H. M.: J. Amer. Pharm. Assoc. (Sci. Ed.) (1946) 35, 266.

7. Hudson, L. D., Tyler, M. and Petty, T. L.: Curr. Ther. Res. (1973) 15, 367.

8. Simmons, F. E. R., Simmons, K. J. and Bierman, C. W.: J. Allergy Clin. Immunol. (1975) 56, 347.

9. Hendeles, L. and Weinberger, M.: Drug Intell. Clin. Pharm. (1977) 11, 424.

10. Habersang, S., Leuschner, F., Stroman, F., Domenico, A. and Schlichegroll, A. v.: Arzneim. Forsch. (Drug. Res.) (1977) 27, 22.

11. Armitage, A. K., Boswood, J. and Large, B. J.: Brit. J. Pharmacol. (1961) 17, 196.

12. Hardtmann, G. E., Koletar, G., Pfister, O. R., Gogerty, J. H. and Iorio, L. C.: J. Med. Chem. (1975) 18, 447.

13. Diamond, L., Adams, G. K., Bleidt, B. and Williams B.: J. Pharmacol. Expt. Ther. (1975) 193, 256.

14. Villani, F. J., Mann, T. A., Wefer, E. A., Hannon, J., Larca, L. L., Landon, M. J., Spivak, W., Vashi, D., Tozzi, S., Danko, G., del Prado, M. and Lutz, R.: J. Med. Chem. (1975) 18, 1.

15. Davies, G. E.: J. Pharm. Pharmac. (1973) 25, 681.

16. DeAngelis, G. G., and Hess, H. J. E.: U.S. Patent (1975) No. 3,890,321.

17. Lipinski, C. A., Stam, J. G., DeAngelis, G. G., Hess, H. J. E.: Pyrimidinones and Hydroxy Pyrimidines. U.S. Patent (1977) No. 3,922,345.

18. Littner, M. R.: Lung (1977) 154, 187.

19. Schmidt, G., Engelhardt, G., Puschmann, S.: U.S. Patent (1977) No. 4,021,557.

20. Broughton, B. J., Chaplen, P., Knowles, P., Lunt, E., Pain, D. L., Wooldridge, K. R. H., Ford R., Marshall, S., Walker, J. L. and Maxwell, D. R.: Nature (1974) 251, 650.

21. Zimmermann, I., Ulmer, W. T. and Roesch, A.: Arzneim.-Forsch. (Drug Res.) (1977) 27, 1999.

22. Roszkowski, A. P., Ferraresi, R. W., Schuler, M. E., Sullivan, B. J.: Fed. Proc. (1974) 33, 2019.

23. Diamond, J.: German Patent (1977) No. DT 27-13-389.

24. Belej, M., Elenewich, J., Touhey, B., Defelice, A., Smart, A., Diamond, J.: Pharmacologist (1978) 20, 266.

25. Goose, J. and Blair, A. M.: Immunol. (1969) 16, 749.

26. Mota, I.: Immunol. (1964) 7, 681.

27. Stotland, L. M. and Share, N. N.: Can. J. Physiol. and Pharmacol. (1974) 52, 1114.

28. Stotland, L. M. and Share, N. N.: ibid., 1119.

29. Dungan, K. W., Cho, Y. W., Gomoll, A. W., Aviado, D. M. and Lish, P. M.: J. Pharmacol. Expt. Ther. (1968) 164, 290.

30. Thompson, W. J. and Appleman, M. M.: Biochem. (1971) 10, 311.

31. Taylor, W. A., Francis, D. H., Sheldon, D. and Roit, I. M.: Int. Arch. Allergy (1974) 46, 104.

32. Evans, D. P., Lewis, J. A. and Thomson, D. S.: Life Sci. (1973) 12, 327.

RECEIVED August 6, 1979.

15

# Prospects for a Prostaglandin Bronchodilator[1]

CHARLES V. GRUDZINSKAS, JERAULD S. SKOTNICKI[2], SOW-MEI L. CHEN, M. BRAWNER FLOYD, JR., WILLIAM A. HALLETT, ROBERT E. SCHAUB, GERALD J. SIUTA, ALLAN WISSNER, and MARTIN J. WEISS

Metabolic Disease Research Section, Medical Research Division, American Cyanamid Company, Lederle Laboratories, Pearl River, NY 10965

FRANZ DESSY

UCB S.A. Division Pharmaceutique, rue Berkendael 68, 1060 Brussels, Belgium

## I. Introduction

The reports in 1968 that $PGE_1$ and $PGE_2$ could relax or block the constriction of isolated human bronchial tissue by mechanisms apparently not involving the adrenergic or cholinergic receptors (3,4; also see 5,6,7), and the subsequent observations that upon aerosol administration bronchodilation could be induced in asthmatic subjects (8,9; also see 10-13) spotlighted the prostaglandins as a potentially important new approach to bronchodilator therapy. However, it also was apparent that the natural prostaglandins would not find clinical application, since they induce cough and irritation of the upper respiratory tract. (Other problems associated with their use: delayed onset of action, short duration of effect, headaches, and also the inherent chemical instability of the 11-hydroxyprostaglandins.) Nevertheless, because their mechanism of action was different from that of the known bronchodilators (4), the prostaglandins did represent an important and exciting lead to further advances in bronchodilator therapy. Obviously this was a situation certain to delight the heart and challenge the skill of medicinal chemists, and we at Lederle in collaboration with a pneumopharmacology group at UCB (Brussels) undertook an extensive investigation into the synthesis and structure-activity evaluation of a relatively large number of prostaglandin congeners, as did chemistry-biology teams at many of the other pharmaceutical houses. An additional positive consideration was the realization that in the overall context of prostaglandin medicinal research, the prospects for a successful bronchodilator development appeared to be more promising than for most other possibilities. Since aerosol application would enable the prostaglandin to be introduced directly to the target organ, the requirement for oral efficacy would be avoided and the probability of a greater selectivity of effect increased -- a major consideration in view of the broad spectrum of prostaglandin biology.

Since several excellent recent reviews of prostaglandin chemistry are available (14,15,16), we will limit the chemical discussion to the development at Lederle and elsewhere of the synthesis of prostaglandin analogs by the convergent conjugate-addition approach and by the derivatization of l-$PGA_2$, available

0-8412-0536-1/80/47-118-301$16.40/0

in relatively abundant amounts from the Carribean sea coral Plexaura homomalla (esper). However, a comprehensive bronchodilator structure-activity review of the prostaglandins is presented.

The structure of l-$PGE_1$ is shown below; l-$PGE_2$ has a second double bond (cis) between $C_5$ and $C_6$. For purposes of this discussion, the $C_1$ to $C_7$ acid chain is referred to as the α-chain and the allylic alcohol $C_{13}$ to $C_{20}$ chain as the β-chain.

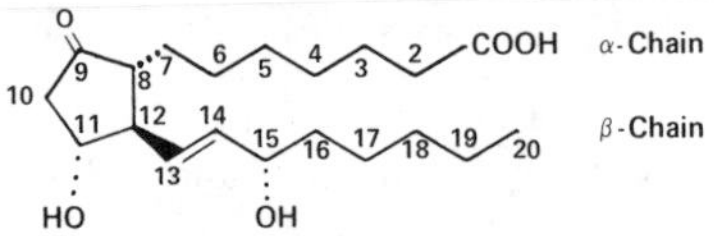
α-Chain
β-Chain
COOH
HO
OH

$PGE_1$

## II. Total Synthesis By The Conjugate Addition Procedure

In order to adequately explore the prostaglandin potential it was apparent that it would be necessary to prepare a relatively large number of prostaglandin congeners of diverse structure in amounts sufficient for extensive biological evaluation. Thus, success would depend in large measure upon the availability of efficient, relatively convenient, and flexible synthetic procedures. In our view at the time, it appeared that these requirements would be satisfied by a process based on the stereospecific introduction of a fully elaborated trans-1-alkenyl β-chain into a cyclopentenone already bearing the ω-carboxyalkyl α-chain via the 1,4-addition of an organometalic reagent; this "conjugate-addition approach" is illustrated in Scheme 1 for the synthesis of l-$PGE_1$. [For examples of this synthetic concept see references 17-56. At the time our studies were initiated there was, to our knowledge, no reported example pertinent to this concept (57).]

SCHEME 1 CONJUGATE ADDITION APPROACH

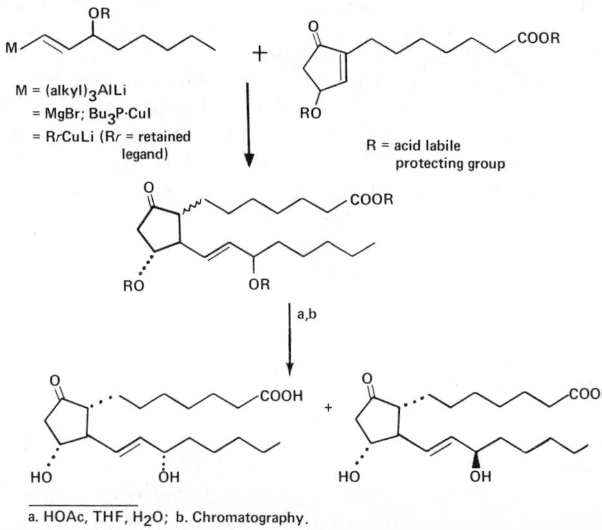
OR
M
COOR
M = (alkyl)3AlLi
= MgBr; Bu3P·CuI
= RrCuLi (Rr = retained legand)
RO
R = acid labile protecting group
COOR
RO
OR
a,b
COOH
HO
OH
COOH
HO
OH

a. HOAc, THF, $H_2O$; b. Chromatography.

We have found this approach in most respects to be the efficient and flexible procedure we originally envisioned and it has produced adequate amounts not only of a large number (>500) but also a broad variety of prostaglandin congeners for biological evaluation. Although this method lends itself best to the synthesis of analogs with modified β-chains, compounds with variations in the α-chain, and in the ring itself also have been prepared.

The successful application of the conjugate addition concept required a satisfactory resolution of two basic synthetic problems.

The first involved the development of useful procedures for the preparation of the 2-alkylcyclopent-2-en-1-ones, synthetic precursors for the 11-deoxyprostaglandin congeners, and of the corresponding 4-hydroxycyclopentenones required for the 11-hydroxy series. In particular, for our study of β-chain variations, convenient preparations of relatively large quantities of cyclopentenones 1-4 having the standard α-chains were necessary. Flexibility was another essential prerequisite since it was in the course of cyclopentenone synthesis that we proposed to obtain entry to those congeners embracing modified α-chains. Our efforts, largely successful, along these lines are discussed directly below.

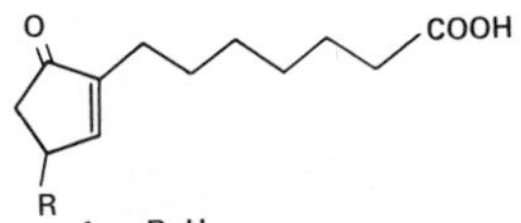

1 R=H
2 R=OH

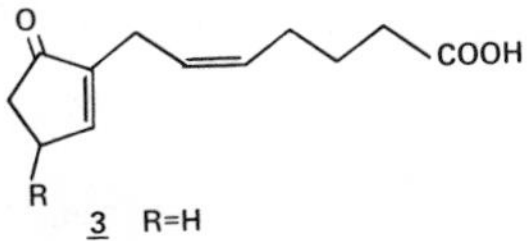

3 R=H
4 R=OH

Our synthetic approach also required the development of effective methods for the stereospecific introduction of the various *trans*-1-alkenyl β-chains. Our investigations with respect to this problem are described below following the cyclopentenone discussion.

A word about optical isomers: if the starting cyclopentenone and β-chain precursors have not been resolved, then two racemates are formed which in the $\Delta^{13}$-15-hydroxy series are almost always separable by simple silica-gel chromatography yielding both the *dl*-15α and *dl*-15β(*epi*) epimers. Thus, in principle, optically active products are obtainable by resolution of either of the two synthons. It is interesting to note that in general the conjugate addition process produces a slight excess of the 15β-epimer (36,39). [In the case of the $\Delta^{13}$-*cis*-prostaglandins, this procedure provides the 15β- epimer with high stereoselectively (22).]

## A. Cyclopentenone Precursors to 11-Deoxyprostaglandins

The search for a general method which would be applicable to both large-scale preparations and to analog studies resulted in a construction of cyclopentenones based on the alkylation of 2-carbalkoxycyclopentanone (58,59,60) followed by a sequence of steps to remove the carbalkoxy group and introduce unsaturation (61,62). Although the number of steps necessary to prepare the modified prostaglandin after introduction of the α-chain is not an appealing aspect of this approach, the yields were good and the cyclopentenones so obtained proved to be useful intermediates for the preparation of a large number of analogs because of the highly convergent nature of the conjugate addition method. The general procedure for the synthesis of these cyclopentenones is illustrated in Scheme 2.

SCHEME 2

GENERAL METHOD OF CYCLOPENTENONE PREPARATION

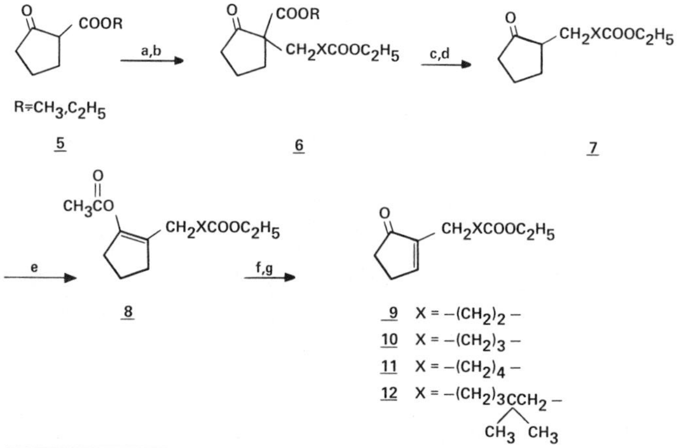

O, COOR; $R=CH_3, C_2H_5$ 5 —a,b→ O, COOR, $CH_2XCOOC_2H_5$ 6 —c,d→ O, $CH_2XCOOC_2H_5$ 7

—e→ $CH_3CO$ (O), $CH_2XCOOC_2H_5$ 8 —f,g→ O, $CH_2XCOOC_2H_5$

9 $X = -(CH_2)_2-$

10 $X = -(CH_2)_3-$

11 $X = -(CH_2)_4-$

12 $X = -(CH_2)_3C(CH_3)_2CH_2-$

a. NaH, glyme; b. $Br(I)CH_2XCOOC_2H_5$, △, glyme; c. HCl, aq. HOAc, △; d. *p*-TSA, EtOH, △; e. *p*-TSA, $Ac_2O$, △, remove HOAc (ref. 63); f. $Br_2$, $CHCl_3$, aq. $CaCO_3$; g. LiBr, $Li_2CO_3$, △, DMF (ref. 64).

Certain variations in the α-chain were introduced by the use of the appropriate alkylating agent, $BrCH_2XCOOR'$ (62). The various cyclopentenones prepared in this way include the homologous series 9, 10, and 11 and the precursor 12 (see Scheme 3) for the 3,3-dimethylprostaglandin series.

SCHEME 3

3,3-DIMETHYL PRECURSORS

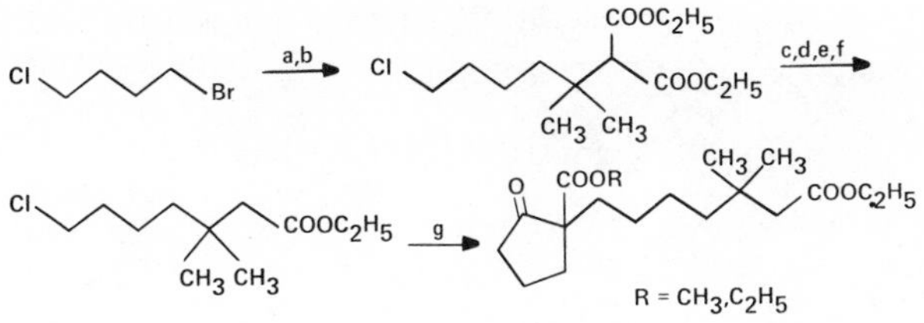

a. Mg, $Et_2O$; b. add to diethyl isopropylidenemalonate and CuI·$Bu_3P$; c. KOH, aq. iPrOH; d. diglyme, △; e. $SOCl_2$; f. EtOH, benzene, collidine; g. sodiocyclopentanone-carboxylate in presence of NaI, glyme.

Other modified α-chain derivatives were prepared by further transformations of the 4-,5-, and 7- carbon chains found in cyclopentenone esters 9 (see Scheme 4), 10 (Scheme 6) and 11 (Scheme 8), respectively (62). For these operations the methoxime group proved to be a useful blocking group for the cyclopentenone moiety, deblocking being easily achieved with aq.HCl in acetone. Scheme 4 shows the preparation of cyclopentenones 16 and 18, precursors for the synthesis of 3-oxa- and 3-thia-11-deoxyprostaglandins (62). The transformation of the 4-carbon side-chain intermediate methoxime 13 to the cyclopentenones 22 and 24 required for the preparation of 4-hydroxy and 4-methoxy-11-deoxyprostaglandins is illustrated in Scheme 5.

Application of a malonic acid extension procedure with substituted malonates to the cyclopentenone pentanoate 10 afforded the cyclopentenone precursors for various 2-substituted 11-deoxyprostaglandins (Scheme 6) (62). The preparation from 10 of cyclopentenone intermediates for the synthesis of 2-nor-(62), 2,3-methano-, and 3-thia-4-homo-11-deoxyprostaglandins (49) is described in Scheme 7.

The cylopentenone heptanoate 11, the precursor for 11-deoxyprostaglandins having the natural $PGE_1$ α-chain, also was homologated to the 8- and 9-carbon chain cyclopentenones (62) as illustrated in Scheme 8.

Scheme 9 describes the preparation of the cycloalkenones 38, 39, and 41, intermediates for the synthesis of 11-deoxy-$PGE_2$, 10a-homo-11-deoxy-$PGE_1$ (61), and 11-deoxy-3-thia-4-nor-$PGE_1$ (49), respectively. The first of these cycloalkenones was obtained by adaptation of a literature procedure (46,65), and the latter two by the general method of Scheme 2.

SCHEME 4

PREPARATION OF 3-OXA AND 3-THIA PRECURSORS

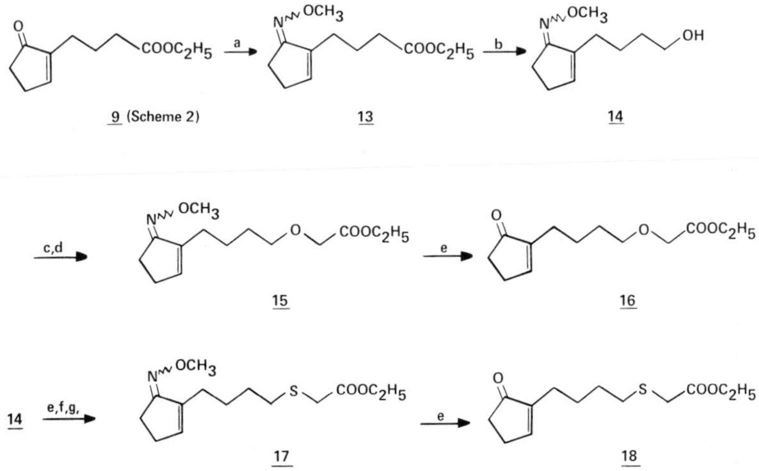

9 (Scheme 2) →a 13 →b 14

→c,d 15 →e 16

14 →e,f,g, 17 →e 18

a. $CH_3ONH_2 \cdot HCl$, pyridine, EtOH; b. $iBu_2AlH$, toluene, 0°; c. BuLi, THF, 0°; d. $BrCH_2CO_2C_2H_5$, THF, △; e. 2N HCl, acetone, △; f. TsCl, pyridine; g. $NaSCH_2COOC_2H_5$, glyme.

SCHEME 5

PREPARATION OF 4-OXY PRECURSORS

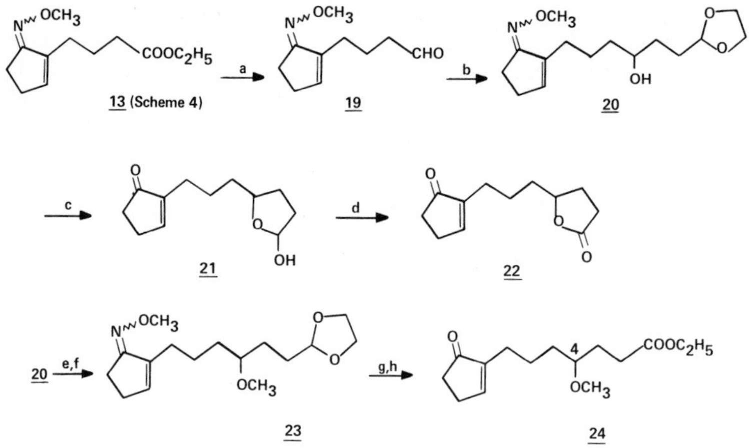

13 (Scheme 4) →a 19 →b 20

→c 21 →d 22

20 →e,f 23 →g,h 24

a. 1 equiv. $iBu_2$ AlH, −78°; b. $BrMgCH_2CH_2CH$(1,3-dioxolan-2-yl), THF, 0°; c. pyruvic acid, dil HCl, acetone; d. Jones oxidation; e. NaH, THF; f. $CH_3I$; g. aq. $H_2CrO_4$; h. $p$-TSA, EtOH, △.

SCHEME 6

PREPARATION OF 2 - SUBSTITUTED PRECURSORS

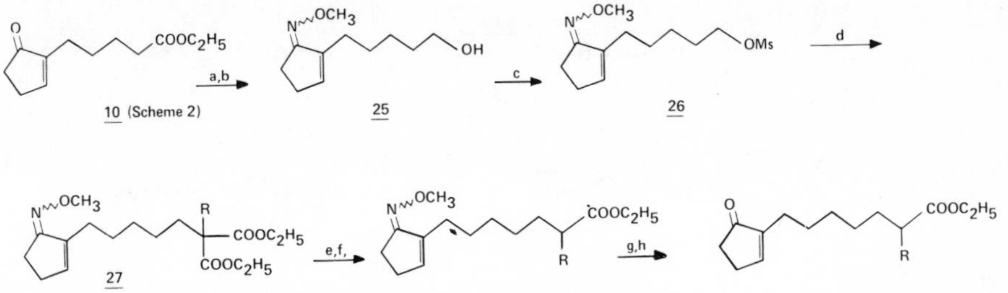

10 (Scheme 2) → a,b → 25 → c → 26 → d →

27 → e,f, → g,h →

28 R = $CH_3$
29 R = $C_2H_5$
30 R = F
31 R = $C_6H_5$

a. $CH_3ONH_2$·HCl, pyridine, EtOH; b. *i*$Bu_2AlH$, toluene, 0°; c. $CH_3SO_2Cl$, $Et_3N$, $CH_2Cl_2$; d. $NaRC(COOC_2H_5)_2$, DMF, △; e. KOH, aq. EtOH; f. free acid, diglyme,△; g. HCl, aq. acetone,△; h. *p*TSA, EtOH.

SCHEME 7

PREPARATION OF 2-NOR, 2,3-METHANO, AND 4-HOMO-3-THIA PRECURSORS

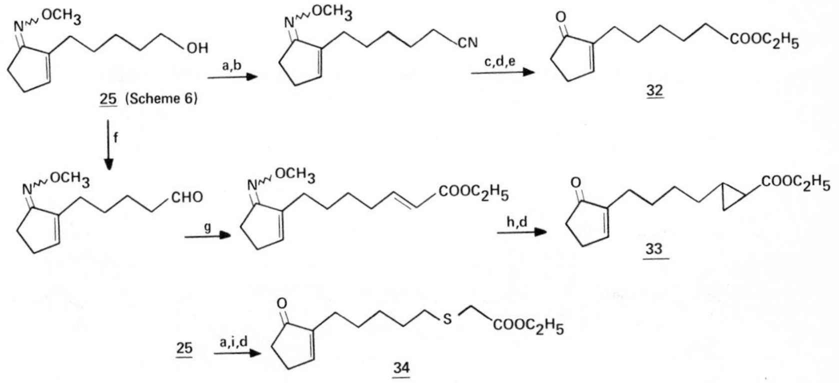

25 (Scheme 6) → a,b → c,d,e → 32

25 → f → g → h,d → 33

25 → a,i,d → 34

a. $CH_3SO_2$ Cl, $Et_3N$, $CH_2Cl_2$; b. NaCN, DMF, △; c. NaOH, aq. EtOH, △; d. HCl, aq. acetone, △; e. *p*-TSA, EtOH; f. Collins oxidation; g. $(C_6H_5)_3P = CHCOOC_2H_5$; h. $CH_2 = SO(CH_3)_2$; i. $NaSCH_2COOC_2H_5$, glyme.

SCHEME 8

PREPARATION OF 2-HOMO AND 2a,2b-BISHOMO PRECURSORS

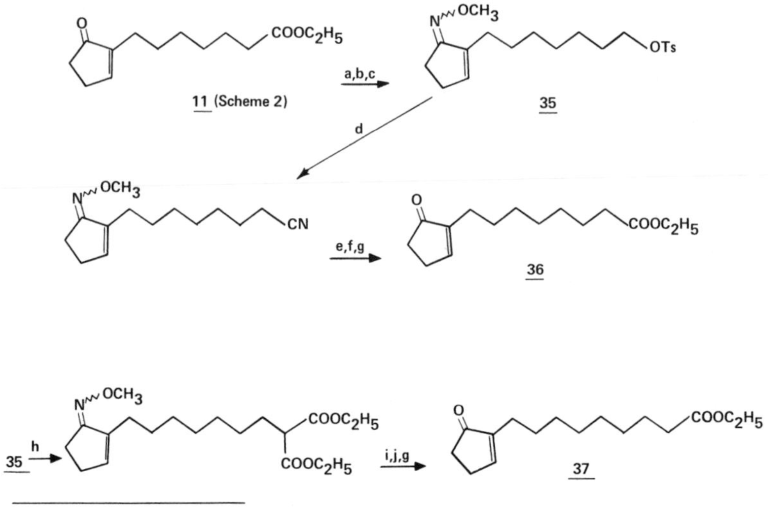

11 (Scheme 2) → a,b,c → 35 → d → e,f,g → 36

35 → h → i,j,g → 37

a. $CH_3ONH_2 \cdot HCl$, pyridine, EtOH; b. $i Bu_2AlH$, toluene, 0°; c. TsCl, pyridine; d. NaCN, DMF; e. NaOH, aq. EtOH,△; f. HCl, aq. acetone,△; g. pTSA, EtOH,△; h. $NaCH(COOC_2H_5)_2$, DMF, △; i. KOH, aq. MeOH; j. free acid, xylene, △.

SCHEME 9

PREPARATION OF 5,6-*CIS*, 10a-HOMO, and 4-NOR-3-THIA PRECURSORS

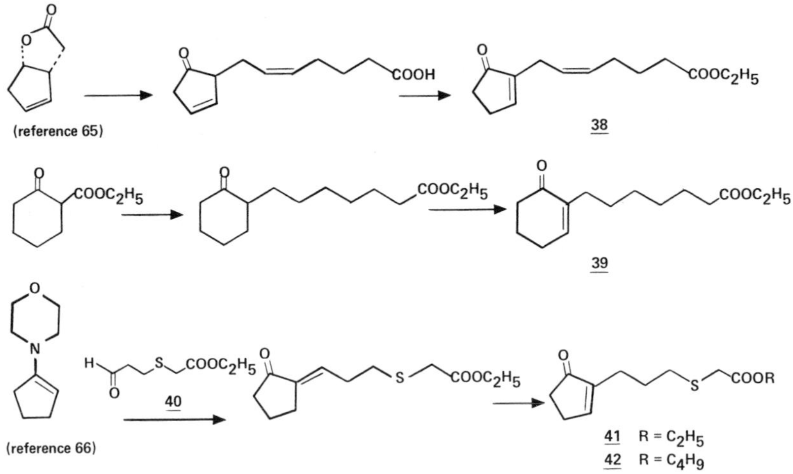

(reference 65) → → 38

→ → 39

(reference 66) 40 →

41 R = $C_2H_5$

42 R = $C_4H_9$

TABLE I

CYCLOPENTENONE PRECURSORS TO 11-DEOXYPROSTAGLANDIN ANALOGS

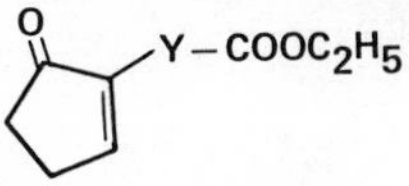


| CYCLOPENTENONE | Y | SCHEME |
|---|---|---|
| 9 | $-(CH_2)_3-$ | 2 |
| 10 | $-(CH_2)_4-$ | 2 |
| 32 | $-(CH_2)_5-$ | 7 |
| 11 | $-(CH_2)_6-$ | 2 |
| 36 | $-(CH_2)_7-$ | 8 |
| 37 | $-(CH_2)_8-$ | 8 |
| 12 | $-(CH_2)_4C(CH_3)(CH_3)CH_2-$ | 2,3 |
| 16 | $-(CH_2)_4OCH_2-$ | 4 |
| 41 | $-(CH_2)_3SCH_2-$ | 9 |
| 42 | $-(CH_2)_3SCH_2-$ (butyl ester) | 9 |
| 18 | $-(CH_2)_4SCH_2-$ | 4 |
| 34 | $-(CH_2)_5SCH_2-$ | 7 |
| 28 | $-(CH_2)_5CH(CH_3)-$ | 6 |
| 29 | $-(CH_2)_5CH(C_2H_5)-$ | 6 |
| 30 | $-(CH_2)_5CH(F)-$ | 6 |
| 31 | $-(CH_2)_5CH(C_6H_5)-$ | 6 |
| 33 | $-(CH_2)_4$  | 7 |
| 22 | $-(CH_2)_3$ 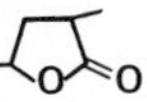 | 5 |
| 24 | $-(CH_2)_3CH(OCH_3)(CH_2)_2-$ | 5 |
| 38 | $-(CH_2CH=CH(CH_2)_3-$ (*cis*) | 9 |
| 39 | 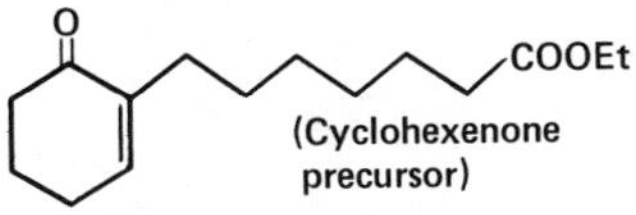 (Cyclohexenone precursor) | 9 |

The cyclopentenone synthons utilized for the preparation of the various 11-deoxyprostaglandin congeners are listed in Table I. In general, these compounds were designed to give analogs in which metabolic inactivation by fatty-acid β-oxidation was blocked or, at the least, hindered.

### B. Cyclopentenolone Precursors to 11-Oxy and 11-Thio Prostaglandins

The preparation of the cyclopentenolones required for the application of the conjugate-addition process to 11-hydroxy-prostaglandins has been the subject of much study (67). The original method (58) for the synthesis of the $PGE_1$ precursor 45 involved overall allylic hydroxylation of a 4-unsubstituted cyclopentenone such as 43, as shown in Scheme 10. In the first step, allylic bromination is not selective but produces by-products which contribute to a lowering of the yield. Solvolysis conditions are critical and, in our experience, this operation is best carried out with $AgBF_4$ in aqueous acetone, providing an overall yield after purification of ca 40%. Introduction of alkoxy groups, ultimately leading to 11α-alkoxy-11-deoxyprostaglandins, may be accomplished by substitution with an appropriate alcohol in the solvolysis step (68,69).

SCHEME 10

4-OXYCYCLOPENTENONES VIA ALLYLIC BROMINATION

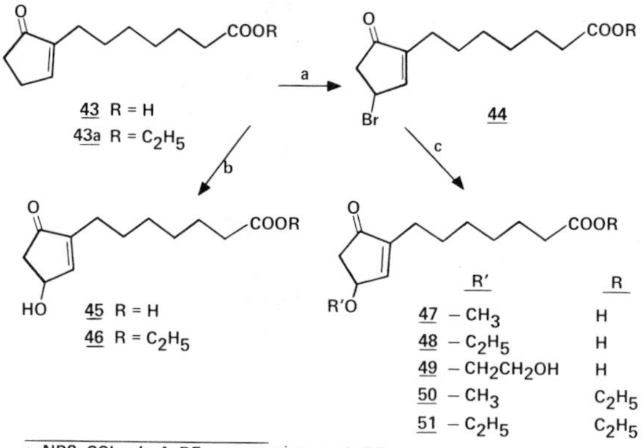

| | R' | R |
|---|---|---|
| 47 | $-CH_3$ | H |
| 48 | $-C_2H_5$ | H |
| 49 | $-CH_2CH_2OH$ | H |
| 50 | $-CH_3$ | $C_2H_5$ |
| 51 | $-C_2H_5$ | $C_2H_5$ |

a. NBS, $CCl_4$; b. $AgBF_4$, aq. acetone; c. $AgBF_4$, R'OH, 2,6-lutidine.

Since the above sequence was not applicable to the $PGE_2$ series (side chain double bond), alternative methods had to be developed (17). Most of these procedures are general and indeed are more efficient for preparing cyclopentenolones than is the allylic hydroxylation process, even in those cases where the latter is applicable. An example of one of these newer methods, as applied to the preparation of the $PGE_2$ precursor 53, is shown in Scheme 11 (18). The key feature of this process is the quantitative isomerization of the 3-hydroxy isomer 52 to the desired 4-hydroxycyclopentenone 53, presumably by acid-catalyzed addition-elimination reactions. That the 3-isomer is the synthetic equivalent of the 4-isomer creates additional valuable synthetic approaches to this critical synthon.

SCHEME 11

PREPARATION OF $PG_2$-SERIES CYCLOPENTENOLONE

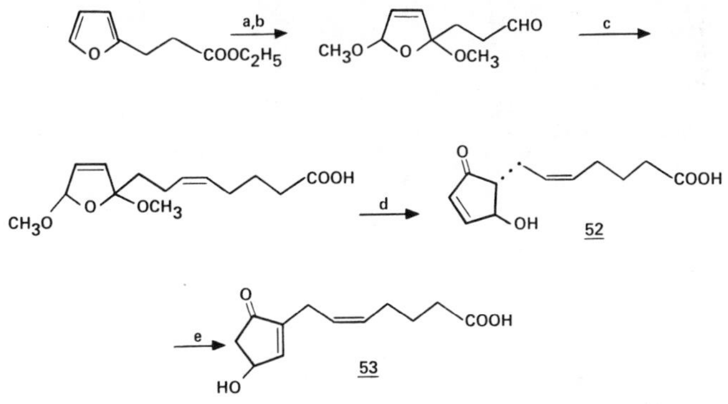

a. $Br_2$, $Na_2CO_3$, MeOH; b. $i Bu_2AlH$, toluene, $-78°$; c. $(C_6H_5)_3P = CH(CH_2)_3COONa$, DMSO; d. phosphate buffer, pH 6, aq. dioxane, $\triangle$; e. 2 N $H_2SO_4$, aq. dioxane, $\triangle$.

It also is possible to prepare cyclopentenones with ring substituents other than hydroxy by exchange reactions if conditions are properly chosen [Scheme 12 (69)]. Thus, the 4-methoxycyclopentenone 54 was prepared from 53 by methanolysis in the presence of sulfuric acid (18). Treatment of 54 with methanolic 2-mercaptoethanol in the presence of a catalytic amount of sodium methoxide gave the thioether 55, again as a consequence of .addition-elimination reactions. A procedure which allowed exchange of the ring methoxy group in 54 with a different alcohol, but preserved the methyl ester, utilized the semicarbazone derivative of 54. Thus, treatment of this semicarbazone, prepared in situ, with acetic acid in ethylene glycol resulted in exchange of the methoxy group with solvent to give 56. Restoration of the carbonyl function by exchange hydrolysis with α-ketoglutaric acid gave the desired 4-(2-hydroxyethoxy)cyclopentenone 57.

SCHEME 12

PREPARATION OF 4-SUBSTITUTED CYCLOPENTENONES

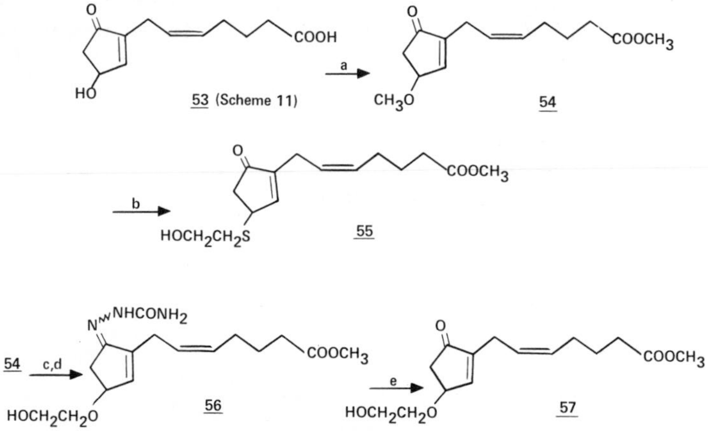

a. $H_2SO_4$, $CH_3OH$, △; b. $HSCH_2CH_2OH$, $NaOCH_3$, $CH_3OH$; c. $H_2NNHCONH_2$, ethylene glycol; d. HOAc, ethylene glycol, 90°; e. α-ketoglutaric acid, HCl, aq. THF.

SCHEME 13

FURANCARBINOL PROCESS

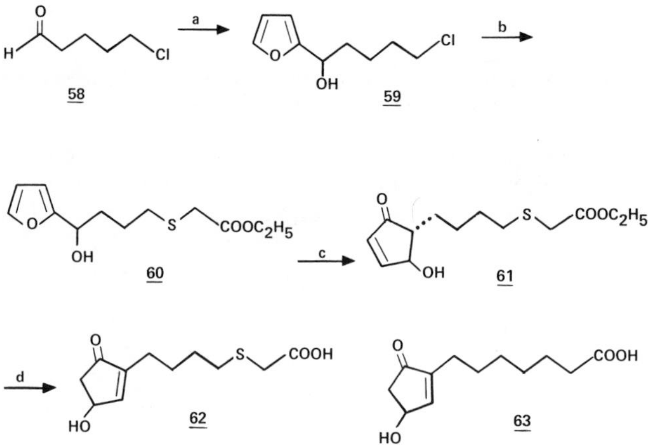

a. 2-furyl lithium, THF, –78 to O°; b. $NaSCH_2$ $COOC_2H_5$, EtOH; c. 2N HCOOH, aq. dioxane, △; d. 0.5M $H_2SO_4$, aq. dioxane, △.

In an important and valuable extension of the furanoid process it was found that alkyl 2-furancarbinols also could be rearranged effectively to 4-hydroxycyclopentenones (70,71), as illustrated in Scheme 13 for the preparation of the cyclopentenone 62 which serves as precursor to the 3-thiaprostaglandin $E_1$ series. Although this particular example is one in which the allylic hydroxylation process also is inapplicable, we prefer the furancarbinol process for the preparation of the 4-hydroxycyclopentenone 63 required for the synthesis of 11α-hydroxyprostaglandins bearing the natural $PG_1$ α-chain.

For the conjugate-addition reactions which produce the prostaglandin skeleton, it is necessary to block all the hydroxy and carboxy functions. The ether blocking groups which we have found useful include tetrahydropyranyl (THP) and trimethylsilyl (TMS). Both of these ethers are readily cleaved with aqueous acetic acid under conditions compatible with the stability of 11-oxy PGE derivatives. These same two groups also serve to esterify the carboxy function. Thus, a hydroxyacid can be blocked in one operation by conversion to a "bis-THP" or "bis-TMS" derivative. Alkyl esters also may be used, but the alkyl 11-hydroxy-9-ketoprostanoates produced can not be converted to the free acids by chemical means.

The cyclopentenones with functionality at the 4-position are listed in Table II. Those compounds with THP blocking groups were prepared from the corresponding free alcohols using dihydropyran (pTSA catalysis) in dichloromethane solution (28). The TMS blocked cyclopentenones were obtained by treatment with chlorotrimethylsilane (TMS-Cl) and hexamethyldisilazane (HMDS) in pyridine solution (72). In these instances the Scheme reference of Table II refers to the parent hydroxy compound.

## C. The Conjugate Addition Step. Preparation Of The Organometallic Reagents

The 1-alkenyl organometallic reagents required for the introduction of the β-chain can be prepared cleanly in the requisite trans configuration by convenient procedures. Furthermore, the 1,4-transfer of the trans-1-alkenyl ligand is accomplished with essentially absolute preservation of the trans-stereochemistry, and in a highly stereoselective manner so that the trans-relationship to the 11α-substituent is obtained (73). The final all-trans configuration of the substituents on the cyclopentanone ring is established upon equilibration (74), for which the mild acid-catalyzed deblocking procedures usually are adequate.

In general, the trans-1-alkenyl organometallic reagents are prepared from the corresponding terminal acetylene (e.g., 77 and 79, Scheme 14). These intermediates are available by condensation of the appropriate aldehyde or ketone with ethynyl

TABLE II

CYCLOPENTENONE PRECURSORS TO 11-SUBSTITUTED PROSTAGLANDIN ANALOGS

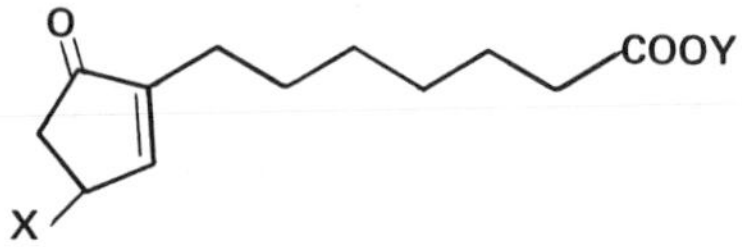

O, X, COOY

| | X | Y | SCHEME |
|---|---|---|---|
| 64 | $(CH_3)_3SiO-$ | $-Si(CH_3)_3$ | 10 |
| 65 | THPO– | –THP | 10 |
| 66 | $CH_3O-$ | –THP | 10 |
| 67 | $(CH_3)_3SiOCH_2CH_2O-$ | $-Si(CH_3)_3$ | 10 |
| 68 | $THPOCH_2CH_2O-$ | –THP | 10 |
| 50 | $CH_3O-$ | $-C_2H_5$ | 10 |
| 51 | $C_2H_5O-$ | $-C_2H_5$ | 10 |

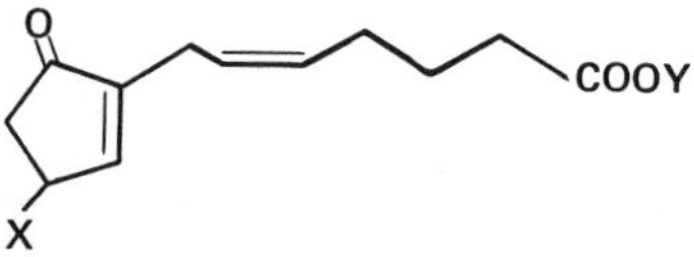

O, X, COOY

| | X | Y | SCHEME |
|---|---|---|---|
| 69 | $(CH_3)_3SiO-$ | $-Si(CH_3)_3$ | 11 |
| 70 | THPO– | –THP | 11 |
| 54 | $CH_3O-$ | $-CH_3$ | 12 |
| 71 | $(CH_3)_3SiO(CH_2)_2O-$ | $-CH_3$ | 12 |
| 72 | $(CH_3)_3SiO(CH_2)_2S-$ | $-CH_3$ | 12 |

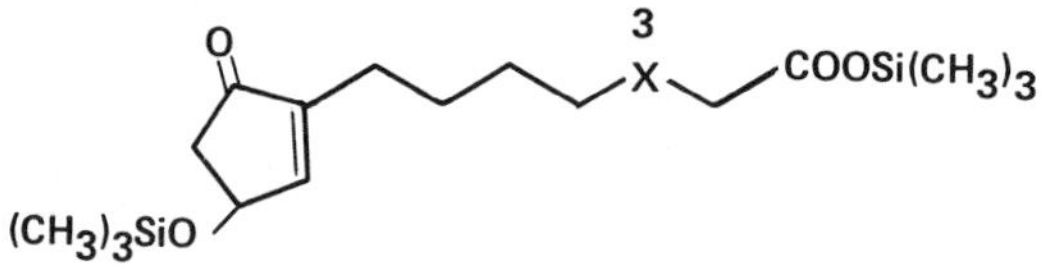

O, $(CH_3)_3SiO$, 3, X, $COOSi(CH_3)_3$

| | X | SCHEME |
|---|---|---|
| 73 | –S– | 13 |
| 74 | –C(CH$_3$)(CH$_3$)– | (prepared from 11-deoxy precursor 12 by allylic hydroxylation procedure) |

magnesium chloride (76) or propargylmagnesium bromide (78), which also serves to introduce the hydroxy function. The hydroxy group is protected as an acid-labile ether, commonly tetrahydropyranyl (THP), trimethylsilyl (TMS), triethylsilyl (TES), triphenylmethyl (trityl, Tr) or mono-p-methoxytrityl (MTr) derivatives. Other laboratories have utilized 2-(2-methoxypropyl) and 1-(1-ethoxyethyl) protecting groups (41).

SCHEME 14

PREPARATION OF HYDROXYALKYNES

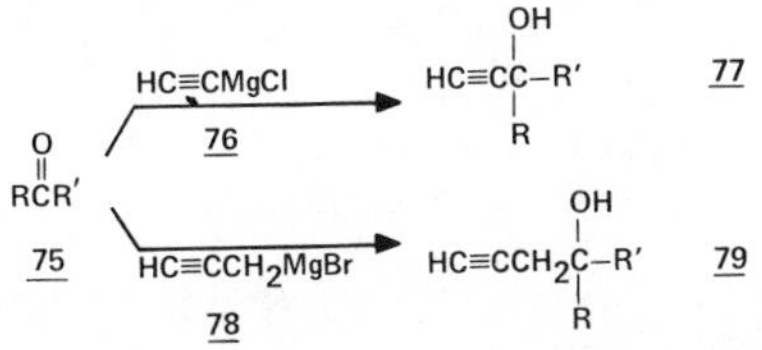

Three types of organometallic reagents have been employed in our laboratories: lithio-1-alkenyltrialkylalanates, lithio-1-alkenylcuprates, and 1-alkenyl Grignards (copper I catalyzed). Our experience with these reagents is described in the next several Schemes.

In its most direct application, the alanate conjugate-addition procedure (Scheme 15), developed in our laboratories, involves initial cis-hydroalumination of a terminal acetylene to give, after treatment with an alkyllithium, a trans-1-alkenylalanate (25,28). Thus, the cis-hydroalumination of 3-trityloxy-1-octyne (80) with diisobutylaluminum hydride (DAH) provided the trans-vinylalane 81. The use of the bulky trityl group is critical since other blocking groups, even one as bulky as t-butyl, give the cis-vinylalane (28,54). Methyllithium treatment of alane 81 furnished the trialkylvinylalanate 83, which undergoes 1,4-addition reactions with the appropriate cyclopentenones.

SCHEME 15

PREPARATION OF LITHIO 1-ALKENYL-TRIALKYLALANATES

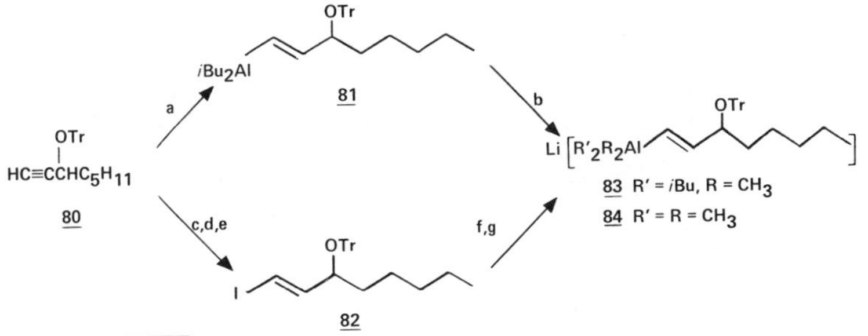

a. *i*Bu$_2$AlH; b. CH$_3$Li, 0°; c. diisoamylborane; d. (CH$_3$)$_3$NO; e. NaOH, I$_2$; f. 1 eq. BuLi or 2 eq. *t* BuLi, – 78°; g. (CH$_3$)$_3$Al.

The addition of DAH to trityloxyalkynes such as 80 is not clean and is accompanied with considerable allylic carbon-oxygen and oxygen-trityl cleavage, which accounts for the low yields of the overall process (54). (Excellent yields of 15-deoxyprostaglandins are obtainable in the absence of an oxy function in the β-chain.) In order to avoid the problems resulting from DAH-ether interaction, an alternative, more circuitous synthesis of lithium 1-alkenyltrialkylalanates was developed (39,54). This approach utilized 1-iodo-trans-1-alkenes, prepared by the Syntex procedure (21) involving successive treatment of a 1-alkyne with diisoamylborane, trimethylamine oxide, and $I_2$/NaOH. After lithiation with either one equivalent of butyllithium or two equivalents of t-butyllithium (75), exposure of the resulting vinyl lithium reagent to trimethylaluminum provided the lithio alkenylalanate 84 required for the conjugate addition process.

Alkenyl copper reagents, such as 87-90, also prepared via vinyl iodides such as 85 or 86, have proven to be reliable reagents for the introduction of the standard as well as many modified β-chains (22,23,26,29,31,32,34-37,72). The alkenylcopper reagents are of three types: lithio divinylcuprates (87), lithio mono vinylcuprates (88,89) containing an inert ligand, and vinylcopper reagents (90) which have received little synthetic attention (Scheme 16).

SCHEME 16

ALKENYL CUPRATE REAGENTS

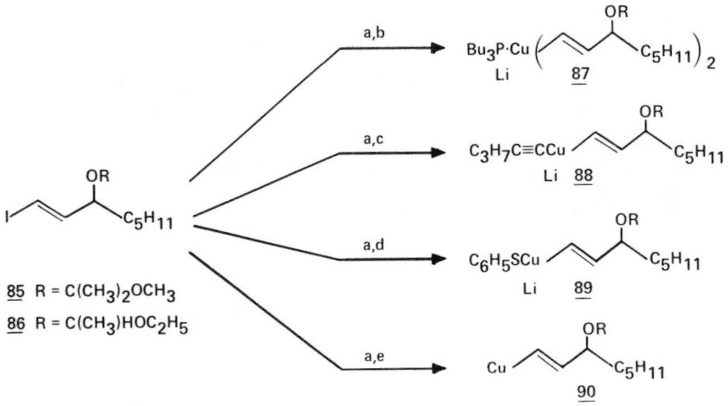

85 R = $C(CH_3)_2OCH_3$

86 R = $C(CH_3)HOC_2H_5$

87 ($Bu_3P \cdot Cu$, Li, 2 × vinyl ligand); 88 ($C_3H_7C{\equiv}CCu$, Li); 89 ($C_6H_5SCu$, Li); 90 (Cu)

a. BuLi, b. $Bu_3P \cdot CuI$; c. $C_3H_7C{\equiv}CCu$, HMPTA; d. $C_6H_5SCu$; e. CuI, HMPTA.

Since a divinylcuprate such as 87 is derived from two molecules of the vinyl iodide intermediate, its use entails the waste of one equivalent of the valuable vinyl iodide. Consequently, mixed cuprate reagents such as 88 and 89 have been developed which substitute a non-transferable ligand for one of the two vinyl moieties (75,76). A popular ligand is 1-pentyne (76,77). 1-Pentynyl lithio cuprates are prepared by dissolving 1-pentynylcopper (I) in ether with the aid of a solubilizing agent such as tributylphosphine or the water soluble hexamethylphosphorous triamide (HMPTA), and then treating with one equivalent of an alkenyl lithium. [Recently, 4-methoxy-4-methylbutyne was reported to be an inert ligand that requires no solubilizing agent (78).]

The lithio cuprate conjugate-addition procedure for the preparation of l-$PGE_1$ methyl ester has been studied in considerable detail by Sih, who introduced this useful process to prostaglandin synthesis (37).

Recently, Corey has rekindled interest in vinylstannanes as intermediates for alkenyl lithium reagents (79,80,81), and we (52,55) and others (53,56) have utilized this method to prepare various β-chain precursors (Scheme 17). We find hydrostannation of terminal acetylenes to be a facile and high yield reaction, whereas iodovinylation is a capricious and tedious transformation. Thus, treatment of 3-triethylsilyloxy-1-octyne 91 with tributylstannane (TBS) in the presence of azobisisobutyronitrile (AIBN) gave stereospecifically an excellent yield of 1-tributylstannyl-3-triethylsilyloxy-trans-1-octene (92), which when lithiated with butyllithium and treated with pentynylcopper provided the requisite lithio cuprate 93. The use of TBS to prepare homovinylic ethers such as 96 and 97 gave a 10:1 mixture of trans and cis isomers.

SCHEME 17

LITHIO CUPRATES VIA HYDROSTANNATION

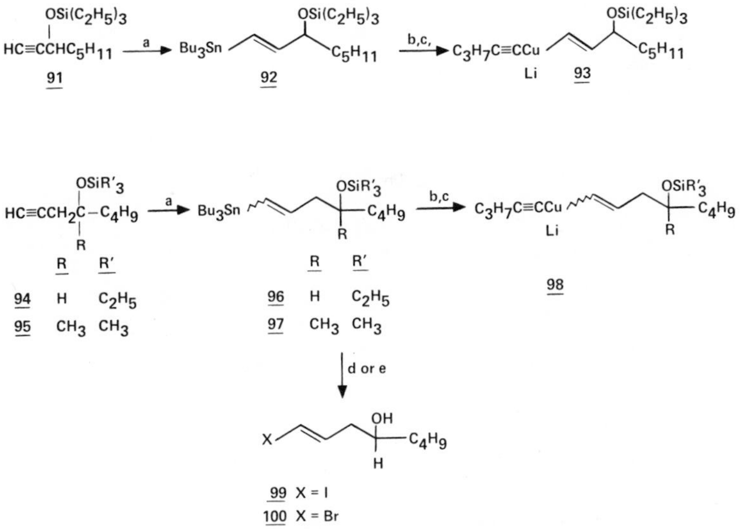

$HC\equiv CCH(OSi(C_2H_5)_3)C_5H_{11}$ (91) $\xrightarrow{a}$ $Bu_3Sn$–CH=CH–CH($OSi(C_2H_5)_3$)$C_5H_{11}$ (92) $\xrightarrow{b,c}$ $C_3H_7C\equiv CCu(Li)$–CH=CH–CH($OSi(C_2H_5)_3$)$C_5H_{11}$ (93)

$HC\equiv CCH_2C(OSiR'_3)(R)-C_4H_9$ $\xrightarrow{a}$ $Bu_3Sn$–CH=CH–$CH_2$–C($OSiR'_3$)(R)–$C_4H_9$ $\xrightarrow{b,c}$ $C_3H_7C\equiv CCu(Li)$–CH=CH–$CH_2$–C($OSiR'_3$)(R)–$C_4H_9$ (98)

| | R | R' |
|---|---|---|
| 94 | H | $C_2H_5$ |
| 95 | $CH_3$ | $CH_3$ |

| | R | R' |
|---|---|---|
| 96 | H | $C_2H_5$ |
| 97 | $CH_3$ | $CH_3$ |

96, 97 $\xrightarrow{d \text{ or } e}$ X–CH=CH–$CH_2$–C(OH)(H)–$C_4H_9$

99 X = I
100 X = Br

a. $Bu_3SnH$, AIBN, 130°; b. BuLi; c. $C_3H_7C\equiv CCu$, HMPTA, d. $I_2$, $Et_2O$; e. $Br_2$, $CCl_4$.

Vinylstannanes also can be employed for the stereospecific preparation of the corresponding vinyl iodides and vinyl bromides as shown in Scheme 17, the transformation proceeding with retention of stereochemistry (52,53).

The use of copper(I)-catalyzed Grignard reagents derived from trans-1-alkenyl (27) or alkyl bromides (30) also has been satisfactorily demonstrated in our laboratories. With alkenyl Grignards some $\Delta^{13}$-cis product is produced, the cis-trans ratio being dependent upon the temperature at which the Grignard reagent is formed. An important advantage of the Cu(I)-catalyzed Grignard addition procedure is its potential for production scale, since conjugate addition proceeds smoothly at 0°, rather than in the -78° to -20° range required for alkenylcopper reagents.

## D. Preparation Of The β-Chain Precursors

### 1. 15-Deoxy Series

The organometallic derivatives required for the introduction of a 15-deoxy β-chain, not otherwise oxygenated, were obtained most conveniently by hydroalumination of a terminal acetylene with diisobutylaluminum hydride and conversion in situ to the lithio alanate 102 required for conjugate addition. In the absence of other oxy functions in the β-chain this process produces 15-deoxyprostaglandins such as 103 and 104 conveniently and in excellent yield, as high as 80-90% for the 11,15-bisdeoxy series (Scheme 18) (25,54).

SCHEME 18

PREPARATION OF *dl*-11,15-BISDEOXY–$PGE_1$ AND 15-DEOXY – $PGE_1$

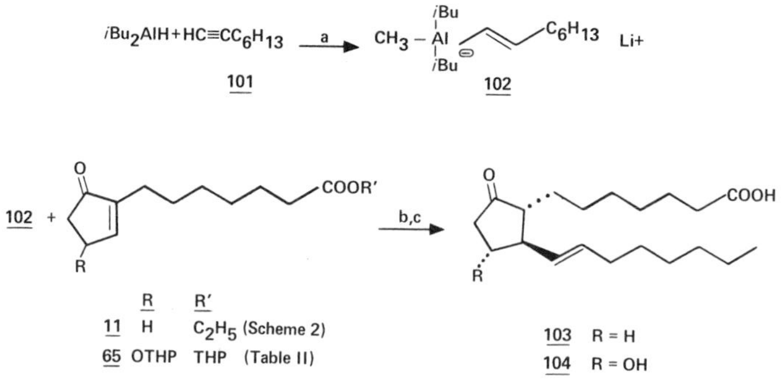

$iBu_2AlH + HC{\equiv}CC_6H_{13}$ —a→ $CH_3-Al^{\ominus}(iBu)_2$–CH=CH–$C_6H_{13}$ Li+

101 102

102 + [cyclopentenone, R, COOR′] —b,c→ [R, COOH]

| | R | R′ |
|---|---|---|
| 11 | H | $C_2H_5$ (Scheme 2) |
| 65 | OTHP | THP (Table II) |

103 R = H

104 R = OH

a. $CH_3Li$; b. conjugate addition at ambient temperature; c. saponification for 103 or mild acid hydrolysis for 104.

## 2. $\Delta^{13}$-15-Hydroxy Series

The preparation of the organometallic intermediates which can be used for the introduction of the natural $\Delta^{13}$-15-hydroxy β-chain is discussed in the previous section (Schemes 15-17).

## 3. 13,14-Dihydro-15-Hydroxy Series

Since biological activity also is associated with 13,14-dihydro derivatives, a method for the direct introduction of this β-chain was devised based upon the conjugate addition of the Grignard reagent derived from either 3-t-butoxyoctyl bromide (107) or iodide (110), the syntheses of which are illustrated in Scheme 19 (30).

SCHEME 19

PREPARATION OF 13,14-DIHYDRO – 15-HYDROXY PRECURSORS

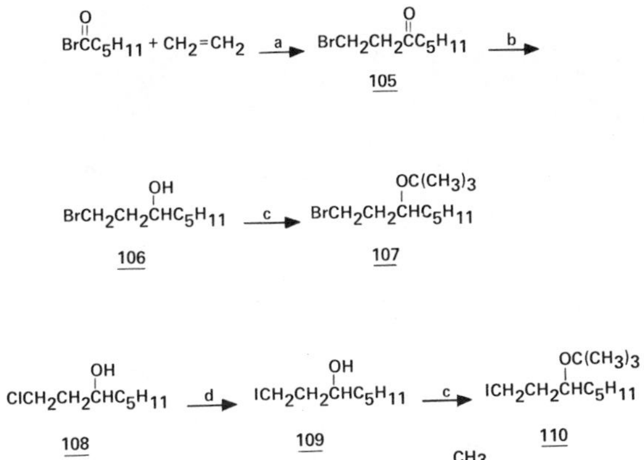

$BrC(=O)C_5H_{11} + CH_2{=}CH_2 \xrightarrow{a} BrCH_2CH_2C(=O)C_5H_{11}$ (105) $\xrightarrow{b}$

$BrCH_2CH_2CH(OH)C_5H_{11}$ (106) $\xrightarrow{c}$ $BrCH_2CH_2CH(OC(CH_3)_3)C_5H_{11}$ (107)

$ClCH_2CH_2CH(OH)C_5H_{11}$ (108) $\xrightarrow{d}$ $ICH_2CH_2CH(OH)C_5H_{11}$ (109) $\xrightarrow{c}$ $ICH_2CH_2CH(OC(CH_3)_3)C_5H_{11}$ (110)

a. $AlBr_3$, $BrCH_2CH_2Br$; b. $NaBH_4$, EtOH; c. $CH_3C(CH_3){=}CH_2$, $H_2SO_4$, $CH_2Cl_2$; d. NaI, acetone.

## 4. 15-Hydroxy β-Chains Potentially Resistant To PG 15-Dehydrogenase. Introduction

The major route of prostaglandin metabolic inactivation involves oxidation of the 15-hydroxy group by PG 15-dehydrogenase (82). As is well known, this is an exceptionally rapid process which takes place in the lung and other organs. Accordingly an intensive effort was mounted in a search for biologically active congeners in which this metabolic process could be expected to be blocked or inhibited.

It was anticipated that such compounds would produce a more prolonged duration of effect and also might prove to be more potent and perhaps orally effective as well. Among the structural features which we introduced into the 15-hydroxyprostaglandin molecule in the course of this investigation were the 15-methyl, 15,19-methano-20-nor, 16-alkyl, 16,16-dimethyl, 16,16-trimethylene, 17,17-dimethyl, 16-cyclopentyl-17,20-tetranor, 16-hydroxy, 16-methoxy, and 16-aryloxy-17,20-tetranor moieties. The synthesis of the various β-chain synthons required for their introduction are described below in this section.

### a. 15-Hydroxy-15-alkyl Series

The preparation of the 15-methyl-15-hydroxy β-chain precursor 113 is illustrated in Scheme 20 (48). Note that the 15-hydroxy group in the 15-methylprostaglandin product is both allylic and tertiary so that considerable care has to be taken during the acid-catalyzed deblocking procedure following conjugate addition (82a).

SCHEME 20

PREPARATION OF 15-METHYL – 15-HYDROXY PRECURSOR

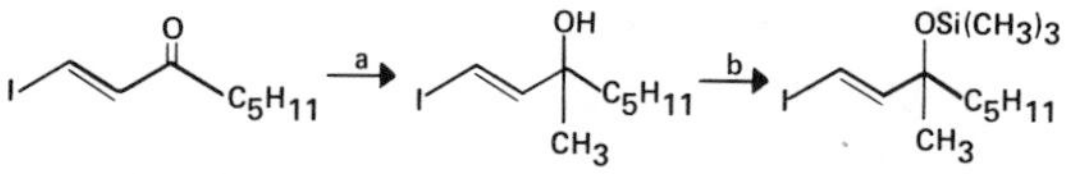

111 → (a) 112 → (b) 113

a. $CH_3MgI$; b. $(CH_3)_3SiCl$, imidazole, DMF.

Analogs in which the β-chain features an alicyclic ring incorporating a tertiary 15-hydroxy function were prepared as shown in Schemes 21 and 22. [A group from the Ono Laboratories recently has reported an alternative synthesis of the methyl ester of 117 (83).] The actual configurations of the 15,16-trimethylene precursors 121 and 122 have not been unequivocally determined. However, with these two intermediates all four possible 11-deoxy-$PGE_1$ congeners 123 were prepared. Although in one instance we were able to separate the $C_{15}$ epimers by silica-gel chromatography, this was not possible in the other case. We also have prepared one pair of $C_{15}$ epimers in the 11-hydroxy series 124, but were unable to effect a separation of the epimeric racemates (84).

SCHEME 21

PREPARATION OF 15,19-METHANO–20-NOR-$PGE_1$ AND $PGE_2$

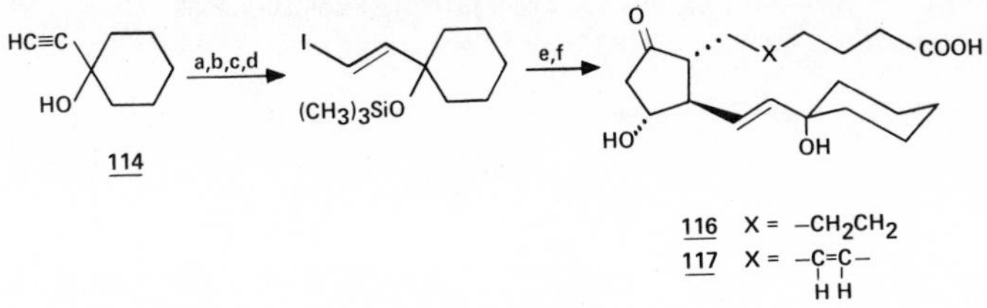

114

116 X = $-CH_2CH_2$

117 X = $-C{=}C-$ (H H)

a. diisoamylborane; b. $(CH_3)_3NO$; c. $I_2$, NaOH; d. $(CH_3)_3SiCl$, imidazole, DMF; e. cuprate addition to cyclopentenone 64 or 69; f. HOAc, THF, $H_2O$.

SCHEME 22

PREPARATION OF 15,16-TRIMETHYLENE – $PGE_1$

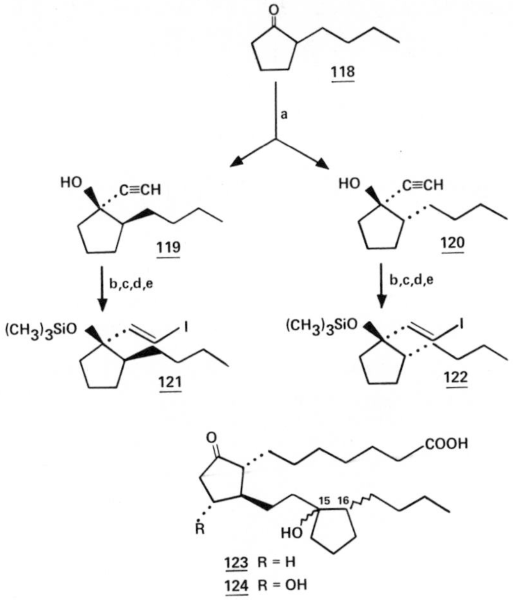

118

119

120

121

122

123 R = H

124 R = OH

a. HC≡CMgBr, $Et_2O$; b. diisoamylborane; c. $(CH_3)_3NO$; d. $I_2$, NaOH; e. $(CH_3)_3SiCl$, imidazole, DMF.

### b. 15-Hydroxy-16-Alkyl Series

The 16-methyl and ethyl β-chain synthons 131 and 132 were prepared in a straightforward manner as illustrated in Scheme 23 (48).

SCHEME 23

PREPARATION OF 16-ALKYL – 15-HYDROXY PRECURSORS

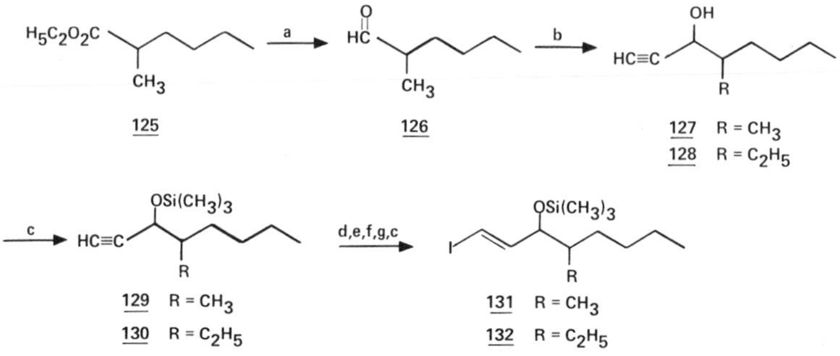

$H_5C_2O_2C$ ... 125 →(a) HC(=O) ... 126 →(b) HC≡C ... OH, R: 127 R = $CH_3$; 128 R = $C_2H_5$ →(c) HC≡C ... $OSi(CH_3)_3$, R: 129 R = $CH_3$; 130 R = $C_2H_5$ →(d,e,f,g,c) I ... $OSi(CH_3)_3$, R: 131 R = $CH_3$; 132 R = $C_2H_5$

a. *i*$Bu_2AlH$; b. LiC≡CH·EDA; c. $(CH_3)_3SiCl$, imidazole, DMF; d. diisoamylborane; e. $(CH_3)_3NO$; f. $I_2$,NaOH; g. HOAc, THF, $H_2O$, chromatography.

### c. 15-Hydroxy-16,16-Dialkyl Series

The synthesis of the vinyl iodide 136 required for the introduction of the 16,16-dimethyl β-chain is shown in Scheme 24 (48). In this and related series, the choice of blocking group is critical, since hindrance by the adjacent *gem*-dimethyl moiety increases the stability of the protecting ether. Thus, conditions necessary for effective hydrolysis of the bulky trityl or *t*-butyldimethylsilyl ethers were too vigorous and resulted in partial disruption of the allylic 15-hydroxy system, and in the 11-hydroxy series, of the β-ketol moiety as well. On the other hand, the usually very labile trimethylsilyl ether was now sufficiently stable to survive the conditions of conjugate addition.

SCHEME 24

PREPARATION OF 16,16-DIMETHYL – 15-HYDROXY PRECURSOR

H(C=O) ... 133 →(a) HC≡C ... OH 134 →(b) HC≡C ... $OSi(CH_3)_3$ 135 →(c,d,e,b) I ... $OSi(CH_3)_3$ 136

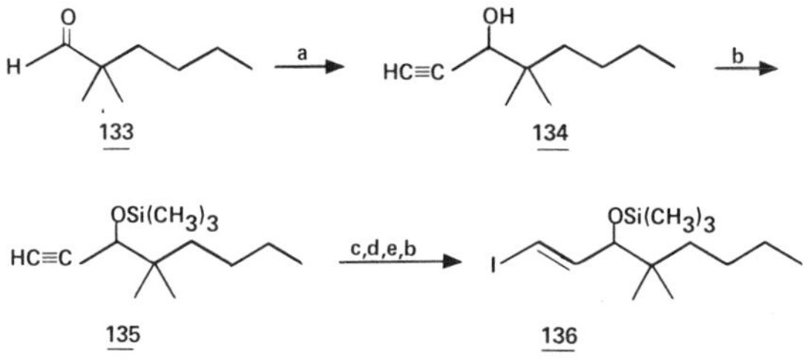

a. HC≡CMgBr; b. $(CH_3)_3SiCl$, imidazole, DMF; c. diisoamylborane; d. $(CH_3)_3NO$; e. $I_2$, NaOH.

Scheme 25 illustrates the synthesis of the 16,16-trimethylene β-chain precursor 143 (46). It is worth noting that attempts to reduce ester 138 directly to aldehyde 140 with 1 equiv. of diisobutylaluminum hydride at -78° gave mainly starting ester and alcohol 139 but no aldehyde. Apparently the bulky trimethylene moiety induces a collapse of the intermediate aluminate reduction product, generating free aldehyde which then undergoes further reduction to alcohol 139. The desired aldehyde 140 was satisfactorily prepared by reduction of ester 138 to alcohol 139 followed by partial oxidation with Collins reagent.

SCHEME 25

PREPARATION OF 15-HYDROXY – 16,16-TRIMETHYLENE PRECURSOR

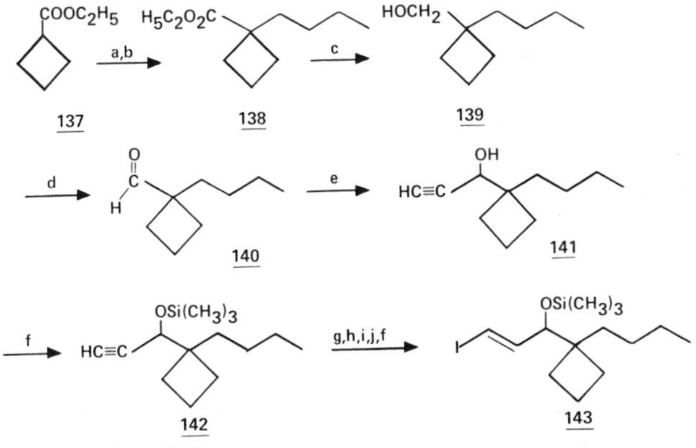

$COOC_2H_5$ 137 —a,b→ $H_5C_2O_2C$ 138 —c→ $HOCH_2$ 139

—d→ 140 —e→ HC≡C, OH 141

—f→ HC≡C, $OSi(CH_3)_3$ 142 —g,h,i,j,f→ I, $OSi(CH_3)_3$ 143

a. $LiNC_6H_{11}(iC_3H_7)$; b. $C_4H_9I$, DMSO; c. $iBu_2AlH$; d. Collins oxidation; e. LiC≡CH·EDA, f. $(CH_3)_3SiCl$, imidazole, DMF; g. diisoamylborane; h. $(CH_3)_3NO$; i. $I_2$, NaOH; j. HOAc, THF, $H_2O$, chromatography.

### d. 15-Hydroxy-17,17-Dialkyl Precursor

The 17,17-dimethyl (48) and 16-cyclopentyl-17,20-tetranor (85) β-chain precursors were prepared without incident as shown in Schemes 26 and 27.

SCHEME 26

PREPARATION OF 17,17-DIMETHYL – 15-HYDROXY PRECURSORS

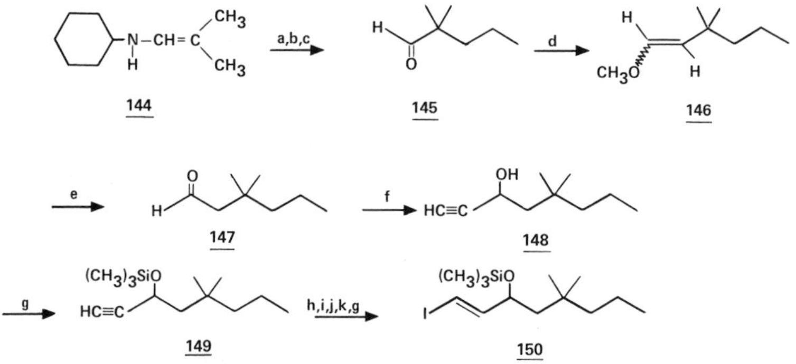

144 →(a,b,c) 145 →(d) 146 →(e) 147 →(f) 148 →(g) 149 →(h,i,j,k,g) 150

a. BuMgCl, b. PrBr; c. HCl; d. BuLi, $CH_3OCH_2PØ_3Cl$; e. $HClO_4$; f. HC≡CMgCl; g. $(CH_3)_3SiCl$, imidazole, DMF; h. diisoamylborane, i. $(CH_3)_3NO$; j. $I_2$, NaOH; k. HOAc, THF, $H_2O$, chromatography.

SCHEME 27

PREPARATION OF 16-CYCLOPENTYL – 15-HYDROXY – 17,20-TETRANOR PRECURSOR

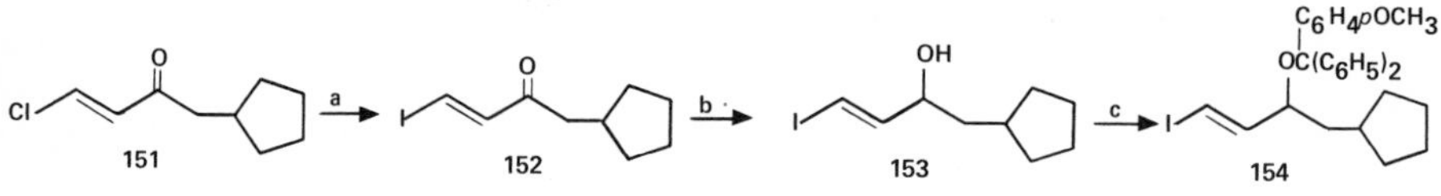

151 →(a) 152 →(b) 153 →(c) 154

a. NaI, acetone; b. $NaBH_4$, EtOH; c. *p*-methoxytrityl chloride, pyridine.

SCHEME 28

PREPARATION OF 15,16-DIHYDROXY PROSTAGLANDINS

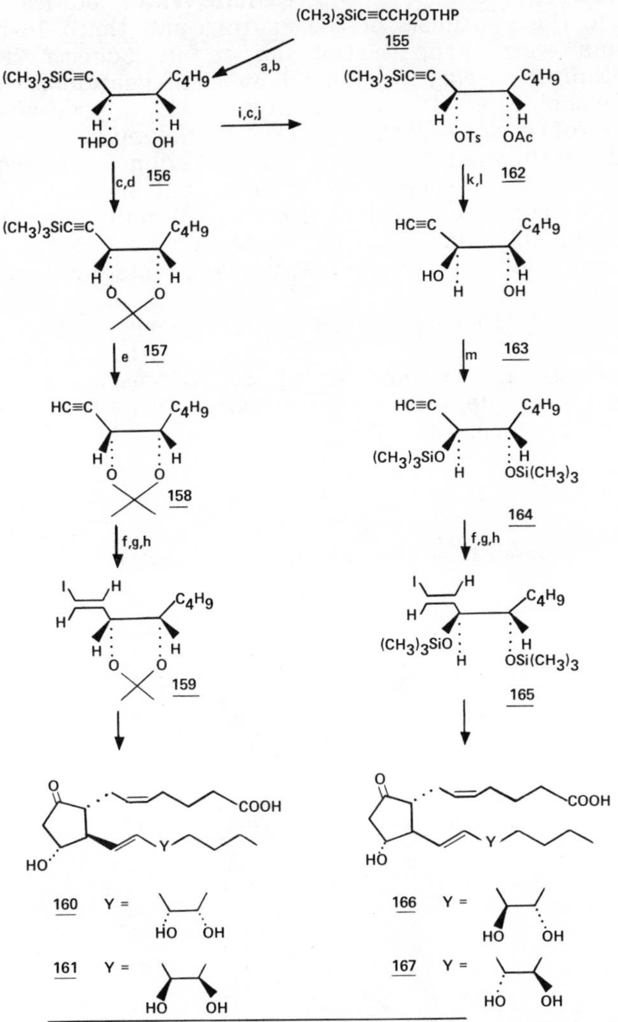


a. BuLi, $ZnI_2$, THF; b. $C_4H_9CHO$; c. EtOH, HOAc, $H_2O$; d. $(CH_3)_2C(OCH_3)_2$, $HClO_4$; e. $K_2CO_3$, MeOH; f. diisoamylborane; g. $(CH_3)_3NO$; h. $I_2$, NaOH; i. $Ac_2O$, pyridine; j. TsCl, pyridine; k. $CaCO_3$, $H_2O$, THF; l. KOH, $H_2O$, MeOH; m. $(CH_3)_3SiCl$, imidazole, DMF.

### e. 15,16-Dihydroxy Series

The outstanding activity observed for the 15-deoxy-16-hydroxy series (see below) prompted the preparation of 15,16-dihydroxy derivatives (72). The intermediate vinyl iodides 159 and 165 leading to the synthesis of the erythro and threo 16-hydroxyprostaglandins were prepared as shown in Scheme 28. The erythro configuration was introduced by condensation of protected propargyl alcohol 155 with valeraldehyde, which proceeds with a high degree of stereoselectivity (86). Solvolysis of erythro tosylate 162 established the threo configuration. The conjugate addition step in both series was carried out by the thiophenol mixed cuprate procedure, which afforded all four possible racemates 160, 161, 166 and 167. [A Syntex group recently reported the preparation of 13-cis-16-hydroxyprostaglandins (44).]

### f. 15-Hydroxy-16-Methoxy Series

Introduction of a methoxy group at $C_{16}$ was accomplished in the erythro series starting with the monotetrahydropyranyl diol 156 as shown in Scheme 29 (43).

SCHEME 29

PREPARATION OF ERYTHRO 15-HYDROXY – 16-METHOXY PRECURSORS

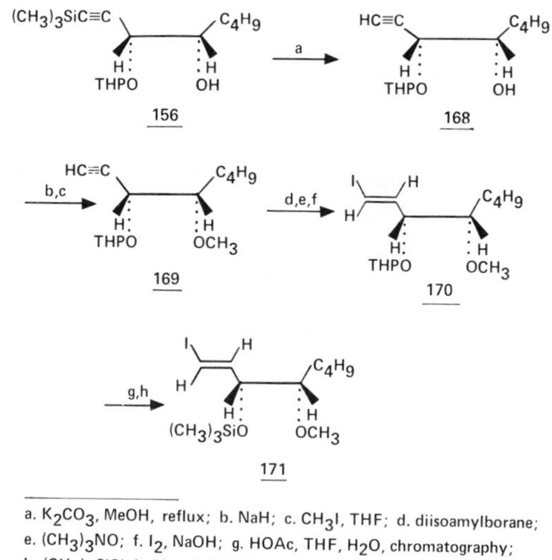

$(CH_3)_3SiC{\equiv}C$ ... $C_4H_9$; H, THPO; H, OH — 156 →(a) HC≡C ... $C_4H_9$; H, THPO; H, OH — 168

→(b,c) HC≡C ... $C_4H_9$; H, THPO; H, $OCH_3$ — 169 →(d,e,f) I, H, H ... $C_4H_9$; H, THPO; H, $OCH_3$ — 170

→(g,h) I, H, H ... $C_4H_9$; H, $(CH_3)_3SiO$; H, $OCH_3$ — 171

a. $K_2CO_3$, MeOH, reflux; b. NaH; c. $CH_3I$, THF; d. diisoamylborane; e. $(CH_3)_3NO$; f. $I_2$, NaOH; g. HOAc, THF, $H_2O$, chromatography; h. $(CH_3)_3SiCl$, imidazole, DMF.

### g. 15-Hydroxy-16-Aryloxy-17,20-Tetranor Series

Considerable interest has developed in the fertility control potential of 16-aryloxy-$PGF_{2}\alpha$ derivatives (87,88). In order to determine the effect of these modifications on bronchodilator activity, we synthesized several 11-deoxy-16-aryloxy analogs via the conjugate addition route (89). The β-chain precursors 172 and 173 were prepared as shown in Scheme 30. Conjugate addition (thiophenol procedure) of the cuprates generated from 172 and 173 to cyclopentenones 11 and 38, respectively, gave the p-fluoro analog 174 and the m-trifluoromethyl analog 175.

SCHEME 30

PREPARATION OF 16-ARYLOXY – 15-HYDROXY – 17,20-TETRANOR PRECURSORS

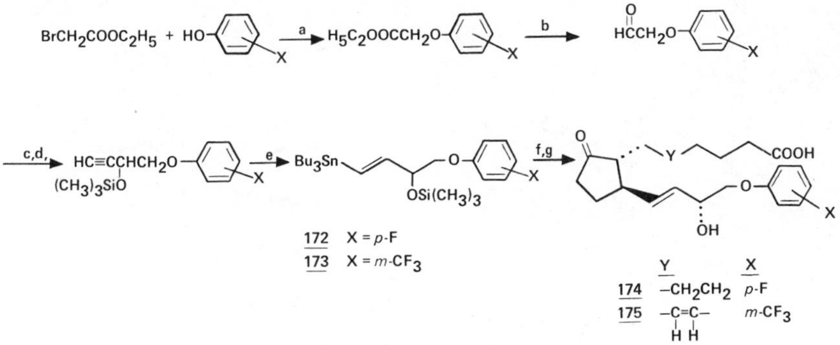

$BrCH_2COOC_2H_5$ + HO–C₆H₄–X →(a) $H_5C_2OOCCH_2O$–C₆H₄–X →(b) $HC(=O)CH_2O$–C₆H₄–X

→(c,d) $HC{\equiv}CCH(OSi(CH_3)_3)CH_2O$–C₆H₄–X →(e) $Bu_3Sn$–CH=CH–CH(OSi(CH_3)_3)–CH_2–O–C₆H₄–X →(f,g) product

172 X = *p*-F
173 X = *m*-CF$_3$

| | Y | X |
|---|---|---|
| 174 | $-CH_2CH_2$ | *p*-F |
| 175 | –C=C– (H H) | *m*-CF$_3$ |

a. $K_2CO_3$, acetone, reflux; b. *i*$Bu_2AlH$, toluene, –75°; c. HC≡CMg Cl, THF; d. $(CH_3)_3SiCl$, imidazole, DMF; e. $Bu_3SnH$, AIBN, 140°; f. conjugate addition *via* thiophenol-cuprate to cyclopentenones 11 and 38; (Table I); g. saponification.

### 5. 15-Deoxy-16-Hydroxy Series

### a. Introduction

As another probe of β-chain SAR, we considered the possibility that certain of the prostaglandin receptor sites are less demanding than others in their binding requirements. If indeed this is the case, it is conceivable that a shift of the 15-hydroxy function to a nearby carbon atom in the flexible β-chain still might allow the molecule to assume a conformation sufficient for a proper fit to one particular organ receptor, but not to others with more stringent requirements, thus leading to increased biological selectivity. To examine this concept we undertook the synthesis of various 15-deoxy congeners having a hydroxy group at $C_{13}$, $C_{16}$, $C_{17}$, or $C_{20}$ or a 15-hydroxymethyl group (33, also see reference 35).

SCHEME 31

PREPARATION OF 15-DEOXY – 16,17, OR 20-HYDROXY AND 15-DEOXY-15-HYDROXYMETHYL PRECURSORS

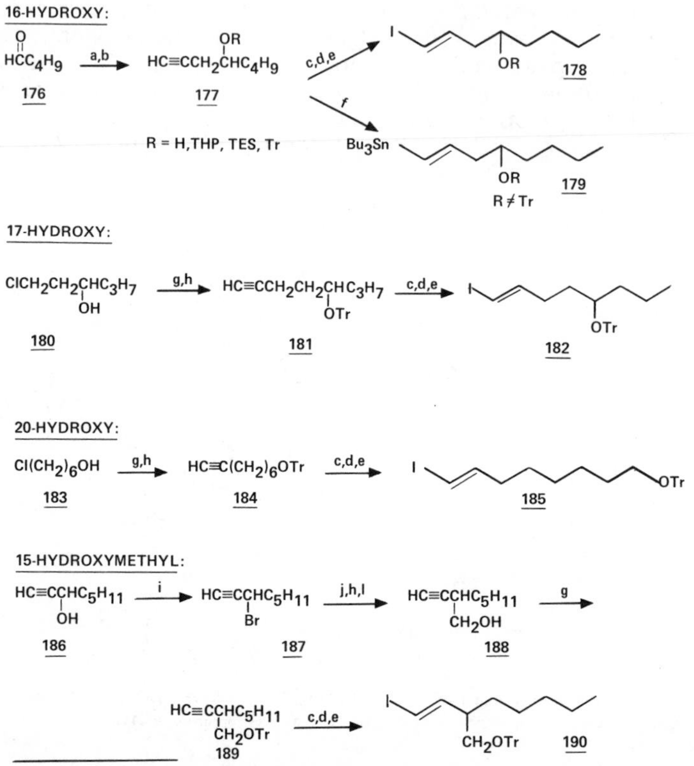


a. HC≡CCH$_2$MgBr; b. dihydropyran, *p*TSA or trityl chloride, pyridine, or $(C_2H_5)_3$ SiCl, imidazole, DMF; c. diisoamylborane; d. $(CH_3)_3$ NO; e. $I_2$, NaOH; f. $Bu_3SnH$, AIBN, 140°; g. TrBr, pyridine; h. LiC≡CH·EDA; i. $(C_6H_5)_3$ P·Br$_2$; j. Mg, Et$_2$O; k. HCHO; l. H$^+$ to hydrolyze methylenedioxy by-product [HC≡CCH $(C_5H_{11})$ CH$_2$O]$_2$CH$_2$.

SCHEME 32

PREPARATION OF 15-DEOXY – 13-HYDROXY – PROSTAGLANDINS

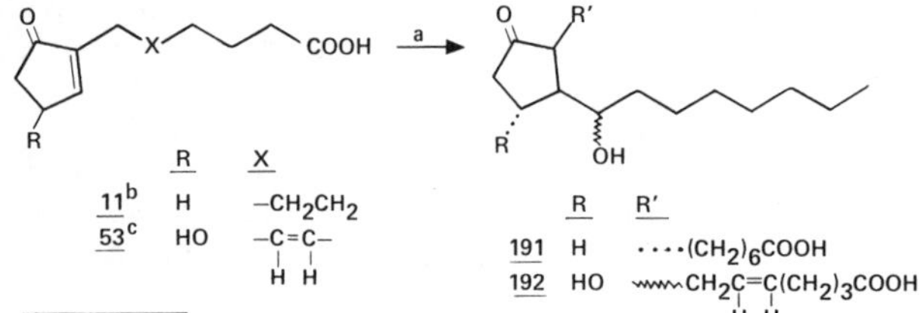


a. octanol, $(C_6H_5)_2CO$, 350 nm.; b. Scheme 2; c. Scheme 11.

Syntheses for the β-chain precursors required for the preparation of the 15-deoxy-16-hydroxy, 17-hydroxy, 20-hydroxy or 15-hydroxymethyl derivatives are shown in Scheme 31 (33). The 15-deoxy-13-hydroxy analogs were obtained by a benzophenone sensitized photo-addition of 1-octanol to the appropriate cyclopentenone as illustrated in Scheme 32 (90).

The 15-deoxy-16-hydroxyprostaglandins proved to be potent bronchodilators, whereas the other derivatives were relatively uninteresting. Therefore, further studies were concentrated in this series and followed three approaches: 1) homologation of the β-chain, 2) introduction of a 16 or 17-methyl group to sterically crowd the 16-hydroxy function, and 3) restoration of allylic character by introducing unsaturation at $C_{17}$-$C_{18}$ (55, see 24,35, 40,42 and 47 for related studies). The requisite β-chain intermediates were prepared in a similar fashion to that of 178 or 179 (Scheme 31) by condensation of propargyl magnesium bromide with the appropriate aldehyde or ketone (55).

### b. 15-Deoxy-16-Hydroxy-16-Substituted Series

Of the various 16-hydroxy analogs clearly the most interesting were the 16-methyl derivatives, and further development of this series was undertaken (55). Among the analogs prepared were compounds featuring a 13-*cis* double bond (Scheme 33), the vinyl iodide for which was obtained *via* diimide reduction (22) of the 1-iodo-1-alkyne 199, a 17-*trans* double bond (203, Scheme 33) which restored allylic character to the molecule, and various alternatives for the 16-methyl group such as ethyl, vinyl, cyclopropyl, 2-propenyl and *trans*-1-propenyl (Scheme 34). The synthesis of the 16-hydroxy-16,20-methano β-chain precursor 206a also is shown in Scheme 34.

It should be noted that the various 15-deoxy-16-hydroxyprostaglandins prepared in the course of our studies consisted of two racemates (~1:1 by $^{13}C$ NMR) epimeric at $C_{16}$, which were not separable by TLC or HPLC. However, introduction of an allylic double bond ($\Delta^{17}$ or 16-vinyl) frequently made separation feasible. A 17-methyl group (4 racemates) also allowed separation into two components. Of necessity, the compounds were tested as the racemic mixture, although it is likely that biological activity largely resides with only one of the four diastereomers (40,56).

### 6. 13-Thia Series

Classical medicinal chemistry has often recognized the isosteric relationship of sulfur and the vinylene group. Accordingly, we have prepared several 13-thia-15-hydroxy analogs, which in isosteric terms also may be considered congeneric to the $\Delta^{13}$-15-deoxy-16-hydroxy series. These 13-thia congeners were

SCHEME 33

PREPARATION OF 15-DEOXY – 16-HYDROXY – 16-METHYL PRECURSORS

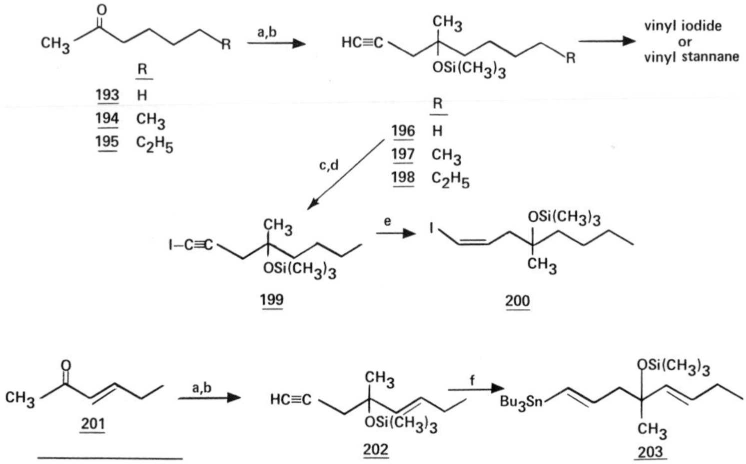

vinyl iodide or vinyl stannane

| | R |
|---|---|
| 193 | H |
| 194 | $CH_3$ |
| 195 | $C_2H_5$ |

| | R |
|---|---|
| 196 | H |
| 197 | $CH_3$ |
| 198 | $C_2H_5$ |

199 200

201 202 203

a. $HC{\equiv}CCH_2MgBr$, $Et_2O$; b. $(CH_3)_3SiCl$, imidazole, DMF; c. BuLi; d. $I_2$; e. diimide; f. $Bu_3SnH$, AIBN, 140°.

SCHEME 34

PREPARATION OF 15-DEOXY – 16-HYDROXY – 16-SUBSTITUTED PRECURSORS

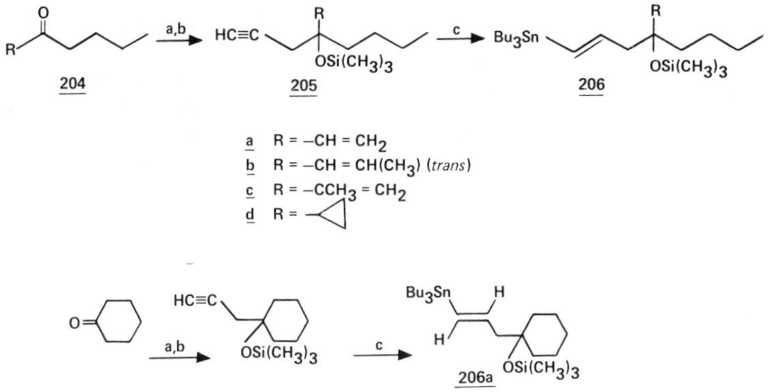

204 205 206

a R = $-CH=CH_2$
b R = $-CH=CH(CH_3)$ (*trans*)
c R = $-CCH_3=CH_2$
d R = cyclopropyl

206a

a. $HC{\equiv}CCH_2MgBr$; $Et_2O$; b. $(CH_3)_3SiCl$, imidazole, DMF; c. $Bu_3SnH$, AIBN, 130°.

prepared as shown in Scheme 35 by the Michael addition of 1-mercapto-2-heptanol (208) to the appropriate cyclopentenone providing 11-deoxy-13-thia-$PGE_1$ (209) and 13-thia-$PGE_2$ (210) (91).

Although the stereochemistry of these analogs is not unequivocally established, model experiments involving the addition of simple mercaptans to cyclopentenone 11 (no 4-hydroxy group) indicate that a 4:1 trans-cis (8-iso) ratio of 11-deoxy products (209) is obtained. The isomeric situation for the 11-hydroxy analog 210 is more complicated. Treatment of the $E_2$ analog 210 with dilute HCl in tetrahydrofuran gave 13-thia-$PGA_2$ (211) and the cyclic ether 212 as the result of an acid-catalyzed intramolecular addition of the 15-hydroxy group to the enone double bond. The stereochemistry shown for 211 and 212 can be assigned with confidence since the acid conditions used to dehydrate 210 are sufficient to epimerize an 8-iso-PG to the 8-normal configuration (74).

SCHEME 35

PREPARATION OF 13-THIA–PROSTAGLANDINS

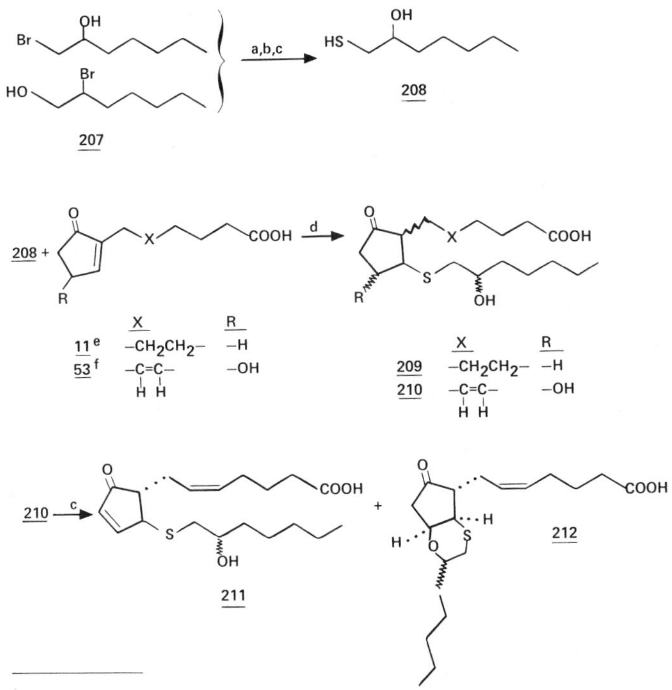

207 → (a,b,c) → 208

208 + cyclopentenone → (d) → 209, 210

| | X | R |
|---|---|---|
| 11[e] | $-CH_2CH_2-$ | –H |
| 53[f] | –C(H)=C(H)– | –OH |

| | X | R |
|---|---|---|
| 209 | $-CH_2CH_2-$ | –H |
| 210 | –C(H)=C(H)– | –OH |

210 → (c) → 211 + 212

a. $NH_2CSNH_2$; b. NaOH; c. $H_3O^+$; d. $Et_3N$; e. Scheme 2; f. Scheme 11.

## III. Modifications at $C_1$, $C_9$ and $C_{11}$

We also have investigated the effect on biological activity which results from the alteration or replacement of the PG functional groups at $C_1$, $C_9$, or $C_{11}$. In general, our synthetic starting point for these studies was l-$PGA_2$ (213), its esters 214 and 215 (92), and the corresponding 15-epimers (93). These substances are particularly attractive for analog synthesis since they are readily available from the relatively abundant and accessible Carribean Sea coral Plexaura homomalla (esper). (For other congener syntheses based upon transformations with l-$PGA_2$ and its esters see references 94-97.)

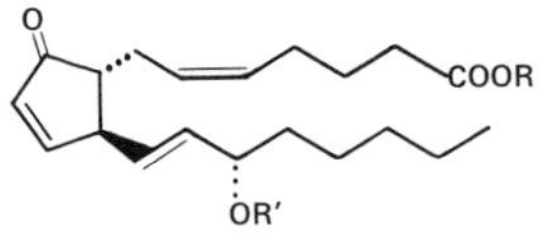

| | R' | R |
|---|---|---|
| 213 | H | H |
| 214 | H | $CH_3$ |
| 215 | $\overset{O}{\overset{\Vert}{C}}CH_3$ | $CH_3$ |

### A. 11-Deoxy-11-Substituted Analogs

Introduction of a large variety of groups to the 11-position was accomplished readily by appropriately catalyzed Michael additions to l-$PGA_2$ or its esters (98). By this approach, we introduced alkyl, vinyl, phenyl, acylthio, alkylthio, cyano (convertable to carboxamido and carboxyl), nitromethyl, and malonyl groups. These products, with the exception of the alkyl, vinyl and phenyl derivatives for which only the 11α-epimer was observed, were 11α/β epimeric mixtures, with the less hindered α-epimer usually predominating. In some instances these mixtures could be separated, but if not they were submitted for assay as such.

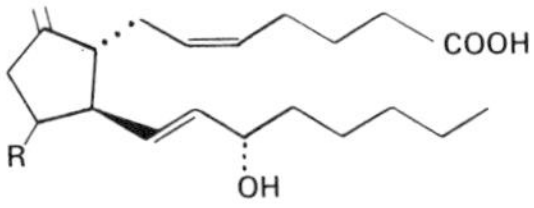

| | R | | R | | R |
|---|---|---|---|---|---|
| 216 | ···H | 221 | ···$C_6H_5$ | 226a | ····CN |
| 217 | ···$CH_3$ | 222 | ···$SCH_3$ | 226b | ◀ CN |
| 218 | ···$C_2H_5$ | 223 | ∿∿ $SCOCH_3$ | 227 | ∿∿ $CONH_2$ |
| 219 | ···$CH(CH_3)_2$ | 224 | ∿∿ $CH(COOC_2H_5)_2$ (diester) | 228 | ∿∿ COOH |
| 220 | ···$CH{=}CH_2$ | 225 | ∿∿ $CH_2NO_2$ | | |

l-11-Deoxy-$PGE_2$ (99), a compound of some interest as a base for structure-activity correlations, was obtained by conjugate reduction of diester 215 with sodium cyanoborohydride (100), and subsequent Jones oxidation and saponification.

The 11α-hydroxymethyl congener was of especial interest, particularly in view of our success with the transposition of hydroxy from $C_{15}$ to $C_{16}$. The introduction of this group was accomplished conveniently by the benzophenone-photosensitized addition (101) of methanol to l-$PGA_2$ diester 215 (102). [Other reports (103,104) of this reaction, and of an alternate synthesis (105,106) have appeared.] Irradiation of $PGA_2$ diester 215 in methanol, followed by chromatography gave both the 11α- and 11β- hydroxymethyl congeners 229 and 231, respectively, which were saponified to the corresponding acids 230 and 232. Isopropanol also added readily to $PGA_2$ diester by this procedure, however only a single product, the 11α-isomer 233, was isolated; saponification afforded the acid 234.

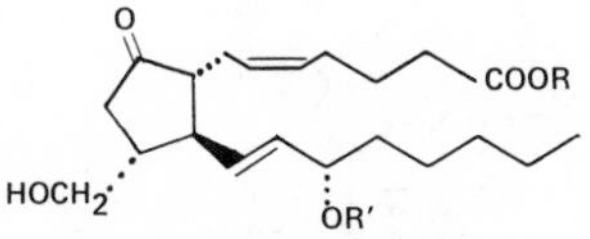

| | R | R' |
|---|---|---|
| 229 | $CH_3$ | $COCH_3$ |
| 230 | H | H |

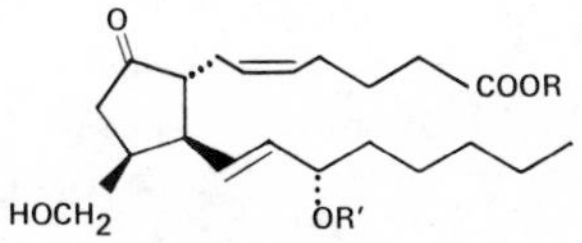

| | R | R' |
|---|---|---|
| 231 | $CH_3$ | $COCH_3$ |
| 232 | H | H |

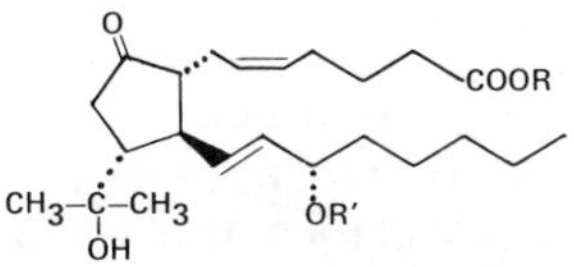

| | R | R' |
|---|---|---|
| 233 | $CH_3$ | $COCH_3$ |
| 234 | H | H |

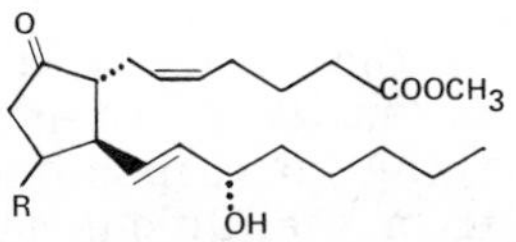

| | R |
|---|---|
| 235 | ····$SCH_2CH_2OH$ |
| 236 | ◀$SCH_2CH_2OH$ |

None of the above noted 11-substituted analogs was more than minimally effective in our bronchodilator assays. However, 11α-(2-hydroxyethylthio)$PGE_2$ methyl ester (235) did prove to be a potent bronchodilator of sufficient interest to warrant clinical investigation (see Section VB). This compound was prepared as a separable mixture with its 11β-epimer 236 by the addition of 2-mercaptoethanol to l-$PGA_2$ methyl ester (214) (69,107).

### B. $C_9$ Derivatives: Hydrazones and Ketals of 11-Deoxy-13,14-dihydro-$PGE_1$

These studies were carried out with 11-deoxy-13,14-dihydro-$PGE_1$ (237), since this compound was of high potency in our bronchodilator assays, and was readily available from l-$PGA_2$ diester (215) by catalytic hydrogenation and saponification. Treatment with the requisite reagent under standard conditions afforded the 9-carbonyl derivatives 238-243 shown in Table III (108).

TABLE III

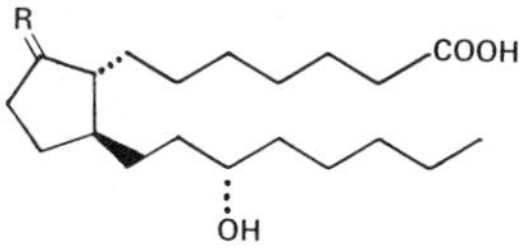

237 R = O

238 R = NOH

239 R = $NOCH_3$

240 R = $NNHCONH_2$

241 R = NNH–$C_6H_4$–COOH

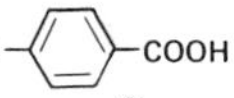

242 R = NNH–$C_6H_3Cl_2$

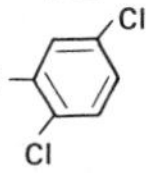

243 R = $NNHCSNHCH_2CH{=}CH_2$

A variety of 9-ketals were prepared from either methyl ester 245 (obtained from l-$PGA_2$ diester 215 by hydrogenation followed by selective hydrolysis) or acid 246, by the usual ketalization techniques involving treatment of the ketone with an excess of the requisite diol, dithiol or hydroxythiol in the presence of an acid catalyst (109). Saponification of the ester afforded the corresponding acids listed in Table IV. [A recent report from the Upjohn laboratories describes the facile preparation of the ethylene ketal of $PGE_2$ (110).]

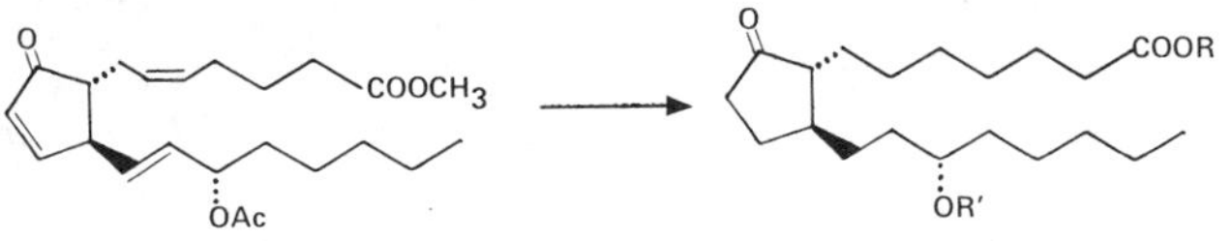

215

| | R | R′ |
|---|---|---|
| 244 | $CH_3$ | $COCH_3$ |
| 245 | $CH_3$ | H |
| 246 | H | H |

TABLE IV

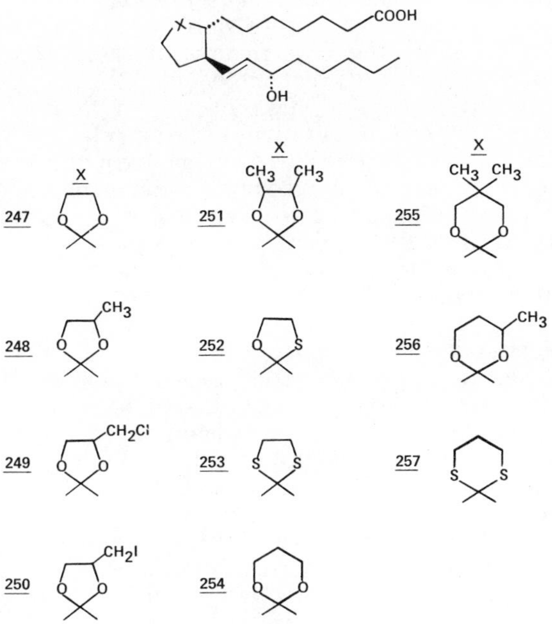

| | X | | X | | X |
|---|---|---|---|---|---|
| 247 | | 251 | | 255 | |
| 248 | | 252 | | 256 | |
| 249 | | 253 | | 257 | |
| 250 | | 254 | | | |

## C. $C_1$-Derivatives: Amides and Esters

Several carboxylic acid derivatives of 11-deoxy-13,14-dihydro-$PGE_1$ (237) were prepared via the acid chloride 258 and are listed in Table V. In addition the decyl ester 264 and the dimethylaminoethyl ester 265 of 15-deoxy-16-hydroxy-$PGE_2$ were obtained by the mixed anhydride method (111,112).

TABLE V

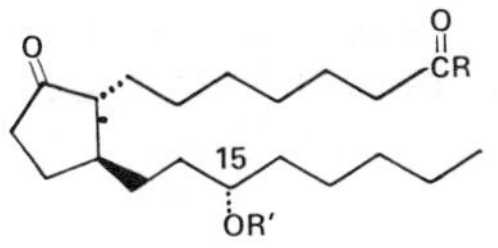

| | R′ | R |
|---|---|---|
| 258 | $COCH_3$ | Cl |
| 259 | H | $NH(CH_2)_3N(CH_3)_2$ |
| 260 | H | $OC_{10}H_{21}$ |
| 261 | H | NHOH |
| 262 | H | $NH_2$ |
| 263 | H | $NHC_6H_5$ |

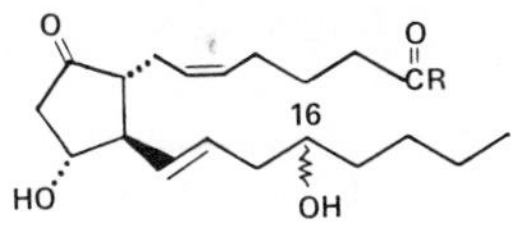

| | R |
|---|---|
| 264 | $OC_{10}H_{21}$ |
| 265 | $OCH_2CH_2N(CH_3)_2$ |

## IV. Bronchodilator Assays

Although the prostaglandin molecule has been subjected to one of the more intensive structure-activity studies in the history of medicinal chemistry, the significance of many of the structure variations has not been fully reported, and the effect on bronchodilator activity often remains unknown. In this review we will attempt to identify those structure-activity relationships that are apparent from our own studies as well as from those described in the literature. Recent discussions published concerning the effect of prostaglandins on the bronchial tree include those by Rosenthale (113) and by Karim and Adaikan (114). In addition, Schaaf has reviewed structure-activity relations in other areas of prostaglandin interest (115).

Our compound evaluation procedure was carried out at the UCB laboratories in Brussels. It is based upon an initial screening in four to six guinea pigs by the Konzett-Rossler method, wherein the ability of an I.V. administered prostaglandin to reverse a bronchoconstriction induced by 5-hydroxytryptamine or histamine is measured and an $ED_{50}$ is determined (46,116). This is a standard assay which in one or another modification is used by most of the other laboratories active in this field, although in several instances aerosol administration is favored. The capacity of a compound to induce a prolonged relaxation was evaluated by the effect (and $ED_{50}$) of the initial dose against a second and third spasmogenic challenge, administered at five minute intervals. Only positive responses to this aspect of the assay are viewed as signigicant since salbutamol does not produce a prolonged effect. The activities reported for our analogs in the tables that follow are derived from this Konzett-Rossler assay and are based on a comparison of $ED_{50}$ data.

For further evaluation, selected compounds are submitted to a dog assay (117,118) in which the prostaglandin is administered by aerosol to an anesthetized pilocarpine bronchoconstricted dog (n=3 to 6) and the decrease in airway resistance is recorded; at the same time effects on the cardiovascular system (femoral pressure, pulmonary pressure, heart rate) are noted. This experiment is allowed to proceed for one hour, which also permits an assessment of the compound's ability to produce a prolonged bronchodilation. In this assay salbutamol maintains its effect for the entire hour, whereas isoproterenol and l-$PGE_1$ lose theirs within the first twenty minutes. At the conclusion of the study a standard dose of isoproterenol is administered to determine the animal's maximum capacity to respond.

A major problem has been the lack of a reliable assay capable of detecting the irritant and cough-inducing properties associated with the natural prostaglandins. Inasmuch as a prostaglandin bronchodilator would have to be free of this liability in order to receive serious consideration as a therapeutic agent, the absence of an appropriate assay represents a critical weakness in our compound evaluation procedure.

Several attempts to resolve this problem have been described. An assay utilizing young beagle dogs preselected for their consistent susceptibility to $PGE_2$-induced coughing (on average only four of 25 animals respond) has been reported by a May and Baker group (119). However, at least one compound (20-ethyl-11-deoxy-$PGE_2$, M&B 26,693) selected by this procedure nevertheless proved to be a bronchial irritant (120). Recently a cat assay also has been claimed to be useful in this respect (121). As yet there has been no reported confirmation from other laboratories; in our own laboratory we have been unable to duplicate the reported results. Finally, an assay involving a spasmogen-induced bronchoconstriction in the monkey has been noted by Weissberg (122). This procedure also is claimed to be useful in determining potential irritant liability. Again, there have been no reports from other laboratories concerning this procedure.

## V. Significance of the Prostaglandin Functional Groups

The initial thrust of our investigation was to determine which of the prostaglandin functional groups and structural features were critical for bronchodilator activity. Toward this end, we have prepared in the $E_1$ and/or $E_2$ series, the 11,15-bisdeoxy, 11-deoxy, and 15-deoxy analogs, derivatives of the 9-carbonyl and carboxylic acid functions, as well as congeners representing modifications of the $\Delta^{13}$ *trans* double bond or the replacement of the cyclopentane ring with a cyclohexane ring. [To the extent studied, racemic prostaglandins are half as active as the natural enantiomers (47,123).]

### A. 11-And 15-Hydroxy Groups

The significance of the 11- and/or 15-hydroxy functions for bronchodilator activity is demonstrated in Table VI. Substantial activity clearly obtains in the 11-deoxy series, but the 15α-hydroxy group apparently is an essential feature, although this requirement can be satisfied by a hydroxy group at $C_{16}$; see section VIII F. Nevertheless it is noteworthy, that in the Konzett as well as other assays, even a primitive prostaglandin such as 11,15-bisdeoxy-$PGE_1$ produces a real PG-like effect, albeit with much diminished potency.

Generally, inversion of the 15-hydroxy group to the 15-*epi* configuration results in an essential loss of activity (113), as does oxidation of this group to a ketone which is the major product of metabolic inactivation.

TABLE VI

RELATIVE IMPORTANCE OF 11- AND 15-HYDROXY GROUPS

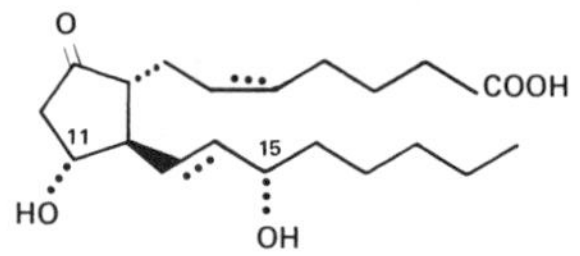

| | RELATIVE POTENCY | |
|---|---|---|
| | SEROTONIN | HISTAMINE |
| 1. *l*-$PGE_1$ | 100 (STD) | 100 (STD) |
| 2. *l*-11-DEOXY-$PGE_0$[a] | 15 | 135 |
| 3. *dl*-11-DEOXY-$PGE_1$ | 44 | 13 |
| 4. *l*-11-DEOXY-$PGE_2$ | 6.5 | 8.4 |
| 5. *dl*-15-DEOXY-$PGE_1$ | 0.1 | 0.2 |
| 6. *dl*-15-*epi*-$PGE_1$ | 0.2 | 0.2 |
| 7. *dl*-11,15-BISDEOXY-$PGE_2$ | 0.02 | 0.35 |
| 8. *dl*-11-DEOXY-15-DEHYDRO-$PGE_0$[b] | $<$0.01 | 0.65 |

a. NO UNSATURATION; b. 15-KETO.

Both 11-deoxy-$PGE_1$ and 11-deoxy-$PGE_2$ showed good activity in our Konzett assay (Table VI). Rosenthale and co-workers (113) found 11-deoxy-$PGE_1$ to be equipotent with l-$PGE_1$ against acetylcholine-induced bronchoconstriction in the guinea pig on aerosol administration. In their hands, 11-deoxy-$PGE_2$ was considerably less effective, and 11-deoxy-$PGF_{2}\beta$ had 10% the potency of l-$PGF_{2}\beta$ (see C). In addition, as will be apparent from the discussion which follows, we and others have found many 11-deoxy derivatives to possess substantial and even outstanding activity in the Konzett assay. Although most examples of this series which were submitted to the pilocarpine dog assay produced significant bronchodilation, we have been unable to find even one 11-deoxy-$\Delta^{13}$-trans prostaglandin capable of inducing the maximum bronchodilatory effect observed with l-$PGE_1$ or isoproterenol, even in some instances at several times the apparent maximum effective dose (Fig. 1). Several 11-deoxy derivatives are believed to have undergone clinical trial, but to our knowledge they have all failed.

## B. $C_{11}$-Substitution

The effect produced by replacing the 11α-hydroxy function with other groups also was investigated. $C_{11}$ congeners in many instances are readily accessible (section III A), and a relatively large number were prepared (Table VII). Only two groups were consistent with substantial activity, the small cyano group (entry 1) and the 2-hydroxyethylthio group (entry 12). It is interesting that hydroxymethyl, acetylthio, methyl and vinyl, as well as methoxy and ethoxy in the 16,16-dimethyl series all failed to give compounds of interest. Other $C_{11}$ substituents exhibiting

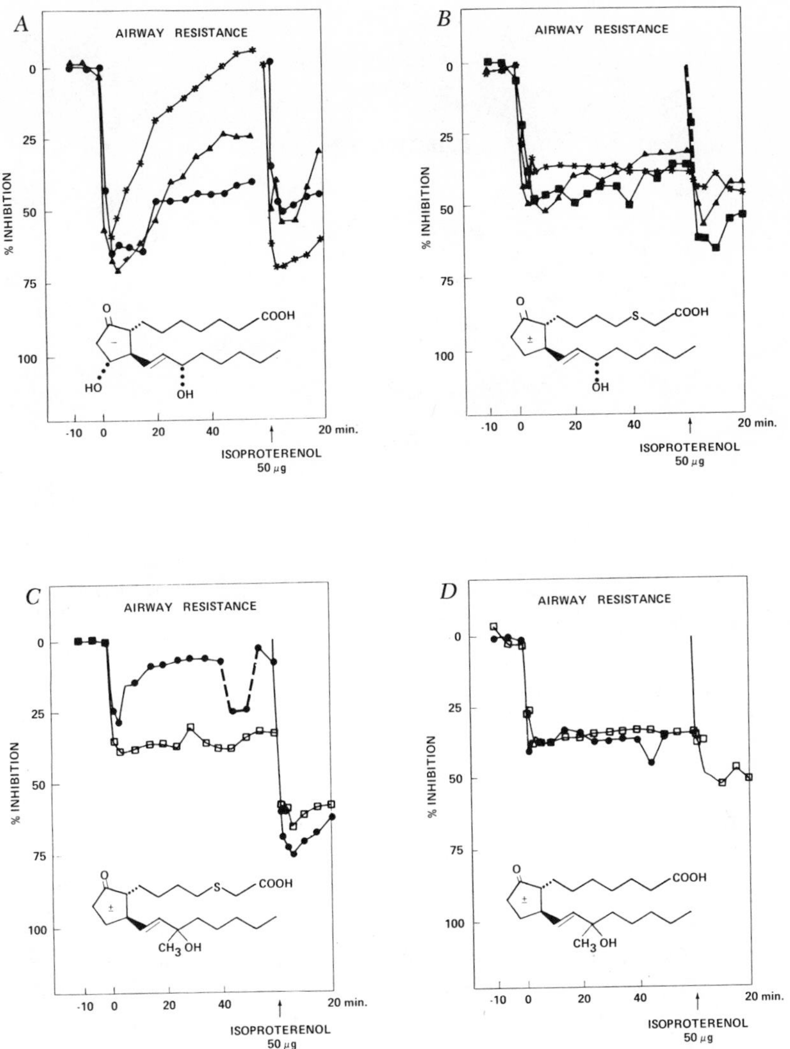


*Figure 1. Bronchodilator activity of (A)* l-*$PGE_1$; (B)* dl-*3-thia-11-deoxy-$PGE_1$; (C)* dl-*15-methyl-11-deoxy-3-thia-$PGE_1$; and (D)* dl-*15-methyl-11-deoxy-$PGE_1$ in pilocarpine-bronchoconstricted dogs (aerosol) (▲) 16 μg (n = 3); (●) 1.6 μg (n = 3); (✱) 0.16 μg (n = 3); (■) 900 μg (n = 4); (□) 160 μg (n = 3)*

## TABLE VII

### $C_{11}$-SUBSTITUTION

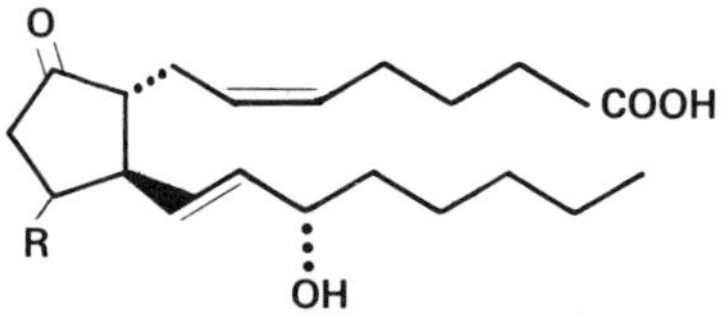

| R | RELATIVE POTENCY SEROTONIN | RELATIVE POTENCY HISTAMINE |
|---|---|---|
| 1. α-OH (*l*-$PGE_2$) | 100 (STD) | 100 (STD) |
| 2. $\Delta^{10}$ (*l*-$PGA_2$) | 0.2 | 11 |
| 3. α-H (*l*-11-DEOXY-$PGE_2$) | 19 | 16 |
| 4. α-$CH_3$ | 0.4 | 1.7 |
| 5. α-$CH{=}CH_2$ | 0.08 | 0.07 |
| 6. α-$SCOCH_3$ | 0.2 | 2.2 |
| 7. α/β-CN | 27 | 16 |
| 8. α-$CH_2OH$ | 0.3 | 1.3 |
| 9. β-$CH_2OH$ | <0.03 | 0.6 |
| 10. α-$OCH_2CH_2OH$ (*dl*-$E_1$)[a] | 2.7 | 2.4 |
| 11. α-$OCH_2CH_2OH$ (*dl*-$E_2$)[a] (METHYL ESTER) | 0.8 | 0.6 |
| 12. α-$SCH_2CH_2OH$ (METHYL ESTER) | 16 | 18 |
| 13. α/β-$SCH_2CH_2OH$ (*l*-$E_1$) | 18 | 18 |
| 14. α/β-$SCH_2CH_2CH_2OH$ (METHYL ESTER) | 0.5 | 0.7 |
| 15. α/β-$SCH_2CH_2SH$ (METHYL ESTER) | <0.03 | 0.08 |

a. PREPARED BY TOTAL SYNTHESIS USING CYCLOPENTENONE 67 OR 71.

reduced activity include $-C_2H_5$, $-C_6H_5$, $-SCH_3$, $-SC_2H_5$, -COOH, $-CONH_2$, $-CH_2NO_2$, $-CH(COOC_2H_5)_2$, $-C(CH_3)_2OH$, piperidino, pyrolidino and cyclohexyl (98,113,124,125).

The 2-hydroxyethylthio observation was pursued with the synthesis of many related compounds, a few of which are included in Table VII (69). However, the effect of this substituent proved to be quite structure specific. Thus, homologation of the chain (see entry 14), replacement of sulfur with oxygen (11), and replacement of hydroxy with sulfhydryl (15) or with methyl were ineffective. On clinical investigation, l-11-deoxy-11α-(2-hydroxyethylthio)-$PGE_2$ methyl ester (I) at aerosol doses as high as 800 μg in asthmatic patients failed to produce a consistent bronchodilation (69).

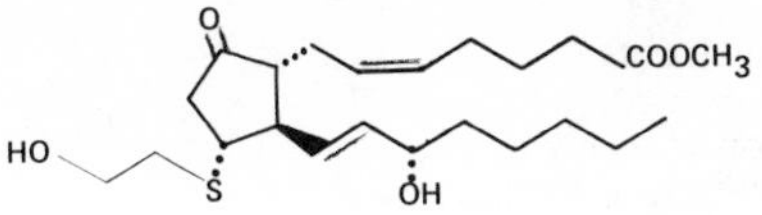

I

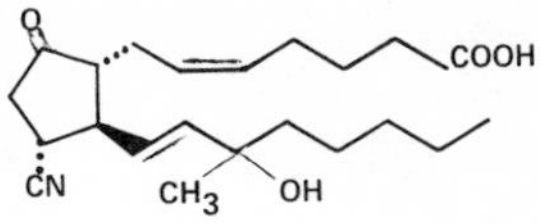

II

A similar study of $C_{11}$ substitution was carried out by a Wyeth team (113,124,125) who found cyano to be the only group of interest. In their assay (Konzett, histamine agonist, aerosol administration), 11α-cyano-11-deoxy-$PGE_2$ had 1% and the 15(R/S)-methyl derivative (II) 10% the activity of l-$PGE_2$. The cyano group, as well as the methyl group, also were effective 11α-substituents in the $PGF_2β$ series (see section C).

Muchowski recently reported dl-11-deoxy-11α,12α-difuoromethylene-$PGE_2$ (III) to have 5x the potency of l-$PGE_2$ in a guinea pig assay (histamine agonist) when administered by aerosol, and to be equipotent when administered by the intravenous route (126,127). The 13,14-dihydro derivative IV was similarly active, as were the $E_1$ and $E_0$ counterparts. Interestingly, the 11α,12α-methylene analogs were essentially inactive. In a clinical trial with mildly asthmatic patients neither III or IV were sufficiently effective to be of interest (126).

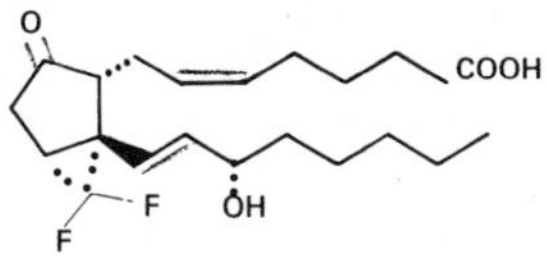

III

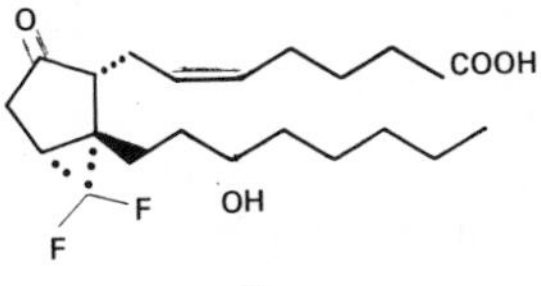

IV

## C. $C_9$ Modifications

### 1. $PGF_{2}\beta$

The relative potencies of several of the standard prostaglandins are shown in Table VIII. In addition to the E series prostaglandins, l-$PGA_2$ and l-$PGF_{2}\beta$ exhibit significant, albeit weaker, bronchodilator activity. The latter compound (WY-15019) was evaluated in asthmatic subjects and found to be ineffective at the dose (200 μg) studied. In fact, an immediate mild bronchoconstriction was noted after inhalation by asthmatic subjects (128). The epimeric $PGF_{2}\alpha$ is a potent bronchoconstrictor in animal models and in man, and asthmatic subjects are markedly hyperreactive to it. Indeed it has been suggested that at least for a significant portion of the asthmatic population it may be an important natural factor in the development of the disease (7,12, 129).

TABLE VIII

BROCHODILATOR ACTIVITY OF THE STANDARD PROSTAGLANDINS



| | RELATIVE POTENCY | |
|---|---|---|
| | SEROTONIN | HISTAMINE |
| 1. *l*-$PGE_1$ | 100 (STD) | 100 (STD) |
| 2. *l*-$PGE_2$ | 18 | 52 |
| 3. *l*-$PGA_2$ | 1 | 3 |
| 4. *l*-$PGF_{2\beta}$ (WY-15109) | 1 | 5 |

### 2. Carbonyl Derivatives

It is apparent that structural changes at $C_9$ markedly effect activity and consequently we have prepared a variety of $C_9$ carbonyl derivatives, mainly hydrazones and ketals, of l-11-deoxy-13,14-dihydro-$PGE_1$, itself a highly potent compound in our assays (Table VI, entry 2). Several of these modifications, particularly ethylene ketalization, are consistent with bronchodilator activity (Table IX). It is unlikely that these derivatives are acting as prodrugs since the onset of action is so immediate and regeneration of the 9-keto function would not be expected at the physiological pH of the lung.

### 3. 9-Deoxy Derivatives

This series was investigated by the Wyeth group (113).

TABLE IX

BRONCHODILATOR ACTIVITY OF HYDRAZONES AND KETALS OF 11-DEOXY-13,14-DIHYDRO-$PGE_0$

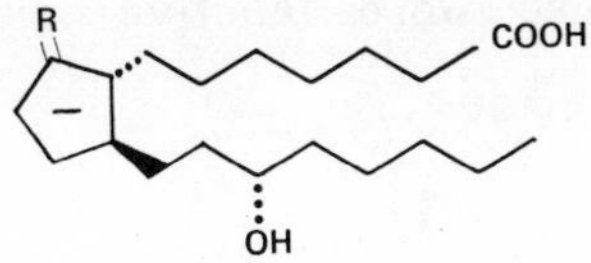

| R | Relative Potency: Serotonin | Relative Potency: Histamine |
|---|---|---|
| 1. = O | 100 (STD) | 100 (STD) |
| 2. = NOH | 10 | 3 |
| 3. = $NOCH_3$ | 6 | 20 |
| 4. = NNH–$C_6H_4$–COOH  | 80 | 48 |
| 5. = $NNHCSNH_2$ | 18 | 0.5 |
| 6. = $NNHCONHCH_2CH = CH_2$ | 31 | 0.8 |
| 7. 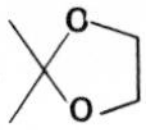 | 36 | 80 |
| 8. 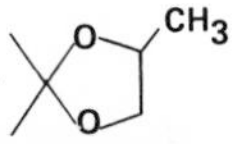 | 900 | 60 |
| 9. 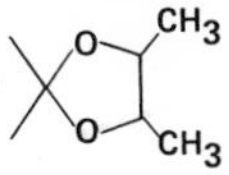 | 9.5 | 1.1 |
| 10. 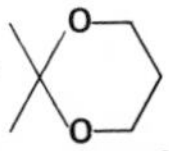 | – | 3 |
| 11. 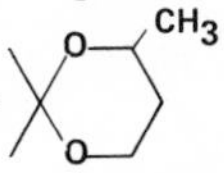 | 5 | 7 |
| 12. 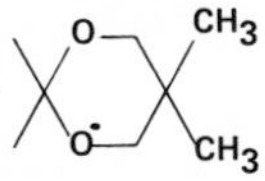 | 10 | 12 |

The following groups were weakly active or inactive:

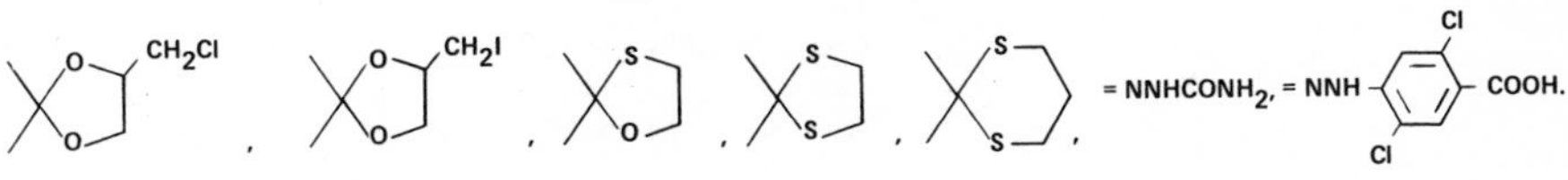

$CH_2Cl$, $CH_2I$, , , , = $NNHCONH_2$, = NNH–(Cl, Cl)–COOH.

The 9-methylene derivative V of 9,11-bisdeoxy-$PGE_2$, which represents an analog wherein the $sp^2$ character of the 9-carbonyl group is retained, was essentially inactive (<0.001 x $PGE_2$). The 9β-hydroxymethyl and 9β-formyl derivatives VI and VII, which can be seen as homologs of 11-deoxy-$PGF_{2}$β and 11-deoxy-$PGE_2$, respectively, also were inactive, as was the 9-dehydro derivative VIII.

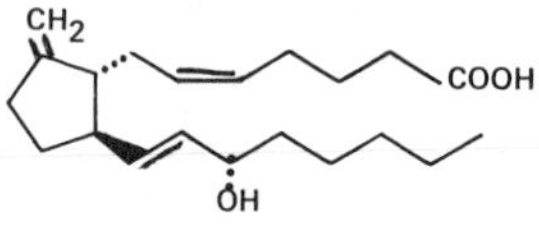

V 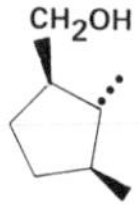 VI  VII 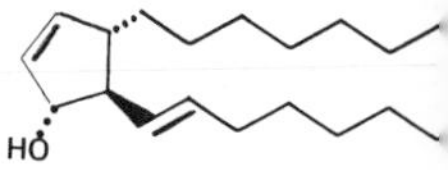 VIII

Muchowski and co-workers have described the synthesis and bronchodilator activity of a series of ring halogenated prostaglandins. Several of these compounds showed excellent activity in the Konzett assay (vs. histamine) on intravenous or aerosol administration (Table X). Phase I evaluation of the most potent member of the series, 9-deoxy-9β-fluoro-$PGE_2$ (IX), however, revealed a cough liability which precluded further clinical investigation (126,130).

TABLE X

9- AND 11- HALO PROSTAGLANDINS

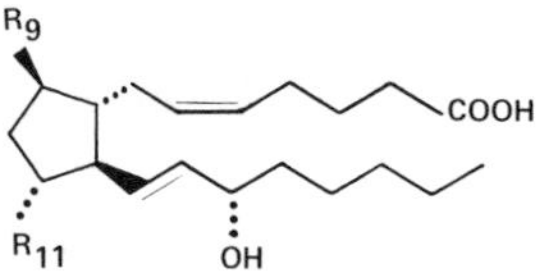

| | $R_9$ | $R_{11}$ | | KONZETT I.V. | KONZETT AEROSOL |
|---|---|---|---|---|---|
| IX | F | OH | | 4X $PGE_2$ | 2.5X $PGE_2$ |
| X | OH | F | | 0.4X $PGE_2$ | – |
| XI | OH | Cl | | 0.5X $PGE_2$ | – |
| XII | OH | OH | ($PGF_{2\beta}$) | | |

## D. 10a-Homo Series

Expansion of the cyclopentanone ring to a cyclohexane ring proved disappointing, providing compounds with only marginal activity (XIII:<0.001 x l-$PGE_2$) (61).

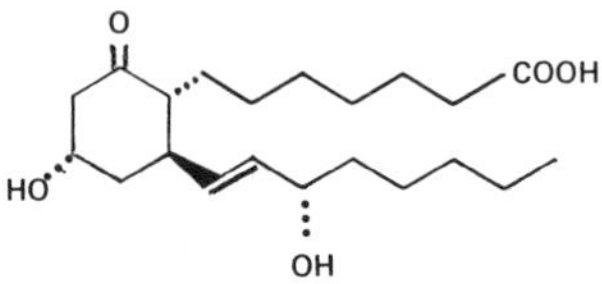

XIII

## E. $C_1$ Modifications

A large number of prostaglandin esters and amides have been reported in the patent literature. Although little is known concerning the biology of these derivatives, it generally is accepted that at least the simple methyl ester usually produces effects equivalent to that of the parent acid. From our own experience we are able to confirm this view as it applies to our bronchodilator assays. In a limited study we have found that a decyl ester and certain amides retain activity, but of considerably diminished potency.

An effort involving several laboratories also has been made along classical medicinal chemistry lines to identify biologically acceptable functional or pro-drug equivalents of the carboxylic acid group. Thus far the following groups have been reported.

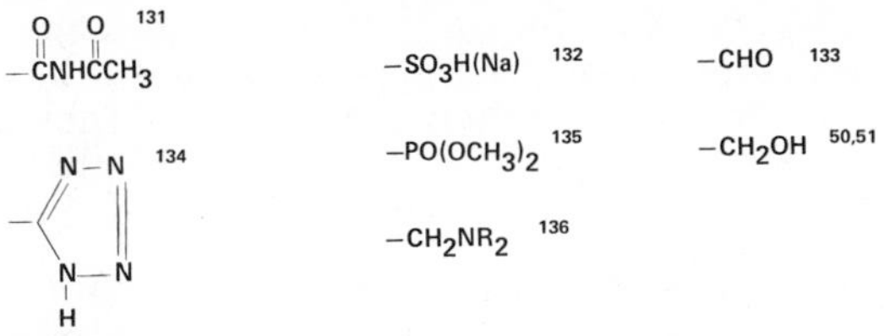

$-C(=O)NHC(=O)CH_3$ [131] $-SO_3H(Na)$ [132] $-CHO$ [133]

tetrazolyl (N–N, N–N, H) [134] $-PO(OCH_3)_2$ [135] $-CH_2OH$ [50,51]

$-CH_2NR_2$ [136]

One such example, the imide XIV (CP-27,987, Pfizer), has been studied in the clinic with what appears to be some initial success (131). This compound when administered by aerosol (6-140 μg) induced an effect and duration of action similar to that of isoproterenol. Side-effects included headaches and a transient increase in heart rate at the higher doses. A mild irritation of the throat and some coughing was noted at all doses, but these effects also were induced by the vehicle without drug.

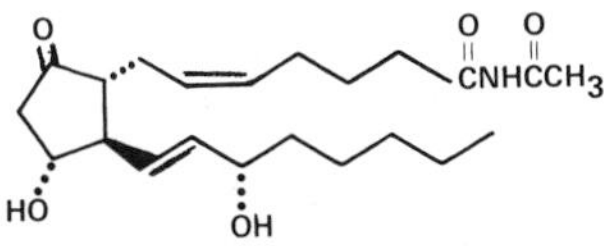

O O ‖ ‖ CNHCCH3 — HO — OH — XIV

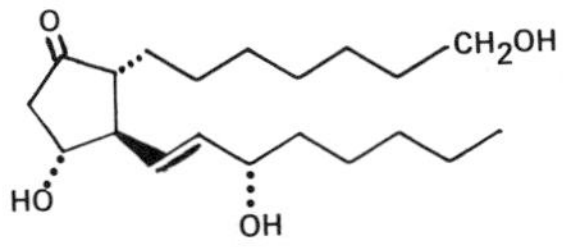

$CH_2OH$ — HO — OH — XV

The only other bronchodilator information available concerning this series of carboxylic acid equivalents is a report that $PGE_1$ and other carbinols (XV) (50,51) and 15-deoxy-16-hydroxyprostaglandin carbinols will relax ginea pig trachea (131a).

## F. 13,14-Double Bond Variations

### 1. 13,14-dihydro Analogs

Compounds in which the 13,14-double bond is saturated are

sometimes referred to as members of the $PGE_0$ class. Although one group has reported that 11-deoxy-$PGE_0$ is only poorly active in the aerosol Konzett assay (124), we have found this compound to possess a high degree of bronchodilator potency in the I.V. Konzett (Table VI) and aerosol pilocarpine dog assays.

In the 11α-hydroxy series potency was substantially diminished, by 90% for $PGE_0$ (124) and by 99% in the 15-deoxy-16-hydroxy-16-methyl series (I.V. Konzett; Table XX) (137).

### 2. 13,14-Cis-Vinylene Analogs

The synthesis of $\Delta^{13}$-cis-15-hydroxyprostaglandins has been reported (22,27,138), but with one exception the biological consequences of this variation have not been described. A Syntex group (138) has noted the relative inactivity of a series of $\Delta^{13}$-cis-16-hydroxy-$PGE_1$ derivatives (0.005 x $PGE_1$ in I.V. Konzett; see Table XV for $\Delta^{13}$-trans counterparts). In the 15-deoxy-16-hydroxy-16-methyl series we also have found that this modification almost completely abolishes bronchodilator activity, the $\Delta^{13}$-cis analog retaining less than 0.5% of the activity of the corresponding $\Delta^{13}$-trans derivative (137).

Replacement of the trans double bond with a triple bond also has been described (139), but bronchodilator testing data has not been reported.

### 3. 13-Thia Analogs

The isosteric relationship of sulfur and vinylene has often been recognized, and on occasion an exchange of one for the other has provided analogs of interest. However, this concept has not proven useful in the prostaglandin series, the 13-thia derivatives (see Scheme 35) having less than 1% the activity of the parent $\Delta^{13}$-15-deoxy-16-hydroxy (or $\Delta^{13}$-15-hydroxy) compound (91).

## VI. α-Chain Variations

A major route of prostaglandin metabolic inactivation is β-oxidation of the carboxylic acid α-chain (82). Consequently we have made an extensive search for structure modifications which, while consistent with biological activity, would block or at the least hinder this metabolic route. An additional advantage for this approach was the possibility that an α-chain modification also might produce a compound resistant to PG 15-dehydrogenase, since this enzyme is known to be sensitive to structure changes at remote sites on the prostaglandin molecule (140,140a,140b). The results of our investigation are presented in Tables XI and XII. Also included in Table XI are a series of $C_2$-$C_6$ alkyl substituted derivatives studied by Bartmann and his colleagues of the Hoechst laboratories (141).

## A. Alkyl and Alkoxy Substitution

From the data of Table XI it is apparent that bronchodilator activity is drastically reduced by substitution on $C_2$-$C_4$. On the other hand, methyl substitution at $C_5$ or at $C_6$ provided compounds with equivalent or even enchanced potency. It is conceivable that the increased activity of the 5-methyl analog, which would not be expected to retard β-oxidation, is in fact a reflection of increased resistance to PG 15-dehydrogenase.

TABLE XI

EFFECT OF α-CHAIN SUBSTITUTION UPON BRONCHODILATOR ACTIVITY

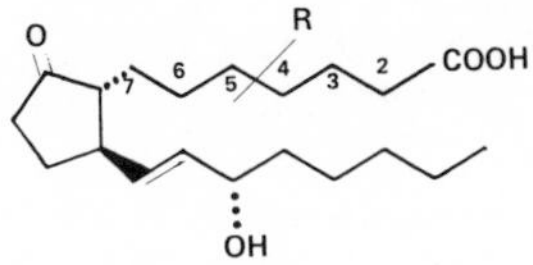

| R | LEDERLE RELATIVE POTENCY SEROTONIN | HISTAMINE | R | HOECHST RELATIVE POTENCY HISTAMINE |
|---|---|---|---|---|
| 1. H (NORMAL) | 100 (STD) | 100 (STD) | 9. H (NORMAL) | 100 (STD) |
| 2. 2-$CH_3$ | <0.1 | 1 | 10. 2-$CH_3$ | 6 |
| 3. 2-$C_2H_5$ | 0.12 | 2.3 | 11. 2-$C_2H_5$ | <0.2 |
| 4. 2-$C_6H_5$ | 0.01 | 0.05 | 12. 2-$C_4H_9$ | <0.2 |
| 5. 2,3-METHANO(*t*) | 0.6 | 154 | 13. 3-$CH_3$ | 3 |
| 6. 3,3-DIMETHYL | <0.001 | <0.1 | 14. 4-$CH_3$ | 2 |
| 7. 4-$OCH_3$ | 0.2 | 1.4 | 15. 5-$CH_3$ | 400 |
| 8. 4-OH (Na SALT) | 0.12 | <0.1 | 16. 5-$C_2H_5$ | 20 |
| | | | 17. 6-$CH_3$ | 170 |

## B. 3-Thia and 3-Oxa Series

In Table XII is shown the effect of isosteric replacement of the 3-methylene moiety by oxygen or sulfur. Only a limited number of examples were studied so that a definitive assessment as to the effect of these substitutions is not really possible. The one 3-oxa analog (entry 2) possessed about 1-3% the activity of the parent compound. Results with the 3-thia derivatives (entries 3, 10, 17) were variable, but the 11α-hydroxy-16,16-trimethylene member (17) of this series was about as active as the parent 3-methylene derivative. In the pilocarpine dog assay, dl-3-thia-11-deoxy-$PGE_1$ (3) produced a nice prolongation of effect (Fig. 1). At total doses of 0.16-900 μg it reduced bronchoconstriction by 50%. In contrast to l-$PGE_1$, which was substantially more potent but short acting, these effects persisted for the duration of the experiment (1 h). On the other hand, the maximum effect (50%) that could be attained at any dose was

TABLE XII

EFFECT OF SUBSTITUTION WITHIN THE
α-CHAIN UPON BRONCHODILATOR ACTIVITY

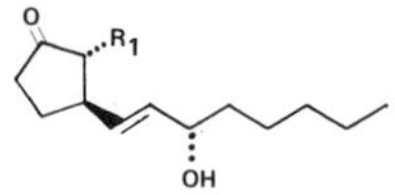

O, $R_1$, OH

| | $R_1$ | RELATIVE POTENCY SEROTONIN | RELATIVE POTENCY HISTAMINE |
|---|---|---|---|
| 1. |  COOH NORMAL | 100 (STD) | 100 (STD) |
| 2. | 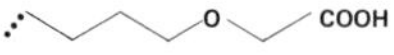 O COOH | 3 | 1.5 |
| 3. | 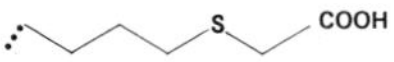 S COOH | 13 | 117 |
| 4. | 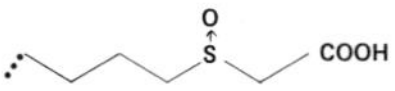 O ↑ S COOH | <0.01 | <0.01 |
| 5. |  S COOH (4-NOR) | <0.01 | <0.01 |
| 6. | 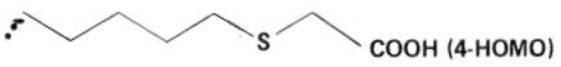 S COOH (4-HOMO) | <0.01 | <0.01 |

O, $R_2$, (H)HO, 16, OH

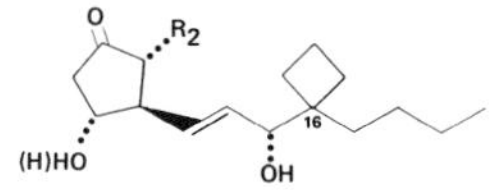

| | 11-DEOXY SERIES $R_2$ | SEROTONIN | HISTAMINE |
|---|---|---|---|
| 7. |  COOH | 100 (STD) | 100 (STD) |
| 8. | 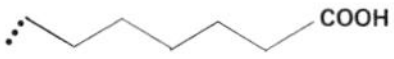 COOH | 38 | 92 |
| 9. | 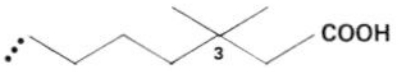 3 COOH | <0.2 | <0.1 |
| 10. |  S COOH | 4.2 | 2.4 |
| 11. | 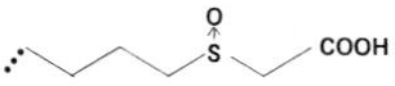 O ↑ S COOH | 0.25 | 0.11 |
| 12. |  COOH 2-NOR | 24 | 7 |
| 13. |  COOH 2-HOMO | <0.2 | <0.07 |
| 14. | 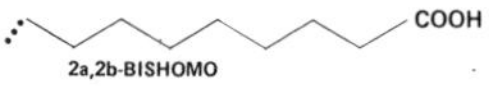 COOH 2a,2b-BISHOMO | <0.2 | <0.07 |

| | 11α-HYDROXY SERIES $R_2$ | SEROTONIN | HISTAMINE |
|---|---|---|---|
| 15. |  COOH | 100 (STD) | 100 (STD) |
| 16. |  COOH | 200 | 290 |
| 17. |  S COOH | 63 | 154 |

ENTRIES 2, 3: REF 39; 4: REF 142; 5, 6: REF 49; 7-16: REF 46; 17: REF 142a.

significantly less than the maximum bronchodilator effect of l-$PGE_1$ (70% inhibition at 0.16-16 μg) or of isoproterenol (70% inhibition at 50 μg) similarly administered. The 15-methyl derivative (Fig. 1) gave similar results in both assays. The 16,16-dimethyl analog, although equipotent in the Konzett assays, proved to be bronchoconstrictive in the dog. Note that the 3-sulfinyl derivative, (entry 4), a possible 3-thia metabolite, is not active.

## C. Variation in Chain Length and Double Bond Isomerization

Several investigations indicate that the length of the α-chain is critical for high activity. Thus, in the 11-deoxy-$PGE_1$ series, a study (Table XIII) by the Hoechst group showed that the abbreviated 5-carbon and 6-carbon α-chain derivatives were inactive and that the 2-homo analog (8 carbons) was only 10% as potent as the parent compound (143). In the 11-deoxy-16,16-trimethylene-$PGE_1$ series, compounds having 8- and 9-carbon α-chains (Table XII; entries 13, 14) were ineffective, although the latter compound should give the parent member of the series by metabolic β-oxidation. However, the 2-nor derivative (12) retained some potency (7-24%). In the 3-thia series neither the 6-atom or 8-atom analog (Table XII; entries 5, 6) were effective compounds. That the former compound (4-nor) was inactive is surprising since examination of space-filling models indicates a good similarity in chain length between its α-chain and that of $PGE_2$.

It is worth noting that a 2a,2b-bishomo-$PGF_2α$ derivative (9 carbon α-chain) has been reported to display potent abortifacient activity (144).

TABLE XIII

EFFECT OF α-CHAIN LENGTH ON BRONCHODILATOR ACTIVITY

O, $(CH_2)_nCOOH$, OH

| n | RELATIVE POTENCY HISTAMINE |
|---|---|
| 1. 4 (BISNOR) | <0.002 |
| 2. 5 (NOR) | <0.002 |
| 3. 6 (NORMAL) | 100 (STD) |
| 4. 7 (HOMO) | 10 |

The Hoechst group has described an effective variation obtained by shifting the 5,6-double bond of 11-deoxy-$PGE_2$ to the adjacent 4,5-position. The resulting analog (XVI; HR-102) is considerably more potent than $PGE_2$, but unfortunately it induced a cough in patients during initial Phase I studies, precluding further clinical investigation (141).

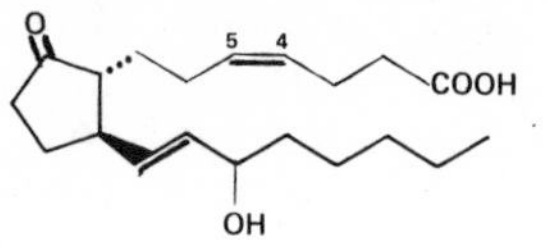

XVI

A 5(6)-dehydro-11-deoxy-$PGE_2$ derivative (acetylenic $C_5$-$C_6$ bond) proved to be only a very weak bronchodilator (146).

D. Miscellaneous

Many other α-chain modifications have been reported (Table XIV). Most of these changes appear to have been consistent with biological activity in one or another assay, but except for entry 6, no reports concerning bronchodilator activity have apeared.

TABLE XIV

α-CHAIN MODIFICATIONS

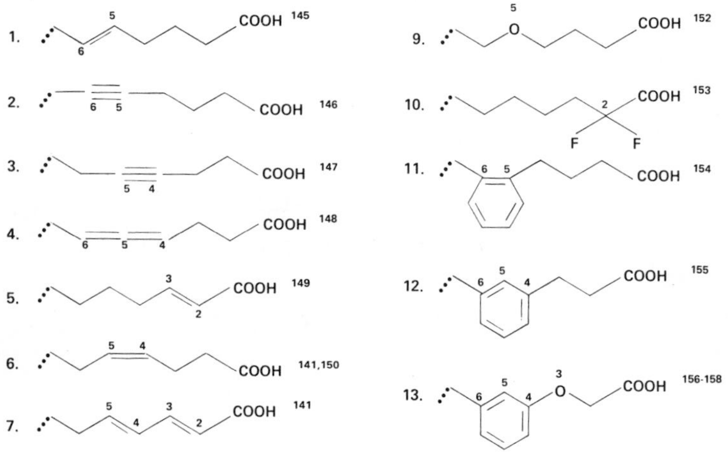

| Entry | Ref. | Entry | Ref. |
|---|---|---|---|
| 1. | 145 | 9. | 152 |
| 2. | 146 | 10. | 153 |
| 3. | 147 | 11. | 154 |
| 4. | 148 | 12. | 155 |
| 5. | 149 | 13. | 156-158 |
| 6. | 141,150 | | |
| 7. | 141 | | |
| 8. | 151 | | |

VII. β-Chain Modifications

The primary agent of prostaglandin metabolic inactivation is PG 15-dehydrogenase (82). We and others have undertaken an intensive search for substitutents which, when positioned at or in the proximity of $C_{15}$, would block or inhibit the action of this enzyme and which also would be compatible with biological activity. Such compounds might prove to be more potent and/or efficacious, but primarily they would be expected to produce a biological effect of prolonged duration. Our efforts along these lines in the 11-deoxy series are summarized in Table XV, and in the 11α-hydroxy series in Table XVI.

## A. 15-Methyl Derivatives

Although $C_{15}$-methylation has given prostaglandins with dramatically enhanced effects as orally active, long lasting inhibitors of gastric acid secretion (159) and to a lesser extent as abortifacients (160), this modification has proven to be a major dissapointment for the development of improved bronchodilators.

In the 11-deoxy series, the 15-methyl-$PGE_1$ member (Table XV; entry 2) was quite effective in our Konzett assays, but only moderately so in the pilocarpine dog assay. However, an Ayerst group has reported (161,162) that the l-15(S) enantiomer (XVII, doxaprost) showed high activity and a prolonged duration of effect in several assays. Similar results have been reported for 15-vinyl (RU-22078) and 15-ethynyl-11-deoxy derivatives (141, 163). On the other hand, introduction of the 15-methyl group (R/S) into $PGE_2$ resulted in a radically diminished potency in our Konzett assay. A limited study (13) of the 15(S)enantiomer XVIII in 6-normal and 6-asthmatic subjects appears to support the Konzett determination, as this compound was at best only weakly effective at a dose (200 μg, aerosol) which is about four times the apparent minimal effective dose reported for l-$PGE_1$ (10,11,164). (No irritant effects were reported in this study.) These results are also in accord with those of Strandberg and Hedqvist (6), who found that in an isolated human bronchial strip assay 15-methyl-$PGE_2$ (XVIII) produced a weak and inconsistent effect.

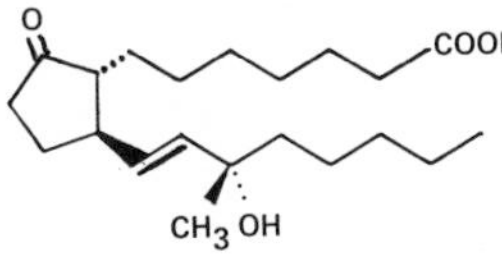

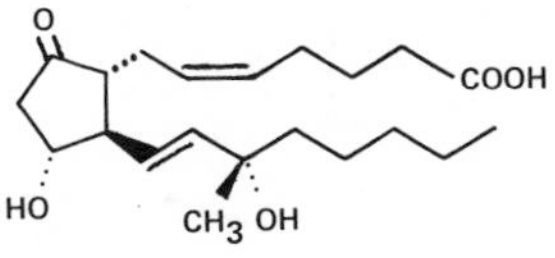

## B. 16,16-Dimethyl Derivatives

The 16,16-dimethyl substitutent, like $C_{15}$-methylation, has produced striking results for the inhibition of gastric acid secretion (165) and an enhanced potency as a uterine smoth muscle stimulant (166), but has proved to be equally dissapointing for the development of a prostaglandin bronchodilator. In both the 11-deoxy and 11α-hydroxy series, introduction of the 16,16-dimethyl group was consistent with retention and perhaps even enhancement of activity in our Konzett assays, and a prolongation of effect was noted by Strandberg and Hedqvist (6) in their guinea pig studies. However, as with the 15-methyl series, these observations could not be confirmed in other systems. In our pilocarpine dog assay (Fig. 2), dl-16,16-dimethyl-$PGE_2$ was

TABLE XV

11-DEOXY-15,16 AND 17- SUBSTITUTED PROSTAGLANDINS

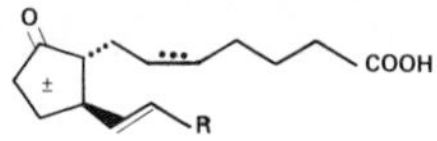

COOH

R

| | R | SERIES | RELATIVE POTENCY SEROTONIN | RELATIVE POTENCY HISTAMINE |
|---|---|---|---|---|
| 1. | 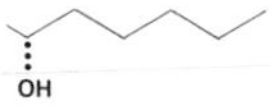 OH | (*l* $E_2$) | 100 (STD) | 100 (STD) |
| 2. | 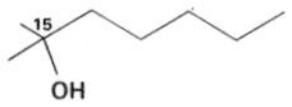 15, OH | (*dl* $E_1$) | 74 | 125 |
| 3. | 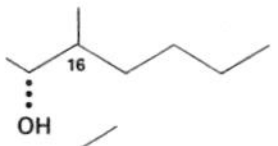 16, OH | (*dl* $E_1$) | 150 | – |
| 4. | | (*dl* $E_2$) | 385 | 925 |
| 5. | 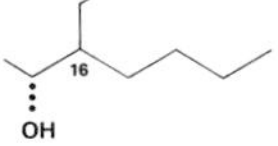 16, OH | (*dl* $E_1$) | 53 | – |
| 6. | | (*dl* $E_2$) | 6.5 | 18 |
| 7. | 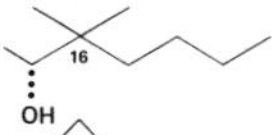 16, OH | (*dl* $E_1$) | 20 | 127 |
| 8. | | (*dl* $E_0$) | 25 | 89 |
| 9. | 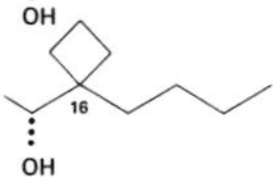 16, OH | (*dl* $E_1$) | 26 | 220 |
| 10. | | (*dl* $E_2$) | 68 | 240 |
| 11. | 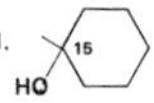 15, HO | (*dl* $E_1$) | 2.2 | 3.4 |
| 12. | 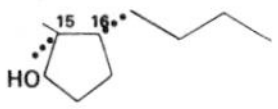 15 16, HO | (*dl* $E_1$) | 4.6 | 20 |
| 13. | 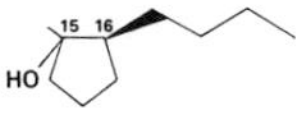 15 16, HO | (*dl* $E_1$) | – | 800 |
| 14. | 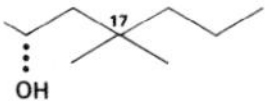 17, OH | (*dl* $E_1$) | 0.1 | 0.6 |
| 15. | 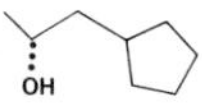 OH | (*dl* $E_1$) | 83 | 378 |
| 16. |  15 16, OH OH | (*dl* $E_1$) | <1.6 | 89 |
| 17. | 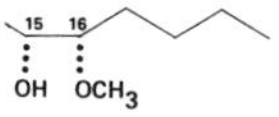 15 16, OH $OCH_3$ | (*dl* $E_1$, Et ester) | 13 | <16 |
| 18. | 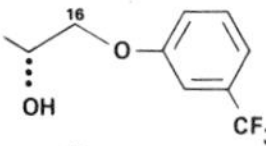 16, O, OH, $CF_3$ | (*dl* $E_2$) | <0.16 | <0.16 |
| 19. | 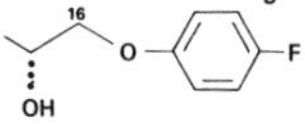 16, O, F, OH | (*dl* $E_2$) | TOXIC | TOXIC |

ENTRIES 2-8, 14:REF 48; 9-10:REF 46; 11-13:REF 84; 15:REF 85; 16:REF 72; 17:REF 43; 18, 19:REF 89.

TABLE XVI

15,16 OR 17-SUBSTITUTED PROSTAGLANDINS

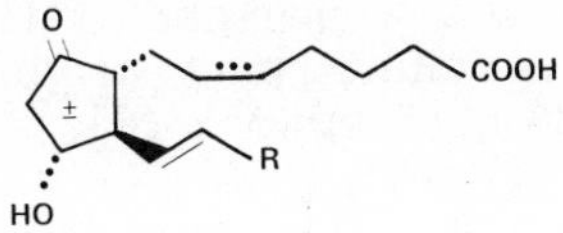

| R | SERIES | RELATIVE POTENCY SEROTONIN | RELATIVE POTENCY HISTAMINE |
|---|---|---|---|
| 1. (*l* $PGE_2$) | 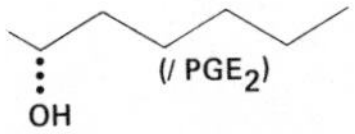 | 100 (STD) | 100 (STD) |
| 2. | 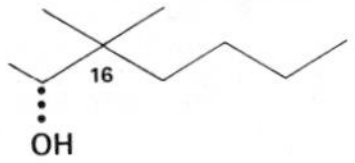 (*dl* $E_2$) | 164 | 435 |
| 3. | 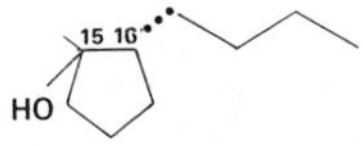 (*dl* $E_2$) | 135 | 173 |
| 4. | 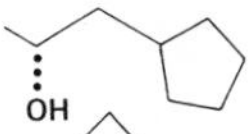 (*dl* $E_1$) | 195 | 54 |
| 5. | 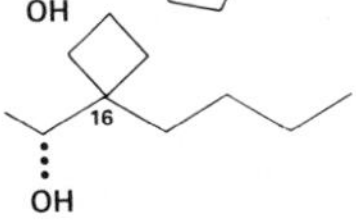 (*dl* $E_1$) | 162 | 76 |
| 6. | (*dl* $E_2$) | 56 | 38 |
| 7. | 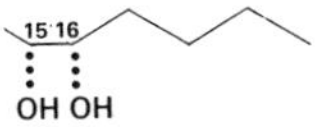 (*dl* $E_2$) | 8 | 4 |
| 8. | 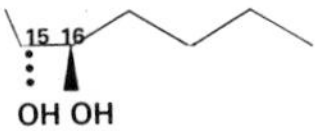 (*dl* $E_2$) | 2 | 2 |
| 9. | 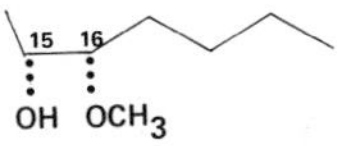 (*dl* $E_2$) | 0.2 | 17 |
| 10. | 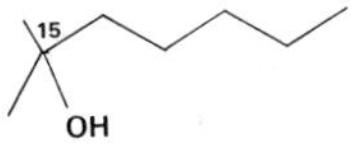 (*dl* $E_2$) | 3 | 3 |
| 11. | 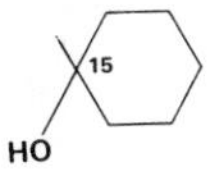 (*dl* $E_1$) | 3 | 1 |
| 12. | (*dl* $E_2$) | 3 | 2 |

ENTRIES 2:REF 108, 167; 3, 11, 12:REF 84; 4:REF 85; 5, 6:REF 46; 7, 8:REF 72; 9:REF 43; 10:REF 82a, 108.

only weakly efficacious, although its effect was prolonged. When tested as the free acid or methyl ester against isolated human bronchi (11 strips) it failed to relax any of the strips and indeed proved to be a consistent and potent contractor (6). [Another laboratory reports a marginal relaxant effect, 0.08 X $PGE_1$ (114).] The $PGE_1$ counterpart produced either no effect or only a slight contraction (5 strips) (6).

It should be noted that in all published studies with human bronchi strips, as well as in our own experience, $PGE_1$ is reported to induce relaxation, although with a potency much less than that of isoproterenol. On the other hand, we and three other laboratories have noted mixed effects for $PGE_2$, a contractor in some instances and a dilator in others (5,6,7). Based on a comparison of response curves and cross tachyphylaxis experiments, Gardiner has suggested that $PGE_2$ can stimulate either $PGE_1$ (relaxor) or $PGF_{2}\alpha$ (contractor) receptors (5).

### C. Cycloalkyl Derivatives

In contrast to the 16,16-dimethyl series, we have found that introduction of the closely related 16,16-trimethylene (spiro-cyclobutyl) group gave analogs with high activity not only in the Konzett assays, but also in the pilocarpine dog assay (46). Thus, 16,16-trimethylene-$PGE_1$ (XIX) (Table XVI; entry 5) appears to be a very potent compound capable of producing an effect of prolonged duration (Fig. 2). 16,16-Trimethylene-$PGE_2$ (46) and its 20-nor derivative gave similar results in the Konzett assay. Unfortunately, both XIX and the $PGE_2$ counterpart produced a short-lived pulmonary hypertension in dogs at effective dose levels, precluding further development of these compounds.

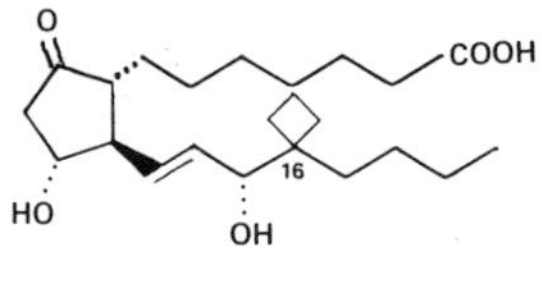

O COOH 16 HO OH

XIX

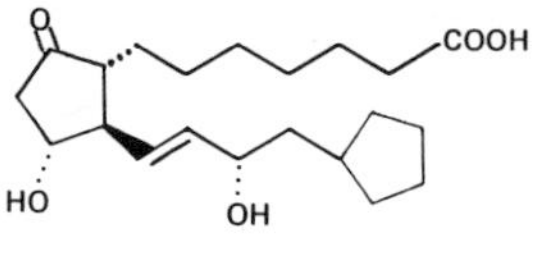

O COOH HO OH

XX

16-Cyclopentyl-17,20-tetranor-$PGE_1$ (XX) also is of interest, since in the pilocarpine assay it is perhaps the most potent prostaglandin we have yet seen (Fig. 3); however, in contrast to the 16,16-trimethylene series, it is a short-acting compound.

A group from Miles Laboratories also has synthesized a series of analogs incorporating a cycloalkyl feature in the β-chain. Testing was carried out with the isolated guinea pig trachea (Table XVII). These studies again demonstrate the bronchoconstrictor potential of 16-alkyl derivatives (168a).

TABLE XVII

β-CHAIN MODIFICATIONS (MILES)

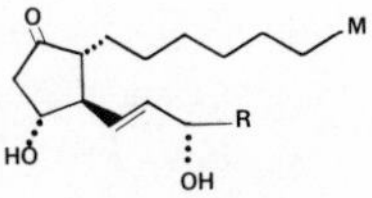

| | | M | R | GUINEA PIG TRACHEA |
|---|---|---|---|---|
| 1. | TR 4010 | COOH |  (STD) | R2 |
| 2. | TR 4051 | $COOCH_3$ |  (STD) | R2 |
| 3. | TR 4723 | $COOCH_3(E_2)$ |  16 | C1 |
| 4. | TR 4510 | COOH | 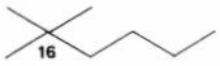 16 | CO |
| 5. | TR 4117 | COOH | 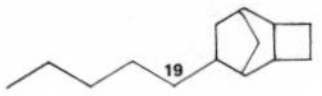 19 | O |
| 6. | TR 4144 | COOH |  16 | C2 |
| 7. | TR 4098 | COOH | 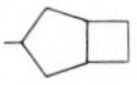 | R2 |
| 8. | TR 4120 | $COOCH_3$ |  | C2 |
| 9. | TR 4713 | $CH_2OH$ | | |
| 10. | TR 4726 | $COOC_2H_5(E_2)$ | | |
| 11. | TR 4078 | $COOCH_3$ | | R3 |
| 12. | TR 4248 | $COOCH_3$ |  | R3 |
| 13. | TR 4569 | $CH_2OH$ | | R3 |
| 14. | TR 4690 | $COOCH_3$ |  | R3 |
| 15. | TR 4673 | $CH_2OH$ | | R3 |
| 16. | TR 4681 | COOH | 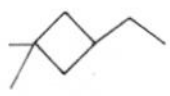 | R3 |
| 17. | TR 4688 | $CH_2OH$ | | R2 |
| 18. | TR 4692 | $COOCH_3$ | 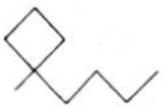 | O |
| 19. | TR 4645 | $CH_2OH$ | | O |
| 20. | TR 4882 | $COOCH_3$ | 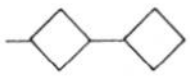 | C4 |
| 21. | TR 4881 | $CH_2OH$ | | O |
| 22. | TR 4796 | $COOCH_3$ | 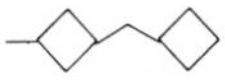 | C3 |
| 23. | TR 4832 | $CH_2OH$ | | O |

C = CONSTRUCT; R = RELAX; O = WEAK; 4 = STRONG. SEE REFERENCE 51 FOR DESCRIPTION OF ASSAY AND EXPLANATION OF RESULTS.

ENTRIES 1-7:REF 168; 8-10:REF 45; 11-23:REF 51.

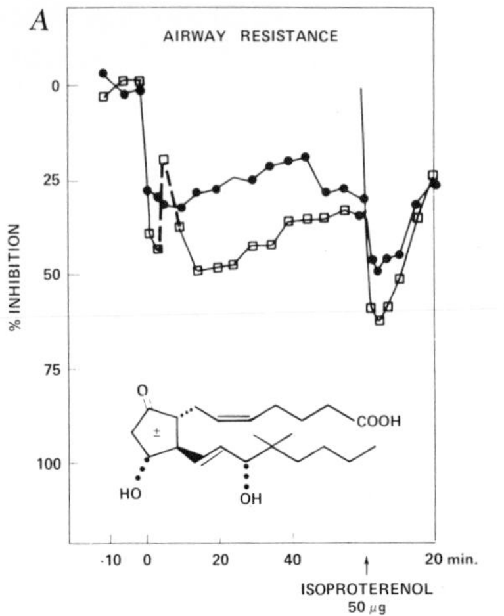


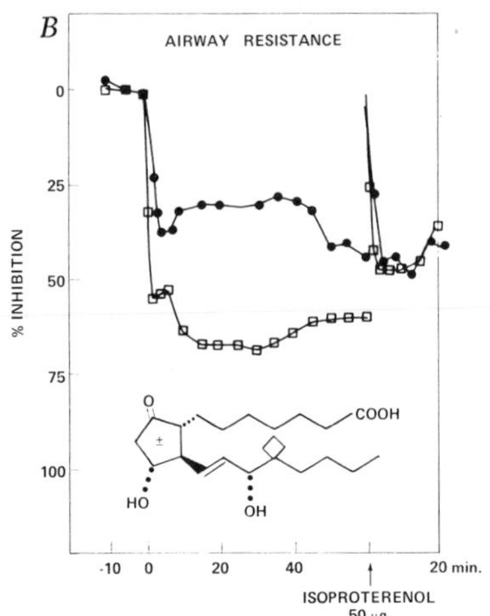


*Figure 2. Bronchodilator activity of (A)* dl-*16,16-dimethyl-PGE$_2$ and (B)* dl-*16,16-trimethylene-PGE$_1$ in pilocarpine-bronchoconstricted dogs (aerosol) (□) 160 μg (n = 3); (●) 1.6 μg (n = 3)*

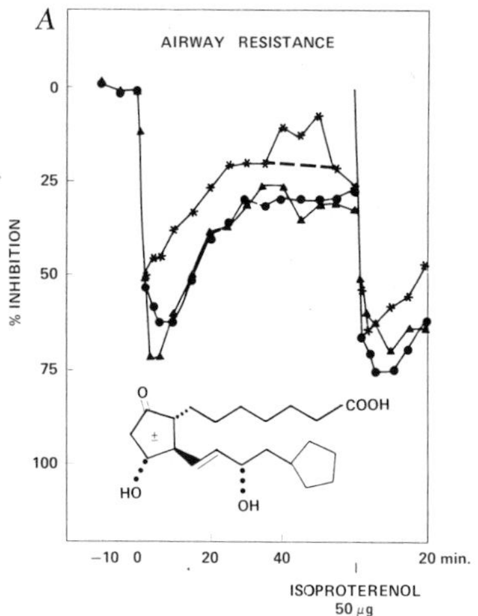


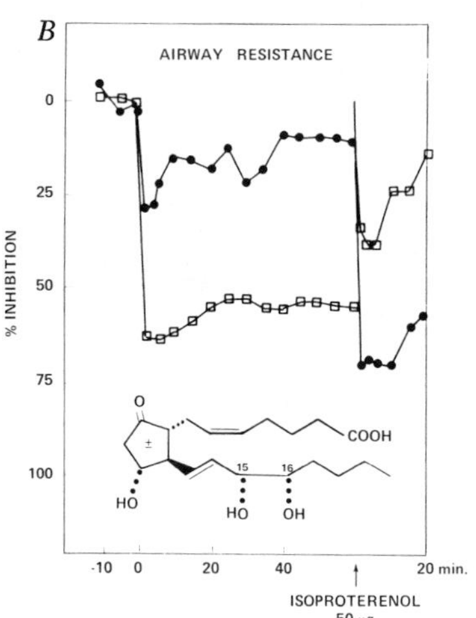


*Figure 3. Bronchodilator activity of (A)* dl-*17,20-methano-PGE$_1$; and (B)* dl-erythro-*16-hydroxy-PGE$_2$ in pilocarpine-bronchoconstricted dogs (aerosol) (▲) 16 μg (n = 3); (●) 1.6 μg (n = 3); (✱) 0.16 μg (n = 3); (□) 160 μg (n = 3)*

15- and 16-Hydroxy derivatives in which the cycloalkyl group incorporates the carbinol carbon also have been prepared. Three examples are illustrated below. The cyclohexyl derivatives XXI and XXII produced relatively weak bronchodilator responses in both the Konzett and pilocarpine dog assays. However, the cyclopentyl derivative XXIII, structurally closer to the natural prostaglandins, shows high potency in both assays, but induced a transient increase in dog pulmonary arterial pressure in the course of the latter assay (84).

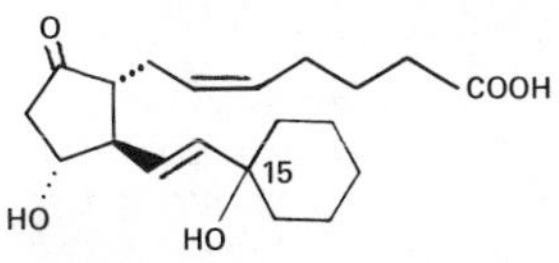

XXI 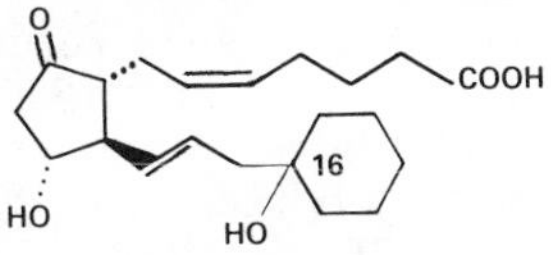 XXII 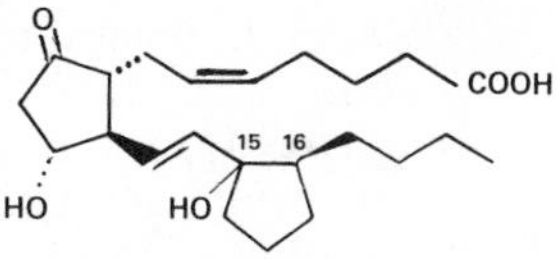 XXIII

D. Other $C_{16}$ Substitutents

In our Konzett assay, 11-deoxy-16-methyl derivatives showed exceptionally high potency (48), an observation also made by a Wyeth group (113). However, further examination of 11-deoxy-16(R/S)-methyl-$PGE_1$ (XXIV) in the pilocarpine dog assay indicated this compound to be relatively ineffective and of no interest. Another member of this series, 16(S)-methyl-20-methoxy-$PGE_2$ (XXV, YPG-209), has been reported to be 230 times as potent as $PGE_2$ in the guinea pig vs. histamine-induced spasms. It also is claimed to be orally effective in this model without concommitant hypotension or diarrhea (169). This is the first claim, that we are aware of, for oral activity for any prostaglandin bronchodilator and we await the results of further studies with this compound.

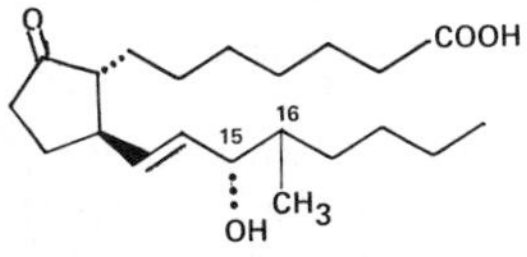

XXIV 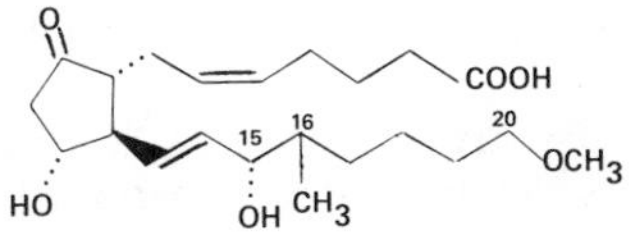 XXV

Larger groups at $C_{16}$ [ethyl, methoxy (43), 16,16-ethylene dithio (170)] as well as the 16-keto group (170) are not consistent with significant activity. On the other hand, the minimally bulky 16-methylene derivative of $PGE_2$ methyl ester (ONO-481CD) is reported to be a potent relaxor of guinea pig trachea (114). The diminished activity found for the erythro (XXVI) and threo 16-hydroxy $PGE_2$ derivatives in the Konzett assay is suprising in view of the high potency found in the 15-deoxy-16-hydroxy series (see below). Although neither the threo nor the erythro

16-hydroxy-$PGE_2$ analogs was capable of producing a maximum effect in the pilocarpine dog model, the erythro derivative was among the longest acting congeners we have studied (Fig. 3).

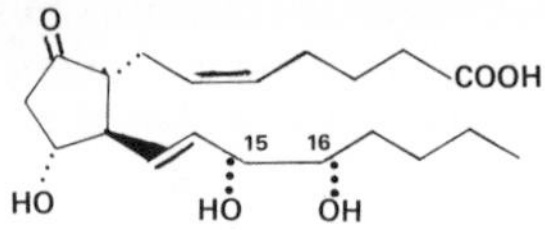

XXVI 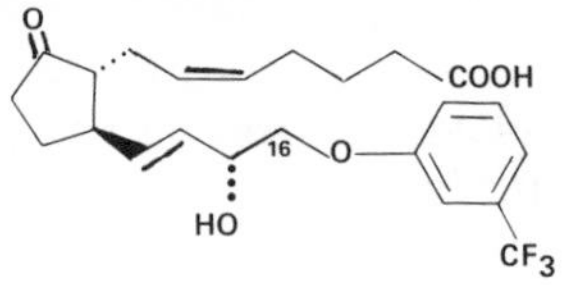 XXVII

It also is interesting that the 16-m-trifluoromethylphenoxy-17,20-tetranor moiety (see XVII; also Table XV, entry 18) which abolished bronchodilator efficacy in the 11-deoxy series, when incorporated into $PGF_2\alpha$ provides one of the most potent prostaglandin abortifacients yet reported (87,88). Furthermore, the p-fluorophenoxy-11-deoxy-$PGE_2$ analog (19) was one of the very few congeners tested in our assays which was toxic. 16-Phenoxy-17,20-tetranor-$PGE_2$ is described as a very potent contractor of isolated human and guinea pig trachea (16 x $PGF_2\alpha$!) (114). Although 17-phenyl-18,20-trinor-$PGE_2$ is reported by one laboratory to be an active bronchodilator in the guinea pig assay and even produced relaxation in a human bronchial strip assay (2 of 5 preparations), Karim and Adaikan (114) claim it and its 15-methyl derivative to be strong constrictors of isolated human and guinea pig trachea (31 and 20 x $PGF_2\alpha$, respectively).

## E. β-Chain Length

In general, it appears that homologation of the β-chain gives compounds with similar or diminished potency. One such example, 20-ethyl-11-deoxy-$PGE_1$ (M & B 26,693), was submitted to clinical investigation (121,122). In eight male non-asthmatic volunteers at a dose of 250 μg (aerosol) M & B 26,693 produced significant bronchoconstriction. At the same dose six of the eight subjects coughed and/or experienced a burning sensation in the throat. The bronchoconstrictor effect is believed to be associated, at least in part, with the cough response.

In the 15-deoxy-16-hydroxy series we have noted a loss of potency on homologation of the β-chain, although in the unsubstituted 16-hydroxy series this was manifested only with the 20-propyl derivative (see below). Abbreviation of the chain by one carbon (20-nor congener) in the 16,16 trimethylene series did not effect the activity (46).

## F. 15-Deoxy-16-Hydroxy Series

The possibility that certain of the prostaglandin receptors might be less demanding than others in their binding requirements led us to prepare a series of analogs wherein the 15-hydroxy function was repositioned to $C_{13}$, $C_{16}$, $C_{17}$, or $C_{20}$ on the flexible β-chain or replaced by a 15-hydroxymethyl group. The results of this study are summarized in Table XVIII. The only compound which provided good activity was the 15-deoxy-16-hydroxy derivative, which is a mixture of 4-diastereomers. Pappo and Collins (40) have shown that only the l-16(S) diastereomer is effective as an inhibitor of gastric acid secretion and we accordingly make the likely assumption that only one of the four isomers is active as a bronchodilator.

TABLE XVIII

BRONCHODILATOR ACTIVITY AS A FUNCTION OF β-CHAIN HYDROXYL POSITION

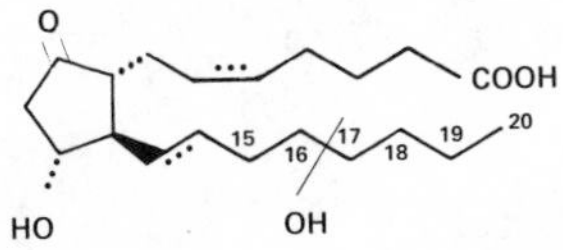

| | | RELATIVE POTENCY | |
|---|---|---|---|
| | | SEROTONIN | HISTAMINE |
| *l* | $PGE_2$ | 100 (STD) | 100 (STD) |
| *dl* | 15-DEOXY-$PGE_1$ | 0.5 | 0.4 |
| *dl* | 15-DEOXY-13-HYDROXY-$PGE_0$ | 0.03 | <0.002 |
| *dl* | 15-DEOXY-16-HYDROXY-$PGE_1$ | 110 | 48 |
| *dl* | 15-DEOXY-17-HYDROXY-$PGE_1$ | 0.4 | 1.9 |
| *dl* | 15-DEOXY-20-HYDROXY-$PGE_1$ | 0.3 | 1.1 |
| *dl* | 15-DEOXY-15-HYDROXYMETHYL-$PGE_2$ | 0.1 | 0.2 |

Further exploration of this series provided the results summarized in Tables XIX, XX and XXI. Table XIX gives the Konzett results for the secondary 16-hydroxy series (55). Activity approximately equivalent to that of l-$PGE_2$ was noted for the dl 15-deoxy-16(R/S)-hydroxy derivatives (entries 2 and 3) of $PGE_1$ and $PGE_2$. Furthermore these analogs have shown good potency and efficacy in the pilocarpine treated dog (Fig 4). Konzett activity is maintained for the 20-methyl (9, 10) and 20-ethyl (11) homologs, but appears to fall off with the 20-propyl derivative (12). Introduction of the trans $\Delta^{17}$ bond (13-15), which restores allylic character to the hydroxy function, or a 17-methyl group (16-20, Fig 4) also was consistent with high activity. Homologation in the $\Delta^{17}$ series led to enhanced potency. Interestingly, dialkylation at $C_{17}$ with the trimethylene group (21) almost abolished activity-compare the 17 methyl analog (19) and the 15-hydroxy-16,16-trimethylene derivatives of Table XVI, entrees 5 and 6.

The 16-methyl derivatives (Table XX) also were of high potency, the $E_2$ member even appearing to display an enhancement of activity --contrast the poor response (3%) observed for 15(R/S)-15-methyl-$PGE_2$ (Table XVI, entry 10). However, in this series homologation of the β-chain or introduction of the $\Delta^{17}$

## TABLE XIX
## BRONCHODILATOR ACTIVITY OF 15-DEOXY-16-HYDROXYPROSTAGLANDINS

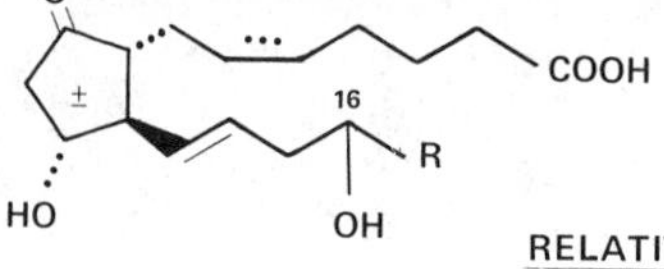

O
COOH
±
16
R
HO
OH

| / $PGE_2$ R | | SERIES | RELATIVE POTENCY SEROTONIN 100 (STD) | HISTAMINE 100 (STD) |
|---|---|---|---|---|
| 1. | 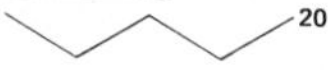 20 | $E_0$ | 0.5 | 0.4 |
| 2. | | $E_1$ | 110 | 48 |
| 3. | | $E_2$ | 19 | 50 |
| 4. | | $A_2$ | 0.7 | 1.1 |
| 5. | | $B_1$ | 0.3 | 0.4 |
| 6. | | $F_{1\alpha}$ | $<0.03$ | 0.06 |
| 7. | | $F_{1\beta}$ | 0.05 | 0.05 |
| 8. | | $F_{2\beta}$ | 0.4 | 0.3 |
| 9. |  21 | $E_1$ | 57 | 23 |
| 10. | | $E_2$ | 110 | 38 |
| 11. |  22 | $E_2$ | 31 | 37 |
| 12. |  23 | $E_2$ | 16 | 10 |
| 13. | 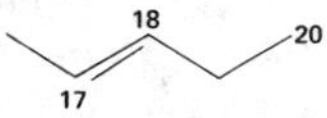 17, 18, 20 | $E_1$ | 5.6 | 7.7 |
| 14. | 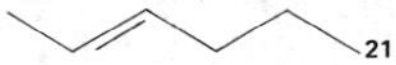 21 | $E_1$ | 25 | 21 |
| 15. |  22 | $E_1$ | 30 | 25 |
| 16. |  17, 20 | $E_2$ | 50 | 175 |
| 17. |  17, 21 | $E_2$ (UPPER*) | 122 | 64 |
| 18. | | $E_2$ (LOWER*) | 17 | 17 |
| 19. |  17, 22 | $E_2$ (UPPER*) | 36 | 17 |
| 20. | | $E_2$ (LOWER*) | 12 | 17 |
| 21. | 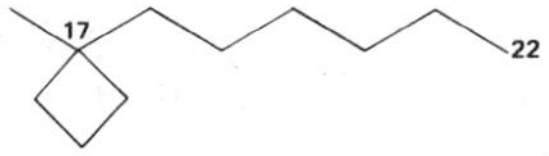 17, 22 | $E_2$ | 0.4 | 1.2 |

*UPPER AND LOWER REFER TO RELATIVE $R_f$ ON SILICA-GEL.

TABLE XX

BRONCHODILATOR ACTIVITY OF 15-DEOXY-16-HYDROXY-16-METHYLPROSTAGLANDINS

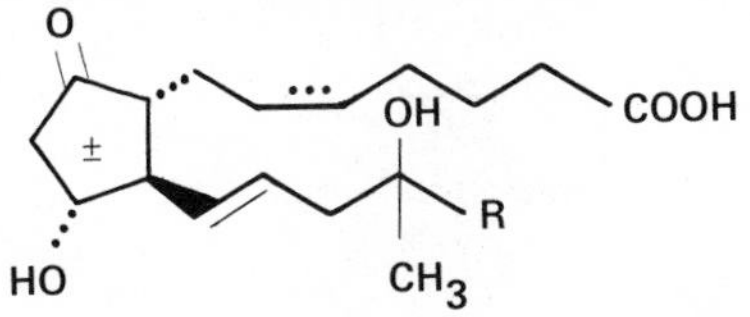

| | R | SERIES | RELATIVE POTENCY SEROTONIN | RELATIVE POTENCY HISTAMINE |
|---|---|---|---|---|
| | / $PGE_2$ | | 100 (STD) | 100 (STD) |
| 1. | 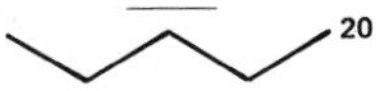 (chain to C-20) | $E_0$ | 0.11 | 2.3 |
| | | $E_1$ | 66 | 166 |
| | | $E_2$ | 300 | 156 |
| | | $E_2$ (13-*CIS*) | 0.3 | 0.4 |
| | | $A_2$ | 0.16 | 0.4 |
| | | $D_2$ | 0.04 | – |
| 2. | 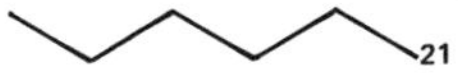 (chain to C-21) | $E_2$ | 9.4 | 22 |
| 3. |  (chain to C-22) | $E_2$ | 30 | 27 |
| 4. | 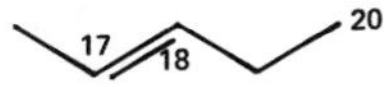 (17,18-ene, chain to C-20) | $E_2$ (UPPER*) | 1 | 1.5 |
| 5. | | $E_2$ (LOWER*) | 25 | 19 |

* UPPER AND LOWER REFER TO RELATIVE $R_f$ ON SILICA-GEL.

## TABLE XXI

### BRONCHODILATOR ACTIVITY OF 15-DEOXY-16-HYDROXY-16-SUBSTITUTED PROSTAGLANDINS

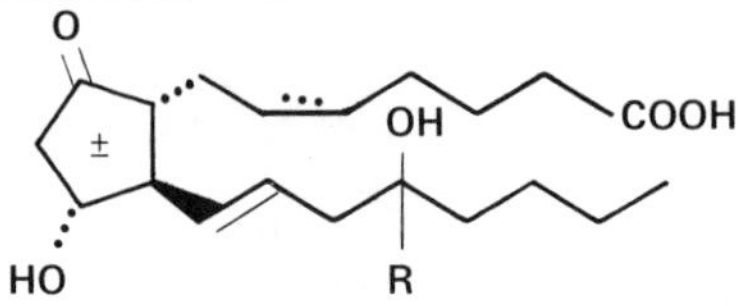

| | R | SERIES | RELATIVE POTENCY SEROTONIN | RELATIVE POTENCY HISTAMINE |
|---|---|---|---|---|
| | / $PGE_2$ | | 100 (STD) | 100 (STD) |
| 1. | –H | $E_1$ | 100 | 48 |
| 2. | –H | $E_2$ | 19 | 50 |
| 3. | $-CH_3$ | $E_1$ | 66 | 166 |
| 4. | $-CH_3$ | $E_2$ | 303 | 156 |
| 5. | $-CH=CH_2$ | $E_1$ | 52 | 89 |
| 6. | $-CH=CH_2$ | $E_2$ | 380 | 533 |
| 7. | 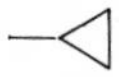 cyclopropyl | $E_2$ | 7.2 | 3.9 |
| 8. | $-C(CH_3)=CH_2$ | $E_2$ | 2 | 2.3 |
| 9. | $-CH=C(CH_3)H$ | $E_2$ | 0.5 | 1.4 |
| 10. | 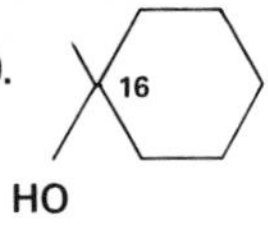 HO, 16 (cyclohexyl ring) | (16,20-METHANO) | 5.9 | 5 |

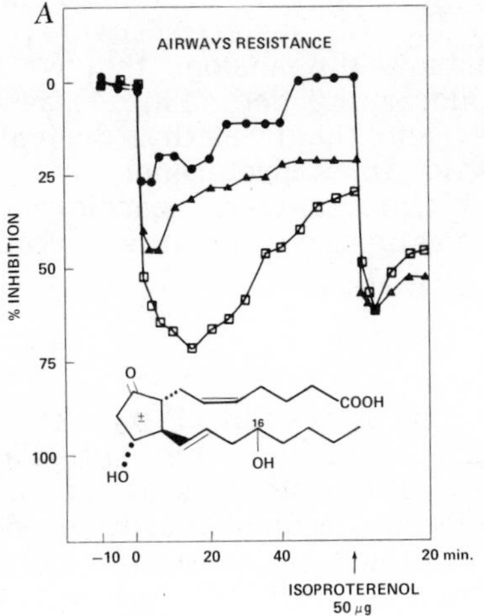


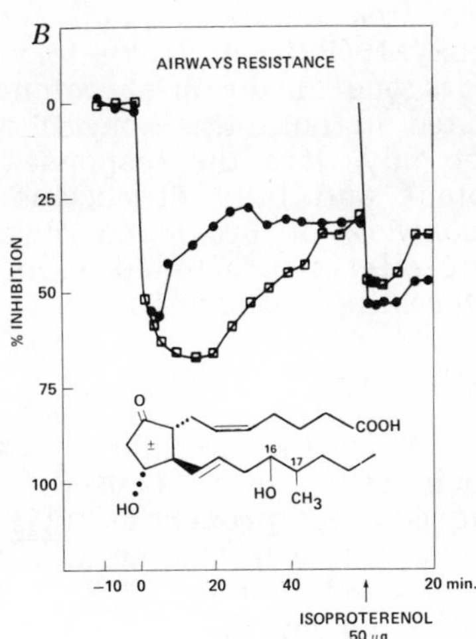


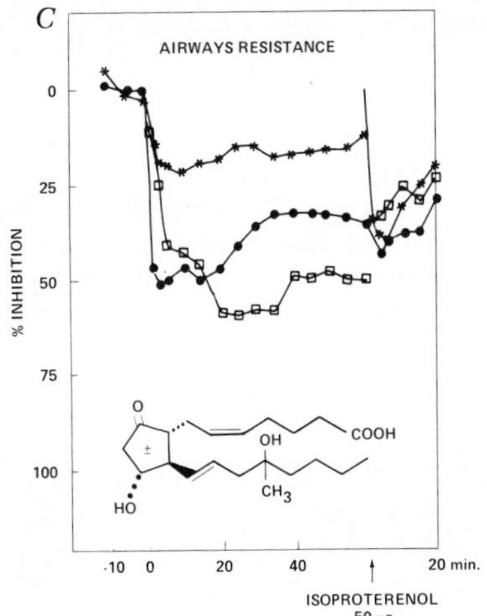


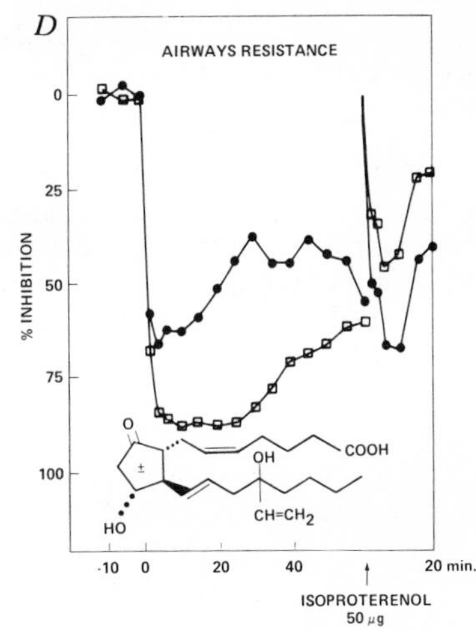


*Figure 4. Bronchodilator activity of (A)* dl-*15-deoxy-16-hydroxy-PGE$_2$; (B)* dl-*15-deoxy-16-hydroxy-17-methyl-PGE$_2$; (C)* dl-*15-deoxy-16-hydroxy-16-methyl-PGE$_2$; and (D)* dl-*15-deoxy-16-hydroxy-16-vinyl-PGE$_2$ in pilocarpine-bronchoconstricted dogs (aerosol) (□) 160 μg (n = 3); (▲) 16 μg (n = 3); (●) 1.6 μg (n = 3); (✱) 0.16 μg (n = 3)*

bond seems to be deactivating. Substitution of a vinyl group at $C_{16}$, but not of a larger alkenyl group or even cyclopropyl, also gave compounds of high potency (Table XXI). Indeed *dl*-15-deoxy-16(R/S)-hydroxy-16-vinyl-$PGE_2$ (4-diastereomers!) (entry 6) is one of the most potent prostaglandin analogs that we have tested in both the Konzett and pilocarpine dog (Fig. 4) assays. Not only were the responses to it (and the 16-methyl derivative) potent and fully efficacious relative to isoproterenol, but they also were of prolonged duration. Unfortunately, cardiovascular side-effects precluded clinical investigation of either of these interesting compounds.

## VIII. Prostacyclins

Since the exciting discovery of prostacyclin ($PGI_2$, XXVIII), much effort has focused on its vasodilator and anti-platelet aggregating properties (171,172). $PGI_2$ also seems to induce bronchodilation in pharmacologically or immunologically broncho-constricted animals (173). When studied in asthmatic patients, $PGI_2$ sodium salt (XXIX) and 20-methyl $PGI_2$ sodium salt were protective at what is claimed to be non-bronchodilator effective doses against non-specfically induced bronchoconstriction. The compounds were administered five minutes before challenge and an effect was observed for at least 15 minutes (174). Similar observations have been made with $PGE_1$ and $PGE_2$ (164). Cardiovascular side-effects were noted in the prostacyclin experiments.

$PGI_2$ also was administered to healthy volunteers and patients *via* aerosol and I.V. infusion. At doses of 200 or 400 μg (aerosol) in 12 patients, ten showed no respiratory changes, one improved, and one responded with bronchoconstriction. The inhaled prostacyclin induced systemic effects resembling those produced by I.V. infusion (175).

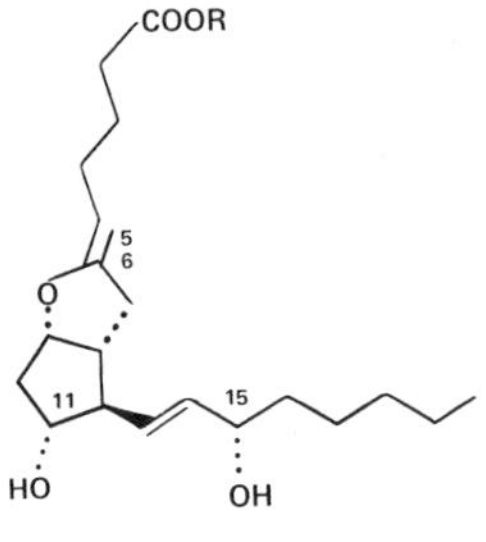

| | R |
|---|---|
| XXVIII | H |
| XXIX | Na |

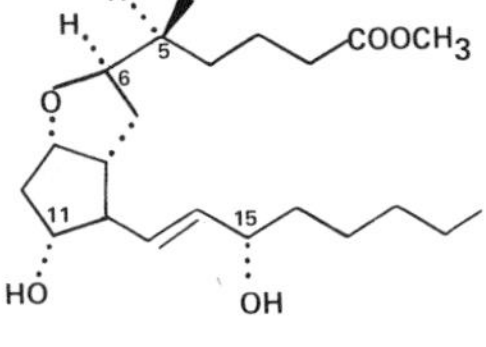

| | R |
|---|---|
| XXX | H |
| XXXI | I |

Our Konzett results obtained for $PGI_2$ sodium salt (XXIX), (176,177), the 5,6-dihydro derivative ($PGI_1$ methyl ester, XXX, 178,179), and its iodo analog, XXXI, are listed in Table XXII (180). The weak activity of XXIX perhaps is due to the rapid inactivation of prostacyclin. It is noteworthy that iodo ether XXXI is a potent bronchodilator in the guinea pig with a prolonged duration of effect.

TABLE XXII

BRONCHODILATOR ACTIVITY OF $PGI_2$ AND $PGI_1$

| | RELATIVE POTENCY | |
|---|---|---|
| | SEROTONIN | HISTAMINE |
| *l*-$PGE_2$ | 100 (STD) | 100 (STD) |
| XXIX | 0.04 | 0.6 |
| XXX | 0.9 | 6.2 |
| XXXI | 16 | 16 |

## IX. Summary and Critique

Clearly the initial promise of the prostaglandins remains to be fulfilled. At least nine candidates have been submitted to clinical investigation and all but one have failed to produce a significant bronchodilator effect (Table XXIII). Furthermore, the one compound (entry 1) which appears to have been effective does not seem to possess any obvious advantages over the natural prostaglandins.

Since all eight failures apparently were selected, at least in part, on the basis of data obtained from a guinea pig Konzett-Rossler assay, the question arises as to the predictive capability of this widely used model for the selection of effective prostaglandin bronchodilators. However, in point of fact, four of the failures (entries 2-5) provided relatively modest Konzett responses, about 1-20% that of l-$PGE_1$, and therefore only one of these compounds (3) can be considered to have been tested at an appropriate multiple of the apparent l-$PGE_1$ minimally effective dose [(50-100 μg)10,11,164]. Accordingly, the possibility remains that "weak" candidates may not have been studied at sufficiently high dose levels.

TABLE XXIII

CLINICAL INVESTIGATIONS

| | CANDIDATE | SECTION | KONZETT POTENCY | CLINICAL RESULTS |
|---|---|---|---|---|
| 1. | 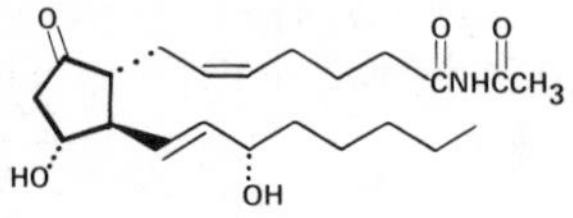 CP-27,987 | V.E. | NOT REPORTED | EFFECTIVE AT 18-35 μg DOSE. MILD IRRITANT, CARDIOVASCULAR EFFECTS[131] |
| 2. | 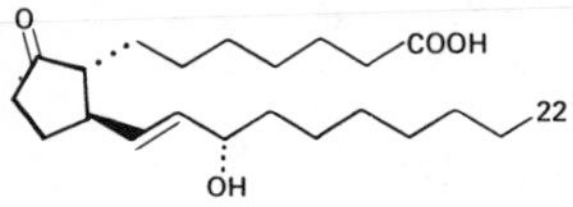 | VII.E. | $\frac{1}{14}$ $PGE_2$ | COUGH AND BRONCHO-CONSTRICTION AT 250 μg (2.5-5 x $PGE_1$ MED)[122] |
| 3. | 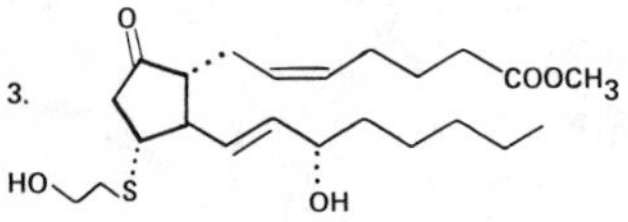 | V.B. | $\frac{1}{6}$ $PGE_1$ | INEFFECTIVE AT 800 μg (8-16 x $PGE_1$ MED)[69] |
| 4. | 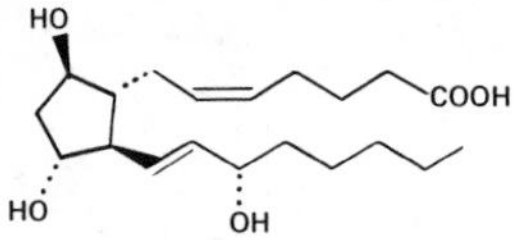 ($PGF_{2\beta}$) | V.C.I. | $\frac{1}{100}-\frac{1}{20}$ $PGE_1$ | INEFFECTIVE AT 200 μg MILD BRONCHOCONSTRICTION (2-4 x $PGE_1$ MED)[128] |
| 5. | 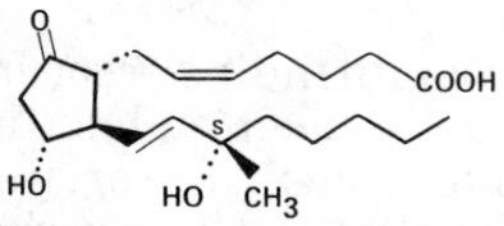 | VII.A. | $\frac{1}{8}$ $PGE_1$ | POSSIBLY WEAKLY EFFECTIVE AT 200 μg. NO IRRITATION. (2-4 x $PGE_1$ MED)[12] |
| 6. | 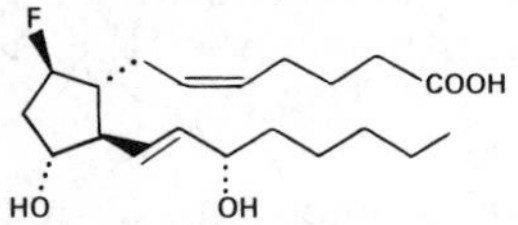 | V.C.3 | 2.5-4 $PGE_2$ | IRRITANT IN PHASE I STUDY.[126,130] |
| 7. | 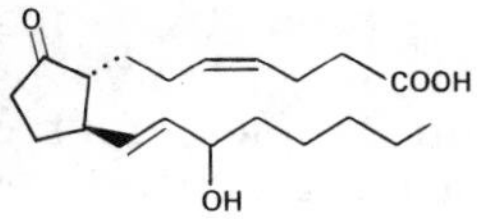 | VI.C. | >$PGE_2$ | COUGH IN PHASE I STUDY[141] |
| 8. | 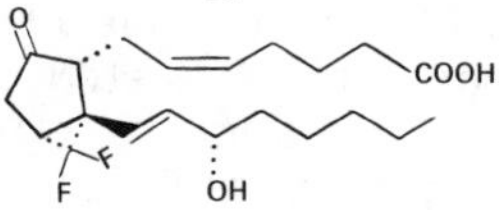 | V.B. | 1-5 $PGE_2$ | INEFFECTIVE[126] |
| 9. | 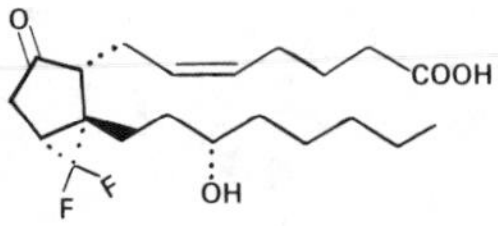 | V.B. | 1-5 $PGE_2$ | INEFFECTIVE[126] |

Two of the failed analogs (6,7) which were reported to be more active than $PGE_1$ or $PGE_2$ in the Konzett assay had to be withdrawn from testing during phase I studies when they produced a cough response, so that evaluation as to Konzett predictability with these compounds was not possible. Two of the above-noted "weak" candidates (2,4) also induced constrictor and/or cough responses, precluding testing at higher dose levels. These observations again emphasize the critical need for a reliable assay capable of evaluating the cough and irritant potential of candidate compounds.

Finally, two other compounds (8,9), more active in the Konzett assay than $PGE_2$, were found to be ineffective in man. These two closely related analogs represent the only clean cut test of Konzett predictability, clearly an inadequate trial. Therefore, as of this writing, any judgement as to the validity of the Konzett assay must remain moot. One other point is worth noting. Five of the eight failures were 11-deoxy derivatives, which recalls our observation concerning the general inability of members of this class, despite high activity in the Konzett assay, to produce fully efficacious and maximal responses in our pilocarpine dog assay. Indeed, the only fully elaborated PGE analog clinically tested was 15(S)15-methyl-$PGE_2$ (5), which by the Konzett assay has about one-eighth the potency of l-$PGE_1$, and which when tested at only four times the latter's apparent minimal effective dose, may have produced a weak bronchodilation.

Not only has it not been possible to develop an improved prostaglandin, but the high promise of the initial clinical observations with the natural prostaglandins is not fully supported by subsequent studies. Thus it appears that in some subjects $PGE_1$, even at twice the apparent MED, does not produce a maximal effect (compared with isoproterenol) (10). Also there is at least one report which claims that $PGE_2$, when administered to asthmatic subjects, usually induces bronchoconstriction rather than dilation (7). It has been suggested that there are two PG-sensitive receptor sites, one responding to $PGE_1$ and inducing relaxation, the other responding to $PGF_{2}\alpha$ and inducing constriction (5). Indeed, it has been postulated that in a significant proportion of the asthmatic population the disease is a manifestation of an increase in number and/or sensitivity of the latter site (181,182,183). Thus $PGE_2$, which appears to interact with either receptor (5), generally behaves like $PGE_1$ in normal subjects and like $PGF_{2}\alpha$ in asthmatic subjects. Bronchoconstrictive capability amongst the prostaglandin congeners also may be more common than is generally believed; mild constrictor effects were noted for three of the clinical failures. Also, our studies with the guinea pig and dog assays, and the studies reported by others using isolated guinea pig or human lung strips indicate that alkylation at $C_{15}$ or $C_{16}$ in the $E_1$ or $E_2$ series often may result in compounds which at the least produce an initial constriction.

With respect to structure-activity correlations it is possible to make the following generalizations, based mainly on Konzett data, and bearing in mind that in some instances the supporting evidence is quite meager.

1. The 15-hydroxy group in the natural (15S) configuration or a 16-hydroxy group (probably 16S) is essential for good activity.

2. The 11α-hydroxy group is not required for high potency in the guinea pig, but note our earlier reservations concerning the efficacy of the 11-deoxy series in the dog. Thus far a suitable replacement for this group has not been identified.

3. Whether the 9-carbonyl group is an essential feature is an open question. Compounds with this function derivatized have shown activity as have 9β-ol ($PGF_2β$) and 9-deoxy-9β-fluoro derivatives, but the latter types have not held up on clinical investigation.

4. The carboxylic acid function has been replaced with an acidic imide funtion ($CONHCOCH_3$) with retention of clinical activity. Very little else has been reported concerning the biological effects of other carboxylic acid "equivalents". Simple carboxylic esters are biologically active.

5. Reduction of the $\Delta^{13}$-trans double bond has given mixed results, there being reports claiming retention of high potency and in other instances considerable diminution. Replacement of the trans configuration with a double bond in the cis configuration has not been consistent with good activity.

6. The size of the cyclopentane ring and the 7 atom length of the α-side chain appear to be fairly specific for high potency. Both abbreviation and homologation of the β-chain seem to be consistent with activity, but apparently neither produces an important enhancement of effect. However, note the reported activity of the 20-methoxy derivative XIV, YPG-209.

7. Substitution at $C_2$, $C_3$ or $C_4$ has been deactivating. One 3-oxa derivative was poorly active, but two of three 3-thia derivatives showed a fairly good retention of bronchodilator effect. Methyl substitution at $C_5$ or $C_6$ has been more rewarding, providing compounds of high potency. A shift of the 5,6 double bond ($E_2$ series) to the 4,5-position also maintained excellent activity, but the resulting compound was cough-inducing in the clinic.

8. Introduction of alkyl substitutuents at $C_{15}$ or $C_{16}$ of the 15-hydroxy series and at $C_{16}$ or $C_{17}$ of the 16-hydroxy series has provided compounds of high potency. However, bronchoconstrictive effects often have been noted and high activity has not been demonstrable for the 15-hydroxy series in our pilocarpine dog assay.

9. The carry-over of structure-activity principles proven important for the inhibition of gastric acid secretion or for antifertility effects to the bronchodilator field has been most disapointing. The introduction of the 15-methyl, 16,16-dimethyl, 16-aryloxy or 2a,2b-bishomo moieties has not provided compounds of bronchodilator interest. On the other hand, members of the 15-deoxy-16-hydroxy series have been effective in all three areas (184).

Acknowledgements

The authors wish to express their gratitude to Rita Hines for the typing of this manuscript and to Maria Román, Shara Chue, Christine Muller and Barbara McCormack for the preparation of the schemes and figures.

## REFERENCES AND NOTES

1. Prostaglandins and Congeners. 24 For the previous paper in this series see Chen, S.-M.L. and Grudzinskas, C.V., Prostaglandins, in press.
2. Cyanamid Educational Award Recipient (1977-1979); Department of Chemistry, Princeton University, Princeton, New Jersey.

## LITERATURE CITED

3. Sweatman, W.J.F. and Collier, H.O.J., Nature, (1968), 217, 69.
4. Sheard, P., J. Pharm. Pharmac., (1968), 20, 232.
5. Gardiner, P.J., Prostaglandins, (1975), 10, 607.
6. Strandberg, K. and Hedqvist, P., Acta Physiol. Scand., (1977), 100, 172.
7. Mathe´, A.A., Acta Physiol. Scand., [Suppl]., (1976), 441, 1.
8. Cuthbert, M.F., Brit. Med. Jour., (1969), 4, 723.
9. Cuthbert, M.F., Proc. Roy. Soc. Med., (1971), 64, 15.
10. Herxheimer, H. and Roetscher, I., Europ. J. clin. Pharmacol., (1971), 3, 123.
11. Kawakami, Y., et al., ibid., (1973), 6, 127.
12. Mathe´, A.A. and Hedqvist, P., Amer. Rev. Respir. Dis., (1975), 111, 313.

13. Smith, A.P., The International Research Communications System (I.R.C.S.), (1974), 2, 1457.
14. Bindra, J.S. and Bindra, R., "Prostaglandins Synthesis", Academic Press, Inc., New York, 1977.
15. Mitra, A., "The Synthesis" of Prostaglandins", John Wiley and Sons, New York, 1977.
16. Crabbe´, P., "Prostaglandin Research", Academic Press, New York, 1977.
17. Bindra, J.S. and Bindra, R., "Prostaglandin Synthesis" Academic Press, Inc., New York, (1977), 120-137.
18. Floyd, M.B., J. Org. Chem., (1978), 43, 1641.
19. Sih, C.J., Price, P., Sood, R., Salomon, R.G., Peruzzotti, G., and Casey, M., J. Amer. Chem. Soc., (1972), 94, 3643.
20. Alvarez, F.S., Wren, D., and Prince, A., J. Amer. Chem. Soc., (1972), 94, 7823.
21. Kluge, A.F., Untch, K.G., and Fried, J.H., J. Amer. Chem. Soc., (1972), 94, 7827.
22. Kluge, A.F., Untch, K.G., and Fried, J.H., J. Amer. Chem. Soc., (1972), 94, 9256.
23. Sih, C.J., Salomon, R.G., Price, P., Sood, R., and Peruzzotti, G., Tetrahedron Lett., (1972), 2435.
24. Pappo, R. and Collins, P.W., Tetrahedron Lett., (1972), 2627.
25. Bernady, K.F. and Weiss, M.J., Tetrahedron Lett., (1972), 4083.
26. Sih, C.J., Salomon, R.G., Price, P., Peruzzotti, G., and Sood, R., Chem. Comm., (1972), 240.
27. Bernady, K.F. and Weiss, M.J., Prostaglandins, (1973), 3, 505.
28. Floyd, M.B. and Weiss, M.J., Prostaglandins, (1973), 3, 921.
29. Sih, C.J., Heather, J.B., Peruzzotti, G.P., Price, P., Sood, R., and Lee, L.-F.H., J. Amer. Chem. Soc., (1973), 95, 1676.
30. Schaub, R.E. and Weiss, M.J., Tetrahedron Lett., (1973), 129.
31. Heather, J.B., Sood, R., Price, P., Peruzzotti, G.P., Lee, S.S., Lee, L.-F.H., and Sih, C.J., Tetrahedron Lett., (1973), 2313.
32. Arndt, H.C., Biddlecom, W.G., Peruzzotti, G.P., and Woessner, W.D., Prostaglandins, (1974), 7, 387.
33. Floyd, M.B., Schaub, R.E., and Weiss, M.J., Prostaglandins, (1975), 10, 289.
34. Arndt, H.C., Biddlecom, W.G., Kluender, H.C., Peruzzotti, G.P. and Woessner, W.D., Prostaglandins, (1975), 9, 521.
35. Dajani, E.Z., Driskill, D.R., Bianchi, R.G., Collins, P.W., and Pappo, R., Prostaglandins, (1975), 10, 733.
36. Sih, C.J., Salomon, R.G., Price, P., Sood, R., and Peruzzotti, G., J. Amer. Chem. Soc., (1975), 97, 857.

37. Sih, C.J., Heather, J.B., Sood, R., Price, P., Peruzzotti, G., Lee, L.-F.H., and Lee, S.S., J. Amer. Chem. Soc., (1975), 97, 865.
38. Poletto, J.F., Bernady, K.F., Kupfer, D., Partridge, R., and Weiss, M.J., J. Med. Chem., (1975), 18, 359.
39. Bernady, K.F., Poletto, J.F., and Weiss, M.J., Tetrahedron Lett., (1975), 765.
40. Collins, P.W., Dajani, E.Z., Bruhn, M.S., Brown, C.H., Palmer, J.R., and Pappo, R., Tetrahedron Lett., (1975), 4217.
41. Arndt, H.C., Biddlecom, W.G., Peruzzotti, G.P., and Woessner, W.D., Prostaglandins, (1976), 11, 569.
42. Bruhn, M., Brown, C.H., Collins, P.W., Palmer, J.R., Dajani, E.Z., and Pappo, R., Tetrahedron Lett., (1976), 235.
43. Hallett, W.A., Wissner, A., Grudzinskas, C.V., Partridge, R., Birnbaum, J.E., Weiss, M.J., and Dessy, F., Prostaglandins, (1977), 13, 409.
44. Bornatsch, W. and Untch, K.G., Prostaglandins, (1977), 14, 617.
45. Arndt, H.C., Biddlecom, W.G., Hong, E., Myers, C., Peruzzotti, G.P., and Woessner, W.D., Prostaglandins, (1977), 13, 837.
46. Skotnicki, J.S., Schaub, R.E., Weiss, M.J., and Dessy, F., J. Med. Chem. (1977), 20, 1042.
47. Collins, P.W., Dajani, E.Z., Driskill, D.R., Bruhn, M.S., Jung, C.J., and Pappo, R., J. Med. Chem., (1977), 20, 1152.
48. Skotnicki, J.S., Schaub, R.E., Bernady, K.F., Siuta, G.J., Poletto, J.F., Weiss, M.J., and Dessy, F., J. Med. Chem., (1977), 20, 1551.
49. Skotnicki, J.S., Schaub, R.E., Weiss, M.J. and Dessy, F., J. Med. Chem., (1977), 20, 1662.
50. Kluender, H.C. and Peruzzotti, G.P., Tetrahedron Lett., (1977), 2063.
51. Arndt, H.C., Gardiner, P.J., Hong, E., Kluender, H.C., Myers, C., and Woessner, W.D., Prostaglandins, (1978), 16, 67.
52. Chen, S.-M.L., Schaub, R.E., and Grudzinskas, C.V., J. Org. Chem., (1978), 43, 3450.
53. Collins, P.W., Jung, C.J., Gasiecki, A., and Pappo, R., Tetrahedron Lett., (1978), 3187.
54. Bernady, K.F., Floyd, M.B., Poletto, J.F., and Weiss, M.J., J. Org. Chem., (1979), 44, 1438.
55. Grudzinskas, C.V., Chen S.-M.L., Floyd, M.B., Lenhard, R.H., Schaub, R.E., Siuta, G.J., Weiss, M.J., Wissner, A., Dessy, F., and Van Humbeeck, L., "Chemistry, Biochemistry and Pharmacological Activity of Prostanoids", Pergamon Press, Oxford, (1979), page 243.

56. Pappo, R., Collins, P.W., Bruhn, M.S., Gasiecki, A.F., Jung, C.J., Sause, A.W., and Schulz, J.A., "Chemistry, Biochemistry, and Pharmacological activity of Prostanoids", Pergamon Press, Oxford, (1979), page 17.
57. Posner, G.H., Org. React., (1972), 19, 1.
58. Heslinga, L., Van Gorkom, M., and Van Dorp, D.A., Rec. Trav. Chim., (1968), 87, 1421.
59. Novak, L. and Szantay, C., Synthesis, (1974), 353.
60. Bagli, J.F. and Bogri, J., J. Org. Chem., (1972), 37, 2132.
61. Floyd, M.B. and Weiss, M.J., J. Org. Chem., (1979), 44, 71.
62. Bernady, K.F., Poletto, J.F., and Weiss, M.J., U.S. Patent 3,884,953; manuscript in preparation.
63. House, H.O. and Kramar, V., J. Org. Chem., (1963), 28, 3362.
64. Joly, R., Warnant, J., Nomine, G., and Bertin, D., Bull. Soc. Chim. France, (1958), 366.
65. Grieco, P.A. and Reap, J.J., J. Org. Chem., (1973), 38, 3413.
66. Burton, T.S., Caton, M.P.L., Coffee, E.C.J., Parker, T., Stuttle, K.A.J., and Watkins, G.L., J. Chem. Soc. (Perkin I), (1976), 2550.
67. Mitra, A., "The Synthesis of Prostaglandins", John Wiley and Sons, New York, (1977), 247.
68. Weiss, M.J. and Floyd, M.B. Jr., U.S. Patent, 3,876,690.
69. Floyd, M.B., Schaub, R.E., Siuta, G.J., Skotnicki, J.S., Grudzinskas, C.V., Weiss, M.J., Dessy, F., and Van Humbeeck, L., manuscript in preparation.
70. Floyd, M.B. Jr., U.S. Patent 4,076,732.
71. Piancatelli, G. and Scettri, A., Tetrahedron Lett., (1977), 1131.
72. Hallett, W.A., Wissner, A., Grudzinskas, C.V., and Weiss, M.J., Chem. Letters, (1977), 51.
73. Sih, C.J., Price, P., Sood, R., Salomon, R.G., Peruzzotti, G., and Casey, M., J. Amer. Chem. Soc., (1972), 94, 3643.
74. Pike, J.E., Lincoln, F.H., and Schneider, W.P., J. Org. Chem., (1969), 34, 3552.
75. Corey, E.J. and Beames, D.J., J. Amer. Chem. Soc., (1972), 94, 7210.
76. Posner, G.H., Whitten, E., and Sterling J.J., J. Amer. Chem. Soc., (1973), 95, 7788.
77. Castro, C.E., Gaughan, E.J., and Owsley, D.C., J. Org. Chem., (1966), 31, 4071.
78. Corey, E.J., Floyd D., and Lipshutz, B.H., J. Org. Chem., (1978), 43, 3418.
79. Corey, E.J. and Wollenberg, R.H., J. Amer. Chem. Soc., (1974), 96, 5581.
80. Corey, E.J. and Wollenberg, R.H., Tetrahedron Lett., (1976), 4705.

81. Corey, E.J. and Wollenberg, R.H., J. Org. Chem., (1975), 40 2265.
82. Ramwell, P. and Shaw, J. "Prostaglandins, Annals of the New York Academy of Sciences", New York, 1971, 200-217.
82a. Yankee, E.W., Axen, U., and Bundy, G.L., J. Amer. Chem. Soc., (1974), 96, 5865.
83. Niwa, H. and Kurono, M., Chem. Lett., (1977), 1211.
84. Wissner, A., Bernady, K., and Weiss, M.J., unpublished results.
85. Schaub, R.E. and Weiss, M.J., U.S. Patent 3,884,969.
86. Chwastek, H., Le Goff, N., Epsztein, R., and Baran-Marszak, M., Tetrahedron, (1974), 30, 603.
87. Binder, D., Bowler, J., Brown, E.D., Crossley, N.S., Hutton J., Senior, M., Slater L., Wilkinson, P., and Wright, N.C.A., Prostaglandins, (1974), 6, 87.
88. Dukes M., Russell, W., and Walpole, A.L., Nature, (1974), 250, 330.
89. Weiss, M.J., Hallett, W.A., and Wissner, A., unpublished results.
90. Wissner, A., J. Org. Chem., (1977), 42, 356.
91. Wissner, A., unpublishable results.
92. Schneider, W.P., Hamilton, R.D., and Rhuland, L.E., J. Amer. Chem. Soc., (1972), 94, 2122.
93. Weinheimer, A.J. and Spraggins, R.L., Tetrahedron Lett., (1969), 5185.
94. Crabbe´, P., Garcia, G.A., and Rius, C., Tetrahedron Lett., (1972), 2951.
95. Crabbe´, P., Garcia, G.A., and Valarde, E., Chem. Comm., (1973), 480.
96. Crabbe´, P. and Guzmán, A., Chem. and Ind., (1973), 635.
97. Vogel, P. and Crabbe´, P., Helv. Chim. Acta., (1973), 56, 557.
98. Grudzinskas, C.V. and Weiss, M.J., Tetrahedron Lett., (1973), 141.
99. Crabbe´, P. and Guzmán, A., Tetrahedron Lett., (1972), 155.
100. Borch, R.F., Bernstein, M.F., and Durst, H.D., J. Amer. Chem. Soc., (1971), 93, 2897.
101. Fraser-Reid, B., Holder, N.L., and Yunker, M.B., Chem. Comm., (1972), 1286.
102. Grudzinskas, C.V. and Weiss, M.J., unpublished results.
103. Bundy, G.L., Tetrahedron Lett., (1975), 1957.
104. Guzman, A. and Muchowski, J.M., Tetrahedron Lett., (1975), 2053.
105. Kiyoshi, S., Ide, J., and Oda, O., Tetrahedron Lett., (1975), 3021.
106. Ide, J. and Sakai, J., Tetrahedron Lett., (1976), 1367.
107. Weiss, M.J. and Siuta, G.J., U.S. Patent 4,085,272.
108. Schaub, R.E. and Weiss, M.J., unpublished results.
109. Schaub, R.E., Floyd, M.B. Jr., and Weiss, M.J., U.S. Patent 3,932,463.

110. Cho, M.J., Bundy, G.L., and Biermacher, J.J., J. Med. Chem., (1977), 20, 1525.
111. Hoffmann, E. and Faiferman, I., J. Org. Chem., (1964) 29, 748.
112. Morozowich, W., U.S. Patent 3,890,372.
113. Rosenthale, M.E., Dervinis, A., and Strike, D., "Adv. in Prostaglandin and Thromboxane Research", Vol. 1, (1976), Samuelsson, B. and Paoletti, R. (ed.), Raven Press, New York, page 477.
114. Karim, S.M.M. and Adaikan, P.G. in "Prostaglandins: Physiological, Pharmacological and Pathological Aspects", Karim, S.M.M. (ed.), University Park Press, Baltimore, (1976), pages 353-355.
115. Schaaf, T.K., "Annual Reports in Medicinal Chemistry", Vol. 12, (1977), Academic Press, New York, page 182.
116. Dessy, F., Maleux, M.R., and Cognioul, A., Arch. int. Pharmacodyn. Ther., (1973), 206, 368.
117. Lulling, J., El Sayed, F., and Lievens, P., Med. Pharmacol. Exp., (1967), 16, 481.
118. Lulling, J., Lievens, P., El Sayed, F., and Prignot, J., Arzneim.-Forsch, (1968), 18, 995.
119. Caton, M.P.L. and Crowshaw, K., "Biochemical Aspects of Prostaglandins and Thromboxanes" Intra-Science Research Foundation Symposium, Santa Monica, California, (1976).
120. Caton, M.P.L. and Walker, J.L., "Abstracts, VIth. International Symposium on Medicinal Chemistry", Brighton, England, (Sept. 7, 1978), page 108.
121. Gardiner, P.J., Copas, J.L., Elliott, R.D., and Collier, H.O.J., Prostaglandins, (1978), 15, 303.
122. Weissberg, R.M., Bradshaw, J. B., and Garay, G.L., J. Pharmacol. exp. Ther., (1978), 205, 246
123. Ramwell, P.W., Shaw, J.E., Corey, E.J., and Andersen, N., Nature (London), (1969), 221 1251.
124. Rosenthale, M.E., Dervinis, A., Kassarich, J., Singer, S., and Gluchmann, M.I., "Advances in the Biosciences 9, International Conference on Prostaglandins, Vienna, September 25 to 28, 1972", Pergamon Press, Oxford, (1973), page 229.
125. Strike, D.P., Kao, W., and Rosenthale, M., 167th Nat. Meeting ACS, March 31 - April 5, 1974, Abs. No. Med. 030.
126. Muchowski, J.M., "Chemistry, Biochemistry and Pharmacological Activity of Prostanoids", Pergamon Press, Oxford, (1979), page 39.
127. Crabbe´, P. and Cervantes, A., Tetrahedron Lett., (1973), 1319.
128. Hamosh, P. and Taveira Da Silva, A.M., Prostaglandins, (1975), 10, 599.
129. Hedqvist, P. and Mathé, A.A., "International Symposium on Asthma, 2d, Augusta, Mich., 1976" Academic Press, New York, 1977, 131-146.

130. Arróniz, C.E., Gallina, J., Martínez, E., Muchowski, J.M., and Velarde, E., Prostaglandins, (1978), 16, 47.
131. Spector, S.L. and Ball, R.E., Jr., Annals of Allergy, (1977), 38, 302. March 27-30, 1977.
131a. Kluender, H.C., Biddlecom, W.G., Woessner, W.D., and Gardener, P.J., "Chemistry, Biochemistry and Pharmacological Activity of Prostanoids", Pergamon Press, Oxford, (1979), page 370.
132. Belgium Patent 816512 (Derwent 00093W/01).
133. Hayashi, M., Kori, S., and Endo, H., U.S. Patent 3,953,435.
134. Nelson, N.A., Jackson, R.W., and Au, A.T., Prostaglandins, (1975), 10, 303.
135. Woessner, W.D. and Kluender, H.C., private communication.
136. Fitzpatrick, T.M., Alter, I., Corey, E.J., Ramwell, P.W., Rose, J.C., and Kot, P.A., J. Pharmacol. Exp. Ther., (1978), 206, 139.
137. Chen, S.-M.L. and Grudzinskas, C.V., Prostaglandins, in press.
138. Bornatsch, W. and Untch, K.G., Prostaglandins, (1977), 14, 617.
139. Fried, J., Lee, M.-S., Gaede, B., Sih, J.C., Yoshikawa, Y., and McCracken, J.A., "Advances in Prostaglandin and Thromboxane Research", Vol. 1, (1976), Samuelsson, B., and Paoletti, R. (ed.), Raven Press, New York, page 183.
140. Nakano, J., Anggard, E., and Samuelsson, B., European J. Biochemistry, (1969), 11, 386.
140a. Ohno, H., Morikawa, Y., and Hereta, F., J. Biochem., (1978), 84, 1485.
140b. Powell, W.S., Hammarström, S., Samuelsson, B., Miller, W.L., Sun, F.F., Fried, J., Lin, C.H., and Jarabak, J., Eur. J. Biochem., (1975), 59, 271.
141. Bartmann, W., Beck, G., Lerch, U., Teufel, H., Babej, M., Bickel, M., Schoelkens, B., and Seeger, K., "Chemistry, Biochemistry and Pharmacological Activity of Prostanoids", Pergamon Press, Oxford, (1979), page 193.
142. Skotnicki, J.S. and Dessy, F., unpublished results.
142a. Floyd, M.B., Schaub, R.E., and Dessy, F., unpublished results.
143. Floyd, M.B. and Dessy, F., unpublished results.
144. Karim, S.M.M. and Ratnam, S.S., "Advances in Prostaglandin .and Thromboxane Research", Vol. 2., (1976), Raven Press, New York, 733.
145. Bundy, G.L., Daniels, E.G., Lincoln, F.H., and Pike, J.E., J. Amer. Chem. Soc., (1972), 94, 2124.
146. Lin, C.H., Stein, S.J., and Pike, J.E., Prostaglandins, (1976), 11, 377
147. Lin, C.H. and Stein, S.J., Syn. Comm., (1976), 6, 503.
148. Crabbe´, P. and Fried, J.H., U.S. Patent 3,879,438.
149. Takagi, et al., Prostaglandins, (1978), 14, 791.
150. Tarpley, W. G. and Sun, F.F., J. Med. Chem., (1978), 21, 288.
151. Nelson, N.A., U.S. Patent 3,920,723.

152. Nelson, N.A., U.S. Patent 3,931,279.
153. Smith, H.W., U.S. Patent 4,099,015.
154. Buckler, R.T., Ward, F.E., Hartzler, H.E., and Kurchacova, E., Eur. J. Med. Chem. Chimica Therapeutica, (1977), 12, 463.
155. Smith, H.W., U.S. Patent 4,121,038.
156. Nelson, N.A., Jackson, R.W., Au, A.T., Wynalda, D.J., and Nishizawa, E.E., Prostaglandins, (1975), 10, 795.
157. Morton, D.R. and Morge, R.A., J. Org. Chem., (1978), 43, 2093.
158. Morton, D.R. and Thompson, J.L., J. Org. Chem., (1978), 43, 2102.
159. Robert, A. and Margerlein, B.J., "Advances in the Biosciences 9, International Conference on Prostaglandins, Vienna, September 25 to 28, 1972", Pergamon Press, Oxford, (1973), page 247.
160. Bygdeman, M., Borell, U., Leader, A., Lundström, V., Martin, J.N. Jr., Eneroth, P., and Green, K., "Advances in Prostaglandin and Thromboxane Research", Vol. 2., (1976), Raven Press, New York, 693.
161. Greenberg, R., Smorong, K., and Bagli, J.F., Prostaglandins, (1976), 11, 961.
162. Bagli, J.F., Greenberg, R., Abraham, N.A., and Pelz, K., Prostaglandins, (1976), 11, 981.
163. Kao, W. and Strike, D.P., Prostaglandins, (1978), 16, 467.
164. Pasargiklian, M., Bianco, S., Allegra, L., "Adv. in Prostaglandin and Thromboxane Res.", Vol. 1, (1976), Samuelsson, B. and Paoletti, R. (ed.), Raven Press, New York, page 461.
165. Nylander, B. and Anderssen, S., "Adv. in Prostaglandins and Thromboxane Research", Vol. 2, (1976), Samuelsson, B. and Paoletti, R. (ed.), Raven Press, New York, page 521.
166. Karim, S.M.M., Sivasamboo, R., and Ratnam, S.S., Prostaglandins, (1974), 6, 349.
167. Margerlein, B.J., Ducharme, D.W., Magee, W.E., Miller, W.L., Robert, A., and Weeks, J.R., Prostaglandins (1973), 4, 143.
168. Kluender, H., "Prostaglandins Synthesis, Structure and Properties", Medical Foundation of Buffalo, April 9, 1976.
168a. Arndt, H.C., Biddlecom, W.G., Peruzzotti, G.P., and Woessner, W.D., Prostaglandins, (1976), 11, 569.
169. Tomioka, K., Terai, M., and Maeno, H., Arch. Int. Pharmacodyn. Therap., (1977), 226, 224.
170. Kao, W. and Rees, R.W., Prostaglandins, (1978), 16, 461.
171. Moncada, S., Bunting, S., and Vane, J.R., Nature, (1976), 263, 663.
172. Bunting, S., Gryglewski, R., Moncada, S., and Vane, J.R., Prostaglandins, (1976), 12, 897.
173. J. Amer. Med. Assoc., (1977), 238, 1714.

174. Bianco, S., Robuschi, M., Ceserani, R., Gandolfi, C., and Kamburoff, P.L., Pharmacol. Res. Comm., (1978), 10, 657.
175. Szczeklik, A., Gryglewski, R.J., Nizankowska, E., Nizankowska, R., and Musial, J., Prostaglandins, (1978), 16, 651.
176. Whittaker, N., Tetrahedron Lett., (1977), 2805.
177. Nicolaou, K.C., Barnette, W.E., Gasic, G.P., Magolda, R.L., and Sipio, W.J., Chem. Comm., (1977), 630.
178. Nelson, N.A., J. Amer. Chem. Soc., (1977), 99, 7362.
179. Johnson, R.A., Lincoln, F.H., Nidy, E.G., Schneider, W.P., Thompson, J.L., and Axen, U., J. Amer. Chem. Soc., (1978), 100, 7690.
180. Chen, S.-M.L. and Dessy, F., unpublished results.
181. Mathé, A.A., Hedqvist, P., Holmgren, A., and Svanborg, N., Br. Med. J., (1973), 1, 193.
182. Smith, A.P., "Prostaglandins: Physiological, Pharmacological and Pathalogical Aspects", ed S.M.M. Karim, MTP, Lancaster, UPP, Baltimore, (1976), pages 83-102.
183. Newball, H.H. and Lenfant, C., Respir. Physiol., (1977), 30, 125.
184. Floyd, M.B., unpublished results.

RECEIVED August 6, 1979.

# INDEX

# INDEX

## B

## C

## D

## E

## N



## O



## P

**U**



**V**



**X**